VIDEO

HANDBOOK

Co-authored

by

MORTON G. SCHERAGA
Allen B. Du Mont Labs.

and

JOSEPH J. ROCHE
co-author Radio Data Book,
editor Radio Maintenance Mag

SECOND PRINTING

William F. Boyce, Publisher

ACKNOWLEDGEMENTS

This book is the result of the efforts of many individuals and firms, without whose cooperation and assistance it would not have been possible. The authors wish to acknowledge their indebtedness and express their thanks to the following individuals who worked on the production of the book, provided much of the necessary information, and helped them to obtain illustrations:

Carmen Auditore, Leonard W. Bidwell, Michael J. Blasi, Alice Boyce, William F. Boyce, Robert Cavanagh, Sam Coombs, Dr. Allen B. Du Mont, Dr. Thomas T. Goldsmith, Joseph Green, Errol Jones, Bob Loewi, E.D. Lucas, Jr., Joseph M. Matera, Bernie Miller, Charles Monroe, Jerry O'Neill, Rita Roche, Jacob Ruiter, Susanna Scheraga, Daniel Shacher, Irving Shane, Norman Silverstein, and Paul Ware.

Special thanks are due to Victor M. Turner and George A. Baker, who did the art work, and to Isidor I. Gross, who helped in the final preparation of the manuscript.

Thanks are also due to the following manufacturers, whose assistance in providing information helped make the book complete:

National Broadcasting Company, Allen B. Du Mont Laboratories, Eastman-Kodak Co., Tel-O-Tube Corporation, Raytheon Corp., Philco Corp., Hallicrafters Co., Tel-Instrument Co. Kay Electric Co., Transvision, Inc., Televiser Magazine, Technical Appliance Corporation, Radio Corporation of America, Farnsworth Television and Radio Corporation, Columbia Broadcasting Company, General Electric Company, Westinghouse Electric Corporation, Scott Radio Laboratories, Telrex, Inc., American Phenolic Corporation, J.F.D. Manufacturing Co., Workshop Associates, Inc., Ward Products Corporation, and Spellman Television Company.

To all these and the many others too numerous to list, the authors express their sincere appreciation.

Joseph J. Roche
Morton G. Scheraga

Montclair, N.J.
May, 1949

CONTENTS

SECTION 12

SECTION 13

SECTION 14

TELEVISION

PAST, PRESENT AND FUTURE

1-1 After decades of scientific development, television is no longer a laboratory curiosity, but a full-fledged industry destined to contribute its share to man's welfare and standard of living. Few other developments have been so long predicted and awaited, and few other industries have had so many false starts before finally becoming practical realities.

What is television? Why has it been so long sought? Is it the motion picture brought into the home, or radio with vision? Perhaps the word itself will help us answer some of these and other questions. Literally, its translation from Greek or Latin means the art of seeing at a distance. These words are an exact description of television. Through the medium of television we are able to view distant places from the privacy of our homes.

The entertainment and educational possibilities of television are almost limitless. Spot news pick-ups, coverage of sporting events, the drama of the theater, musical concerts, are only a few of the programs already being transmitted. Television's ability to let you see as well as hear your favorite radio programs, comedians, artists and speakers will enrich your leisure hours.

Present experimental and full-time programs indicate the educational advantages of television. Children learn quickly from a picture, and several excellent programs, devoted entirely to children, have already appeared. They provide entertainment and at the same time, teach patriotism, tolerance, facts about distant peoples and countries, and other useful lessons.

Classroom demonstrations with television receivers have been tried in high schools and colleges, and suggest the possibilities of mass education via television. Renowned lecturers can reach large audiences without having to travel to them. An important use of such facilities has been demonstrated in medical schools. A television camera, suspended over a patient in a hospital operating room, sent close-up pictures to medical students seated around distant receivers. If these students had actually been in the operating room itself, they would not have had as good a view as that obtained by television.

Scientist, lawyer, laborer . . . we shall all derive benefits from television. Television combines the sound of radio with the information of the newspaper, the entertainment of the theater and the motion picture. It is a unique development, borrowing from all fields of communication. It will develop its own specialists and techniques and evolve as an art in itself.

Is television really here? From almost every standpoint it has arrived. Using the year 1948 as a reference, we can find facts to substantiate this:

a. At the end of 1948, 42 cities in 28 states had television stations bringing television to almost 70 million persons.

b. Well over 100 commercial television stations had been authorized by the Federal Communications Commission. Applications for additional stations totaled more than 300. By the end of 1950, 150 stations are expected to be in operation.

c. Estimates indicate that 900,000 television receivers were produced in 1948, bringing the total number in the country close to a million. Production estimates for coming years indicate there will be 3 million television receivers in use by 1950; 10 million by 1953.

d. Several television networks are already in operation, linking distant cities together. One means of connecting stations is being provided by the American Telephone and Telegraph Company, which has been laying coaxial lines between television areas. New York, Philadelphia, Baltimore, Washington, Richmond, Buffalo, Cleveland, Toledo, Detroit, Chicago, Milwaukee and St. Louis have been linked by cable and relay. By 1951, this intercity network will be extended to the Pacific Coast, making possible nation-wide television transmission. The extensive network plans of the A.T. & T. system are shown on the map of Figure 1.

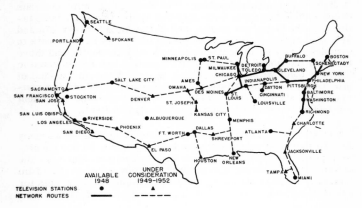

Figure 1. Network routes of the American Telephone and Telegraph Company, showing the cities which will be linked by coaxial cables.

e. With increases in the production of television receivers and the entrance of new manufacturers into the field, competition will become keener and prices lower. Approximately 100 manufacturers are now in the business of making television receivers and kits. Although the present price range of receivers extends from about $100 to $2500, the average retail price of receivers in volume production during 1948 was around $400. This figure is expected to drop each year. It is not unlikely that large screen receivers will be available within two years for less than $200, thus bringing television into the price range of the lower income groups.

f. Television is one of the country's fastest growing industries. Leaders in the industry estimate that by 1953, five years from today, it should represent an over-all capital investment of $2,630,000,000 and give employment directly and indirectly to as many as 292,000 persons. Its effectiveness as an advertising medium may result in a ten percent increase in the sale of many products.

In considering television as an industry, it is necessary to break it down into its essential components. They are television broadcasting, the manufacture, distribution and servicing of television receivers, industrial television, and military television.

1-2 Television Broadcasting. The Federal Communications Commission has made provision for approximately 1,000 stations, in the band now in use, and in the band between 475 and 890 megacycles, set aside for future use. The FCC expects to complete channel assignments in the low band shortly, and there is every likelihood that additional channels will be allocated in the high band within the next few years. Although the cost of television station installations varies greatly, $300,000 is a conservative estimate for a complete unit. To supply the equipment for 1,000 stations will require an industry in itself.

A station originating network programs may employ as many as 150 persons; a small station in a city under 50,000 population, perhaps as few as seven or ten. In addition, there are the artists, script writers, and advertising copy writers. The film industry, which is already supplying a number of programs for use by television outlets, will create further employment.

The following estimated figures give a clue to the possible scope (employees and investment) of the television broadcasting industry in 1953:

Employees

Full-time employees in stations	15,000
Advertising agencies, artists, etc	12,000
Film supplies	2,000
Manufacturers of equipment	3,000
Total	32,000

Investment

Television transmitters	$70,000,000
Manufacturing facilities	10,000,000
Total	$80,000,000

1-3 Television Receiver Manufacturing. By 1953, 10 million television receivers are expected to be in use. To place a receiver in a home requires many steps and many hands: among them, purchase of parts from specialized suppliers, assembly by the manufacturer, distribution through jobbers and dealers, installation and servicing, etc. A statistical breakdown of this phase of television activity based on an estimate for 1953 appears below:

Employees

In receiver factories	40,000
Distributors, dealers, installation and service	50,000
Parts suppliers	75,000
Total	165,000

Investment

Television receivers	$2,000,000,000
Manufacturing facilities	225,000,000
Total	$2,225,000,000

1-4 Television Networks. In order to supply the 200 television stations contemplated in 1953, some 20,000 miles of coaxial cable will be necessary to provide network-program service. Micro-wave radio relaying facilities may add another 20,000 miles of circuit connections.

The number of employees to install and service this network equipment is estimated at 10,000. The investment in cables and radio relay facilities will be $100,000,000.

1-5 Industrial Television. Television has many non-entertainment uses such as in department store advertising, mass education through private facilities, aircraft navigation, plant protection, and traffic control. The estimates of employment and investment in this field by 1953 are:

Employees needed for manufacture, installation and maintenance, 30,000.

Investment required for equipment, $200,000,000.

1-6 Theater Television. Commercial application of theater television has not advanced to any great extent thus far, but, in order to compete against home receivers, it is expected that half of the nation's film theaters may be equipped to show televised events on large theater screens. Theaters would need their own pick-up equipment and relay facilities, requiring additional employees. The possibilities for 1955 in this field are:

Employees for installation, maintenance and operation, 10,000.

Investment for theater equipment and pick-up and relay facilities, $50,000,000.

1-7 Military Television. Military applications of television are veiled in secrecy, but we do know of the use of television to control robot planes and operate guided missiles. If world events continue to require military preparedness on a large scale, such applications of television will be constantly expanded.

1-8 Future Developments. The full potentialities of television have not yet been realized. With the improvements that will come in program quality as more and more advertisers look to this new medium as a means of selling, there will also be technical advances to make program coverage even more exciting. As radio now spans continents, so will television. The international olympics, the coronation of a foreign king, travelogs in distant countries, all will make television a more entertaining and educational medium. "Two-way television" will make it possible for two entertainers located in distant cities to appear on the same screen, or for two political candidates to debate an issue though they are separated by a great distance. Political campaigns, conventions, congressional hearings will all be influenced by television, which will make the public more acutely aware of its governments representatives and operation. It is not beyond the realm of possibility that international television will create a better understanding among peoples of different lands and serve as a potent instrument of peace.

The use of television in airplanes will become a practical reality. Stations will have camera-equipped planes as part of their remote pick-up equipment. The airplanes will be able to take off at a moment's notice to give the viewing audience a birds-eye view of floods, forest fires, rescues at sea, volcanic eruptions, and other newsworthy happenings.

Further studies of the transmission and reception of signals at very high frequencies may make it possible to use built-in antennas and eliminate the need for outdoor installations.

An inevitable development, no matter what the manifold applications of television will be, is color television. All the beauties of art and nature will take on more vivid reality when televised in color.

Television is the long sought goal of man to span time and space. No other medium more adequately fulfills man's dream of bringing the world into his home.

1-9 Color Television. In 1946, the Federal Communications Commission held hearings to determine whether or not to allow standardization of a color television system. The proponents of black-and-white television argued that no low cost, all-electronic color system had been demonstrated and that it would be unfair to deprive the public of the already perfected black-and-white system. The backers of color television, particularly the Columbia Broadcasting System which had developed a combined electronic and mechanical color system, maintained that the engineering methods of color transmission had been fully worked out and would very shortly make black-and-white television obsolete. The FCC's decision when finally handed down gave the "green light" to black-and-white television, on the basis that the color system developed by CBS had several limitations which would prevent the full commercial exploitation of television. The FCC also indicated that other methods of color transmission had been demonstrated at the hearings which showed promise of the development of an all electronic color system. Lack of sufficient data on the various methods prevented the establishment of acceptable standards at the time of the hearings, and it is expected that at least five more years of laboratory research will be required before a practical color system can be evolved. The rapid growth of black-and-white television since 1946 bears out the wisdom of the FCC's decision.

1-10 Television vs. Radio Broadcasting and Motion Pictures. Although television is actually a specialized form of radio, it requires not only certain modifications of familiar radio circuits, but also various new circuits, techniques, and equipment. Whereas standard radio transmission involves the conversion of sound into electrical energy at the transmitter and the reconversion of electrical energy into sound at the receiver, television requires that light be converted into electricity at the transmitter and back again into light at the receiver.

Television is similar to motion pictures in many respects since both media reproduce on a viewing screen a series of images which create the illusion of uninterrupted motion. The methods used to obtain the illusion of motion in television and in the motion picture are considerably different, but, since both media must satisfy the requirements of the human eye, there are certain salient features of each which are identical. An understanding of how motion pictures create the illusion of motion is an excellent stepping stone in learning the more complex system used in television. To understand either medium, some of the elementary properties and functions of the human eye must be known.

THE HUMAN EYE AND THE TELEVISION SYSTEM

1-11 How the Eye Sees. Just as radio achieves the duplication of sound and the properties of the ear, so must any television system possess the remarkable powers of the eye to see and reproduce an image. A study of the characteristics of the human eye and how it sees will unfold many of the mysteries of television systems, past and present, and explain the need for many of the features in these systems. With this understanding of the visual organs of the body, the reader will appreciate how closely present day television imitates the functions of the eye in order to accomplish its purpose.

A sketch of the structure of the human eye is shown at the top of Figure 2, and a cross-section of a simple camera is shown in the bottom half for purposes of comparison. When taking a picture with such a camera, the first step is the focusing of the light reflected from the subject so that it will form a sharp image on the sensitized film. This is accomplished by changing the position of the lens with respect to the subject. If after the focusing operation is completed, the subject is moved further away from the camera, it becomes necessary to repeat the focusing procedure. This is necessary because the lens is not capable of simultaneously focusing on objects at different distances from the camera.

The eye employs a very similar focusing system. Its lens is composed of an elastic, transparent material, whose curvature and focal length are controlled by a number of tiny muscles. These muscles automatically adjust the focal length of the lens so that no matter what the distance is to the object, the image always falls perfectly in focus upon the back wall of the eye. It is because of this automatic focusing property of the lens that we are able to look at objects close at hand and then almost instantly look at objects in the distance.

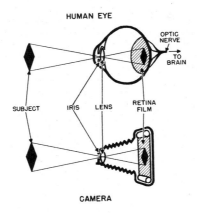

Figure 2. The action of the human eye is similar to that of a camera.

The back wall of the eye is known as the retina and like the film in the camera, receives the image. Whereas the camera film is composed of millions of tiny light-sensitive particles of silver which are acted upon in various degrees by the light received from the subject, the retina is coated with a material known as the visual purple, in which are embedded about 18,000,000 light-sensitive elements called rods and cones. The light which enters the camera strikes the film which is later chemically processed to form the image on its surface. In the eye, the information gathered by the millions of rods and cones must be conveyed in a systematic pattern to the brain through the fibers of the optic nerve, which is attached to the retina. All of the rods and cones function independently of each other and send their "nerve currents" through separate fibers. Thus, what the eye actually sees is a picture composed of many stimulations from these minute elements of the retina. Each element contributes its share of information, depending upon how much light from the object falls on it. Finally, the brain coordinates these stimulations into what we call sight.

The extraordinary flexibility of the eye is further exemplified by the fact that as you read across this page, the light reflected from the printed words is constantly changing. Therefore, as soon as the rods and cones convey one message to the brain, they must be ready to send succeeding messages as you scan from word to word. The sense of sight thus consists of millions of successive impulses sent to the brain from the elements of the retina.

Another element of the eye which will enable us to appreciate its corresponding part in the television system is the iris. The iris is the ring-shaped, colored matter in the eye which we refer to when we speak of the color of someone's eyes. The opening in the center of the iris is the pupil. The light rays which enter the eye must pass through the pupil. The iris regulates the size of this opening automatically so that the amount of light which passes into the eyeball remains approximately the same. In bright sunshine, the iris closes down the pupil to a very tiny pinpoint so that excessive light does not enter the eye. At night, the iris opens fully to let in all available light. The control over the amount of light is likewise important when taking a picture with a camera in order not to "overexpose" or "underexpose" the film. Similarly, television cameras are equipped with an iris or adjustable diaphragm which the operator sets according to the brightness of the scene.

1-12 Persistence of Vision. The foregoing description of how the eye transforms light rays from a "still" object into sight does not explain how we are able to perceive continuous motion. The ability to perceive motion is based upon another characteristic of the rods and cones; that is, they do not instantly respond to changes in light intensity, but have a lag of about one-tenth of a second. Likewise, the eye must be stimulated for a definite period of time, depending upon the intensity of light, before an impression will register on the retina. In order to observe a moving object, the eye must register each successive motion at least 1/500,000th of a second in bright light. Once this impression has been registered, the lag characteristic of the eye will hold it until the next impression is made. If these impressions occur at intervals of less than one-tenth of a second, the eye will blend them into a sensation of continuous motion. This lag characteristic of the eye is called persistence of vision and makes possible the motion picture and television.

1-13 The Repetition Rate of Images. Motion picture film offers an excellent example of how the eye sees moving objects by virtue of its persistence characteristic. A typical film is shown in Figure 3 and is seen to consist of a series of still pictures, each of which differs slightly from the next. When film is run through a projector, each still picture or "frame" is held in front of the lens for a definite period of time while the light is projected through it onto the screen. The shutter then cuts off the light while the still picture is removed and the next one moved before the lens. The shutter then opens and the next image is projected. If the successive still pictures are projected rapidly enough, the image formed in the eye by one frame will persist through the dark interval between frames and blend into the next image.

Figure 3. A strip of motion picture film.

In early motion pictures 16 frames were flashed on the screen during each second, but at the low light levels used in theaters a definite flicker was noticeable. In other words, even though the average one-tenth second lag of the eye would be expected to eliminate flicker effects when more than ten frames are projected per second, still, the illumination of each scene was not sufficiently high to register a persisting impression from as many as 16 frames per second.

Present day motion pictures overcome the effects of flicker by projecting 24 frames per second and, by the action of the shutter, project each frame twice. There are thus produced

48 separate projected pictures per second and no interrupted motion is visible. As will be explained later, the modern all electronic television system provides 30 frames per second, each of which is broken into half-frames or "fields", thereby giving, in effect, 60 pictures per second.

1-14 Breaking the Picture into Elements. We have already shown how it is possible to break down a moving scene into a

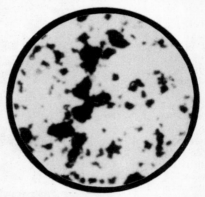

Figure 4. Greatly enlarged portion of a photographic negative. (Courtesy Eastman Kodak Co.)

succession of complete pictures and still retain the illusion of continuous motion. This technique is satisfactory for motion pictures, but falls short of the requirements of television. No television system has yet been developed which enables us to show a complete picture in even a single frame. The "dissecting" of the continuous motion has to be carried further; successive frames must be broken into elements. To appreciate how a picture may be divided into small elements and still appear uniformly solid, we can examine the methods employed in photography and photoengraving to reproduce a scene in a newspaper or book.

The scene is first photographed with a camera and transferred to film. If the developed image on the film is examined under a microscope, it will be found to consist of many tiny grains of silver, as shown in Figure 4. These silver elements are so deposited that in the darker portions of the picture they are closely bunched together, while in the lighter shades, they are more finely dispersed or do not exist at all. Because the grains are so fine, they appear as a solid picture to the naked eye.

To print the picture on paper with ink, the photograph is now etched onto a copper or zinc plate. Examination under a microscope of a picture reproduced from such a photoengraving reveals an even coarser distribution of black and white dots than appeared on the photographic film. In the photoengraving process, the film is projected onto a sensitized metallic plate through a transparent screen which is ruled with tiny squares.

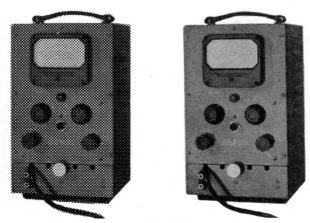

Figure 5. Coarse and fine half-tone engravings.

The image which is formed on the metallic surface consists of many small dots. In light portions of the picture they are extremely tiny and little ink is deposited from them, whereas in the darker portions they are larger and even run together. Figure 5 shows the same picture made from photoengravings of different screen fineness. At the left, the dots are easily visible to the naked eye, while in the engraving to the right the dots are hardly discernible.

The silver grains and printed dots show how a picture can be divided into a pattern of separate elements, each element contributing a portion of light or darkness to the combined image. Since there are about 18 million rods and cones on the retina, the eye can see this many detailed elements in a photograph or photoengraving. The finest screens used for photoengravings contain about 14,400 elements per square inch. The full resolving capabilities of the eye are thus hardly taxed by the details in the best photoengraving when viewed from a distance of several inches.

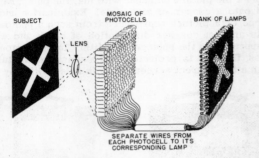

SUBJECT   LENS   MOSAIC OF PHOTOCELLS   BANK OF LAMPS

SEPARATE WIRES FROM EACH PHOTOCELL TO ITS CORRESPONDING LAMP

Figure 6. The Carey television system.

1-15 Proper Viewing Distance. Not only does the number of elements in a picture determine how pleasing the overall effect will be to the eye, but the distance from the eye to the picture must be considered as well. For example, if the coarse engraving shown to the left in Figure 5 is viewed from several feet, the large dots will no longer be distinguishable and the picture will appear as uniform as the one shown in the right of Figure 5, but which is viewed at a distance of several inches.

The proper viewing distance is extremely important in television, for it determines the picture size that is most comfortable for viewing. For example, it is entirely possible for a television picture to be too large for the size of a room. The average person watches a moving picture (in the theater or on a television set) most comfortably from a distance roughly 10 to 12 times the height of the picture. Thus, an 8'' x 10'' image will be viewed most satisfactorily by the average eye at a distance of approximately eight feet. Sitting nearer only increases eye strain and makes the viewer conscious of the picture elements and coarseness of detail. Moving further away (as was done in comparing the coarse and fine engravings of Figure 5) improves the picture by blending the details together -- but the picture now becomes too small for comfortable viewing. A picture of any given size, then, must be viewed from a definite predeterminable distance.

Any screen size viewed at the proper viewing distance pro-

vides about the same pictorial detail if the screens used contain the same number of picture elements and are of equal brightness. The midget television receiver, with its 3-1/2" x 4-1/2" image, which must be viewed from a short distance, produces just as sharp an image as the projected image receiver which projects images as large as several feet and has to be viewed from greater distances. The only advantage large television screens offer is the ability to accomodate a larger audience more comfortably around the receiver.

1-16 A Simple Television System. It is apparent from the foregoing discussion of picture frames and elements that it is not necessary to reproduce a scene so that it will appear as one continuous mass to the eye.

An early attempt to devise a television system was made by G. R. Carey of Boston in 1875. Carey knew of the properties of the eye and tried to take advantage of this knowledge. He attempted to simulate the action of the retina and optic nerve of the human eye by substituting an electro-mechanical system consisting of photocells and light bulbs. Carey's system also illustrates the basic principle of the conversion of light energy into electrical energy. See Figure 6. In this simple illustration, light from the subject is focused by a lens onto a bank or mosaic of photocells. Each photocell generates an electrical current in proportion to the amount of light which falls on it. This action is very much like the rods and cones in the retina of the eye which produce "nerve currents" when stimulated by light.

If light does not fall on a photocell, it does not produce a current. Thus the photocells receiving the light reflected from the letter X develop currents while the others which do not receive light remain inactive. To convey the electrical information held by the cells, Carey connected each cell through a pair of wires to a lamp located in a bank of lamps. The lamps which receive currents from the active cells light up and reproduce the original image.

This system is impractical because it requires at least 250,000 photocells, pairs of wires, and light bulbs to produce a picture of acceptable detail. Carey's television set-up also failed because the small currents from the photocells could not light the lamps to a sufficient brightness. It remained for Lee de Forest to invent the amplifier tube which could magnify tiny currents before photocells could be put to such use.

The difficulty of running two wires from each photocell to a

light bulb might be overcome by switching a single pair of wires consecutively to each photocell and its corresponding lamp. If this switching is done at a rate which is faster than the persistence characteristic of the eye, the eye will be deceived into seeing a continuous image on the bank of electric light bulbs, rather than a single element at a time. If we also use an amplifier to increase the strength of the photoc⋯ ⋯, Carey's basic television system assumes the mo⋯ ⋯figuration shown in Figure 7. Herein we have the⋯ ⋯n-ciple of all television systems which have since follov⋯ dividing of the picture into elements before transmission, sending an electrical current from each element successively over a single pair of wires, and the reconversion of these currents into light at the receiver.

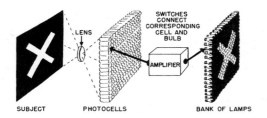

Figure 7. An improved television system using a single pair of wires and an amplifier.

Animated cartoon signs, such as those in Time Square, New York City, are an application of the crude light bulb television system. Figure 8 illustrates their operation. To transmit the simple object, it is first projected from a film onto the photocell bank. The pair of wires is then switched to the photocell in the upper left-hand corner. Simultaneously, the corresponding lamp in the receiving bank lights up to produce the white portion of the image. The switching continues along the top from left to right, illuminating the lamps in succession, and then drops down to the second row and starts across again from left to right. The uniform white background causes equal currents to be given off from the photocells, and so the lamps in the first few rows light up with the same intensity. As the switching proceeds across the third row, the photocells which received no light from the black object do not produce currents to cause their corresponding lamps to glow. By continuing to switch from left to right and down the bank of photocells, we

trace out all the black and white details.

This process of switching from left to right and top to bottom is called scanning and is much like the pattern followed by the eye in reading the lines on this page. This method of scanning has been carried over into all mechanical and electronic television systems.

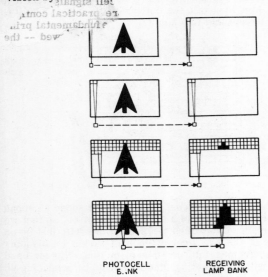

| PHOTOCELL BANK | RECEIVING LAMP BANK |

Figure 8. A practical light bulb television system.

1-17 Nipkow's Mechanical Disc. In 1884 Paul Nipkow announced the first practical mechanical device which overcame the limitations of Carey's method of televising an image. Nipkow devised a rotating metal disc, perforated with small holes arranged in the form of a spiral. The Nipkow disc offered a suitable scanning method for dissecting the object into elements at the transmitter and was also used to reconstruct the image at the receiver. It also introduced the principle of scanning by successive lines rather than individual elements.

The method of linear scanning is illustrated in Figure 9. Consider yourself an observer looking at the picture of the woman through a tiny window which is focused on the upper left-hand

corner   Now move the window to the right across the top of the
picture, and then quickly return to the left, but drop the aperture
down slightly to line number 2. Continue this operation   until
the entire picture has been scanned into, say 20 lines. Suppose
it were now possible to scan all these lines in less than one-
tenth of a second. The observer would not then see the individual lines because the persistence characteristic of the eye
would enable him to retain the impressions, from the first to
last line, and blend them into a unit.

Figure 9. How linear scanning is accomplished.

In the case of a moving scene, if we scan the scene a second
time in the next one-tenth of a second, and so on, so that we
view the entire scene ten times per second, we will just be on
the borderline of the eye's persistence of vision for blending
the successive frames into continuous motion. Nipkow used
this principle with his rotating disc technique by producing 60
scanning lines per inch in each frame, while presenting 20
frames per second. Refer now to Figure 10 for a description
of Nipkow's television system.

The circular disc contains a series of round holes arranged
in a spiral. In practice these holes were made either rectangular or square and were covered with lenses in order to gather
the maximum amount of light. The distance between successive
holes determines the width W of the picture to be reproduced
at the receiving end while the radial distance from the first
(hole 1) to the last hole (20) in the spiral determines the height
H of the picture. Each hole is closer to the center of the disc
by an amount equal to the diameter of the holes.

The object to be televised is focused onto the shaded area
shown in Figure 10. As the disc rotates, each hole sweeps a-
cross the image focused on the shaded area, allowing light to

pass through the disc. If we were to examine the elements of light, passing through the hole in the disc, on a screen behind the disc, they would appear in the fashion shown at the right of Figure 10. The scanning lines are shown only for illustrative purposes. Actually they would blend together if the disc rotated faster than 10 times per second.

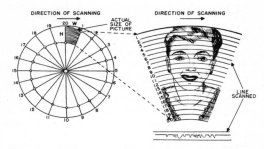

Figure 10. Rotating disc used in Nipkow's television system.

1-18 Converting the Scanning Lines into Electrical Signals. Suppose that instead of a screen, a single photoelectric cell is placed behind the disc. The light falling on the cell from the first hole would cause an equivalent amount of current to flow from the cell. The variations in photoelectric current for one

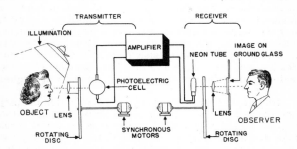

Figure 11. Transmitter and receiver apparatus for a mechanical television system.

of the scanned lines would appear as shown in Figure 10. Then, as the second hole moved across the photocell to produce the second scanned line, the chain of current variations would continue. In this manner, all the light variations in the picture are transformed into a continuous series of electrical signals. The apparatus which was employed in mechanical television transmitters to pick up scenes by this method is shown in Figure 11. The current variations from the photocell are amplified and transmitted on a radio frequency carrier to the receiver.

1-19 Reconstructing the Image at the Receiver. At the receiver, as shown in Figure 11, the current variations are fed to a neon tube whose light output instantly changes in intensity with changes in the current flowing through it. When more light falls on the photocell at the transmitter, the neon tube becomes brighter; when the light fades, it becomes dimmer. The observer looks at the neon light through a scanning disc, identical in size and shape to the one at the transmitter. Both discs run at exactly the same speed, and are synchronized so that when a given hole in the transmitting disc is in front of the photocell, the corresponding hole in the receiving disc is in front of the neon lamp. The observer actually sees a series of flashes through each hole in the receiving disc. Because of his persistence of vision, these flashes blend into a picture which is a reproduction of the one at the transmitter.

Several variations of the Nipkow disc method were used in mechanical systems which were developed after its introduction, but all of them depended upon the principle of linear scanning and used a single photocell and lamp. The improvement over Carey's system which required a multitude of cells and lamps is obvious. The Nipkow mechanical system represented the furthest advance in the art of television until the early 1930's when it was made obsolete by the introduction of the present day cathode ray electronic scanning system. It is well to list the shortcomings of the rotating disc method of television so that the reader may appreciate how they have been overcome when he begins to study the electronic system in the next chapter.

1. Although the Nipkow disc increased the detail in the picture and eliminated the need for a multiplicity of photocells and lamps, its 60 line picture did not possess the detail required for high quality television. Only 1800 impulses of light were produced during a single scanning of the entire picture. It will be recalled that the high quality reproduction of a photograph by the photoengraving process utilizes as many as 14,400 elements in one square inch of picture. The picture detail produced by the mechanical system was therefore far below the standards achieved in printing.

2. It was extremely difficult to synchronize the transmitter disc with the receiver disc. Most types of motor drives developed for mechanical systems were affected by variations in the power line voltage and frequency. These effects were particularly bad when the transmitter and receiver were on different power lines.

3. The light from the neon lamp was insufficient for comfortable viewing over any length of time. Much of the light was lost in a magnifying lens that had to be used to "blow up" the approximately one inch square picture that was obtained with most scanning discs. Some scanning discs were constructed which were as large as several feet in diameter, but even these could only produce a picture several square inches in area.

4. Finally, the mechanical system was cumbersome and difficult to maintain and could not achieve the portability that was required to make television really practical.

1-20 The Transmission Frequency Band Required for Television. Before turning our attention to the modern electronic television system, we can use our knowledge of the characteristics of the human eye and the factors that govern a high quality, detailed picture to set up certain standards. The first consideration is the number of elements desirable in the television image. In order to approach the standards of the 120 line per inch half-tone engraving which has 14,400 elements per square inch, and 8" x 10" television picture must have 960 lines (8 inches times 120 lines per inch) and 1,120,000 elements per frame (80 square inches times 14,400). At the 30 frames per second repetition rate which has been chosen for television, over 30 million elements must be scanned in one second. This is turn requires an equivalent electrical signal varying at a frequency of about 15 million cycles per second. A television channel capable of transmitting this band of frequencies occupies too extensive a portion of the frequency spectrum to be practical. A compromise must be made in the maximum detail of the television image in order to reduce the band width requirements. In practice, the television channel is limited to a band width of six megacycles, part of which is occupied by the sound frequencies that accompany the picture. Only four megacycles of the channel are devoted to the television signal, thereby limiting the picture to less than 200,000 elements. This figure may appear inadequate in comparison to the more than 1,000,000 elements found in a fine half-tone. It should be realized, though, that a television picture is viewed from a greater distance than that used when reading a newspaper or book. The television image will therefore be almost as good as the half-tone under actual viewing conditions.

1-21 Frame Frequency. It was mentioned above that a picture repetition rate of 30 per second has been standardized for the modern television system. This figure was arrived at after careful consideration of flicker effects and po ver line frequencies. At first, a rate of 24 per second was considered because it would coincide with that already established for motion pictures. Since it was to be expected that many television programs would consist of the televising of motion pictures, the problems of synchronizing the two systems could be minimized if both used the same repetition rate.

Even more important than the 24 frame scanning rate of motion pictures was the affect of power line frequency upon the synchronizing circuits. Most of the receivers in this country will be operated from 60 cycle lines. Unless the receiver rectifier circuits which convert the alternating current to direct current are perfectly filtered, some 60 cps or 120 cps ripple will get into the synchronizing circuits. The ripple voltage frequencies would not be a multiple of the picture frequency if the repetition rate were set at 24 per second. Synchronization would be unstable as the power line frequency opposed the frame frequency. Since the repetition rate of the present day television system is 30 cps, which is a multiple of the power line frequency, the problems of synchronization are greatly simplified.

It is realized that some areas in this country are served by 25 cycle lines, but these are few in number when compared to. the preponderance of 60 cycle supplied homes which benefit by a frame frequency of 30 per second. In areas which do not have 60 cycle alternating current, additional filtering may be necessary in the receiver power supply circuits to avoid trouble.

1-22 Consideration of the Number of Lines in the Television Picture. It was pointed out in paragraph 1-14 that an 8" x 10" television picture with detail as good as that of a 120 line per square inch photoengraving would have to have 960 lines. This results in more picture elements than can be transmitted in a 6 megacycle channel. Hence, the present system uses 525 lines. This number of lines produces the maximum number of elements that can be transmitted in the four megacycle portion of the six megacycle television channel allocated to the picture signal.

The reader may wonder whether or not television systems have been built which use more than 525 lines. The answer is yes. In this country and in Europe, television pictures with as many as 1000 lines have been produced. The cost of constructing receivers and transmitters to handle the additional band width required does not result in a proportional improvement in picture quality. It is unlikely that the 525 line standard will be superseded by any other in the near future.

1-23 Allocation of the Television Frequencies. After the width of the standard television channel had been fixed at six megacycles, the problem of finding a sufficient amount of space in the frequency spectrum arose. The space occupied by a television channel can be appreciated by comparing the AM broadcast band with a single television channel as shown in Figure 13. Notice that there are 106, ten kilocycle, channels in the AM band which extends from 540 to 1600 kilocycles. And yet all 106 stations occupy less frequency space than a single television station.

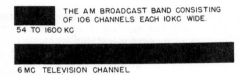

THE AM BROADCAST BAND CONSISTING OF 106 CHANNELS EACH 10 KC WIDE.

54 TO 1600 KC

6 MC TELEVISION CHANNEL

Figure 12. The space occupied in the frequency spectrum by all the a-m stations is less than that allotted to a single television station.

The FCC has therefore allocated a much higher frequency range to television stations than that used for radio broadcasting so that there may be a reasonable number of channels available. These allocations are split into two bands; one extending from 50 to 72 megacycles, and the other from 174 to 216 megacycles. Twelve channels, each six megacycles wide, are available in these two bands. (The FCC originally assigned 13 channels to television in the bands from 44 to 72 mc. and 174 to 216 mc. However, later studies indicated that interference effects which appeared in the television picture were caused by signals from other services in the frequency spectrum. These signals combine with the television signal and produce a beat frequency that falls in the frequency range for which most intermediate frequency amplifiers of television receivers are tuned. To meet the demands of other services for more frequency space and to solve the interference problem, the FCC took channel one (44-50 mc.) away from television. This move will enable receiver manufacturers to design the IF amplifiers to tune to an IF carrier frequency of about 41 mc., which frequency tests have indicated will be less troubled by signal interference from other services.)

The future of television has been carefully planned by the FCC in order to minimize signal interferences between channels. Channel assignments are staggered so that adjacent channels will not be used in the same area. This allows the use of a maximum of seven channels in any one area of the country. The FCC has determined the number of channels which will be available in the various areas of the country and the frequencies which will be used in each area. The reader may refer to Section 12 and readily ascertain how many television stations he will eventually be able to receive in his area. In addition to the stations assigned in the television band below 300 mc., space has been allocated in the region from 475 to 890 mc. to allow for further expansion.

Now that we know what to expect of the electronic television system in picture detail and number of commercial stations, let us begin the study of modern television techniques.

FUNDAMENTALS OF
ELECTRONIC TELEVISION

2-1 The television system in use today is essentially an electronic system. It was made possible by the development of the cathode ray tube which is the heart of both the television transmitter and receiver.

As was pointed out in Section I, all television systems must satisfy the requirements of the human eye. The cathode ray tube does this remarkably well and television as we know it today has been designed around this tube.

The cathode ray tube performs the two most important functions of the television system. At the transmitter, it "sees" the scene to be televised and transforms it into an electrical signal which can be passed on to the television receiver where the second important function takes place. Here again a cathode ray tube is used to take the electrical signal and from it reconstruct the original scene in the form of a visual picture on the viewing screen.

A brief resume of the history and origin of the cathode ray

tube is a good starting point for the discussion of the tube's construction and operation which follow.

The term "cathode ray" was originated in the last century by a scientist, Jules Plucker, who was investigating the properties of gases. His experiments included putting the gases being studied into cylinder-like glass envelopes. In these glass envelopes, there were two metal plates which were connected to a battery. (Figure 1.) The plate connected to the negative end of the battery was called a cathode, while the plate connected to the positive end was given the name anode. In the experimental procedure, a pressure reducing pump was attached to the tube through an opening. It was discovered that as the pressure was reduced, the region of the cathode acquired a definite, greenish glow. Plucker attributed this glow to invisible rays which, he believed, came from the cathode. He therefore called them "cathode rays".

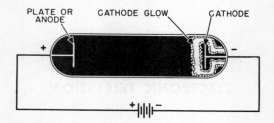

PLATE OR ANODE   CATHODE GLOW   CATHODE

Figure 1. Plucker's simple gas tube.

Although its basic shape and components were changed, the same type of tube was used in later experiments in the study of gases. Still later, the tube found use as an indicating unit using the cathode rays as a pointer. It was found that as an indicator, it functioned best with almost all of the gas pumped out. Nevertheless, the name "cathode ray tube" has remained in use, even though at the greatly reduced pressure now utilized, the green colored region in the neighborhood of the cathode is no longer evident, and the alleged "cathode rays" proved to be merely electrons.

2-2 Modern Cathode Ray Tubes. The modern cathode ray tubes now used in television differ considerably in construction and appearance from Plucker's original gas tube. A Type used in present day receivers is shown in Figure 2. Cathode ray tubes designed for television receivers have been given various names by tube manufacturers. Some of these are "kinescope", "teletron", and "visitron". Since there has been no universal acceptance as yet of a name for the receiver tube, the term "picture tube" will be used in this text whenever reference is made to the receiver cathode ray tube.

Figure 2. A modern cathode-ray tube used in television receivers. (courtesy GE)

Figure 3. The Iconoscope, a cathode-ray tube used in the television camera. (courtesy RCA)

There are several types of cathode ray tubes used in the television camera. One of the earliest designs, illustrated in Figure 3, is known as the "iconoscope". This word stems from the Greek word icos, which means "I see". The name is descriptive of the tube, since it actually does see the scene being televised and can change what it sees into electrical signals.

PICTURE TUBE CONSTRUCTION

2-3 Since the heart of the television camera and receiver is a cathode ray tube, it is best to begin the discussion of the modern electronic television system with a description of this tube. Of the two basic types, the picture tube and the camera tube, the former is more fundamental and a little easier to understand. It is therefore treated first.

Figure 4 shows a cross-sectional drawing of a picture tube, including its component parts and an imaginary electron beam, number 8, to illustrate the action of the various elements of the tube upon the beam.

The modern picture tube consists of five main sections: (a) a glass envelope, (b) a base which is outside the envelope, (c) the electron gun assembly, (d) the deflection plate assembly, and (e) the screen. The cathode, number 5, provides a source of electrons which are attracted in the general direction of the screen, number 19, by the action of the electron gun. These electrons are molded into a very narrow beam, which can be focused to a small point at the screen.

The inside of the screen is coated with a material which lights up when bombarded by the stream of electrons. The property of the screen which causes it to emit light when struck by the electrons is called fluorescence. When properly focused, the electron beam will strike the screen, causing a very small area of the screen to glow. If the face of the tube is viewed, this area will be a small pinpoint of light.

The deflecting plates, numbers 14, 15, 16, 17, can be made to move the beam up, down or sideways (vertically or horizontally). It is possible to apply electrical signals to these plates and cause the beam to move so fast that the eye cannot detect its movement. Since the screen material glows for a short time, even after the electron beam has moved to another position, a pattern can be traced on the screen similar to the one shown in Figure 5. Though the beam is constantly moving while tracing out this rectangular pattern, the pattern actually appears stationary because of the after-glow of the screen and the persistence of the eye.

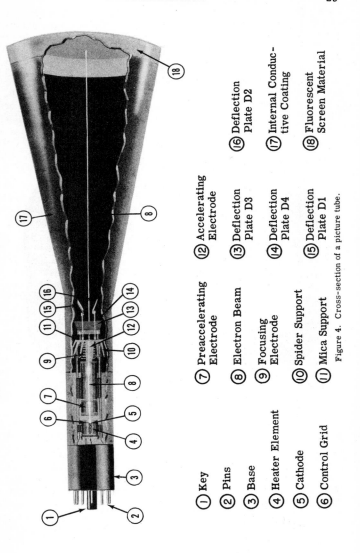

Figure 4. Cross-section of a picture tube.

① Key
② Pins
③ Base
④ Heater Element
⑤ Cathode
⑥ Control Grid
⑦ Preaccelerating Electrode
⑧ Electron Beam
⑨ Focusing Electrode
⑩ Spider Support
⑪ Mica Support
⑫ Accelerating Electrode
⑬ Deflection Plate D3
⑭ Deflection Plate D4
⑮ Deflection Plate D1
⑯ Deflection Plate D2
⑰ Internal Conductive Coating
⑱ Fluorescent Screen Material

2-4 The Electron Gun. The electron gun is so named because it takes the electrons given off by the cathode and accelerates them somewhat in the manner of a gun. The electron gun can be subdivided into four parts: (1) the cathode-grid assembly; (2) the pre-accelerator assembly; (3) the focusing electrode assembly; and (4) the accelerating electrode assembly. The assemblies are all supported by ceramic or glass rods which run the entire length of the electron gun as shown in Figure 4, number 10. These rods are usually made of a non-conducting ceramic or glass material to prevent electrical inter-action between the various parts of the gun.

Figure 5. Illuminated pattern obtained on the screen of a picture tube when the electron beam is rapidly moved vertically and horizontally.

2-5 The Cathode-Grid Assembly. The cathode-grid assembly consists of the heater element, the cathode, the control grid, and other supporting components, as shown in Figure 6. This illustration is an exploded view of the cathode-grid assembly and does not show the actual spacing of the components. The heater element, a coiled wire, is usually made of tungsten or an alloy of tungsten. This material is chosen because it is easily heated to a high temperature when an electrical current passes through it.

The cathode is a thin metal sleeve surrounding the heater coil. The metal sleeve, usually nickel alloy, is coated on one end with a substance which emits electrons in great quantities when heated sufficiently. This substance is usually an oxide, such as caesium oxide. The cathode is electrically insulated from the

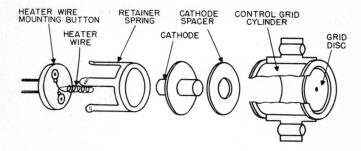

Figure 6. The cathode-grid assembly.

heater and is therefore said to be indirectly heated. Indirect heating is used because it isolates the emission qualities of the cathode from the power source supplying the current to the heater, and permits the use of an alternating current source. If alternating current were applied directly to the cathode to heat it, the flow of electrons would fluctuate according to the frequency of the current. Early cathode ray tubes used a heater-cathode assembly in which the heater itself emitted the electrons. For proper operation, these tubes required a direct current heater supply. Because it is more economical to supply the current for the heater from an a-c source, the indirectly heated cathode is now used almost exclusively.

The control grid in the cathode-grid assembly is a cylinder, completely surrounding both the heater and the cathode. The grid is open at one end, but closed at the other end by a disc. The disc has a small hole in its center to permit the passage of electrons. Since all electrons which pass to the screen must go through the hole in the disc, the grid electrode can assist in controlling the electron flow.

2-6 The Pre-Accelerator Electrode Assembly. The pre-accelerator electrode assembly is shown in Figure 7. It usually consists of two parts, A and B, each of cylindrical shape, with several discs enclosed in them. All of the discs have holes in their centers to permit the passage of the electron stream. This assembly gets its name from the electrical function it performs in the electron gun. It causes the electrons to move more rapidly in the direction of the screen. Its function is essentially the same as that of the accelerator (to be mentioned later), which also increases the speed of the electrons. Since the electrons pass through this electrode before they pass through the accelerator, it has been named the pre-accelerator.

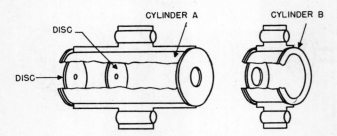

Figure 7. The pre-accelerator electrode assembly.

2-7 The Focusing Electrode Assembly. The focusing electrode assembly performs the function which its name implies. It focuses the electron beam to a fine point on the screen. (Figure

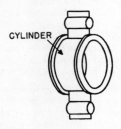

Figure 8. The focusing electrode assembly.

8.) The focusing cylinder is shorter in length than the grid and pre-accelerator electrodes, but is of essentially the same shape. It does not contain the discs included in the grid and pre-accelerator electrode assemblies.

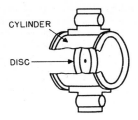

CYLINDER

DISC

Figure 9. The accelerating electrode assembly.

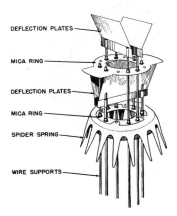

DEFLECTION PLATES

MICA RING

DEFLECTION PLATES

MICA RING

SPIDER SPRING

WIRE SUPPORTS

Figure 10. The deflection plate assembly.

2-8 The Accelerating Electrode Assembly. The accelerating electrode assembly performs the same function as does the pre-accelerator. It increases the speed of the electrons traveling toward the screen. The construction of the accelerating electrode is shown in **Figure 9**.

2-9 The Deflection Plate Assembly. The deflection plate assembly, shown in **Figure 10**, is mounted between the electron gun and the fluorescent screen. This assembly consists of two pairs of rectangular metal electrodes referred to as deflection plates. The four deflection plates are mounted with the aid of two mica rings which support and insulate them from one another and from the electron gun. A spider spring, made of a flexible metal material, centers the deflection plate assembly in the neck of the picture tube. As the electrons travel from the electron gun to the fluorescent screen, they must pass between each of the pairs of plates. The deflection plates are so placed in the tube that if a voltage differential appears across either pair, it will cause the electron beam to be deflected. Since the pairs of plates are mounted at right angles to one another, either horizontal or vertical deflection is possible by applying an electrical signal on the proper pair.

Figure 11. The glass envelope is coated on the inside with a conducting material. The second anode cap is connected to the aquadag coating. (courtesy DuMont)

2-10 The Envelope. All of the elements of the picture tube are mounted inside of a glass envelope. Almost all air is evacuated from this envelope which must be strong enough to withstand the pressure of the atmosphere.

The inside of the glass envelope between the neck and the screen is coated with a conducting material, as shown in Figure 11A. Graphite is the major component of this material which is known commercially as "Aquadag" or "Dixonac". The coating is connected to the accelerating electrode so that it operates at the accelerating potential. In picture tubes which operate at very high accelerating potentials, a small metal contact is fused to the funnel portion of the tube. The second anode and aquadag coating are connected to this contact instead of to a pin in the base. Figure 11B shows a picture tube with this type of construction. When stray electrons approach the coated insides of the tube, the high potential on the coating repels them backward toward the accelerating anode, so that electrons striking the walls of the tube are returned to the circuit. The potential on the conductive coating also eliminates inter-action between the electron beam and electrons rebounding from the screen.

Some picture tubes are equipped with an additional element referred to as an intensifier band. The intensifier band consists of a ring of graphite, coating the inside of the tube envelope. A non-conductive coated area between the intensifier band and the accelerator coating insulates the two coatings from each other. A small metal pin is inserted through the glass at a point where it will contact the intensifier band so that an electrical connection can be made to the band. Since the intensifier ring completely encircles the electron beam, it does not affect the path of the beam once the beam has been deflected. The purpose of the intensifier band is to further accelerate the electrons without making it more difficult to deflect the beam. If the beam is traveling too fast, deflection is quite difficult, requiring extremely large electrical signals on the deflection plates. With an intensifier band tube, it is possible to deflect the beam when it is moving at low speed when deflection is relatively simple. Then, after the beam has been deflected, the voltage on the intensifier band imparts to the beam additional acceleration to provide a brighter image on the screen.

2-11 The Tube Base. Except for the fact that it is larger and usually has more pins, the picture tube base is similar to an ordinary vacuum tube base. The leads which connect to the various parts of the internal assembly of the tube are brought through the glass seal at the end of the tube and are inserted into pins in the base.

2-12 The Fluorescent Screen. The fluorescent screen consists of a thin chemical coating which is deposited on the inside face of the tube. This coating consists of a silicate, sulphide, sulfate, or tungstate, and a binding material which holds the chemical to the glass. The thickness and uniformity of the coating are very critical and must be held within very narrow margins to assure uniform color and light output when the electron beam impinges upon the screen.

OPERATION

2-13 All of the parts of the picture tube just described perform important functions. The principle parts of the picture tube will now be discussed from an electrical standpoint, for the purpose of assisting the reader to understand their operation.

2-14 The Heater Coil. The sole function of the heater coil, or filament, is to heat the cathode to its proper operating temperature. No useful electron emission takes place from the heater coil. The manner in which the heater converts electricity into heat may be understood from a simple discussion of electricity.

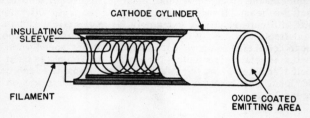

Figure 12. Heater and cathode assembly.

All material consists of small particles called atoms. Included in each atom are small negatively charged particles referred to as electrons. The wire which makes up the heater coil, therefore, consists of atoms and the electrons which are part of them. When a potential is placed across the ends of the heater wire, it causes electrons to be released from their atoms. These electrons move along the wire and constitute a current flow. The moving electrons strike other atoms and electrons which oppose their motion. This opposition is referred to as "resistance". As a result of the opposition or resistance to the electron flow, some of the energy which causes the current to flow is converted into heat.

2-15 The Cathode. The cathode must supply the electrons

which later are formed into the beam which is directed toward the face of the tube. It is placed over the heater coil so that the heat generated by the filament can be radiated to it (Figure 12). The cathode is insulated from the filament so that no electrical inter-action may take place. When heated to a temperature of about 700 degrees centigrade, the oxide coated cathode emits comparatively large amounts of electrons. To perform most efficiently, the cathode must emit the largest possible number of electrons at the lowest possible temperature. It has been found that certain oxides of alkaline earth metals such as caesium meet these requirements and are best suited for the cathode coating.

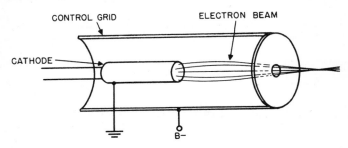

Figure 13. The grid limits the number of electrons which pass to screen.

2-16 The Grid. The electrons emitted from the cathode must pass through the hole in the grid. The grid controls the number of electrons which flow through the accelerator electrodes. When a more negative potential than the cathode potential is placed on the grid, it decreases the number of electrons which pass through the hole in the grid. When the negative charge on the grid is varied, the number of electrons passing through the hole in the grid also varies. The grid can therefore be used to control the number of electrons in the beam, and for this reason, is usually referred to as the control grid. If the negative charge on the grid is great enough, the electron beam will be entirely cut off.

The control that the grid can exert over the electron beam is one of the important features of the picture tube which have made electronic television possible. The greater the number of electrons (beam current) in the beam, the greater will be the light output from the screen. When the television signal is fed to the grid, it controls the passage of the electron beam and thus the intensity of the glow of the screen.

2-17 Grid Action. In order to control the stream of electrons passing to the screen, the grid is placed around the cathode (Figure 13). The cathode and grid in a cathode ray tube function in the same manner as the cathode and grid in a conventional vacuum tube. If the grid were at the same electrical potential as the cathode, the electron beam would be limited only to those electrons which were traveling along an axis which passes through the small hole in the disc at the end of the grid. The action of the disc on the electron beam, however, is not sufficient to limit the beam properly. It also does not provide a means for changing the number of electrons in the beam. Therefore, the grid is given a potential more negative than the cathode and this potential is made variable.

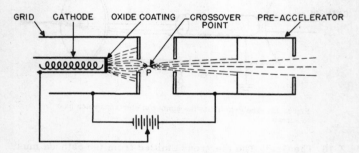

Figure 14. The "crossover" point of the electron beam is between the grid and the pre-accelerator electrode.

Some of the electrons which are emitted by the cathode do not go through the grid opening. This is because the cathode is much more positive than the grid and exerts a greater attracting force on the electrons than do the positive potentials on the more remote accelerating anodes. At the same time the negatively charged grid repels the negative electrons back to the cathode. This action of the grid in repelling electrons is aided by the presence of what is called a "space charge" which exists around the cathode. The space charge is created by the electrons themselves. Some of the electrons in breaking away from the cathode do not have sufficient energy to reach the grid. These electrons hover around the cathode as a sort of electron cloud and sometimes even return to the cathode. The space charge created by these electrons forms a barrier for other electrons which are freed from the cathode. If the new electrons do not possess a sufficient amount of energy to penetrate the space charge, they are forced back to the cathode. With these factors: (1) the negative grid, (2) the space charge, (3) the attraction of the cathode for the electrons, and (4) the small opening in the grid disc, it is very difficult for electrons to pass through the grid to the accelerating assembly beyond. Many electrons, however, break free from the cathode with sufficient energy to overcome these barriers and pass through the opening in the grid.

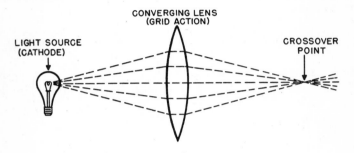

Figure 15. The focusing of an electron beam is similar to the action of a lens on a beam of light.

The electrons which pass through the grid, because of the pulling forces exerted by the positive charges on the accelerating electrodes, converge into a narrow beam. This convergence is due to the relatively high negative potential at the grid which makes each forward traveling electron move toward the axis of the electron beam. The cumulative actions of the electrical fields at the grid and at the pre-accelerator electrode causes the paths of the electrons, which pass through the grid, to meet and cross over at point P as shown in Figure 14. This point is called the "crossover point" and is between the grid and the pre-accelerator electrode.

The field between the grid and the pre-accelerator electrode acts on the electron beam in a manner similar to the action of a lens on a beam of light. In fact, the substitution of an "electrostatic" lens for the grid and pre-accelerating electrode, as shown in Figure 15, may help the reader to understand the action

of these electrical fields in narrowing down the electron beam
to the crossover point.

2-18 The Pre-Accelerator. In early cathode ray tubes the focusing electrode was located right in front of the control grid.
With this type of construction, adjustments of the voltage on the
focusing electrode effected the grid action and changed the intensity of the electron beam. In more modern tubes this inter-
action is prevented by the pre-accelerator electrode which is
inserted between the control grid and focusing anode, as shown
in Figure 16. The pre-accelerator is connected directly to the
second anode and provides the initial acceleration of the electron beam.

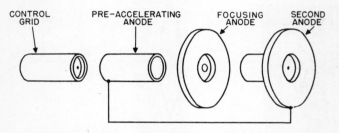

Figure 16. The pre-accelerator electrode is inserted between
the control grid and the focusing anode.

2-19 Focusing Electrode. After the electrons converge at the
crossover point, they begin to spread out again. A means had
to be provided to force the electrons back to the axis of the tube
and retain the narrow beam until it reaches the screen. Two
methods are used in modern picture tubes to focus the beam in
this manner. They are called (1) electrostatic focusing and (2)
electromagnetic focusing. The term focusing is used because
of the similarity to the focusing of a light beam by an optical
system.

Electrostatic focusing is most easily understood by referring to an optical analogy of the action of an electrical field
on an electron beam. With a lens, light rays can be made to
converge to a point and afterwards they will begin to diverge
again. The diverging beam can then be made to converge once
more, by introducing another lens as shown in Figure 17.
By substituting lenses of different curvatures for the second
lens, the distance to the second crossover point can be varied.

If a screen is located a certain distance away, the light rays can be made to cross over, or focus, at the screen by the proper selection of lens curvature.

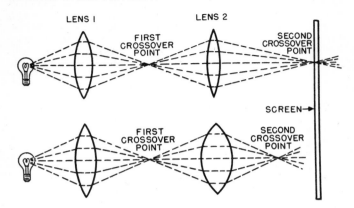

Figure 17. The distance to the second crossover point is determined by the curvature of lens 2.

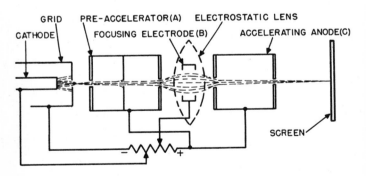

Figure 18. The electrostatic field inside the focusing electrode focuses the electron beam to a second crossover point.

If an "electrostatic lens" and an electron beam are substituted for the optical system and light beam, electrostatic focusing can be illustrated as in Figure 18. As the beam of electrons leaves the pre-accelerator assembly, it is diverging. This divergence is caused by the fact that the focusing electrode, (b), is more negative than the pre-accelerator, (a). The repelling force set up by the more negative focusing electrode slows up the electrons and makes them scatter. As the diverging electrons pass from the focusing electrode, (b), into the field between the focusing electrode and the accelerator, (c), their speed is once more increased, since the accelerating anode is more positive than the focusing electrode. The electrostatic field again acts

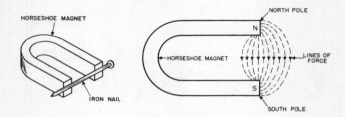

Figure 19. Left, the magnetic field between the poles of the horseshoe magnet pulls the nail to the magnet. Right, the lines of force around a horseshoe magnet.

in the manner of a lens and focuses the electron beam to a second crossover point. This crossover is adjusted so that it occurs at the screen.

The electrostatic focusing action must take place for many different beam currents. These differences in beam current are caused by the potential on the grid. To compensate for this, the potential on the focusing electrode is made variable so that the electrostatic fields on each side of it may be made weaker or stronger to permit the focusing of smaller or larger amounts of beam current.

2-20 Electro-Magnetic Focusing. Electro-magnetic focusing is another method that is used to focus the stream of electrons to a point on the screen. Whereas in electrostatic focusing the focusing action is accomplished by applying d-c voltages to the electron gun in the manner previously discussed, electromagnetic focusing is accomplished by placing a coil of wire over the neck of the picture tube, and passing a d-c current through the coil. Electromagnetic focusing action may be more easily understood by reviewing the basic theories of magnetism.

Between the ends or poles of a horseshoe magnet, such as shown in Figure 19A, there exists a field of magnetic force. The existence of this field can be demonstrated by holding an ordinary iron nail near the poles of the magnet. As the nail is brought close to the poles, the magnetic field will pull the nail to the magnet. When the nail is some distance from the magnet (outside of its magnetic field), there is little pulling action. The extent of the magnetic field surrounding the magnet is determined by the degree to which the metal in the magnet is magnetized.

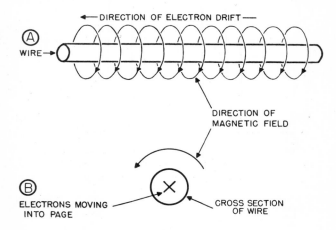

Figure 20. Direction of electron current flow in, and direction of magnetic field surrounding, a wire.

In an attempt to picture a magnetic field, it is assumed that it consists of lines of force or flux. The lines of force around the horseshoe magnet are shown in Figure 19B. Notice that the flux extends in one direction from one pole to another. The pole at which the lines originate is called the north pole, and the pole at which they terminate is called the south pole.

A similar magnetic field surrounds electrons. An ordinary metal wire is made up of atoms which contain electrons. As explained above, each magnetic field has a definite direction; that is, the lines of force travel from one point to another. When no current flows through a wire, the electrons in it lie at random, and the directions of the magnetic fields around the electrons are so different from each other that they effectively cancel out. The net effect is that no magnetic field is set up outside of the wire. However, when a current flows through a wire as shown in Figure 20A, the electrons flow in one direction only.

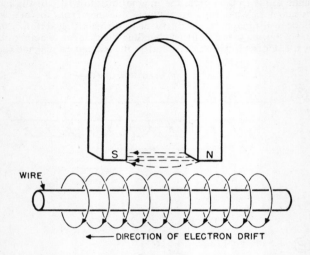

Figure 21. A wire which is parallel to the magnetic lines of force set up by a horseshoe magnet is not influenced by the magnet.

Since the electrons all move in the same direction, their magnetic fields all act in the same direction. This direction is around the axis of the wire. The accumulative effect of the magnetic fields of the electrons acting in the same direction, is the creation of a magnetic field around the wire. Looking at the wire along its axis, as shown in Figure 20B, if the current were going into the page as indicated by the x, the magnetic flux would flow in a circle around the wire in a counter-clockwise direction. If the current in the wire were flowing in the opposite direction, the magnetic flux would flow clockwise.

From the previous discussion, it has been shown that magnetic fields can be produced by two methods:

1. By magnetizing certain metals such as iron (a horseshoe magnet).

2. By sending a current in one direction through a wire.

When a number of fields of magnetic force are merged, they either add to create a more powerful field or cancel each other, resulting in a diminished field. The factor which determines whether they will add or cancel is their direction or polarity.

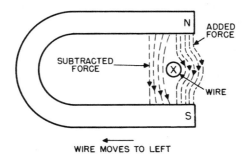

WIRE MOVES TO LEFT

Figure 22. Wire placed at right angles to the lines of force from the horseshoe magnet.

Suppose a wire with a d-c current flowing through it were placed near the poles of a horseshoe magnet, as shown in Figure 21. The wire is parallel to the magnet lines of force set up by the horseshoe magnet. Under these conditions, the magnetic field surrounding the wire is at right angles to the horseshoe's magnetic field. The two fields neither aid nor oppose each other, and therefore, they will not influence one another.

If the wire is now placed at right angles to the lines of flux from the horseshoe magnet, the fields will be in the same direction on one side of the wire, and in opposite directions on the other side. Looking at the end of the conductor, the fields appear as in Figure 22. To the right of the wire, the magnetic fields from the horseshoe magnet and from the current flowing in the wire are in the same direction. To the left of the wire, the directions of the two fields oppose each other. The result of this opposition to the left of the wire and reinforcement to the right of the wire is that of forcing the wire to the left.

If an electron beam is substituted for the wire with current flowing in it, a similar action will take place, and the beam will

be forced into a different path, because a magnetic field surrounds the electron beam in exactly the same manner as it does
a wire carrying a direct current (Figure 23). An electron beam
flowing in the direction indicated and at right angles to a magnetic field will be forced to the left just as was the wire in Figure 22.

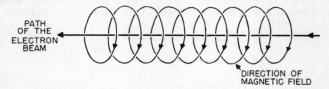

PATH
OF THE
ELECTRON
BEAM

DIRECTION OF
MAGNETIC FIELD

Figure 23. Direction of magnetic field set up by an electron
beam.

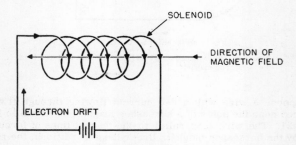

SOLENOID

DIRECTION OF
MAGNETIC FIELD

ELECTRON DRIFT

Figure 24. Direction of magnetic field in a solenoid.

The ability of a magnetic field to move an electron beam from
its path when the beam is traveling at right angles to the field
is the principle upon which magnetic focusing is based.

In magnetic focusing, an electro-magnet is used instead of a
permanent one. An electro-magnet consists of many turns of
wire wound in the shape of a coil. Such a coil of wire is called
a solenoid. If current flows through a solenoid, the addition of
the magnetic fields created around each turn of wire results in
lines of force which travel along the axis of the solenoid, as
shown in Figure 24. If this solenoid is fitted around the neck

of a cathode ray tube in which electrons are flowing, there will be two sets of magnetic fields in action: (1) the field due to the electron beam, and (2) the field due to the current flowing in the solenoid. As shown in Figure 25, electrons (A) traveling along the axis of the solenoid are not affected since the field due to

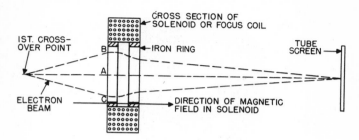

Figure 25. Focusing of an electron beam by a magnetic field inside of a solenoid.

the electrons is parallel to the magnetic field of the solenoid. Electrons which are diverging from the axis of the tube are affected (B and C). The magnetic field due to the diverging electrons is reinforced on one side but opposed on the other side, and thus the electrons are forced back to the axis of the tube. Since the electrons are moving forward, in addition to the side motion resulting from the field surrounding the solenoid, they follow a spiral path through the magnetic field created by the focusing coil. After leaving the magnetic field surrounding the solenoid, they continue to approach the axis of the tube. Electrons (A), (B), and (C), therefore, converge again.

By properly locating the solenoid (referred to as the focusing coil) and correctly adjusting the current through the coil, the paths of electrons passing through the coil can be changed so that all of the electrons meet at the screen to form a small, "focused" spot. If the current in the coil or the location of the coil is changed, the beam will no longer be focused on the screen.

2-21 Focus Coil Construction. Commercial focus coils (Figure 26) are made by winding many turns of wire around a soft iron core. An air gap is left in the center of the iron core (Figure 25) to concentrate the lines of flux at the center of the focus coil. By concentrating the flux in this manner, stray magnetic fields around the coil are reduced and are less likely to magnetize the elements of the electron gun. Concentration of the field increases the efficiency of the coil and reduces the di-

Figure 26. A commercial focus coil. (courtesy RCA)

rect current required to set up a sufficiently strong focusing field.

In practice, the focus coil is moved along the length of the tube neck to obtain the best focusing of the beam on the screen. Fine adjustments of the focusing action are made by changing the current flowing through the coil.

2-22 Electromagnetic Focusing vs. Electrostatic Focusing. Since the use of electromagnetic focusing eliminates the need for a focusing electrode, the electron gun structures used in magnetic tubes are simpler and more economical than those used in electrostatic tubes. The focusing action secured with the electromagnetic focusing system is generally better than that obtained with electrostatic focusing. Electromagnetic focusing usually gives a smaller minimum spot size. This is a distinct advantage as the reader will realize later.

2-23 Deflecting the Electron Beam. Part of the job of creating a television picture on the screen of a picture tube consists of moving or ''deflecting'' the electron beam from side to side and from top to bottom of the screen. Two methods have been devised to provide the control over the electron beam necessary to accomplish this horizontal and vertical deflection. The two methods used are called (1) electrostatic deflection and (2) electromagnetic deflection. The functioning of both of these deflection systems is similar to that of the related methods of electron beam focusing.

2-24 Electrostatic Deflection. In the description of focusing systems, it was explained that electrons carry a negative charge

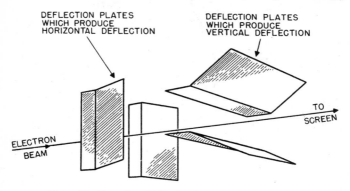

Figure 27. Two pairs of deflection plates mounted at right angles to each other.

and are therefore attracted by positively charged bodies and repelled by negatively charged bodies. It follows then that if a positively charged body is brought close to an electron beam, the beam will be drawn toward it and conversely that the beam will be forced away from a negatively charged body. This is the principle upon which electrostatic deflection is based.

2-25 Electrostatic deflection of the electron beam in a picture tube is accomplished by mounting two pairs of metal plates between the electron gun and the fluorescent screen. The pair of plates which deflect the beam vertically are mounted one above the other and are referred to as the vertical deflection plates. The pair of plates which deflect the beam horizontally are mounted side by side and are known as the horizontal deflection plates. The designations ''vertical'' and ''horizontal'' indicate the direction in which the plates, referred to, move the beam and not to the physical orientation of the plates themselves.

Figure 27 shows two pairs of deflecting plates. The two pairs of plates are mounted at right angles to one another. The ends of the plates nearest the screen are bent outward toward the wall of the tube. This bending is necessary so that the beam will not strike the sides of the plates when it reaches the extreme angles of deflection.

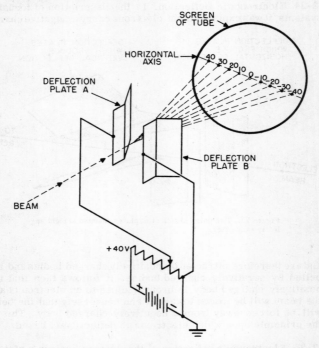

Figure 28. The electron beam is moved horizontally when a d-c potential is applied to the horizontal deflection plates.

With the plates mounted in the tube, it is only necessary to place a potential across the proper pair of plates to secure vertical or horizontal deflection of the beam.

Figure 28 illustrates a pair of horizontal deflection plates across which a variable potential has been placed. When the potential across the plates is zero, the beam is not deflected and strikes the screen at 0.

If the variable resistor is adjusted toward the positive end so that a 10 volt potential difference exists between the plates, the beam will be deflected and will strike the screen at the point marked 10. The deflection takes place in the direction of plate A because it is the positive plate. If the potential difference is

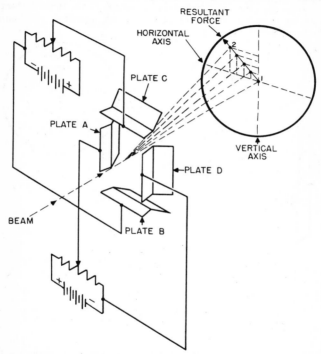

Figure 29. The horizontal and vertical deflection plates, with separate sources of voltage connected to them.

increased to 20 volts, the angle of deflection will be increased, and the beam will strike the screen at the point marked 20. If the voltage is increased to 30 and again to 40, the point at which the electron beam strikes the screen will move to the point marked 30 and then to the point marked 40.

If the leads from the battery are reversed so that deflection plate B becomes the positive plate, the beam will be deflected in the opposite direction. By following the procedure previously outlined, the beam can be made to strike the screen successively at the points marked -10, -20, -30, and -40.

The operation of the vertical deflection plates is identical to that of the horizontal plates except that the plates are mounted one above the other and therefore cause the beam to be deflected up or down. If the upper plate is made positive, the beam

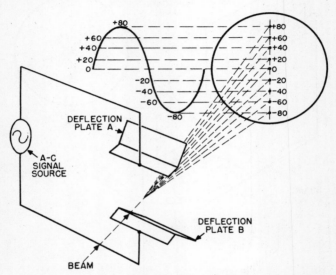

Figure 30. The electron beam traces out a vertical line when a high frequency sine wave is applied to the vertical deflection plates.

will be deflected upward; and if the lower plate is made positive, the beam will be deflected downward.

Figure 29 shows both horizontal and vertical deflection plates. Separate sources of voltage are shown connected across each set of plates. The horizontal plate A and the vertical plate C are positive and as a result, the beam is deflected upward and to the left simultaneously. If the voltage across the horizontal plates is the same as that across the vertical plates, the beam will move between 1 and 2 in the figure as the voltages are increased equally. The beam can be positioned to any part of the screen by applying deflecting voltages of the correct polarity and amplitude.

The cathode ray tube is sometimes used as an indicating device to measure voltages. A voltage to be measured is applied to one set of deflection plates. The position to which the spot is deflected on the screen is directly related to the magnitude of the voltage on the deflection plates, and by measuring the dis-

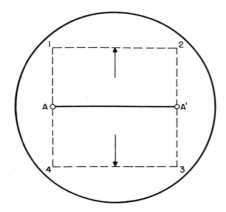

Figure 31. Raster pattern traced out by two sine waves, of equal amplitude, but of different frequency, which are applied to the vertical and horizontal deflection plates.

tance the spot has moved, the voltage on the plates may be determined.

For television purposes, very rapidly varying voltages are applied to the vertical and horizontal deflection plates. To illustrate the effect of a varying voltage on one pair of plates, Figure 30 shows a sine wave voltage connected to the vertical plates. In a single cycle, the voltage starts at zero, increases to a positive maximum of 80 volts, reduces to zero again, falls to minus 80 volts, and returns to zero once more. With this signal applied to the plates, the electron beam will move under its influence and trace out a vertical line. If the sine wave is of low enough frequency (less than 10 cycles/sec.), the beam will move up and down slowly, and the human eye will detect its movement. If a sine wave of higher frequency is applied (about 60 cycles/sec.), the eye will no longer detect the movement of the beam, and the path traveled by the spot will appear as a straight line on the screen.

If a similar voltage is connected to the horizontal plates of a cathode ray tube, a horizontal line will be traced out by the beam.

If alternating voltages of the same amplitude, but of greatly different frequency, are applied simultaneously to both the ver-

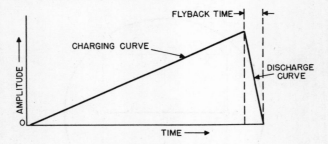

Figure 32. A sawtooth voltage.

tical and the horizontal deflection plates, the pattern on the screen will no longer be a line, but a square. This may be explained with reference to Figure 31. The line A-A' represents the pattern which is obtained if a varying voltage is applied to the horizontal deflection plates only. Imagine now that another varying voltage is applied to the vertical plates at the same time. The result will be the moving of line A-A' up and down at the frequency of the vertical deflecting voltage. If this frequency is greater than 10 c.p.s., the eye will not detect the movement of the line and the screen will appear to be illuminated over an area bounded by points 1, 2, 3, and 4. The action of the electron beam in tracing out the square pattern is known as "scanning". The illuminated pattern which appears on the fluorescent screen by virtue of this scanning action is known as a "raster".

2-26 **Sawtooth Wave.** In television, sine wave voltages are not used to secure the scanning action. For reasons which will be apparent later, it is desirable to use a deflecting signal which will move the beam from left to right and then, almost immediately, return it to its original position. The same is true for vertical deflection where it is desirable to move the beam from the top of the raster pattern to the bottom and then return the beam very quickly to the top again. The deflecting voltage which meets these requirements is shown in Figure 32. Such a signal is called a "sawtooth" because of its shape. If such a voltage is applied to the horizontal deflection plates of a picture tube, the beam will move across the horizontal axis at a uniform rate of speed during the rising portion of the curve. The beam will return rapidly to its original starting point when the sawtooth

Figure 33. Illuminated pattern produced by applying sawtooth voltages, of different amplitudes, to the deflection plates.

voltage drops back to zero. The time consumed during the return is known as the "flyback time" or "retrace time".

A sawtooth voltage is also applied to the vertical deflection plates. When vertical and horizontal sawtooth voltages act on the beam simultaneously, an illuminated pattern, such as shown in Figure 33, is obtained. This pattern is not square, as that shown in Figure 31, because the vertical sawtooth voltage is not as large as the horizontal sawtooth voltage. Later the part which the sawtooth voltages and the scanning raster play, in creating the television picture on the screen, will be explained.

2-27 Electromagnetic Deflection. Electromagnetic deflection

requires the use of coils to influence the beam as does electromagnetic focusing. Figure 34 shows a cross-sectional view of
the neck of a picture tube with a pair of solenoids positioned to
effect horizontal deflection of the beam. Current flows from the
battery through the top coil then through the bottom coil and back

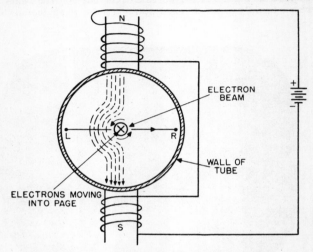

Figure 34. Method of magnetically deflecting the electron beam.

to the battery. The coil is split into two parts, each of which is
connected in series and placed on a different side of the picture
tube. The current through the coil sets up a magnetic field as
indicated by the lines of force. In the figure, the electron beam
traveling through the center of the tube is going into the page
as indicated by the x. The magnetic field, due to the travel of
the electron beam, is re-inforced by the lines of force from
the external field on the left side, while on the right hand side,
the fields oppose. This causes the beam to be forced to the
right. Similarly, another set of deflecting coils placed perpendicular to the coils, shown in the figure, will deflect the beam
up or down, depending upon the direction of the magnetic field
surrounding the coils. Since the current through the coils determines the direction of the magnetic field, it also determines
the direction in which the beam is deflected.

When magnetic deflection is used, the magnetic field must vary
in strength and direction in a manner similar to the varying

voltages on the plates of an electrostatically deflected tube. It has been shown that electrostatic deflecting voltages have a sawtooth shape for television scanning. The strength of the magnetic field must also increase and decrease in a sawtooth fashion. Since the magnetic field surrounding a coil is proportional to the current in the coil, the deflecting current will likewise have a sawtooth shape.

Figure 35. A commercial yoke.

Coils used for electromagnetic deflection consist of many turns of wire and are called solenoids, as in the case of electromagnetic focusing. In order to make a neat and compact arrangement, the vertical and horizontal deflecting solenoids are placed in a cylindrical container called a "yoke". The shape and configuration of the deflection coils in a commercially manufactured yoke are shown in Figure 35.

2-28 Magnetic Focusing vs. Magnetic Deflection. So that the reader will not confuse the action of magnetic fields in focusing the electron beam with the deflecting action, the following is a review of both. In magnetic focusing, the lines of flux around the solenoid placed over the neck of the tube, are parallel to the axis of the tube. A d-c current is fed to the focusing coil to force electrons back to the axis of the electron beam. In magnetic deflection, the lines of flux surrounding the deflecting coils are perpendicular to the axis of the tube. A varying current in the vertical and horizontal deflection coils moves the entire electron beam up and down, or left and right.

The yoke is positioned between the focus coil and the point where the neck joins the funnel portion of the tube, as shown in Figure 36. The electron beam is therefore focused before it reaches the deflection coils. Once the beam has been focused, the deflection coils impart vertical or horizontal motion to it.

2-29 Electromagnetic vs. Electrostatic Deflection. Electromagnetic deflection is preferred over electrostatic deflection when a large diameter picture tube is used. This choice is based mainly on the cost of the circuits necessary to generate the saw-

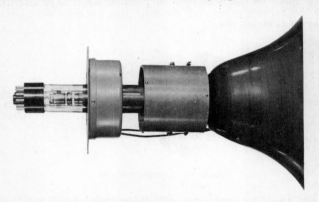

Figure 36. Positions of yoke and focus coils on the neck of a picture tube. (courtesy DuMont)

tooth voltages or currents which deflect the electron beam. With the larger cathode ray tubes, greater accelerating voltages are necessary in order to obtain a sufficiently intense spot on the fluorescent screen. Since the beam is traveling faster, it is more difficult to deflect. If electrostatic deflection is employed with a large tube, sawtooth voltages of very great amplitude are necessary. It is difficult to build circuits which can generate large sawtooth voltages, while large sawtooth currents can be generated with relative economy. With tubes ten inches and larger in diameter, magnetic deflection is preferred; however, in small tubes, seven inches or less in diameter, electrostatic deflection is used because small sawtooth signals are required to deflect the beam, and the electrostatic system is quite inexpensive. Electrostatically deflected tubes are invariably electrostatically focused. A few magnetically deflected tubes, such as the 5TP4, are electrostatically focused.

2-30 Fluorescent Screens. As mentioned previously, the screen of the picture tube is used to produce a visual pattern of the movement of the electron beam. If a screen were not used in a picture tube, a slight glow would be visible where the electron beam struck the glass face of the tube, even though the beam itself is invisible. The glow would not be satisfactory for viewing purposes and, therefore, a screen material is necessary to produce a bright image on the face of the tube. The screen material used is of such a nature that it glows when bombarded by electrons. Some of the chemicals which react in this manner are zinc orthosilicate, calcium tungstate, and zinc sulfide. The intensity and color of the light emitted by a fluorescent screen depends upon: 1 the chemical used in the coating; 2 the thickness of the coating; 3 the velocity of the electrons striking the coating; 4 the number of electrons which strike the coating (beam current); and 5 the length of time that the beam remains in one position on the coating.

The term "fluorescence" was introduced previously in the discussion of picture tube screens. (Section 2-12). Fluorescence is the property of the screen which causes it to glow when it is bombarded by the electron beam. In describing picture tube screens, the term "phosphorescence" is also used. Phosphorescence is a property of the screen material which causes it to glow after the electron beam has been removed. The term "persistence" is used when referring to the phosphorescent property of the screen. A screen which glows for a comparatively long time after being struck by electrons is said to have a long persistency, and a screen which glows for a short time is said to have a short persistency. The persistence of the picture tube screen is important in television, since a certain amount of persistence is desirable to make the television pattern appear stationary to the human eye. As the electron beam moves across the screen, it lights up successive points. Because of the phosphorescent quality of the screen material, the points on the screen glow until the beam scans across them again. This enables the eye to retain an image of the spot between successive scans.

Cathode ray tubes are made with screens which have persistencies of from a few microseconds to as long as several minutes. The persistence and color of the glow of screen materials are designated by letters and numbers. For example, a P1 screen has a green fluorescence with a medium persistence. The P4 screen, used mainly in television, has a white fluorescence and medium persistence. This screen is preferred for television because it produces a black and white picture. Other types of screen are the P7, which has a blue fluorescence and a long yellow phosphorescence, and the P5 and P11 screens, which are blue fluorescent and have a short persistence. The P1, P7, P5, P11, and several other screens are found in tubes used in cathode ray oscillographs.

2-31 Tube Nomenclature. The nomenclature used for cathode ray tubes has been standardized so that the numbers and letters refer to certain characteristics. The first number — 5, 7, 10, 12, 15, etc. — indicates the diameter of the screen in inches. This number is followed by a letter — A, B, C, etc. — which is assigned

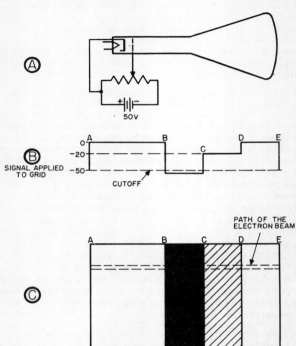

Figure 37. Forming an image on the screen.

to indicate the order in which the tube was developed with respect to tubes of the same diameter. Following this letter is the letter P, which stands for phosphor and another number — 1, 2, 4, etc. — which identifies the type of screen. Examples of picture tubes in use today are the 10BP4, 12JP4, and 15AP4. Illustrating the nomenclature, the 15AP4 tube type has a screen 15 inches in diameter; the "A" indicates that it was the first commercial 15 inch diameter tube to be developed; and the P4 designates the screen as being of the white fluorescent type preferred for use in television receivers.

2-32 Forming an Image on the Screen. If the proper potentials are applied to the elements of the electron gun of a picture tube, an electron beam will be formed. This beam will pass through the tube and strike the screen where, if the beam is properly focused, a small pinpoint of light will appear.

If, in addition to the above, sawtooth signals of sufficient amplitude are applied to the horizontal and vertical deflection plates, a raster will appear on the screen. As described in Section 2-25, a raster is a rectangular pattern of light which appears on the screen when the beam is scanned back and forth and up and down the face of the tube.

In order to form an image on the screen, an additional element of control over the beam is necessary. The number of electrons in the beam must be increased and decreased as the beam moves across the screen. Changes in the number of electrons in the beam will cause some parts of the screen to glow more brightly than others. If the number of electrons in the beam is varied in the proper way, an image will be formed on the screen.

The control, necessary to change the number of electrons in the beam, is provided by the grid. If the potential on the grid is varied, the number of electrons passing through the grid will vary. This function of the grid was described in Sections 2-16 and 2-17.

To illustrate the operation of the tube in forming an image on the screen, assume that a battery and a variable resistor are connected to the grid of a picture tube, as shown in Figure 37A. Assume, also, that sawtooth voltages are being applied to the deflection plates and a raster is being formed on the screen of the tube. When the variable resistor is adjusted to place -50 volts on the grid, the electron beam will be completely cut off, and the screen will be dark. When the resistor is adjusted so that no voltage is placed on the grid, a great many electrons will pass through the grid and the screen will glow brightly. At voltages between zero and -50 volts, the screen will glow with varying degrees of brightness, which can be represented as shades of grey.

If, as the beam is deflected across the screen from left to right, the potential on the grid is varied as shown in Figure 37 B, a portion of the pattern shown in Figure 37C will be formed.

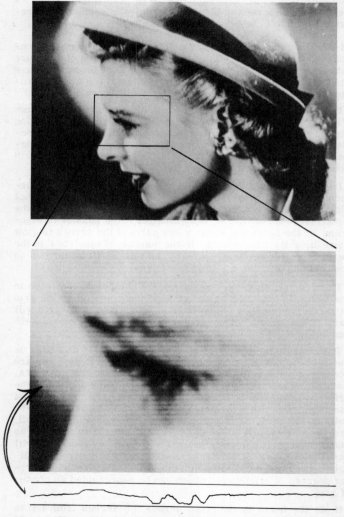

Figure 38. Grid voltage variations necessary to form one line of a picture.

The portion formed will consist of a thin horizontal line.

As the beam scans across the screen from point A to point B, the potential on the grid is zero and the screen will glow brightly. At the moment the beam reaches point B, the voltage on the grid is reduced to -50 volts. This causes the beam to be completely cut off, and the screen does not glow until point C is reached. At this point, the voltage on the grid is raised to -20 volts. Sufficient electrons reach the screen under this condition to cause it to glow dimly, as represented by the grey portion of Figure 37C. The voltage on the grid remains at -20 volts until the beam is scanned to point D. When point D is reached, the potential on the grid is again zero and the screen glows brightly between points D and E.

By this process, one line of the pattern of Figure 37C is formed. When the line has been completed, the action of the sawtooth signal present on the vertical deflection plates moves the beam down slightly. At the same time, the sawtooth signal on the horizontal plates returns the beam, almost immediately, to the left side of the screen. The beam then moves from left to right and another line is formed. This process is repeated until the complete pattern has been formed. All of this takes place in a very short period of time.

It will be remembered that due to the persistence of the screen, it continues to glow after the electron beam has passed over it. This property of the tube in combination with the persistence characteristic of the eye enables the observer to retain the upper portion of the image while the lower portion is being formed. After the complete image has been formed, it fades out very rapidly.

The pattern in Figure 37C is a very simple one, but its formation is essentially the same as that of the complex pictures normally encountered in television. Figure 38 shows a complex picture and the grid voltage variations necessary to create one line of it. Note that each line of this picture is different and requires a different group of grid voltage variations to bring about its formation. This is the only difference between the pattern of Figure 37C and the picture of Figure 38.

The picture tube is used in television receivers, where it reproduces scenes transmitted by the television station. Before a scene can be transmitted over the air it must be transformed into an electrical signal. The major part of the task of transforming a scene into a television signal is performed by the camera tube.

THE CAMERA TUBE

Several types of cathode ray tubes have been devised for the purpose of picking up the television picture. The iconoscope is treated first because an understanding of its operation will prove helpful when discussing other types of camera tubes, such as the orthicon, the image dissector, and the monoscope, which are described in Section 4.

The function of the iconoscope in the television system can be compared to that of the microphone in conventional radio system. The microphone picks up sound and transforms it into an electrical signal. In the television system, the iconoscope picks up light images and transforms them into electrical signals.

The iconoscope is similar in many respects to the cathode ray tube used in the television receiver, and the foregoing discussion

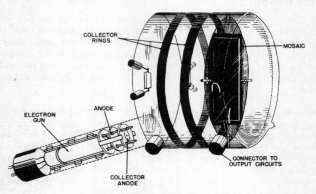

Figure 39. Construction of the Iconoscope.

of the picture tube applies in many cases to the operation of the iconoscope.

2-33 Iconoscope Construction. The modern iconoscope, Fig–

ure 39, consists of six major parts: a the glass envelope; b the tube base; c the electron gun assembly; d the deflection plate assembly; e the mosaic; and f the collector rings. The tube base, the electron gun assembly, and the deflection plates are the same as those in the picture tube. The shape of the glass envelope is quite different as shown in Figure 39. The impor-

Figure 40. The mosaic of an iconoscope tube.

tant parts of the iconoscope which are not used in the picture tube are the mosaic and the collector rings. The mosaic is a sensitized plate which transforms light into an electrical signal. This signal is passed on to the collector ring, which is a conductive coating on the inside surface of the glass envelope.

2-34 The Mosaic. The mosaic is a mica plate coated with a metal film, as shown in Figure 40. The material used to coat the mosaic is a mixture of chemicals consisting mainly of silver oxide. The mosaic is actually covered with millions of small particles, each of which is insulated from its neighbor. This structure is obtained by coating the silver oxide on the thin (0.001 inch) mica sheet, and baking the combination in an oven, until the heat transforms the silver oxide into pure silver. During the transformation, the silver forms into tiny particles or globules which are separated from each other by approximately 0.001 inch. The globules are made responsive to light by the addition of caesium vapor. The caesium vapor combines with the silver and forms a thin film around each globule. The globules when treated in this manner are made responsive to light ("photosensitive"). When a treated globule is exposed to light, it gives off electrons in an amount proportional to the intensity of the light which falls on it. The back of the mica plate, known as the "signal plate," is coated with a conducting material such as aluminum. The aluminum is applied with a brush, spray, or similar method. The mosaic is suspended in the iconoscope by glass members which are molded into the

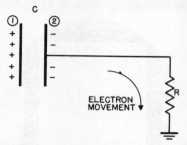

Figure 41. Each globule on the mosaic acts like a condenser.

glass envelope. A connection is provided to couple the signal plate to the outside circuit.

The shape of the iconoscope tube is such that the electron stream from the electron gun strikes the same side of the mosaic as does the light from the scene being picked up.

2-35 Electrical Operation of the Mosaic. Two theories have arisen to describe how the electron beam, the light rays, and the mosaic function to form a television signal. An understanding of either theory would permit the reader to grasp the fundamental problems in forming an electrical signal from an optical signal. Both explanations will, however, be given here.

In both theories of the electrical operation of the iconoscope, the mosaic and the metal back of the mica plate are believed to act as millions of small capacitors, one plate of each capacitor being common to all of the others. The common plate is the metal backing. For the purpose of discussion, it is convenient to visualize one of these small capacitor elements, as shown in Figure 41. When light is focused on the mosaic, each globule emits electrons. The number of electrons emitted depends upon the amount of light to which each globule is exposed; that is, a globule emits more electrons when exposed to a lighter part of the scene than does another globule which is exposed to a darker portion of the scene. In emitting electrons, each globule becomes positively charged. In Figure 41, plate 1, which represents the mosaic, loses electrons and becomes positively charged. This action causes plate 2 to become negatively charged with respect to plate 1. Plate 1 attempts to acquire electrons from the nearest source available in an attempt to become neutral again. The negative plate 2 cannot neutralize the positive plate because of the insulated gap between them.

An electron beam which consists of negatively charged electrons can supply the charges necessary to neutralize the positive side of the capacitor. If an electron beam is allowed to impinge upon plate 1 of the capacitor, the negative charges on plate 2 of the capacitor will be repelled because the electron beam will neutralize or discharge the positive plate 1. The repelled charges, which are electrons, will flow through the resistor R, connected to plate 2. As a result of the current flow, a voltage will develop across the resistor which will be proportional to the original charge on the capacitor. Since the charge was a result of the light to which the capacitor was exposed, the voltage across R is proportional to the amount of light which fell on the capacitor. In this way, light is converted into an electrical potential.

Returning to the mosaic, each globule on the mosaic is a plate of a capacitor. When an image is focused on the mosaic, light rays fall on the globules. The intensity of the light rays falling on any particular globule depends upon the brightness of the part of the scene which is focused on the globule. Thus globules upon which light rays from bright portions of the scene fall, become more positively charged than globules upon which darker portions of the scene are focused.

It will be recalled that an electron gun is mounted in the iconoscope. The electron beam which is created by this gun is made to scan the mosaic in the same manner that the beam in the picture tube scans the picture tube screen. As the beam scans across the mosaic, the electrons in the beam strike each successive globule and equalize the positive charge created by light rays from the scene. As the charge on each globule is equalized, electrons leave the signal plate because it is effectively the opposite plate of a capacitor which has been discharged. The electrons flow through a resistor connected to the signal plate and set up a voltage across it. The voltage changes as the current through the resistor changes, which in turn changes as the electron beam scans across globules which have different positive charges.

The voltage across the resistor consists of a series of electrical impulses which represent the scene focused on the mosaic.

These electrical impulses are the television or "video" signal.
The electron beam which discharges the globules is actually
much larger in diameter than a single globule. The diameter of
the electron beam is approximately 0.01 inch, whereas the average diameter of a globule is approximately 0.001 inch. When
scanning across the mosaic, the electron beam actually dis-

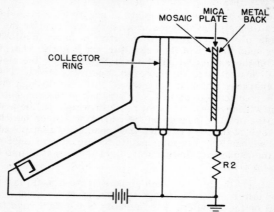

Figure 42. Path of electrons in iconoscope circuit.

charges many globules simultaneously. The signal which appears across the load resistor is then the average of the charges
stored on a number of globules. A group of globules discharged
at any one time by the electron beam is referred to as an "element". An element is the smallest area of the mosaic that can
be resolved by the electron beam.

In the above explanation, there must be a complete circuit a-
round which electrons flow in order for it to be an accurate account of what happens on the mosaic. To satisfy the necessity
for a complete circuit, electrons are said to travel from the
electron beam to the mosaic, from the metal plate on the back
of the mosaic, through the resistor, through the iconoscope power supply, to the cathode, as shown in Figure 42.

The second theory regarding the electrical operation of the
mosaic succeeded the first one after it was learned that the current flowing through the load resistor was many times greater
than the number of electrons which fell on each globule. The
first theory does not explain where the extra electrons in the

output circuit originated. The second theory accounts for this discrepancy and is generally accepted as the more accurate version.

The newer theory continues to assume that the mosaic is made up of tiny capacitor elements which are charged by exposure to light. From this point on, the theories differ.

As the scene being viewed is focused on the mosaic, the photosensitive globules emit electrons. The distribution of the emitted

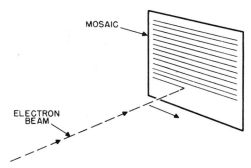

MOSAIC

ELECTRON
BEAM

Figure 43. Scanning motion of electron beam across the mosaic.

electrons, which accumulate in front of the mosaic, is an electrical reproduction of the scene, greater numbers of electrons being present in bright areas and fewer electrons in the darker areas.

The beam of electrons from the electron gun sweeps over the entire mosaic in a number of successive movements from one side of the mosaic to the other, as shown in Figure 43. Each movement or sweep across the mosaic is slightly lower than the previous one until the beam reaches the bottom of the mosaic. At this point, the beam is brought up to the top of the mosaic very quickly and repeats the sweep or "scanning" motion. As the electron beam scans one globule, the beam strikes the globule with sufficient force to cause additional electrons, called "secondary electrons", to be knocked off the atomic structure of the globule, as shown in Figure 44.

The electrons, which are emitted by the mosaic due to the action of the light which is focused on the mosaic, collect in front of the mosaic in a sort of cloud, or space charge. The number of electrons in front of areas of the mosaic which are exposed to bright portions of the scene is greater than in front of areas exposed to the dark portions of the scene. When the electron beam scans across the mosaic and releases secondary electrons, the electrons in the space charge tend to repel the secondary electrons back to the mosaic. Since the space charge is stronger in front of strongly illuminated areas of the mosaic,

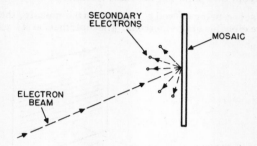

Figure 44. Secondary electrons emitted by a globule on the mosaic.

fewer secondary electrons will be released from these areas. Thus when the electron beam scans across areas of the mosaic which are highly illuminated, very few secondary electrons are emitted, and when the beam scans across dimly illuminated areas, many secondary electrons are emitted.

The secondary electrons flow to the collector ring through the load resistor where they set up a voltage which varies as the beam scans across light and dark portions of the image. This varying voltage is the video signal.

When a scene is focused on the mosaic, a few of the electrons which are released by photo-emission drift to the collector ring and thence to the load resistor. Since only a few reach the collector ring, the difference in potential between the mosaic and the collector ring is but a few volts. Most of the emitted electrons collect around the mosaic and form the space charge. When the electron beam strikes a globule, the number of secondary electrons emitted is greatly in excess of those emitted due to light rays from the scene. This largely increased supply of electrons increases the difference in potential between the mosaic and the collector ring. Therefore, when the electron beam is striking globules, a much larger current flows through the load resistor than results from light rays. The variations in current are in exact synchronism with the motion of the electron beam as it passes over each element. The varying current through the load resistor of the iconoscope forms the picture signal which is transmitted to the receiver, and fed to the grid of the picture tube.

2-36 Iconoscope Efficiency. Only a small portion of the total number of electrons emitted by the mosaic find their way to the collector ring and pass through the load resistor. The electrons which leave the mosaic as a result of photo-emission and secondary emission go to one of three places: 1 they travel to the collector ring; 2 they are repelled by the other electrons which have been emitted before them and return to the globule from which they started; and 3 they are repelled by the electrons emitted before them and return to neighboring globules. It is estimated that only 25% of the electrons which are emitted find their way into the field between the mosaic and the collector ring. Since the potential difference between the collector ring and the mosaic is small, between 15% and 20% of these electrons never reach the collector ring. Therefore, of all the electrons emitted, only 5% or 10% are used in forming the signal.

2-37 Bias Lighting. A method known as "bias lighting" has been developed to increase the efficiency of the iconoscope. As pointed out previously, a great many of the secondary electrons which succeed in escaping from the mosaic do not reach the collector ring because the difference in potential between the mosaic and the collector ring is very small. It has been discovered that many of these electrons collect on the glass wall of the envelope and remain there. The caesium oxide used during the manufacture of the tube not only collects on the mosaic but also on the walls of the envelope. The secondary electrons fall on this caesium oxide surface.

The bias lighting method consists of placing small flashlight bulbs in the camera behind the iconoscope. The photosensitive mosaic is not affected by this light source since the bulbs are behind the signal plate. The light from the bulbs falls on the caesium oxide which has coated the inner surface of the glass envelope, and the electrons which have collected on the caesium oxide are released. In this manner, the electrons which were deposited on the walls of the envelope return to the vicinity of the collector ring. Since the electrons carry a negative charge, they increase the potential difference between the surface of the mosaic and the collector ring and increase the efficiency of the iconoscope. While the increase in efficiency is comparatively small, it is important because it increases the sensitivity of the iconoscope. The improvement in sensitivity makes it possible to reduce the intensity of the light on the scene to be televised. Since the light which must be used is so intense that it is extremely uncomfortable for people to work under, and is also very costly, bias lighting brings about a worthwhile improvement.

2-38 Spurious Secondary Electrons. In addition to its inefficiency, another shortcoming of the iconoscope is the irregular-

Figure 45. Uneven illumination of the test pattern caused by spurious secondary electrons in the iconoscope.

ity of illumination it produces on the picture tube in the television receiver. When light is not falling on the iconoscope mosaic, it would be expected that no image signal would appear at the load resistor. Actually, however, a signal does appear and produces the uneven shading shown in Figure 45. When a scene is televised, the uneven shading is superimposed on the picture. The signals which cause this shading are thought to be secondary electrons which are given off by the mosaic when it is scanned by the electron beam. These secondary electrons accumulate around the mosaic and form an "electron blanket". Many of the electrons emitted during subsequent scannings are repelled by the electron blanket and return to the mosaic. These electrons do not return to their original globules, but "shower" back to others. The result is an uneven distribution of electrons because some portions of the mosaic accumulate more electrons than others. This process takes place whether or not an image is focused on the mosaic. The uneven electron distribution causes different potentials to be set up between the collector ring and various portions of the mosaic. When light from a

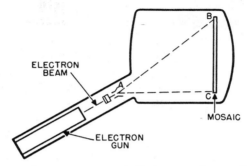

Figure 46. Keystoning occurs in the iconoscope because the electron beam travels unequal paths from the gun to the mosaic.

scene to be televised is focused on the mosaic, the signal voltage developed across the load resistor is a result of the light from the scene, and of the unevenly distributed electrons in the electron blanket.

A way to partially overcome the effects of spurious secondary electrons has been devised. It consists of coupling a signal into the load resistor of the iconoscope to counter balance that portion of the video signal which is a result of spurious secondary electrons. The signal coupled to the load resistor is furnished by a "shading generator". A shading generator produces signals of several different waveforms. The waveform which gives the greatest improvement is selected by the studio technician who monitors the picture.

2-39 Keystoning. In the iconoscope, the electron beam and the scene being viewed are both focused on the front of the mosaic. To accomplish this, the electron beam is projected toward the mosaic at an angle. In this way, the electron gun structure is mounted below the mosaic, leaving the area in front of the mosaic clear so that light rays from the scene to be televised can be focused directly on the mosaic. Because the electron gun is

mounted in this manner, the electrons in the beam must travel
further to reach the top of the mosaic than they do to reach the
bottom of the mosaic. This is illustrated in Figure 46 where
distance AB is greater than distance AC. Since the beam travels
a longer path to reach the top of the mosaic, it has the opportunity to be deflected through a larger horizontal arc than it does

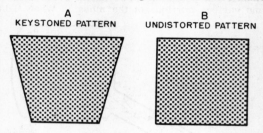

Figure 47. A shows a keystone pattern. B shows correct scanning pattern, obtained on mosaic when keystone distortion is eliminated.

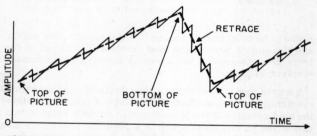

Figure 48. Compensating signal for overcoming keystoning.

at the bottom of the mosaic. As a result, the beam does not
trace out a rectangular pattern, but a distorted shape as shown
in Figure 47A. This pattern resembles a keystone, and thus
the term "keystoning" has been given to the distortion of the
image which occurs in the iconoscope.

Keystoning of the image cannot be tolerated since it results
in the transmission of a distorted picture. To eliminate the

distortion, a compensating signal is combined with the sawtooth voltage which controls the horizontal movement of the beam in the iconoscope. The compensating signal is a sawtooth voltage, as shown in Figure 48. Note that the amplitude of the compensating signal increases as the beam travels downward toward the bottom of the mosaic. Therefore, instead of being constant, the signal which produces the horizontal deflection increases in amplitude as the beam moves downward. When the proper amount of compensation is introduced, the pattern scanned on the mosaic will appear as shown in Figure 47B.

A SIMPLIFIED TELEVISION SYSTEM

2-40 In the transmitter and receiver, many tubes and circuits are used to perform the necessary functions of the electronic

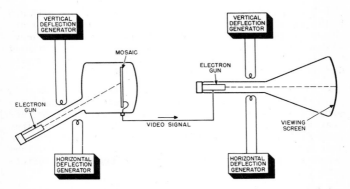

Figure 49. A simplified television system.

television system. While all of these tubes and circuits are important, a clearer understanding of the operation of the television system may be achieved if some of the elements of the system are disregarded and it is assumed that the television system consists of the units shown in Figure 49. Once the operation of the system is understood, the reader will realize the necessity for the additional components and circuits which link and surround the cathode ray tubes in the television camera and receiver.

The simplified system of Figure 49 consists of an iconoscope camera tube, a picture tube, and horizontal and vertical sawtooth deflection generators for both tubes. The mosaic of the camera tube is shown connected to the grid of the picture tube. By simplifying the television system in this way it becomes much easier to visualize the actions which take place in an actual television system, even though the simplified version is not practical.

Assuming that the system of Figure 49 is in operation but that no image is focused on the mosaic in the camera tube, the following actions are taking place.

1 The electron beam in the camera tube is moving back and forth across the mosaic. At the completion of each excursion across the mosaic the electron beam is moved down slightly to begin scanning another line.

2 The electron beam in the picture tube is moving back and forth across the viewing screen. At the completion of each excursion across the screen the beam in the picture tube is moved down slightly to begin scanning another line. The motion of the electron beam in the picture tube is exactly the same as that of the electron beam in the camera tube.

3 The sawtooth signals applied to the horizontal deflection coils of the camera tube and picture tube are of the same frequency (15,750 cps). The sawtooth signals applied to the vertical deflection coils in both tubes are also of the same frequency (60 cps). Because both horizontal signals and both vertical signals are equal, the electron beam in the camera tube moves in exact synchronization with the beam in the picture tube.

4 The electron beams in both tubes move back and forth, tracing a number of horizontal lines starting at the top of the mosaic and viewing screen and moving toward the bottom. Figure 50 illustrates this process at one instant. Both beams have scanned part of the way down and a number of horizontal lines have been formed. In the illustration, only a few horizontal lines are shown. In an actual television system many more lines are used.

If now an image is focused on the mosaic, several additional actions will take place, as follows.

1 As the electron beam in the camera tube scans across the

mosaic, it strikes the globules on the surface of the mosaic and a signal appears at the output of the picture tube.

2 This signal is fed to the grid of the picture tube, where it increases or decreases the number of electrons in the electron beam.

3 As the electron beam in the camera tube strikes globules of the mosaic on which a bright portion of the scene being televised is focused, the signal at the output of the tube increases.

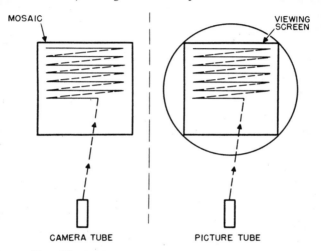

Figure 50. The electron beam scans the mosaic in exact synchronism with the electron beam in the picture tube.

4 When the increased output of the camera tube reaches the grid of the picture tube, it causes the number of electrons in the beam to increase, and thus the screen glows more brightly.

5 As the electron beam in the camera tube strikes globules on which dark portions of the scene are focused, the output to the picture tube decreases, and the number of electrons in the picture tube beam decreases. As a result, the portion of the viewing screen being scanned glows dimly. The positions of the bright and dark portions of the mosaic always correspond to the bright or dark portions of the viewing screen, because the electron beams in the camera and picture tubes are always in the same relative positions.

6 When the electron beams have reached the bottom of the mosaic and viewing screen, a complete image will appear on the viewing screen. This image is a reproduction of the image focused on the mosaic. The scanning action takes place so rapidly that the persistence of the eye (Section 1) and of the screen coating cause us to see a complete image whose structure of lines and elements is barely visible.

7 In order to create the illusion of motion, images are created on the viewing screen in rapid succession. Each image is slightly different than the one preceding it. Successive images are created so rapidly that the eye blends them into one continuously changing picture.

SCANNING

2-41 The method used in the television system, to break down a picture into a series of horizontal lines, which are made up of a series of elements, has been described previously. These horizontal lines appear, to the eye, to blend into a uniform picture if they are presented in very rapid succession. The mechanical television systems which preceeded the electronic system were capable of breaking a picture into 60 horizontal lines. The quality of pictures produced by these systems was very poor because not enough elements could be presented by 60 lines.

The number of lines, into which the mechanical system could break a picture was limited by the speed at which the scanning disc could rotate. The electronic television system which employs cathode-ray tubes overcomes this scanning problem. In the iconoscope and picture tube, the picture is scanned by an electron beam which is practically inertialess. The beam can be made to scan any number of horizontal lines by applying deflection signals of suitable frequency to the vertical and horizontal plates. In the present electronic television system, the number of lines has been standardized at 525 for each complete image. As will be described later, it is not possible to increase the number of lines above this number because of the limitations that have been placed on the channel assigned to each television station. In the following paragraphs the quality and characteristics of the television pictures, which can be obtained with a 525-line system, are discussed.

2-42 Aspect Ratio. The television picture has been designed to have a height 3/4 its width as shown in Figure 51. The ratio of the height of a picture to its width is known as its aspect ratio. The aspect ratio of the standard television picture is therefore three to four. This aspect ratio is used because it has been found, by tests on many persons, to be the most pleasing to the eye, for long viewing periods.

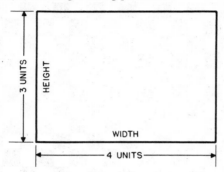

Figure 51. A pattern with a 3 x 4 aspect ratio.

2-43 Picture Elements vs. Bandwidth. The number of elements into which a television system breaks a picture has a direct relation to the width of the channel occupied by the television signal, when it is transmitted over the air. Since the radio frequency spectrum is quite crowded, bandwidth has been the factor which has limited the number of elements in the standard picture. If space were available in the spectrum, it is very probable that the number of lines and elements in the television picture would be greater than at present.

The reader will understand the relationship between bandwidth and the number of elements in the picture by referring to Figure 52A. Assume that the number of checkered squares in the figure is increased until the maximum number, which a 525 line television system can reproduce, is reached. The number of squares in the figure will then be equal to the number of elements into which the system is capable of breaking an image.

Since the elements are square, the height and width of each element will be equal to the width of one horizontal line. In the 525 line picture, there will be 525 elements in a vertical line running from the top to the bottom of the picture. If the aspect ratio is the same as the standard, three to four, there will be 700 elements along each horizontal line (4/3 x 525).

In order to reproduce such a picture on the screen of a picture tube, the signal on the grid of the picture tube would have to be similar to that shown in Figure 52B. As the electron beam scans across each horizontal line, the signal on the grid would

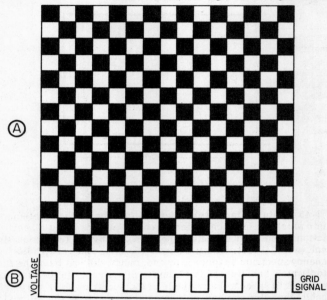

Figure 52. A, checkerboard pattern. Each black and white square is assumed to represent an element in a picture. B, grid voltage which is required to produce checkerboard pattern on the screen of the picture tube.

have to increase and decrease for each white and black element. For the 700 black and white squares on one line, there would be 350 cyclic changes from white to black. In other words, the television transmitter would have to transmit 350 pulses or cycles for each line. Each time a pulse is received and applied to the grid of the picture tube, it increases the number of electrons in the electron beam and the screen glows brightly. At the end of each pulse, the signal on the grid drops and the number of electrons in the beam decreases enough so that the screen is almost completely black. When the next pulse arrives, the process is repeated. Note that for every two picture elements, the signal on the grid must go through one cycle of change.

If one line requires 350 cycles of change, then 525 lines require 525 x 350, or 183,750 cycles. Assuming that the picture is formed in one second, the frequency of the video signal would be 183,750 cps.

If one complete picture, containing 525 lines, was presented to the eye each second, the eye would notice flicker as the elements were traced out line by line, for it will be recalled that at least 10 complete pictures per second must be presented to the eye to prevent flicker. To remove all traces of flicker, as many as 48 pictures are presented each second in motion pictures (24 frames, each projected twice.) In television, as many as 60 pictures are used. The 60 cycle repetition rate of television pictures has been chosen because it equals the frequency of most of the power lines in this country. This is a distinct advantage as the reader will realize when he familiarizes himself with the operation of receiver deflection circuits.

Returning to the checkerboard pattern which would produce 183,750 cycles of voltage for each complete picture scanned by the electron beam, it is apparent that there would be 183,750 x 60 or approximately 11,000,000 cycles per second if 60 pictures were scanned per second. The television channel would have to be 11 megacycles wide if all the shades in the checkerboard pattern were to be reproduced faithfully.

Because it has been impossible to assign an 11 megacycle channel to each television station, several methods have been developed to decrease the frequency of the video signal that is required for a 60 frame television system.

2-44 Interlaced Scanning. Two ways have been devised to reduce the band occupied by the video r-f signal, and at the same time maintain the picture quality possible with a 525 line, 60 frame per second system. The bandwidth is reduced through the use of interlaced scanning and single sideband transmission. Interlaced scanning is discussed here, while single sideband transmission is discussed later in this section. The reader should keep in mind the following points in order to understand what it accomplishes.

   1 The purpose of interlaced scanning is to reduce the number of voltage cycles per second (frequency) of the video signal and thus reduce the band occupied by the video r-f signal.

   2 It is desirable to accomplish this and still retain the picture quality of a 525 line, 60 frame per second system.

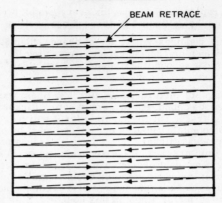

Figure 53A Simple scanning pattern.

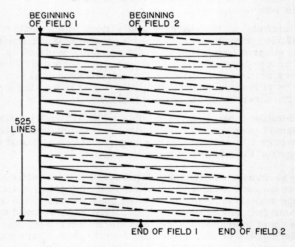

Figure 53B Interlaced scanning pattern.

3 The frequency of the video signal is directly related to the number of lines in each frame and to the number of frames transmitted each second. A reduction in either the number of lines in a frame or in the number of frames transmitted each second will reduce the frequency of the video signal.

To understand interlaced scanning, consider first a simple scanning system in which the electron beam traces out 525 horizontal lines. An example of this method of scanning is illustrated in Figure 53A. The electron beam starts at the top left hand corner and moves across the picture to the right side. The beam then quickly snaps back to the left side and scans the line below. This process is repeated for 525 lines. At the end of the 525th line the beam is at the bottom right hand corner of the picture. With this method of scanning, the beam would trace out 525 lines, 60 times per second.

In the interlaced scanning system the electron beam does not trace out the 525 lines in succession. Instead it skips every other line, tracing out first the odd number lines. When the beam reaches the bottom of the picture, it returns to the top and scans only the even number lines. This method of scanning is shown in Figure 53B. To scan a complete 525 line picture or frame, there are two complete scans or fields. One field contains only the odd number lines and the other field contains only the even number lines. The field repetition rate is 60 cycles per second, but now the picture or frame repetition rate is 30 cycles per second. In other words, two fields containing 262.5 lines each are required to make up a 525 line frame.

The effect of the interlaced scanning system is to deceive the eye into seeing 60 complete pictures or fields per second. The eye blends the odd line fields and the even line fields into a 525 line picture occuring only 30 times per second. The interlaced scanning system is thus very similar to the movie projection system in which 24 frames per second are used, but each frame is projected twice. To the eye it appears that 48 frames are projected each second.

With the interlaced scanning system 30 x 183,750 or approximately 5,500,000 cycles per second must be transmitted to reproduce the checkerboard pattern. The band width is reduced to one half that required with the simple scanning system which presents 60 complete pictures containing 525 lines each. The reduction in band width is accomplished without increasing the flicker effect, because 60 fields of 262.5 lines each are presented using the interlaced system.

The 5.5 megacycle band required for transmitting an interlaced picture is even more than can be allocated to any one television station. As a compromise between the desired number of elements in a picture and the limits of the space in the frequency bands allotted to television, the video signal is limited to 4 megacycles.

2-45 Scanning Signals. To understand interlaced scanning thoroughly, the reader should be familiar with the type of pattern produced by the signals which move the electron beam in the iconoscope and picture tube and cause it to trace out the scanning pattern. The electron beam scans the top line of the mosaic from left to right, returns to the left side of the mosaic

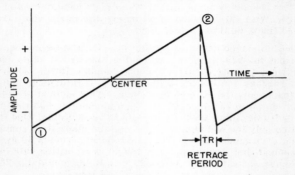

Figure 54. Sawtooth scanning voltage.

skips the second line, and scans the third line as shown in Figure 53B. This process is repeated until the electron beam reaches the bottom of the picture. In tracing out the pattern the beam moves horizontally and vertically. The horizontal motion of the beam in scanning the mosaic is quite rapid, whereas the vertical motion is considerably slower. The signals which are applied to the deflection plates (or coils) of the iconoscope and picture tube to produce the scanning motion are of the sawtooth variety. Figure 54 is a graphic illustration of the sawtooth waveform. The voltage starts at a negative value, increases along a straight line to the zero level (at which point the electron beam is at the center of the mosaic), continues along the straight line to a positive value equal in amplitude to the voltage at which the beam started, and then quickly returns to the initial negative value. If this sawtooth voltage is fed to the horizontal deflecting plates, the electron beam will be deflected from the left side of the mosaic to the right side, return rapidly to the left side, and begin moving across the mosaic again. In each field, using interlaced scanning, there are 262.5 horizontal motions of the beam to one vertical motion of the beam. Therefore a sawtooth voltage of much lower frequency; than the horizontal deflection signal, is applied to the vertical plates to move the beam vertically.

An important characteristic of the sawtooth scanning voltage, shown in Figure 54, is the uniformity, or "linearity", of the voltage rise between points 1 and 2. If the rate were not constant, the electron beam would not move across the mosaic at a uniform speed. This would result in a distorted picture, as shown in Figure 55. A picture distorted in this fashion is said

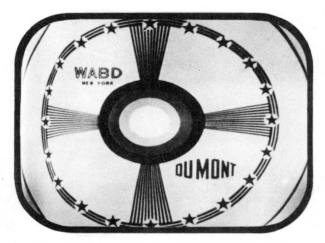

Figure 55. Horizontal distortion of test pattern caused by non-linear scanning.

to be non-linear. A non-linear picture is caused by a sawtooth voltage which has the shape shown in Figure 56. The rising portion of the sawtooth is bent, or non-linear.

It is desirable to keep the time required for the beam to snap back from the right side of the mosaic to the left side as small as possible. In practice this would mean that the portion of the sawtooth voltage represented by Tr in Figure 55 be straight up and down. Unfortunately the circuits necessary to achieve such a condition are too costly to be practical. In practice, the time Tr is generally limited to about 10% of the complete sawtooth waveform.

As mentioned previously, each complete field is scanned 60 times per second. Therefore, the frequency of the sawtooth voltage on the deflection plates which move the beam vertically is 60 cps. In each field there are 262.5 horizontal lines. Therefore, the frequency of the sawtooth voltage on the horizontal deflection plates is 262.5 x 60, or 15,750 cps.

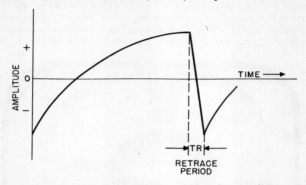

Figure 56. Shape of sawtooth voltage which produces non-linear pattern shown in Figure 55.

2-46 Interlaced Scanning Pattern. Figure 57 illustrates an interlaced scanning pattern. As the horizontal deflecting voltage moves the beam from point 1 to point 1B, the vertical deflecting voltage simultaneously produces a small downward movement of the beam. When point 1B is reached, the beam snaps back to point 2 and scans to point 2B. This process continues until the bottom of the mosaic is reached and the 262nd line is scanned. At the completion of the 262nd line, the beam returns to the left side of the mosaic and starts to trace line 263. It reaches the bottom of the mosaic when halfway through line 263.

When the beam reaches the middle of line 263, the vertical deflecting voltage has reached its peak and commences the vertical retrace. During the vertical retrace period, the beam moves from the bottom of the mosaic back to the top. At the same time, the horizontal deflecting signal continues to move the beam back and forth across the mosaic. Since the retrace time of the vertical deflecting signal is quite short, the beam moves up the mosaic quite rapidly from points 263 to 264 to 265, and finally from 273 to 273.5. These lines which occur during the vertical retrace period are visible on a picture tube screen when no signal is being received. Point 273.5 corresponds to the beginning of the next vertical sawtooth deflecting signal, and the beam is displaced exactly halfway across the mosaic from point 1 where the first scanning line started. The process starts all over again with the beam moving from point 273.5 to point 273.5B of the second field. The lines in the second field fall between the lines in the first field because of the half line displacement at point 273.5. The last line scanned in the

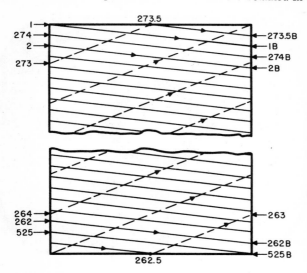

Figure 57. Method of forming interlaced scanning pattern.

second field is from point 525 to point 525B. At this point the vertical sawtooth deflecting signal retraces again and the electron beam starts scanning downward once more from point 1.

In this system of interlaced scanning, some of the horizontal lines are wasted during the interval that the vertical sawtooth deflecting signal is retracing. About 12.5 horizontal lines are wasted in each field. For two fields, or one frame, 25 lines are wasted. In practice, then, for one complete frame, instead of obtaining a picture of 525 horizontal lines, only 500 lines are actually seen. Since the retrace portions of the horizontal and vertical deflecting signals are not used to convey picture information, the electron beam is automatically cut off during the retrace period.

2-47 Blanking Pulses. The scanning lines produced during the vertical and horizontal retrace periods contribute no useful information to the picture, and produce unwanted bright lines in the picture, as shown in Figure 58. The retrace lines are, therefore, obliterated by cutting off the electron beam during the retrace periods. This is accomplished by feeding negative

Figure 58. Retrace lines which would be visible if they were not obliterated by blanking pulses.

pulses to the grid of the iconoscope at the end of each line and at the end of each field. These pulses have the wave shape shown in Figure 59. The duration of each pulse is slightly longer than the retrace time of the sawtooth signals. When the negative pulse is applied to the picture tube grid, the grid becomes so negative with respect to the cathode that no electrons pass through the grid aperture. This controlling feature of the grid electrode was discussed previously under the section on cathode-ray tubes. The method of preventing electrons from passing through the grid during the retrace time of the sawtooth deflecting signals is called "blanking", since the negative pulses effectively blank out the electron beam. The negative pulses which cause blanking of the beam are called blanking or pedestal pulses. The blanking pulses are generated at the television station where they are applied to the iconoscope grid to provide blanking. The pulses are also mixed with the signal output from the iconoscope. A television signal with blanking pulses added is shown in Figure 60. The blanking pulses drive the video signal down to the blank level which corresponds to the grid cut-off bias of the tube. Note that a longer blanking pulse is required

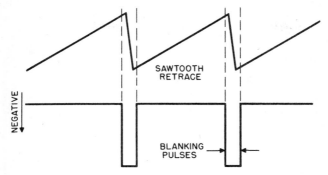

Figure 59. Waveshape and polarity of blanking pulses.

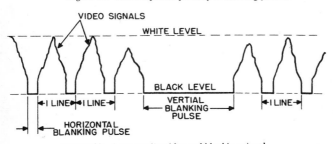

Figure 60. A composite video and blanking signal.

for the vertical blanking than for the horizontal blanking. This is because the retrace time of the vertical sawtooth voltage is longer than that of the horizontal sawtooth voltage. These blanking signals appear at the television receiver where they are fed to the grid electrode of the picture tube.

2-48 Synchronizing Pulses. It was assumed in the foregoing discussion that the deflecting signals which cause the beam to move horizontally and vertically were of a constant frequency.

The circuits used to generate sawtooth signals, however, have a tendency to change frequency, or "drift". Because of the inherent frequency drift of such circuits, the sawtooth scanning voltages in the iconoscope may differ slightly in frequency from the sawtooth voltages which control the scanning of the beam in the picture tube. The picture tube scanning beam would then be out of synchronization with the iconoscope scanning beam and

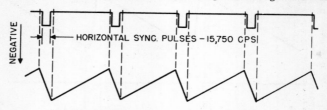

Figure 61. Horizontal sync pulses occur during retrace period of horizontal sawtooth voltage.

would not reproduce the television picture in the same sequence in which it is being scanned in the camera tube.

To keep the frequency of the deflecting signals constant at the transmitter and the receiver, additional signals are fed to the iconoscope sawtooth generator circuits from a synchronizing generator which puts out synchronizing pulses of constant frequency. These synchronizing pulses are mixed in with the video signal and the blanking pulses.

Separate sync pulses are necessary for proper operation of both the horizontal and vertical sawtooth deflecting circuits. At the transmitter these signals are generated, mixed in the proper sequence, and fed to the iconoscope deflection circuits. Special circuits separate the horizontal sync pulses from the vertical sync pulses. The separated horizontal sync pulses are then used to synchronize the horizontal sawtooth voltages while the vertical sync pulses lock the vertical sawtooth voltages. At the receiver, the synchronizing pulses are removed from the combined signal and fed to the sawtooth generators, to maintain their frequencies in step with the sawtooth generators at the transmitter.

The horizontal sync pulses have a square wave shape as shown in Figure 61, and occur at a frequency of 15,750 cps, which is, of course, the same frequency as the horizontal sawtooth scanning voltages. The vertical sync pulse must occur once each field to synchronize the vertical sawtooth voltage, and therefore has a frequency of 60 cps. The shape of the vertical sync pulse is shown in Figure 62. It is actually made up of six small pulses. The vertical sync pulse is formed in this manner to provide synchronization of the horizontal sawtooth generator during the vertical retrace period. This synchronization problem is discussed in greater detail in Section 3.

The sync pulses do not convey picture information. They are merely "keying" signals which are used at the transmitter, and

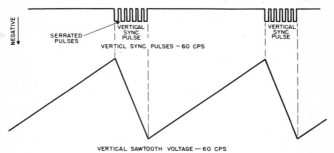

Figure 62. The vertical sync pulse consists of six serrated pulses.

the receiver, to synchronize the sawtooth scanning circuits. These sync pulses could be fed to the iconoscope deflection circuits and then transmitted to the receiver as a separate radio signal. It is much simpler however, to combine the sync signals with the video and blanking signals and transmit them simultaneously. The method by which the signals are combined is explained with reference to Figure 63. The synchronizing pulses are added to the blanking, or pedestal, pulses. The term pedestal pulse is used synonymously with blanking pulse because the blanking pulse serves as a base, or pedestal, upon which the sync pulses are set. Since the blanking pulse must drive the grid of the iconoscope and receiver to cutoff, it represents the black level (the video signal level which produces black on the screen). The sync pulses, being even more negative than the blanking pulses, occur only during the retrace periods when the beam is cut off. The sync pulses cannot, therefore, produce any visible illumination on the screen. They are thus conveniently sent along with the picture information to synchronize the deflection circuits at the receiver with those at the transmitter.

2-49 The Television Signal. Thus far three signals, video, sync, and blanking, have all been mixed together to form the "composite" television signal. Figure 63 shows two horizontal lines of video signal with blanking and sync pulses between them. The maximum amplitude of the signal in the positive direction corresponds to the "white level" (the video signal level pro-

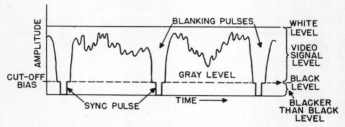

Figure 63. Combined sync, blanking, and video signals.

ducing white on the screen). The "black level" is the bottom of the picture information. This level corresponds to the amplitude of the blanking pulse. At this level the beam is cut off and no illumination of the screen occurs. The sync pulses extend below the black level. The region occupied by the sync pulses is called the blacker than black level or super-sync.

A television signal, such as shown in Figure 63, in which the maximum signal amplitude corresponds to the white level, is said to have a positive polarity. This is the polarity of the signal required at the grid of the receiver picture tube to reproduce the proper shades in the picture, because as the amplitude of the signal is decreased, the voltage on the grid becomes more negative, and the illumination on the screen changes from white to shades of gray. When the signal drops to the blanking or black level, the voltage on the grid is sufficiently negative to cut off the beam and the screen appears black.

When the television signal is transmitted on an r-f carrier, it has a negative polarity, as shown in Figure 64. The negative polarity is desirable because it makes the picture signal more immune to noise. Noise bursts usually effect only the upper and lower limits of the modulating signal. With negative transmission, noise signals are superimposed on the sync signals and occur during the "blacker than black" level, when the electron beam is cut off in the picture tube. In this way the noise does not interfere with the picture information. At the receiver, the polarity of the signal is changed from negative to positive before it is applied to the grid of the picture tube.

2-50 Equalizing Pulses. In addition to the horizontal and vertical sync pulses, another group of pulses is required when in-

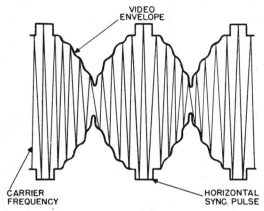

Figure 64. Radio-frequency carrier modulated by the composite video signal. The polarity of the video signal is said to be negative because maximum amplitude of the carrier corresponds to the tips of the sync pulses.

terlaced scanning is used. With interlaced scanning, the even-scanned lines lie midway between the odd-scanned lines. This interlacing of lines takes place because of the half-line displacement at the end of one field and the beginning of the next field. This means that the vertical sawtooth voltage of one field must occur one half line later than the preceeding vertical sawtooth. Since the vertical sawtooth voltages are "keyed" by the vertical sync pulses, it is necessary to make the vertical sync pulses occur one half line after the last horizontal sync pulse in one field, and one full line after the last horizontal sync pulse in the next field. The half line difference in time of the vertical sync pulse with respect to the horizontal sync pulses in two successive fields is brought about by several half line pulses known as equalizing pulses. These pulses occur at twice the frequency of the horizontal sync pulses (or every half line). One group of six equalizing pulses precedes the vertical sync pulse, while another group follows it. Elsewhere in this section the manner in which the equalizing pulses account for the half line displacement is discussed.

2-51 Picture Qualities. In discussing the qualities of a television picture, three terms are used: (1) resolution, (2) contrast, (3) brightness. The term resolution is used to describe the amount of detail that is visible in various objects in a television picture. In this sense, resolution refers to details in both the horizontal and vertical directions.

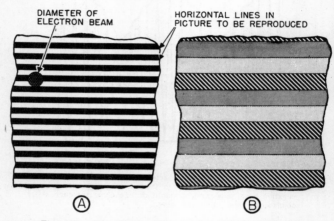

Figure 65   Magnified portion of a picture containing 1,000 horizontal black lines.

2-52 Vertical Resolution. The significance of vertical resolution may be appreciated by a study of the pattern in Figure 65A. This pattern is a magnified portion of a picture which consists of 1,000 horizontal lines, each alternately black and white. The circle represents the diameter of the electron beam in the iconoscope or picture tube. The beam is larger than the thickness of one line. Therefore, when the beam scans the pattern, it cannot distinguish the sharp demarkations between the black and white lines. The signal from the iconoscope mosaic results from a combination of globules, some of which have been exposed to white, and some to black. The beam, in discharging a group of these globules, produces a voltage which represents a mixture of black and white. On the picture tube the pattern does not appear as sharp black and white lines, but as varying shades of grey. See Figure 65B.

In order to reproduce the pattern as black and white lines, the electron beam must have a diameter much smaller than the thickness of the horizontal lines in the picture being televised. Otherwise, the beam cannot transform, or resolve, fine details in the vertical direction. To obtain the maximum resolution

SPACES
BETWEEN
LINES

PATHS OF
ELECTRON
BEAM

Figure 66. Magnified portion of the mosaic showing scanning lines and pattern of horizontal black lines projected on the mosaic.

possible with the present 500 line system, the beams in the iconoscope and in the picture tube must be focused to very small spots. It is essential that the electron beams in the camera and picture tubes be sharply focused at all times, for the vertical resolution is limited by the size of the spots which the electron beams make on the mosaic and on the picture tube screen.

Another factor affecting the vertical resolution of a television system is the number of lines into which it breaks a picture. Figure 66 represents a magnified portion of a mosaic showing the path of the electron beam as it scans 525 horizontal lines. Also shown are a number of horizontal black lines which are projected on the mosaic from a pattern. These horizontal black lines (1, 2, 3, etc) are so thin that they fall between adjacent scanning paths of the electron beam. The black lines, therefore, do not contribute to the signal output obtained from the iconoscope and hence will not appear on the receiver picture tube. Thus, the number of scanning lines in the television system also limits the vertical resolution. The greater the number of lines a television system breaks an image into, the greater is the vertical resolution which can be obtained. Since the number of horizontal lines in the present television picture is fixed at 500 (525 less the 25 horizontal lines that are lost during the vertical retrace time), the maximum possible resolution is predetermined.

2-53 Horizontal Resolution. Horizontal resolution is a measure of the ability of the television system to distinguish between closely spaced vertical details, such as lines. Here again, the diameter of the electron beam is a limiting factor. Horizontal resolution is also limited by bandwidth of the transmitter and receiver circuits, and the channel occupied by the video r-f signal. The reader will recall that the number of elements in the checkerboard pattern which can be reproduced along one line is determined by the bandwidth of the video signal. Since the signal must pass through a number of amplifiers in both the transmitter and receiver, the bandwidth of these amplifiers is an important factor affecting the horizontal resolution. As a rule, the circuits in transmitters are sufficiently broad to pass the full band of video signals. This is also true of the higher priced television receivers, but in many low cost receivers the bandwidth of the i-f amplifiers is not great enough to pass the complete video signal. In this case, the i-f amplifiers become the factor in the system which limits the horizontal resolution.

In small picture television receivers (7 inch or smaller picture tubes), the horizontal resolution is primarily limited by the spot size. The images available on the small screens of these tubes are approximately 4 x 5 inches and less. When 500 horizontal lines are crowded into this small area, the lines are so close together that an extremely small spot size is necessary. The picture tubes used are not capable of producing a spot size small enough to take advantage of the horizontal resolution capabilities of the rest of the system. Since the spot size of the beam limits the number of individual elements that can be reproduced along one line in the horizontal direction, there is little point in employing 4 Mc. amplifiers in receivers using small picture tubes, since the vertical and horizontal resolution is already limited by the size of the picture and the diameter of the electron beam. An amplifier response of 2.5 Mc. is considered sufficient for use with small picture tubes.

It should not be inferred from the above that all small tubes produce comparatively large spots. The size of the beam can be reduced by making the hole in the grid smaller and by increasing the accelerating voltages. This is actually done with small projection tubes which throw the television image onto large screens by means of optical systems.

2-54 Contrast. Contrast refers to the relative intensity of the light and dark areas in a picture. The television pattern of Figure 67A lacks sufficient contrast and therefore appears flat. Figure 67B shows a pattern having too much contrast, and Figure 67C shows a pattern which has proper contrast.

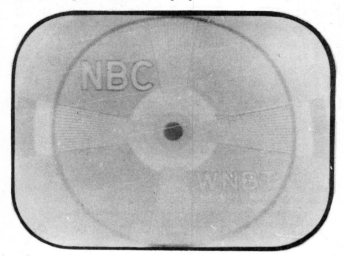

Figure 67A Insufficient contrast.

At the transmitter it is possible to control the contrast by boosting the amplitude of the video signal picked up from the iconoscope. At the receiver the contrast can be controlled by changing the amplification of the video signal in the receiver circuits.

2-55 Brightness. Whereas contrast is a measure of the relative intensity of the light and dark areas in the picture, brightness represents the average intensity of the overall picture. Brightness is controlled at the television receiver by varying the d-c voltage on the grid of the picture tube. The d-c voltage changes the number of electrons flowing to the screen and, therefore, the average illumination.

2-56 Test Patterns. In order to facilitate the adjustment of television transmitters and receivers, test patterns are usually

Figure 67B Too much contrast.

Figure 67C Proper contrast.

transmitted by television stations for several hours during the day.

A typical test pattern is shown in Figure 68A. By observing the test pattern image obtained on the receiver picture tube, several of the characteristics of the overall television system can be determined. Horizontal resolution can be determined by

Figure 68A A typical test pattern.

noting how far in toward the inner circles of the "bulls-eye" the lines in the vertical wedge are resolved. If the lines are distinctly black and white for their entire length, the picture is said to have 350 line horizontal resolution. If the horizontal resolution is poor, then the vertical lines become blurred near the inner circles and the resolution is less than maximum, as indicated by the numbers on the chart. The vertical resolution is measured similarly by observing how far toward the inner circle the lines in the horizontal wedge can be resolved. Figure 68B shows a test pattern having poor resolution. Note that the fine lines in the wedges are not distinctly visible.

The degree of contrast of the television system can also be determined by the use of the test pattern. The inner circles in Figure 68A range from complete black in the center, through several shades of grey, to the white background of the pattern.

Good contrast in a picture is indicated by distinct changes of shade between each circle.

2-57 RMA Test Pattern. The Radio Manufacturers' Association has proposed that the test pattern shown in Figure 69 be used as a standard pattern for test purposes. In addition to en-

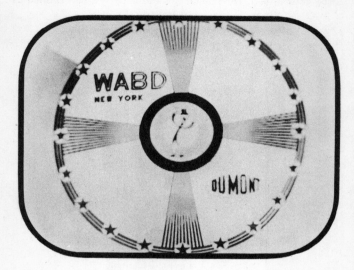

Figure 68B Test pattern with poor resolution, as it appears on screen of picture tube.

abling checks of contrast and resolution to be made, this test pattern provides a means for determining the proper operation of other circuits in the television transmitter and receiver with respect to scanning, brightness, phase shift, focus, plus several other factors. A complete explanation of the RMA test pattern will be found in Section 9.

2-58 The FCC Standard Television Signal. The wave shape of the composite television signal has been standardized by the FCC, so that all stations may transmit uniform waveforms to which all receivers can synchronize. Figure 70 shows the composite video signal, near a vertical synchronizing pulse, for two successive fields. Although this diagram appears complex, it can be readily interpreted by careful study.

2-59 Amplitude Characteristics. The percentage amplitude levels of the various components of the video signal have been standardized to enable proper operation of the receiver. Assuming the peak-to-peak amplitude of the composite signal to by 100%, Figure 70A indicates that 75% plus or minus 2.5% of

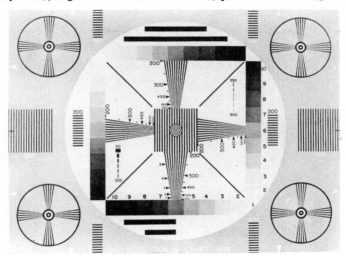

Figure 69. RMA test pattern.

the maximum amplitude is devoted to the picture information contained in the camera signals. The remaining 25% is occupied by the synchronizing pulses. It will be remembered that the blanking level represents black (or grid cutoff) on the cathode ray tube. This makes a convenient reference point to which various shades in the picture can be related; hence at the transmitter, the blanking level (and the synchronizing pulses) are always kept at the same percentage modulation point.

2-60 Frequency Characteristics. The time duration of the various pulses is indicated in percentages of H and V.

H equals the time from the start of one line to start of the next line — or 63.5 microseconds $\left(\frac{1}{15,750} \text{ second.}\right)$

V equals the time from the start of one field to the start of the next field — or 16,667 microseconds $\left(\frac{1}{60} \text{ second.}\right)$

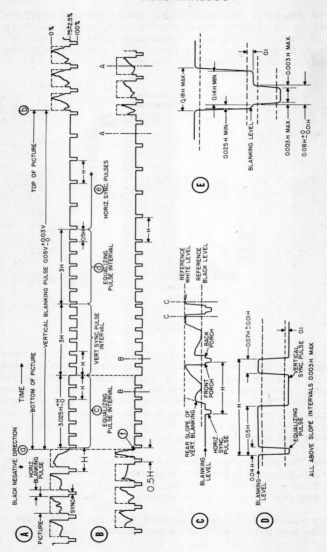

Figure 70. The FCC standard television signal.

Five waveforms are shown in the figure, as follows:

A. Figure 70A shows:

1. The vertical blanking interval extending between points a to b, for a period of 0.05V, or about 14H. 60 vertical blanking pulses occur per second.

2. Superimposed on the vertical blanking pulse are six equalizing pulses (c), extending for 3.025H.

3. Following the first equalizing pulses is the vertical sync pulse, lasting for 3H. The vertical sync pulse has 6 slots, or serrations, to provide continuity of horizontal synchronization during the vertical blanking interval.

4. Six more equalizing pulses (d) follow for a time equal to 3H. The equalizing pulses have a frequency twice the rate of the horizontal sync pulses, and therefore occur 0.5H apart. They are so positioned in the vertical blanking interval as to provide for the half line difference between fields and permit interlaced scanning.

5. Several horizontal pulses (e) occur after the equalizing pulses before the vertical blanking period ends. Each horizontal pulse occurs once each line, and of course, is spaced H time apart.

6. At the end of the vertical blanking interval (b), the cathode ray tube beam is turned on and picture information appears. There then occurs one complete field of lines, with a horizontal blanking pulse of 0.18H occurring between each line.

B. In Figure 70B there is a waveform similar to 70A, except for one important difference. Note that at point f the first equalizing pulse is now displaced only a half line away from the last horizontal sync pulse in the previous field. Likewise, the first horizontal sync pulse after the end of the vertical blanking period occurs one half line before the corresponding horizontal pulse did in the previous field. This accounts for the half line displacement between fields. Otherwise, the vertical blanking intervals for the even and odd line fields would be identical.

1. The scanning of the next complete field now begins and fills in between the lines of the previous field of Figure 70A.

2. At the end of the last line, the beam is back at the beginning of 70A and the start of the next frame.

C. Figure 70C shows an enlarged view of the section marked A-A in Figure 70B.

D. Figure 70D shows section B-B in Figure 70B in greater detail. The exact slope and duration of an, equalizing pulse and a serrated vertical pulse are shown.

E. Figure 70E gives a detailed view of the horizontal sync and blanking pulse shown between points C-C in Figure 70C.

2-61 The Television Channel. It was explained previously that in order to pass all the picture information composed of signals from the elemental sections of the mosaic, the amplifiers in the video sections of the transmitter and receiver must be 4 megacycles wide. Provision has been made, in the allocation of television channels, for the audio signals

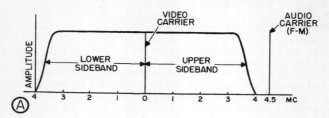

Figure 71A Band of frequencies which would be required for video signal if double side-band transmission were used.

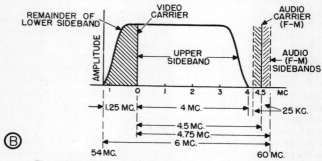

Figure 71B The bandwidth of a television channel is reduced to six megacycles by partially suppressing the lower side-band.

which are transmitted simultaneously with the video carrier and its associated sidebands. The sound accompanying the picture is transmitted on an individual frequency-modulated carrier by a separate transmitter whose frequency is quite close to that of the video transmitter.

If ordinary transmission methods were used to generate the video r-f signal, a band of frequencies 8 megacycles wide would be required to cover the side bands produced. Figure 71A shows a television channel when both sidebands associated with the video carrier are transmitted. This type of transmission is undesirable because of the limited amount of space in the frequency spectrum available for television use. If both sidebands were transmitted, the channel necessary for the video and sound carriers would be 9 megacycles wide. It would also be necessary

Television Frequency Allocations

Channel	Frequencies	Channel	Frequencies
2	54- 60 mc	8	180-186 mc
3	60- 66 mc	9	186-192 mc
4	66- 72 mc	10	192-198 mc
5	76- 82 mc	11	198-204 mc
6	82- 88 mc	12	204-210 mc
7	174-180 mc	13	210-216 mc

Figure 72. Frequency assignments of the twelve television channels.

to provide amplifiers in the transmitter and receiver capable of passing an extremely wide signal. Since both video sidebands contain identical information, it is possible to suppress or filter one sideband at the transmitter and still obtain all the picture information at the receiver. This type of transmission is known as a "vestigial-side band" or "single side-band" system.

Filters are difficult to construct which will cut off the undesired sideband without distorting the remaining 4 megacycle channel. This difficulty is overcome by attenuating a part of the sideband and leaving a 2 megacycle pass band on the low side of the carrier. As a result of this partial sideband suppression, the television channel can be reduced to 6 megacycles as shown in Figure 71B. The video carrier is located 1.25 megacycles from the low end of the channel, with the sideband extending for 4.75 megacycles. The audio carrier, which is frequency modulated with a maximum deviation of plus and minus 25 kc, is fixed 4.5 megacycles from the video carrier, leaving a 0.5 Mc. separation between the sound and picture signals. This separation prevents cross modulation between the two signals in receivers which do not have sharply tuned resonant circuits. The separation between television channels provided by the unused remainder of the lower sideband helps prevent interaction between the video signal and the sound carrier of the next lower channel.

2-62 Television Channel Assignments. The wide 6 megacycle band required for television transmission places severe limits on the number of television stations when compared to AM or FM broadcasting. In order to accommodate a sufficient number of channels, it has been necessary to use very high frequencies. As a compromise with the many broadcasting services demanding space in the ether, the FCC has allocated 12 channels to television between the regions of 54 and 216 Mc. These are divided into a low and high band, channels 2-6 occurring between 54 and 88 Mc, while channels 7-13 extend from 174 to 216 Mc. The frequency limits of the 12 channels is shown in Figure 72. Originally 13 channels were allocated, but due to allocation problems, channel 1 was dropped.

In granting licenses to television stations, the FCC has arranged the channel assignments so that no two adjacent channels are used in any one area. This helps prevent interference between channels, which might occur despite the 2 megacycle guard band that exists in each 6 megacycle channel.

The FCC has made provision for further expansion of commercial television by allocating space in the region between 500 and 1,000 megacycles.

THE COMPLETE ELECTRONIC TELEVISION SYSTEM

2-63 Earlier in this section it was pointed out that, while the camera and picture tubes are the heart of the electronic television system, many other circuits and components are necessary. A few of these components and circuits have already been mentioned. The following is a review of what has already been discussed, and a brief description of other parts of the television system.

Figure 73 illustrates the major parts of the television station and receiver. The television system operates in the following manner:

1. The scene to be televised is focused by the lens system onto the photo-sensitive mosaic of the iconoscope tube in the camera. Each element of the mosaic stores up a charge of electricity proportional to the amount of light focused on it.

2. The camera tube electron gun shoots a stream of elec-

trons at the mosaic, thereby discharging each tiny photocell upon which it impinges. The electron beam is made to scan the mosaic, by means of sawtooth signals supplied from the vertical and horizontal deflection circuits, starting first in the upper left corner and moving in a horizontal line to the right. The beam returns quickly to the left to begin scanning the next line

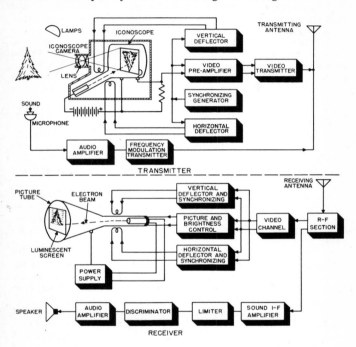

Figure 73. Block diagram of a complete electronic television system.

of photoelectric elements. This process is continued until the entire mosaic is scanned.

3. As each element is discharged by the electron beam, an equivalent electrical signal is produced, consisting of a short pulse. The continuous series of pulses produced forms the video signal. The weak video signal is amplified by the video

pre-amplifier.

4. The output from this amplifier is combined with synchronizing and blanking pulses, which are supplied by the sync generators. The sync pulses control the motion of the electron beam in the camera tube and simultaneously synchronize the electron beam in the receiving picture tube.

5. The composite video signal is fed to the modulator and radio frequency section of the transmitter, resulting in an amplitude-modulated high frequency carrier.

6. The sound signal is generated at the same time in the audio system, which consists of a standard frequency modulation transmitter, operating at a carrier frequency exactly 4.5 megacycles above the frequency of the video carrier. The audio stages include a microphone, audio amplifiers, a frequency modulated generator, and a radio frequency transmitter.

7. The outputs of the video and audio transmitters are fed to the antenna system and radiated.

8. At the receiving point, the antenna picks up the composite picture and sound signals and feeds them to the radio frequency section where they are amplified.

9. The incoming sound and picture signals are separated and fed to separate amplifier systems.

10. The separated video signal passes through several i-f amplifier stages of the video section, is detected and applied to the grid of the cathode ray tube, whose fluorescent screen generates bursts of light proportional to the detected voltage on its grid.

11. The video signal is also fed to the synchronizing circuits of the receiver where the sync pulses are separated from the video information and used to control the electron beam in the picture tube. The beam thus traces out an image identical to that being scanned by the beam in the studio camera tube.

12. The sound passes through a separate i-f amplifier, FM limiter, discriminator, audio amplifier, and speaker system.

The reader should now be familiar with the basic operation of the electronic television system, and well prepared to study its circuit and component details.

If the foregoing description of the fundamentals of the electronic television system has been studied carefully, the reader should have no trouble in understanding the operation and purpose of the transmitting and receiving circuits used in television.

THE TELEVISION RECEIVER

3-1 A television receiver is a complex electronic mechanism. Fifteen or more tubes are required to produce the picture and sound in very small television receivers, while as many as 35 to 40 tubes are used in larger, more expensive models. The reception of ultra-high frequency television signals is accomplished through the use of very critical circuits which require meticulous design and construction.

In a field as young as television, it is not unusual that manufacturers have found many different ways to solve the problems of video circuit design. Time and the all important proving ground in the customer's home will indicate the circuits and designs which perform the best. By familiarizing himself with all of the basic circuits commonly employed in television receivers, the .technician will be able to understand all of the various receivers. With an understanding of fundamentals, the reader will readily appreciate how combinations of the basic circuits may be grouped to make up the numerous commercial receivers now on the market.

Television receivers may be divided into three groups: (1)

Direct view receivers with electrostatic picture tubes, 7 inches or less in diameter; (2) Direct view receivers employing magnetic picture tubes ranging from 7 inches to 20 inches in diameter; (3) Projection receivers in which the image is thrown from the face of the picture tube onto a screen. Picture sizes as large as several square feet are obtained in this manner.

The relative picture sizes of receivers falling into each of these categories are shown in Figure 1. Many basic circuits are common to receivers in all three categories, but there

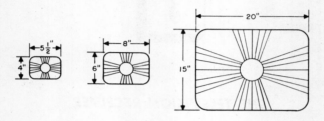

Figure 1. Relative picture sizes of seven inch, ten inch, and projection television receivers.

are wide variations in those circuits which operate the different types of picture tubes and projection systems.

To simplify this discussion of the television receiver and make, it easier for the reader to understand, the receiver will be separated into six basic sections as shown in the block diagram of Figure 2.

   1. The R-F Section
   2. The Video Channel
   3. The Sweep Circuits
   4. The Power Supplies
   5. The Picture Tube
   6. The Sound Channel

All of the basic circuits used in each of the six sections of the receiver will be described in detail in this chapter. At the end of the chapter, combinations of these circuits will be grouped into complete receivers in each of the three categories previously mentioned.

3-2 Block Diagram of a Typical Television Receiver. Before beginning the detailed description of the circuits used in tele-

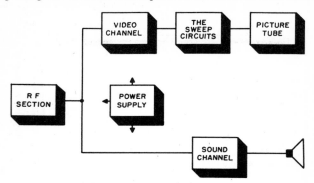

Figure 2. The six basic sections of the television receiver.

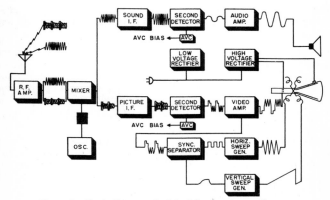

Figure 3. Block diagram of a television receiver with waveforms at input and output of stages.

vision receivers, it is well to summarize the operation of a typical complete unit. This may be accomplished by following a signal through the receiver. The path of the television signal through the receiver is traced with reference to the block diagram shown in Figure 3.

The antenna receives both the sound and picture signals, which are coupled to the receiver input by a suitable transmission line. Referring to the diagram of a typical channel as shown in

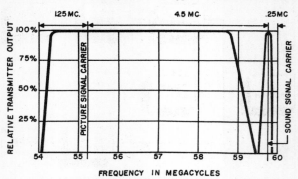

Figure 4. A typical television channel.

Figure 4, it is apparent that the r-f amplifier and mixer tuned circuits must have a bandwidth of 6 Mc, if both the video and sound signals are to be passed.

Television receivers are of the superheterodyne type in which a local oscillator beats with the incoming signals in a mixer stage. Since there are two separate carriers in the r-f and mixer circuits, the local oscillator, beating with each, will produce two i-f signals in the plate of the mixer tube.

The plate of the mixer tube feeds filter networks which separate the video and sound i-f signals, diverting them to the respective i-f systems. After this point in the circuit, there are actually two independent receivers, either of which can operate without the other. One is an FM receiver which reproduces the sound, the other is a video receiver which forms the image on the picture tube.

The sound channel consists of i-f amplifier stages, a limiter, a discriminator, and a conventional audio frequency amplifier.

The video channel begins with the intermediate frequency amplifiers which receive the video i-f carrier from the mixer. After passing through several i-f stages, the video-modulated signal is delivered to a diode detector which acts as a demodulator in the conventional fashion. The detected signal passes through one or more stages of video amplification. The video amplifier response must be essentially flat from below 60 cycles to 4 megacycles. The video signal is finally applied to the grid of the cathode ray tube and varies the intensity of the electron beam according to the shades of black and white in the picture. At the output of the video amplifier there is a circuit which inserts a d-c component on the picture tube grid to reproduce the average brightness of the television picture.

Usually the video signal is tapped at the output of either the video detector or video amplifier and fed to a sync separator tube, which passes the sync pulses and clips off the video information. The sync pulses are then passed through an amplifier in whose plate circuit there are circuits which separate the horizontal and the vertical pulses. These pulses control the operating frequencies of horizontal and vertical sawtooth generators, in order to keep them in step with the transmitter. Both sweep signals are then amplified and fed to the horizontal and vertical deflection plates (or coils). In this way, the beam in the picture tube is synchronized with that in the camera tube at the transmitter.

As the beam in the picture tube sweeps across the fluorescent screen, the signal on the grid of the tube produces the proper variations in the beam intensity and so reconstructs the television picture element by element and line by line.

The power supply requirements of the receiver are two-fold; First, a low voltage (300 to 400 volts) supply is required for the plates and screens of all the tubes, except the cathode ray tube; and second, a high voltage power supply is required for the picture tube. The high voltage required varies between 2,500 and 30,000 volts, depending upon the type and size of the picture tube.

THE R-F SECTION

3-3 The r-f section of a television receiver must perform a number of functions: It must select the desired television signal consisting of sound and picture carriers; it must convert these signals to individual intermediate frequencies; and direct them to the audio and video channels. The r-f section consists of the antenna input circuits, an r-f amplifier (not used in all receivers), the local oscillator for superheterodyne operation, and the mixer. Since there are twelve television channels, extending from 54 to 216 Mc, provision must be made, in the design of these circuits, for great frequency coverage. When tuned to any particular channel, the r-f circuits must have a bandwidth of 4 to 6 Mc, to pass the video and audio signals.

Wide band circuits operating at the high frequencies used for television bring about problems which are not encountered at standard broadcasting frequencies. The layout of the chassis and components, the inductance and capacity of leads, and the interelectrode capacities of tubes become important factors. Miniature tubes have been developed which satisfy the requirements of these high frequency circuits.

Stray inductance and capacitance in the r-f section of a television receiver is so critical that even a slight disturbance of lead or part positioning may cause a previously perfect receiver to become inoperative. In design and manufacture, all parts must be carefully positioned and leads must be kept as short and direct as possible.

Because excessive losses occur if ordinary insulating materials are used at high frequencies, special insulating materials are required in television receivers.

Frequency stability is an important factor in television receivers, because it is much more difficult to design stable equipment for high frequency operation than for use at regular broadcasting frequencies.

3-4 Tubes. Miniature tubes have low interelectrode capacitances and high mutual conductances (gm). Since the gain of an amplifier is proportional to mutual conductance, high mutual conductance miniature tubes simplify somewhat the problem of obtaining high gain amplifiers at television frequencies. Circuit capacity is important because it limits the size of the plate load resistor of the amplifier tuned circuits. The higher the capacity, the lower is the load resistor required for a broad band response characteristic. The gain of an amplifier is proportional to the size of its load resistance, so that it is desirable to make this resistor as large as possible by keeping the circuit capacity low.

In the design of broadcast receivers, pentodes have long been preferred to triodes because of their higher gain and stability. In television receivers, the triode has again assumed importance because of several characteristics which make it superior to the pentode. The triode has fewer grids than a pentode and develops less noise. In highly sensitive television receivers, tube and circuit noise is about 10 microvolts. This is as great as some parts of the input signal. Tubes which generate the least amount of noise are therefore preferred. Triodes produce about one-third as much noise as a pentodes.

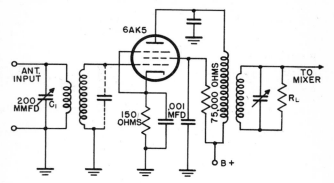

Figure 5. Pentode r-f amplifier.

Another desirable characteristic of the new miniature triodes, designed for high frequency operation, is their reduced grid-to-plate capacitance which makes them less likely to oscillate in amplifier stages. Their lower interelectrode capacitance reduces the degree of tuned circuit loading required in order to obtain a broad band response. Higher plate load resistance increases the amplifier gain of triodes.

Miniature tubes which are suited for broadband high frequency operation because of their low capacities and high mutual conductance are the 6AK5, 6AG5, and 7W7 pentodes, the 6J4, 6J6, and 7F8 triodes.

3-5 R-F Amplifiers. Not all television receivers employ r-f amplifiers. In the primary operating areas of television stations, signals are strong enough so that an r-f amplifier is not necessary.

There are several points in favor of the use of an r-f stage. Increased selectivity and reduced image response result when an r-f amplifier is used. The added gain an r-f amplifier produces, improves the signal-to-noise ratio of the entire receiver, because it minimizes the effects of the noise generated in the mixer tube. An r-f amplifier isolates the oscillator from the antenna and prevents excessive radiation from the receiver, an important factor in crowded urban areas.

Several circuits and circuit variations are used in television r-f stages.

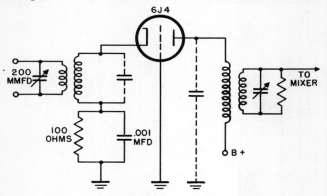

Figure 6. Grounded-grid r-f amplifier.

3-6 Pentode R-F Amplifier. A pentode r-f amplifier is illustrated in Figure 5. The 6AK5 and 7W7, high mutual conductance pentodes, are suitable for broadband, high frequency operation in such a circuit. A double-tuned, over-coupled transformer is used between the grid of the r-f amplifier and the antenna. Its primary is tuned by capacitor C-1 to provide a resonant circuit at the desired frequency. In the plate circuit, another parallel tuned circuit is used, loaded by resistor R-1, to obtain a response characteristic 6 Mc wide. The r-f signal appearing across this resonant circuit is coupled directly to the grid of the mixer stage.

3-7 Grounded-Grid Amplifier. In conventional r-f amplifier circuits, a triode would oscillate if used at television frequencies because of its high interelectrode capacity. The grounded-grid r-f amplifier shown in Figure 6 was designed to eliminate this oscillation without the use of neutralization. The grid of the tube is grounded and acts as a shield between the input and output circuits, thus preventing the tube from oscillating. The input signal is injected into the cathode. The varying r-f signal produces a fluctuating potential difference between the grounded grid and the cathode, causing changes in plate current. The grounded-grid amplifier, using triodes such as the 6J6 or 6J4, is simpler in construction than a pentode amplifier and requires fewer components.

3-8 Cathode-Coupled R-F Amplifier. Figure 7 shows a dual

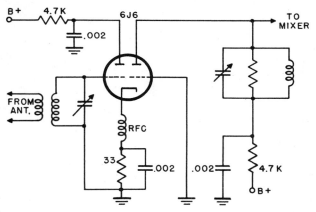

Figure 7. Cathode-coupled r-f amplifier.

triode used as a cathode-coupled amplifier. This circuit is in reality a combination of two amplifiers. The first triode section is used in a cathode-follower circuit with the input signal fed to its grid. Normally, the output of a cathode-follower is taken from the cathode of the tube. The tube shown has a common cathode for both triode sections, and therefore, the output signal of the cathode-follower is connected to the cathode of the second section. The second triode is a grounded grid amplifier, and since in such a circuit the cathode is the input, interstage coupling is complete within the tube.

The addition of the cathode follower stage before the grounded-grid amplifier has several advantages. The input of the cathode-follower has low capacity and broad bandwidth. The additional stage isolates the antenna from the local oscillator better than does a single r-f stage. Oscillator radiation to nearby receivers is therefore negligible. The overall gain of this r-f amplifier is about the same as that of a single pentode. If a dual triode, having separate cathodes, were used, the cathodes would have to be connected together.

3-9 Push-Pull R-F Amplifier. Push-pull r-f amplifiers are found in some receivers. These circuits possess excellent stability at high frequencies. A typical circuit is shown in Figure 8. The input signal is fed from the antenna through a balanced transmission line to the grids of a dual triode. The plate tank circuit consists of a quarter wave section of balanced trans-

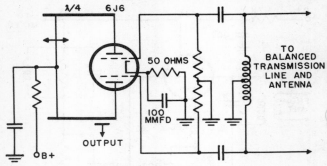

Figure 8. Push-pull r-f amplifier.

mission line. This quarter wave section is equivalent to a high Q parallel-tuned circuit. The transmission line can be tuned over a band of frequencies by moving a shorting bar along the parallel conductors. The push-pull amplifier has high gain, low capacity, and is stable in operation by virtue of its symmetry.

3-10 The High Frequency Oscillator. The purpose of the local oscillator in a television receiver is identical to that of the oscillator in a conventional superheterodyne. The oscillator signal beats with the incoming television signal to produce the picture and sound i-f signals.

An important problem in the design of television receivers is that of oscillator stability. Excessive oscillator drift results in a corresponding intermediate frequency drift and deterioration of the video and audio response. In extreme cases, the oscillator frequency may shift far enough so that the audio carrier output of the mixer stage is moved out of the pass band for which the sound i-f amplifier is tuned.

Temperature change and supply voltage variations are the major causes of oscillator drift. Most materials have a positive temperature expansion coefficient; that is, with a rise in temperature, they expand. As a result, an increase in temperature causes an increase of inductance and capacitance in the oscillator circuit, and a corresponding decrease in frequency. Since ceramic materials have a practically zero temperature coefficient, band switches and sockets are usually made of these materials.

To overcome the effects of capacitance which increases with

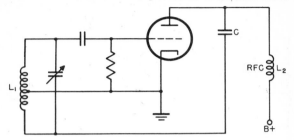

Figure 9. Shunt-fed Hartley oscillator.

temperature, a small capacitor with a negative temperature coefficient is often added across an oscillator coil. Inductance increases may be minimized by the use of suitable types of wire, such as Invar and Nilvar, which have negligible linear expansion coefficients. It is interesting to note that while receiving circuits use high L to C ratios for best efficiency, a low L to C ratio is preferred in oscillators. If the capacitance is made relatively large, it tends to minimize the effects of capacitance changes due to tube warm-up and plate voltage variations.

In order to reduce oscillator "pulling" to a satisfactory point, it is necessary to use separate tubes for the oscillator and mixer stages of a television receiver. Pulling is the tendency of the oscillator to lock in or approach the frequency of a signal near its own frequency (in this case, the incoming r-f signal). The fact that the comparatively high interelectrode capacities of multi-grid converter tubes makes them undesirable at high frequencies, is another reason why separate mixer and oscillator tubes are found in television receivers.

Several types of oscillator circuits are found in television receivers. At present, the Hartley, the Colpitts, and the Ultraudion are the most popular.

3-11 The Hartley Oscillator. The Hartley is one of the simplest self-excited oscillators. Its distinguishing feature is the tapped coil, L-1, used to obtain the feedback necessary for oscillation. A shunt fed circuit is shown in Figure 9. The coil is connected between the plate and the grid. The tap, usually located nearer the grid end, is connected either directly or through a condenser, to the cathode of the oscillator tube. A blocking condenser, C, is used to isolate the high positive d-c voltage on

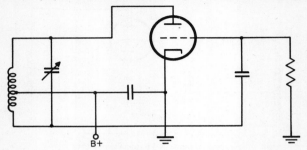

Figure 10. Series-fed Hartley oscillator.

the plate from the negative d-c voltage on the grid. The r-f grid current flows in the lower section of the coil, while the r-f plate current flows in the upper section of the coil. The phasing of the plate and grid currents in the coil is such that positive feedback to the grid is obtained and oscillation takes place.

Both shunt (Figure 9) and series (Figure 10) feed are illustrated to demonstrate the detailed circuit modifications necessary to change from one method of feed to the other. Shunt feed is well adapted to applications in which it is desirable to keep the tuned circuit at ground potential. This is accomplished only at the expense of using a well designed r-f choke in the B plus lead. Series feed eliminates the need for this choke but requires that the tuned circuit be at a high d-c potential (plate voltage) above ground.

The Hartley oscillator does not depend on the grid-plate capacity of the oscillator tube for feedback and will, therefore, work well with almost any type of triode, tetrode, or pentode.

By modifying the basic circuit as shown in Figure 11, the Hartley can be made to cover several widely separated frequencies. In position 1 of the switch, L-5 is in the circuit in combination with capacitor C-1. Other frequencies are obtained by placing inductances L-1, L-2, L-3, or L-4 in parallel with C-1, which is always in the circuit. The number of switch points is determined by the number of television channels which the receiver must cover. The variable capacitor, C-2, is placed in the circuit for fine tuning and to adjust for frequency drift.

3-12 Colpitts Oscillator. The Colpitts oscillator obtains the

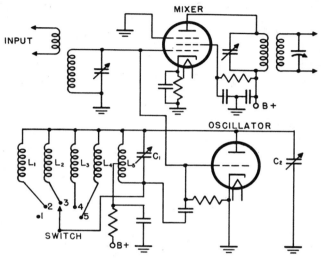

Figure 11. Hartley oscillator for covering widely separated frequencies.

feedback necessary to support oscillation by dividing the tuned circuit into two parts, as shown in Figure 12. This division is accomplished by means of a capacitive voltage divider made up of C-1 and C-2 in series, shunted across L. It will be noticed that the principle involved is the same as that used in the Hartley circuit, except that it is the capacitor which is tapped instead of the coil. The r-f voltage across C-1 is the plate portion, and the r-f voltage across C-2 is the grid portion. The feedback ratio is therefore dependent on the ratio of the two capacitors. The smaller capacitor has the larger r-f voltage across it, since its reactance is greater. Because the ratio of the reactance does not change with frequency, a constant feedback ratio over a wide tuning range can be maintained, providing the reactance ratio is not disturbed. The ratio can be kept constant by adding a separate variable condenser, or by making C-1 and C-2 parts of a split stator condenser.

3-13 Ultraudion Oscillator. The Ultraudion oscillator (Figure 13) has the distinguishing characteristic that there is no visible division between the grid and plate portions of the coil L-1. This circuit has no coil tap as does the Hartley, or capacity divider as does the Colpitts.

In the Ultraudion, the grid-to-cathode capacitance Cg and the

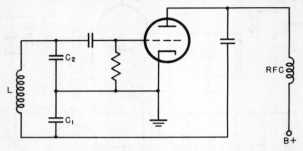

Figure 12. Colpitts oscillator.

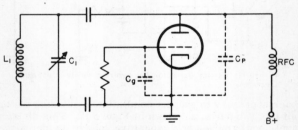

Figure 13. Ultraudion oscillator.

cathode-to-plate capacitance Cp form a voltage divider which performs the same function as do the dividing capacitors used in the Colpitts circuit. In other words, the operation is exactly the same as the Colpitts circuit, except that the dividing capacitances are the interelectrode capacitances of the tube plus stray capacitance in the wiring. This makes the feedback ratio entirely dependent upon the characteristics of the tube, and the stability subject to the heating effects on the tube elements. Adjustment of feedback is possible by the addition of a condenser between the grid and cathode, or plate and cathode, or both. The advantage of the Ultraudion circuit is that it is simple and

requires comparatively few components, since it uses interelectrode capacitances in place of external components.

3-14 The Mixer. In the superheterodyne television receiver,
the mixer's function is the combining of the incoming r-f carrier

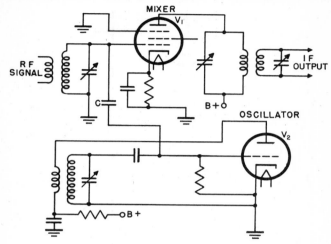

Figure 14. Capacitive-coupled mixer oscillator.

with the receiver's oscillator signal to produce a lower frequency (intermediate frequency). In order to produce this intermediate frequency, the mixer must operate as a non-linear device on the curved portion of the plate characteristic of the mixer tube. In ordinary broadcast receivers, a single tube, known
as a pentagrid converter, often performs the functions of the oscillator and mixer. At television frequencies, the stability of
the oscillator section in a pentagrid converter is very poor. To
avoid excessive frequency drift, separate tubes are used for the
oscillator and mixer stages in current television receivers.

A typical mixer circuit is shown in Figure 14. Here both the
r-f signal and the local-oscillator voltage are applied to the
control grid of a pentode, V-1. Instead of capacitive coupling
to the oscillator through C, inductive coupling may be used. A
circuit using inductive coupling is shown in Figure 15. The use
of two tubes in the circuit arrangements of Figures 14 and 15
results in stable oscillator performance and maximum gain, by

permitting the use of a high transconductance mixer tube.

The greater the conversion efficiency of the mixer stage, the better is the signal-to-noise ratio of the circuit. That is, for a small signal input, more i-f voltage is produced at the plate, which in turn helps to overcome the mixer conversion noise.

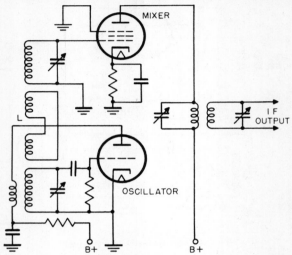

Figure 15. Inductively-coupled mixer-oscillator.

Only the beat frequency of the r-f signal and the oscillator is to be passed on to the i-f stages; hence, the plate tank circuit of the mixer tube is tuned to this intermediate frequency. The r-f and oscillator frequencies in the plate circuit are by-passed to ground.

3-15 Dual Triode Mixer-Oscillator Circuits. A dual triode, such as a 6J6 or 7F8 is often used as a mixer and oscillator. The incoming signal is applied to the mixer grid and the oscillator voltage is injected into the grid or cathode.

In Figure 16, one section of a 7F8 dual triode is connected as a Hartley oscillator. The cathode of this section is capacitively coupled to the cathode of the mixer stage. The intermediate frequency appears in the plate circuit of the mixer triode. In Figure 17, the oscillator voltage is injected into the grid.

A 6J6 which has a single cathode common to both triode sections may also be used as a dual mixer-oscillator tube if it is connected as shown in Figure 18. The r-f input signal is inject-

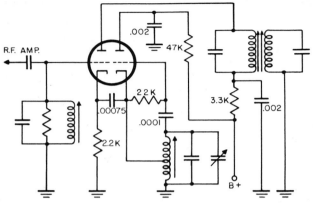

Figure 16. Mixer-oscillator using cathode injection.

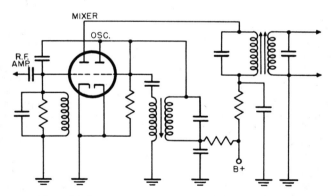

Figure 17. Dual triode mixer-oscillator using grid injection.

ed into the grid of the first section. This sets up a varying voltage across the inductance in the cathode circuit. The second triode is operated as a modified Colpitts oscillator with its grid coil coupled to the inductance in the cathode. Cathode-coupled mixing thus takes place and produces an intermediate frequency in the plate circuit of the mixer section.

Dual triode mixer-oscillator circuits do not exhibit the disadvantages of single tube mixer-oscillator circuits which were

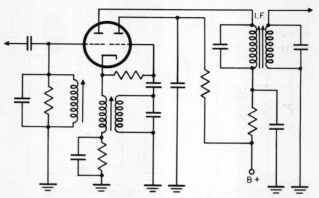

Figure 18. Mixer-oscillator using dual triode with common cathode.

previously mentioned, because there is sufficient isolation between sections of the tubes used to eliminate these effects.

3-16 Separation of Video and Audio I-F Frequencies. In addition to the video i-f frequency signal in the mixer of a television receiver, there is also generated an audio i-f carrier and its associated sidebands. The video i-f frequencies of present receivers range from 25.75 Mc to 26.4 Mc, while the audio i-f carrier may be from 21.25 Mc to 21.9 Mc. In most receivers, the video and audio i-f signals are separated in the mixer stage, and fed to separate amplifiers.

Several methods are employed to separate the signals, all embodying much the same principle. Tuned circuits are placed in the mixer stage. Each circuit is resonated for the desired frequency which is then passed on to the proper i-f amplifier. In Figure 19, a parallel combination consisting of a coil, L-1, and a capacitor, C-1, is placed in the mixer plate circuit and broadly tuned to pass the 4 Mc video signal. The video signal is then fed to the video i-f amplifier. A separate parallel circuit, L2-C2, is tuned to 21.9 Mc, thus developing a maximum voltage at the audio frequency, but very little video signal voltage. The 21.9

Mc sound carrier and its 25 kc sidebands are fed to the audio i-f amplifiers.

In Figure 20, two parallel tuned circuits are again used, but in this case, the resonant circuit (L1-C1) for the picture signal is in the plate circuit, while the tuned circuit (L2-C2) for the

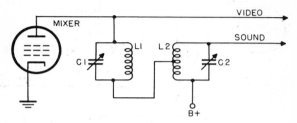

Figure 19. Circuit used to separate the video and audio signals.

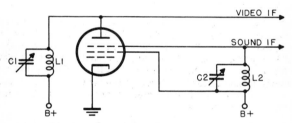

Figure 20. Plate and suppressor-screen tuned circuits for separating video and audio signals.

sound signal is in the suppressor-screen circuit. Still another method uses a series parallel combination as shown in Figure 21. The video signals are developed across the parallel tuned elements (L1-C1) in the plate circuit, while the sound is taken from the capacitor in the series circuit formed by the inductance, L-2, and the capacitance, C-2.

Perfect separation of audio and video signals is not achieved by the above methods, and additional filtering must be employed in the respective i-f amplifiers. Little trouble is encountered with video signals in the audio stages, since spurious amplitude modulation of the FM sound by the picture signals is suppressed in the limiter stages. On the other hand, sound signals can materially affect the picture quality if they are not properly filtered.

Rejection of sound signals which reach the video channel is obtained through the use of wave traps which are discussed later in this section.

3-17 Wide Band Tuned Circuits. The amplifier stages in the

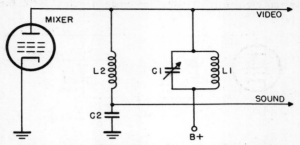

Figure 21. Series and parallel circuits for separating video and audio signals.

r-f and i-f sections of a television receiver are coupled together by tuned circuits consisting of combinations of inductors, capacitors, and resistors. These tuned circuits must be designed and adjusted for a uniform 6 Mc pass band in the r-f circuits and 4 Mc pass band in the video i-f circuits. At the same time, the shape of the response curve of the tuned circuits must be such as to attenuate the frequencies generated by stations operating on adjacent channels.

A simple tuned circuit consisting of a coil and capacitor connected in parallel is shown in Figure 22. This circuit has a characteristic such that when a voltage is applied to it at its resonant frequency, the impedance of the parallel combination is maximum. As the applied voltage is varied in frequency above and below the resonant point, the impedance of the circuit decreases as shown in Figure 23. Several curves are shown in the figure, each curve representing a different value of Q. Q is the ratio of a coils inductive reactance to its resistance. The significance of this ratio is indicated by the shape of the curves in Figure 23. The higher the Q, the sharper is the tuning of the circuit, and the greater is its selectivity. Another important factor is the fact that the higher the Q of a circuit, the higher the voltage developed across it. Thus, Q is a measure of the gain of an amplifier stage which uses tuned circuits.

The simple circuit of Figure 22 is inadequate for coupling television amplifier stages, because it discriminates against frequencies above and below its resonant frequency. In order to obtain a wideband frequency characteristic for r-f, mixer, and i-f stages, a transformer combination is employed as shown in Figure 24.

Several resonant curves can result from this circuit, depend-

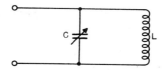

Figure 22. A parallel resonant circuit.

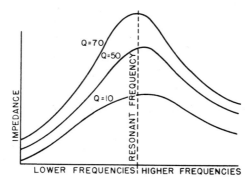

LOWER FREQUENCIES | HIGHER FREQUENCIES

Figure 23. The effect of Q on the selectivity of a parallel tuned circuit.

ing upon the degree of coupling between the primary and the secondary (the coefficient of coupling, is a measure of the amount of magnetic flux linking the primary and the secondary). In Figure 25, three conditions of coupling are shown. A loosely coupled circuit gives the resonant frequency characteristic of the simple tuned circuit. As the coupling is increased, a point is reached where the impedance of the circuit rises to a maximum. This degree of coupling is referred to as "critical coupling". At degrees of coupling greater than critical coupling, the impedance no longer rises, but the curve begins to broaden, resulting in the double humped characteristic of an overcoupled circuit.

The overcoupled circuit approaches the desired response for wideband television amplifiers. However, the dip at the resonant frequency is undesirable. This dip is minimized by shunting the primary and the secondary with low resistances as shown in Figure 26. This lowers the Q of the circuit and consequently

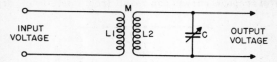

Figure 24. A resonant and coupled coil.

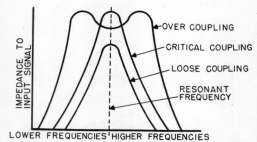

Figure 25. The effect of coupling on the response of a tuned circuit.

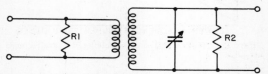

Figure 26. Transformer shunted with resistors to flatten and broaden its response.

its gain, but flattens and broadens the curve to secure the 6 Mc bandwidth required. Figure 27 shows several response curves for different values of loading resistance. Special high gain tubes, such as the 6AC7, 6AK5, 6AU6, and 6J6, have been developed for television to compensate for the reduction in gain resulting from broad band coupling. Gains of approximately 10 to 20 are realized when these tubes are used in broadband circuits.

3-18 Antenna Coupling Circuits. A tuned wideband circuit is required in the antenna input system in order to match the impedance of the antenna transmission line to the first amplifier tube. Two types of coupling circuits are illustrated in Figures 28 and 29. Figure 28 shows an untuned primary and tuned secondary transformer which permits impedance matching through

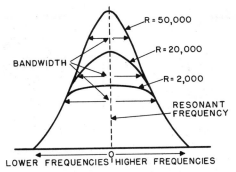

Figure 27. The effect of various values of load resistance on bandwidth of coupling transformers.

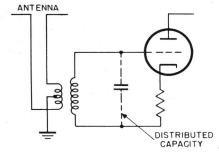

Figure 28. Antenna coupling circuit using untuned primary and tuned secondary.

adjustment of the number of turns in each winding. The secondary winding, and its distributed capacitance, form a resonant circuit. The tuned primary and secondary circuits of Figure 29 give double the signal gain of an untuned primary, tuned secondary circuit, having the same bandwidth. Impedance match is provided for through adjustment in the number of turns and the size of the shunting capacitance.

A third type of coupling is shown in Figure 30. A tuned link, L-2, is added to the double tuned circuit of Figure 29 and results in greater signal gain and selectivity.

The generation of the sound and picture intermediate frequen-

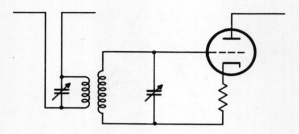

Figure 29. Antenna coupling circuit using tuned primary and secondary.

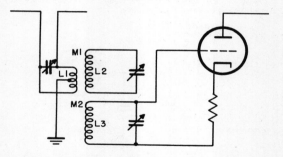

Figure 30. Double tuned antenna coupling circuit with tuned link added.

cies in the mixer stage completes the functions of the r-f section. From this point, the television receiver actually becomes a separate FM sound receiver and a separate video receiver with common power supplies. The sound i-f signal is directed to distinctly separate audio circuits. The picture signals are fed to the video and sweep circuits which control the operation of the picture tube.

THE VIDEO CHANNEL

3-19 The video channel consists of the video i-f amplifiers, the video second detector, the video amplifier, an automatic gain control circuit, and a circuit referred to as the d-c restorer. These stages are arranged as shown in the block diagram of Figure 31. The video channel amplifies the video i-f signals, de-

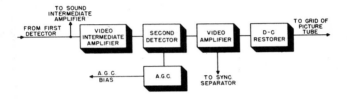

Figure 31. Block diagram of the video channel.

tects them, and brings them up to a level at which they can properly modulate the grid of the picture tube.

The sensitivity, selectivity, and bandwidth of a television receiver, with respect to video signals, is governed mainly by the characteristics of its video i-f amplifiers. Only careful design and construction will bring about the required characteristics.

3-20 Sensitivity. The sensitivity of a television receiver may be defined as the minimum input voltage which will drive the grid of the picture tube from full brightness to cutoff when the receiver is operating at maximum gain. The amplitude of the video signal required at the picture tube to fully modulate the grid in this manner depends upon the design characteristics of the electron gun structure. Although the signal amplitude required varies with different picture tubes, 50 volts may be taken as an average. The gain of the r-f amplifier, the video i-f amplifiers, and the video amplifier must provide sufficient amplification to increase the level of the received signal to the required 50 volts. When the amplification of a receiver is increased, the signal required to provide the necessary 50 volts is reduced. A receiver capable of great amplification can therefore produce satisfactory pictures with very weak input signals. There is, however, a limit to the amount of usable amplification. The amount of usable amplification is governed by the prevailing man made and atmospheric noise. When the noise signals are

Figure 32. Test pattern showning effects of weak signal.

almost as strong as the television signal, a "washed-out", grainy picture is obtained. Noise streaks appear in the picture and synchronization is unstable. Figure 32 is a test pattern showing the effects of a weak signal. The minimum signal from which a satisfactory picture can be reproduced must of necessity be stronger than the prevailing noise.

3-21 Signal to Noise Ratio. The relation between a received signal and the prevailing noise is usually expressed as a ratio, referred to as the signal to noise ratio. In strong signal areas, the signal-to-noise ratio may be as high as 50 or more. The primary operating area of a television station is considered to include all locations where a video signal of more than 500 microvolts may be received. Since the average noise level is normally about 100 microvolts, signal to noise ratios as low as 5 are commonly encountered.

As previously pointed out, the weakest television signal which will produce a usable picture is slightly greater than the noise level. In areas having a noise level of 100 microvolts, a signal of over 100 microvolts is necessary. Such a signal would therefore have a signal to noise ratio of more than one. If the gain of the receiver is sufficient to amplify weaker signals, say 50 microvolts, to a level of 50 volts at the picture tube, so much noise would be amplified along with the desired signals that the picture would be unpleasant to view.

With this understanding of minimum input signal level and the voltage required at the picture tube, it is possible to determine the gain needed in each amplifier stage of the television receiver. To amplify a 100 microvolt signal to a level of 50 volts, the overall amplifier gain must be 500,000 (50 volts divided by 100 microvolts). This gain might be derived in a television receiver in the following manner:

1. An r-f amplifier with gain of 10.
2. I-F amplifier stages with gains between 8 and 15.
3. A video amplifier with a gain between 25 and 50.

If it is assumed that the receiver has three i-f stages, that the r-f amplifier and each i-f amplifier have a gain of 10, and that the video amplifier has a gain of 50, the following amplified voltages will appear at the specified points in the receiver for an input signal of 100 microvolts:

1. At the output of the r-f amplifier—1,000 microvolts.
2. At the output of the 1st video i-f amplifier-10,000 microvolts.
3. At the output of the 2nd video i-f amplifier—100,000 microvolts.
4. At the output of the 3rd video i-f amplifier—1,000,000 microvolts, or 1 volt.
5. At the output of the video amplifier (or the input to the grid of the picture tube) - 50 volts.

Most television receivers now on the market have a gain of about 500,000 and, therefore, have a sensitivity of about 100 microvolts. Some of these receivers may not have an r-f amplifier stage, in which case an extra video i-f amplifier or video amplifier may be used to achieve this sensitivity. A few receivers have sensitivities as low as 1,000 microvolts, which means that they must operate in areas where strong signals exist.

3-22 Bandwidth. Closely associated with the sensitivity of a receiver is the bandwidth of its amplifiers. As the bandwidth of an amplifier is increased, its gain is decreased. The optimum bandwidth for passing the video signal is 4 Mc. To achieve this wideband response at high gain is a very difficult problem. Circuit capacities, tubes, and components must be critically selected. Only high quality receivers have this wideband response and a maximum sensitivity of 100 microvolts. In less expensive receivers which employ small picture tubes, the bandwidth is purposely limited to a value not greater than 3 Mc and often less

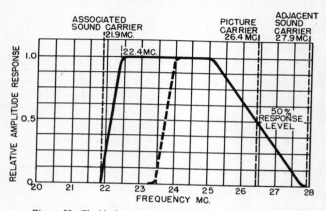

Figure 33. The ideal response curve for a television receiver.

than 2.5 Mc. This means that the gain of each amplifier stage may be increased, and fewer stages used. There is little advantage in using 4 Mc amplifiers with small picture tubes, because the spot size of the electron beam prevents the reproduction of any more detail than contained in a 2.5—3 Mc signal. With large tubes (10 inches or more in diameter) full use may be made of bandwidths of 3.5 to 4 Mc.

3-23 Selectivity. The selectivity of a television receiver reflects in its ability to differentiate between the desired video signal and signals of other frequencies. Selectivity is usually expressed in the form of a curve of output voltage plotted against frequency. The shape of the selectivity curve is chiefly determined by the response of the video i-f amplifiers. The ideal selectivity curve for a television receiver, as shown in Figure 33, is therefore the same as the video i-f response curve. Several important characteristics of the idealized curve should be noted:

1. The response falls to zero at 21.9 Mc. This is the sound

carrier intermediate frequency of the associated television channel. The associated channel sound signals must be greatly attenuated so that they will not pass through the video channel. Should sound signals get into the picture, they will cause annoying band patterns in the picture, as shown in Figure 34. An

Figure 34. Test pattern showing effects of sound in the picture channel.

attenuation of 40 db (a voltage ratio of 100 to 1) will fully reject the associated channel sound carrier.

2. The video signal is uniformly amplified from 22.4 Mc to about 25 Mc. From this point, the slope of the curve falls gradually. At 26.4 Mc, the relative amplitude response is 50%. The bandwidth of the video channel is considered to extend from 22.4 Mc to the point on the response curve where the response has dropped to 50%. The frequency difference between 22.4 Mc and 26.4 Mc is 4 Mc. In other words, the selectivity curve of an ideal television receiver is not flat over its entire 4 Mc bandwidth. The response of the amplifiers is made to slope in this manner because it has been found that an amplifier with this characteristic passes the high frequency components of the television signal with less distortion than an amplifier whose re-

sponse is flat to 4 Mc and then drops off very suddenly. The
dotted portion of the curve represents the response characteristic of a video i-f amplifier, such as used in television receivers with small picture tubes. The pass band of the amplifier
extends from about 23.9 Mc to 26.4 Mc, or 2.5 Mc.

3. The response at 27.9 Mc is zero. This is the sound carrier

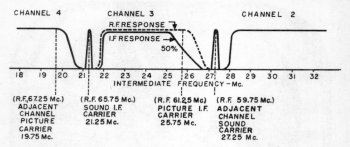

Figure 35. The relationship between the response of a television
receiver, the television signal, and signals in adjacent channels.

intermediate frequency of the higher adjacent television channel
(Figure 35). Since this signal is very close to the picture
carrier, it must be more sharply attenuated than the sound
carrier at 21.9 Mc. An attenuation of 60 db (a voltage ratio of
1,000 to 1) is recommended design practice.

The response characteristic of actual amplifiers does not
normally resemble the ideal selectivity curve shown in Figure
33. To obtain this selectivity, sound traps are placed in the
video i-f amplifier stages. These traps attenuate the sound
carriers on either side of the picture carrier and are responsible for shaping the response curve.

3-24 Intermediate Frequencies. Most manufacturers operate
the receiver local oscillator at a higher frequency than the received signal, so that the video intermediate frequency signal
appears on the low frequency side of the sound intermediate
frequency signal, as shown in Figure 36. The intermediate frequencies indicated in this figure are 21.25 Mc for the sound,
and 25.75 Mc for the video. These are the frequencies employed
in RCA receivers. Other manufacturers sometimes use other
intermediate frequencies. For example, Philco receivers are
designed for a sound intermediate frequency of 22.1 Mc and video
intermediate frequency of 26.6 Mc. G.E. and DuMont employ

21.9 sound and 26.4 video intermediate frequencies.

3-25 Video I-F Amplifier Circuits. To achieve the wideband response required in the video i-f amplifiers, a number of methods are employed. One method utilizes overcoupled band pass amplifiers and another stagger tuned amplifiers. A third type of video i-f amplifier system, now in use in some television re-

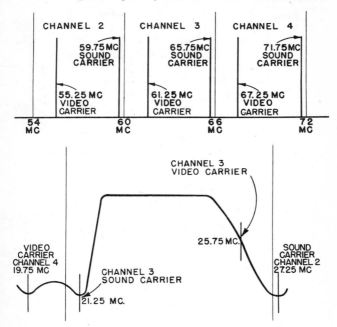

Figure 36. Video and sound r-f frequencies, and video and sound i-f frequencies.

ceivers, is known as the intercarrier sound system or the dome system. Using this system, both the video and audio i-f carriers are amplified together, eliminating the need for a separate sound i-f system.

3-26 Overcoupled Circuits. A typical broadband, overcoupled video i-f amplifier is shown in Figure 37. Except for the fact that its band pass is 4 Mc, this i-f amplifier is identical to the

r-f amplifiers previously described. The response characteristic of the over-coupled i-f transformers Z-1 and Z-2 is shown
in Figure 38. This response is shown compared to that of a
loosely coupled and a critically coupled transformer. With loose
coupling, the response is maximum over a narrow band of fre-

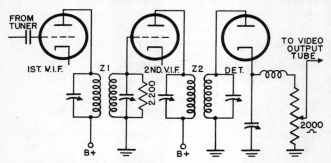

Figure 37. Simplified schematic of broadband overcoupled i-f
amplifier.

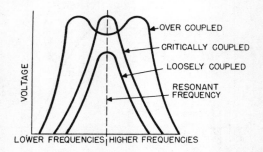

Figure 38. Effect of coupling on the response of a tuned circuit.

quencies. If the transformer is critically coupled, the gain of
the tuned circuit is increased, but is maximum for a narrow
band of frequencies only. Finally, if the transformer is over-
coupled, the response curve broadens to include a wide band of
frequencies.

In a broadband amplifier chain, each stage is not necessarily
tuned to its full bandwidth. Slight compensating effects are made
in each tuned circuit to produce a good overall characteristic.

The i-f response curves of a broadband amplifier chain designed in this manner are shown in Figure 39. The combination of the four curves produces a response which is substantially flat from about 22.5 Mc to 25 Mc.

A combination of over-coupled and peaked resonant circuits

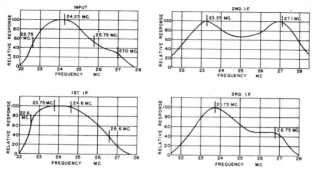

Figure 39. Response curves of the transformers of a broadband amplifier chain.

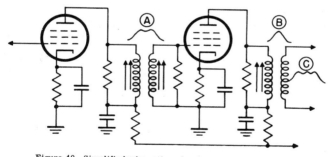

Figure 40. Simplified schematic and response curves of peaked and overcoupled i-f amplifier.

is used in some receivers to obtain a wide response characteristic. By peaking one stage (B), the dip in the over-coupled stage (A) is minimized, as shown in Figure 40. The resultant response is that of curve C.

3-27 Stagger-Tuned Circuits. In a stagger-tuned i-f system, each stage is peaked to a different frequency, and the overall response curve is the result of the combination of peaked stages. In the circuit of Figure 41, four stages of i-f amplification are employed to obtain the necessary wideband frequency response characteristic and adequate gain. The converter plate transformer, T-1, and each successive i-f transformer have one

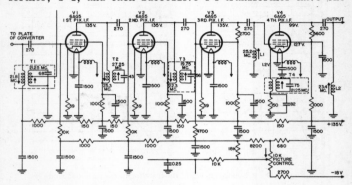

Figure 41. Stagger tuned i-f amplifier channel.

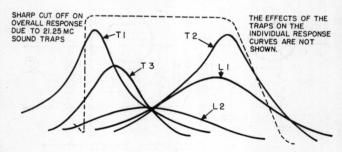

Figure 42. Response curves of stagger tuned i-f amplifier.

tuned circuit each, and each is tuned to a different frequency. The effective Q of each coil is fixed by the shunt plate load or grid resistor, so that the response of all of the stages together produces the desired overall curve. Figure 42 shows the response curves of each stage and the shape of the curve which results from their combination.

In order to obtain this band pass characteristic, the picture i-f transformers are tuned as follows:

Converter transformer	21.8 Mc. (T-1 primary)
First transformer	25.3 Mc. (T-2 primary)
Second i-f transformer	22.3 Mc. (T-3 primary)
Third i-f coil	25.2 Mc. (L-1)
Fourth i-f coil	23.4 Mc. (L-2)

In such a stagger tuned system, the correct overall response curve can not always be obtained by tuning the coils to specified

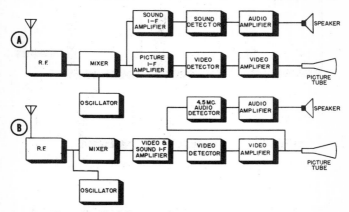

Figure 43. Block diagrams of receivers using conventional and intercarrier sound systems.

frequencies. This results when the values of the components of a tuned circuit are slightly off and change the shape of the response curve of a tuned circuit. By shifting the frequency to which each circuit is tuned, compensation can usually be made for the off value components and the desired response obtained.

The response of the i-f stages of a receiver changes slightly when the picture control is varied due to the Miller effect. This effect results in a change in tube input capacitance as the tube's gain is varied by grid bias changes. The change of input capacitance causes a slight detuning of the preceding i-f coil and a slight change in response. The change is slight, however, and if the receiver is aligned at the correct grid bias, no difficulties are encountered in stagger tuned systems.

3-28 The Intercarrier Sound System. The use of the intercarrier sound system eliminates the need for separate video and audio i-f circuits. This system is in use in a number of receivers and considerably lowers component costs. The intercarrier sound system may be illustrated by comparing the block diagram of a conventional television receiver with that of a receiver using the intercarrier system, as shown in Figure 43. In the conventional receiver, (A), the individual picture and

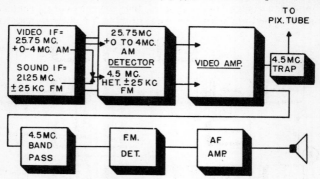

Figure 44. Operation of the intercarrier sound system.

sound carriers are heterodyned in the mixer with the high frequency local oscillator to produce two separate i-f carriers with their associated sidebands. The video carrier is fed to the video i-f amplifier, and then to the video detector. It is further amplified by the video amplifier, and finally impressed upon the grid of the picture tube. Similarly, the FM sound carrier is fed to the sound i-f amplifier, detected, and further amplified to a level sufficient to drive the speaker. Note that two separate i-f amplifying systems are required in such a television receiver circuit.

The operation of the intercarrier sound system is explained with reference to Figure 44.

1. The incoming television signal is heterodyned to produce sound and video i-f carriers.

2. The combined sound and video i-f carriers are amplified by the same i-f amplifying system.

3. The video signal is detected and amplified as usual. It is then fed to the picture tube.

4. The audio signal, separated from the video signal at the video amplifier output, has already been amplified in both the

picture i-f channel and the video stages.

5. The 4.5 Mc FM carrier is fed to an FM detector and audio amplifier.

A simple circuit for separating the sound carrier from the video signal is shown in Figure 45. Since the audio carrier is

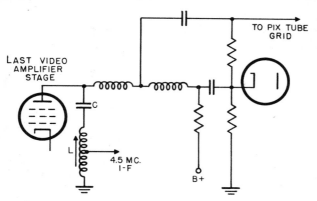

Figure 45. Circuit used to separate the sound carrier from the video signal in intercarrier receiver.

located 4.5 Mc from the video carrier, a 4.5 Mc trap, L-C, placed in the plate circuit of the video amplifier, will permit the separation of the sound signal from the video signal and eliminate all sound in the video signal.

Receivers using the intercarrier system are relatively immune to the effects of oscillator drift, since the sound frequencies are not moved out of the i-f pass band by normal drift of the oscillator.

3-29 Wavetraps. The video i-f response curve obtained with tuned circuits is shown in Figure 46. Such a band pass characteristic does not provide sufficient attenuation at the audio i-f frequency to prevent the audio signal from passing through the video i-f stages. To obtain better selectivity, small wavetraps are inserted in video i-f amplifier stages. These traps consist of sharply tuned parallel resonant circuits tuned to the frequency of the audio carrier. They are often referred to as "sound traps", because their purpose is the removal of the sound carrier.

The sound traps must attenuate two frequencies, the associated sound carrier heterodyned to 21.9 Mc and the adjacent channel sound carrier which is heterodyned down to 27.9 Mc. Adjacent channel interference is not serious in as much as stations are not assigned to adjacent channels in any one area. The effect may be troublesome, though, when a receiver is located be-

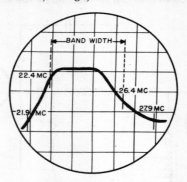

Figure 46. Video i-f response curve using tuned circuits only.

tween two large cities and can pick up television signals located in adjacent channels.

A parallel resonant sound trap presents a high impedance to the signal for which it is tuned. Thus, when inserted in the grid

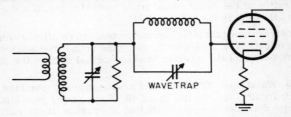

Figure 47. Simplified circuit of i-f amplifier with grid wavetrap.

circuit of an amplifier, as shown in Figure 47, it is in series with the signal path and effectively blocks the unwanted sound i-f signal. Since the trap is very sharply tuned, it does not reject the desired frequencies. A second trap is usually incorporated in the next stage to attenuate the adjacent channel audio carrier signal at 27.9 Mc.

Cathode wavetraps are also used to reject unwanted signals. When inserted in the cathode of a video i-f amplifier stage (Figure 48), a trap is in series with the input signal and prevents the amplification of the sound carrier and its associated sidebands.

Sound traps usually consist of a fixed capacitor and a slug

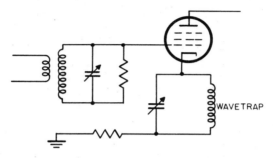

Figure 48. Simplified circuit of i-f amplifier with cathode wavetrap.

tuned coil, which can be adjusted to resonate at the correct frequency. They are often pretuned and sealed at the factory, so that they require no further adjustment. In some cases, they must be aligned whenever the video i-f amplifiers require servicing.

With the sound traps properly tuned, the overall video response curve of a receiver should be similar to that shown in Figure 49. This is the ideal wave shape, for it contains only the video signals.

3-30 Overcoupled I-F Amplifier with Wave Traps. The G.E. Model 801 receiver is an example of a design using an over-coupled i-f amplifier with wavetraps. See Figure 50. Three 6AC7 tubes are used in the three-stage video i-f amplifier. The transformers T-1, T-2, T-3, and T-4 are over-coupled and loaded with resistor to obtain a response curve 4 Mc wide. This type of circuit does not result in sufficient attenuation of the associated sound carrier or the adjacent channel sound carrier. A suitable response curve is obtained in the circuit of Figure 50 by the addition of wavetraps. A third winding is added to each video transformer and tuned to trap out the audio carrier and its associated sidebands. The trap in T-1 is tuned to 27.9 Mc to provide rejection at the adjacent channel audio i.f., while the traps in T-2, T-3, and T-4 are tuned to 21.9 Mc, the audio i.f. in the channel being received. The combination of sound traps

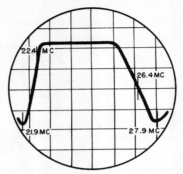

Figure 49. Response curve of video i-f amplifier with sound traps properly tuned.

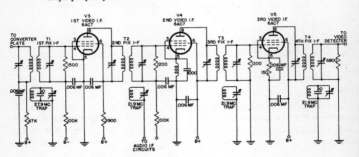

Figure 50. Overcoupled i-f amplifier with wavetraps.

and over-coupled transformers results in the response curve shown in Figure 51.

Wavetraps are inserted in the RCA circuit shown in Figure 41 in the following manner: The first three traps form absorption circuits. The first trap (T-1 secondary) is tuned to the associated sound i-f frequency. The second trap (T-2 secondary) is tuned to the adjacent channel sound i-f frequency. The

third trap (T-3 secondary) is tuned to the adjacent channel picture carrier frequency. The fourth trap (T-4 secondary) is in
the cathode circuit of the fourth picture i-f amplifier, V-4, and
is tuned to the associated sound carrier i-f frequency. The
primary of T-4, in series with the resistor and capacitor,
forms a series resonant circuit at the frequency to which L-2

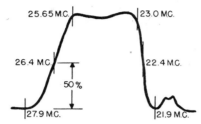

Figure 51. Response curve of i-f amplifier channel using over-
coupled transformer and sound traps.

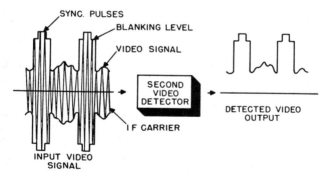

Figure 52. Input and output waveforms of the second detector.

is tuned (23.4 Mc). This provides a low impedance cathode circuit at 23.4 Mc, permitting the tube to operate at high gain. At
the resonant frequency of the secondary of T-4 (21.25 Mc), the
wavetrap acts as high impedance in the cathode circuit and greatly reduces the gain of the amplifier. The 21.25 Mc audio i-f
signals are therefore attenuated.

3-31 The Video Second Detector. The amplified video i-f signal passes from the last i-f amplifier to the second video detector, which demodulates the carrier leaving the video, blanking, and synchronizing information. The wave form of the signal at the output of the detector is shown in Figure 52. At the present time, all television receivers utilize diode detectors as shown in Figure 53. This detector is similar to that used in the or-

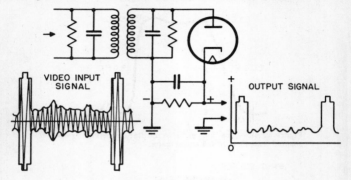

Figure 53. Diode detector and waveform.

dinary superheterodyne receiver, except that it must pass a wider band of frequencies and maintain the proper polarity of the video signal.

3-32 Signal Polarity. When a signal passes through a vacuum tube, a 180° phase shift takes place, and as a result, the polarity of the signal is reversed. In ordinary sound receivers, the polarity of the signal at the speaker is not important. In television receivers, the video signal must be of the proper polarity, otherwise a negative picture will be obtained on the screen of the picture tube, as shown in Figure 54. The proper polarity to obtain a positive picture depends upon whether the signal is fed to the grid or to the cathode of the picture tube. The correct polarity when the video signal is applied to the grid of the picture tube is shown in Figure 55a. The polarity must be reversed if the signal is fed to the cathode of the picture tube, as shown in Figure 55b. Since the polarity of the signal is reversed each time it passes through a stage, the number of stages in the receiver, following the video detector, determines the polarity of the signal at the picture tube.

3-33 Positive and Negative Detectors. A modulated i-f carrier contains identical positive and negative picture information above and below the a-c axis. When a diode detector is connected as shown in Figure 53, a positive detected signal results. This is because the signal above the a-c axis drives the plate of the diode positive with respect to the i-f signal ground, and

Figure 54. Test pattern showing negative picture caused by improper polarity of grid of picture tube.

the diode conducts, whereas the signal below the a-c axis does not cause the diode to conduct.

By reversing the plate and cathode connectors, as shown in Figure 56, the signal below the a-c axis may be detected, giving a polarity opposite that obtained with the circuit shown in Figure 53.

3-34 Detector Frequency Response. The frequency response of the second detector should be linear up to 4 or 5 Mc. Slightly above these frequencies, the response of the detector should fall off sharply to attenuate the i-f carrier and the harmonics produced by distortion in the detector. In older receivers which used an r-f frequency of 12.75 Mc, the ratio of the i-f carrier frequency to the highest video frequency was 3 to 1. With this small ratio, it was difficult to separate the 4 Mc video band from the intermediate frequency signal. It was necessary to add a number of band pass filters to obtain good frequency response over the 4 Mc video band and at the same time attenuate high frequency signals. The new video i-f frequency of 26.4 Mc has

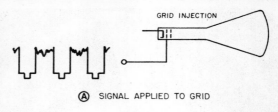

Ⓐ   SIGNAL APPLIED TO GRID

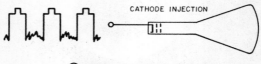

Ⓑ   SIGNAL APPLIED TO CATHODE

Figure 55. Polarity of signal required at grid and cathode of picture tube.

simplified the problem somewhat, although filter circuits are still used to maintain optimum frequency response.

Figure 57 shows a complete video detector incorporating a band pass filter. The diode load resistance, R-1, is very low (3,300 ohms compared to the 2 megohms found in ordinary circuits). This low value of load resistance permits the detector to pass a wide band of frequencies. L-1 and L-2 constitute a band pass filter whose upper limit is approximately 5 Mc. Higher frequencies are greatly, attenuated by L-1 and L-2, and in addition are by-passed by capacitor C-1.

While a low value of load resistance used in a detector results in the required wide frequency response, it reduces the efficiency of the detector. As a result, the output of the signal obtained is but 1 or 2 volts. This signal is not of a great enough amplitude to properly drive the picture tube. In order to bring the signal up to the required level, it is passed through a number of video amplifier stages.

3-35 Direct-Coupled Video Detector. The d-c component of the detected video signal is proportional to the average brightness of the transmitted scene. When passed through an ordinary amplifier, the d-c component of a signal is lost. In a television receiver, the d-c component must be maintained in some

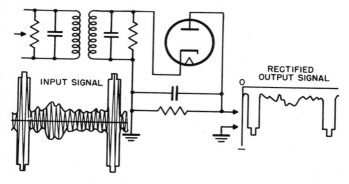

Figure 56. Diode detector and waveform.

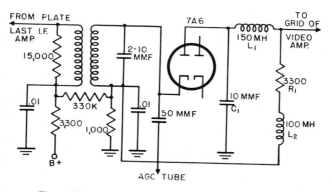

Figure 57. Schematic of video detector with bandpass filter.

way so that the average brightness of the transmitted scene will be conveyed to the picture tube. One method used to accomplish this is through the use of a direct-coupled video detector and video amplifier. Direct-coupling passes on the d-c component which would normally be lost in other circuits. The G.E. Model

801 receiver uses the direct-coupled video detector shown in Figure 58.

The video i-f signal is transformer-coupled to the cathode circuit of the detector. A negative signal is developed across the 1,500 ohm diode load resistor, R-1. L-1, C-1 and the input cap-

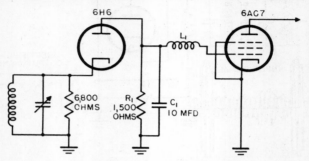

Figure 58. Direct coupled video detector.

acity of the video amplifier together comprise a band pass filter. The filter is direct-coupled to the grid of the video amplifier, and the d-c voltage drop across R-1 provides grid bias for the video amplifier.

3-36 Push-Pull Detectors. A signal somewhat greater than that available from a regular diode detector can be obtained through the use of a push-pull detector. The circuit of a push-pull detector is shown in Figure 59. The video i-f signal is fed to the plates of a dual diode through a balanced transformer. The cathodes of the dual diode are tied together. The operation of this detector is identical to that of a full-wave rectifier. One diode conducts the positive portion of the i-f signal, and the other, the negative portion. The detected signal is developed across the diode load resistor, R-1, and is of positive polarity.

3-37 Video Amplifiers. The function of the video amplifier in a television receiver is similar to that of an audio amplifier in an ordinary sound receiver.

In a sound receiver, the signal at the output of the second detector is not great enough to drive the loudspeaker, and must be passed through one or more stages of audio amplification before being applied to the speaker.

In a television receiver, the signal at the video second detect-or is not of sufficient amplitude for proper operation of the pic-ture tube. It is passed through the video amplifying stages to bring it up to the necessary amplitude. As mentioned previous-ly, the signal at the output of the last video amplifier must be

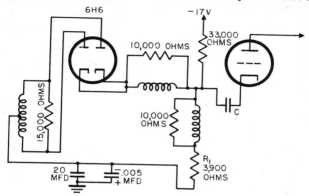

Figure 59. Push-pull video detector.

of a pre-determined polarity. This polarity is determined by whether or not the signal is fed to the grid or cathode of the pic-ture tube.

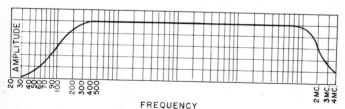

FREQUENCY

Figure 60. Response curve of video amplifier.

3-38 Frequency Response. The video amplifier should have a frequency response uniform from approximately 30 cycles to 4 Mc, as shown by the curve of Figure 60. Ordinary resist-ance-capacitance coupled amplifiers, such as shown in Figure 61, cannot provide this frequency response characteristic, since at high frequencies, the interelectrode capacity of the tube bypasses the signal to ground, while the coupling capacitor Cc has a large enough reactance to block some of the low frequency output voltage.

3-39 Phase Distortion. When á signal is passed through an

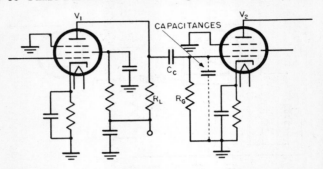

Figure 61. Simplified schematic of resistance coupled amplifier.

amplifier, it is delayed slightly. This delay usually varies with the frequency of the input signal, and when signals of more than one frequency are fed into an amplifier, the amount of delay is different for each frequency. This difference in delay is referred to as phase distortion. Phase distortion of the video signal will cause the picture to appear smudged and blurred, as shown in Figure 62. This type of distortion must be kept to a minimum.

3-40 High Frequency Compensation. The capacitance between the various elements of a video amplifier circuit and ground tend to reduce the high frequency response of the amplifier. To keep these shunting capacities to a minimum, circuit components must be carefully placed, lead lengths kept short, and lowloss tube sockets used. Video amplifier tubes, such as the 6AC7 have been carefully designed to give a minimum of interelectrode capacity. When all these precautions have been taken, the shunting capacity will still be 20 to 30 mmf. This capacity is great enough to cause appreciable loss of high frequency response.

To compensate for this loss, an inductance may be placed in series with the load resistor of an amplifier, as shown in Figure 63. The value of this inductance is so chosen, that at low frequencies its effect is negligible. At high frequencies, the in-

ductive reactance becomes great enough to increase the load
resistance of the amplifier. The point at which the impedance
of the inductance begins to increase the effective load resistance corresponds to the frequency at which the response of the
amplifier begins to fall off due to the shunting capacitance. The

Figure 62. Test pattern showing effect of phase distortion.

increased load resistance gives a greater voltage drop and a
resulting greater output voltage, which compensates for the drop
caused by the shunting capacitance. This method of high frequency compensation is referred to as shunt-peaking.

The effects of shunt capacitance may also be compensated for
by adding an inductance in series with the output coupling capacitor, or an amplifier, as shown in Figure 64. The coupling
capacitor, Cc, and the inductance form a series resonant circuit. This method, referred to as series-peaking, is more desirable than shunt-peaking, since it permits the use of a slightly higher load resistance which gives greater gain. Phase distortion with series-peaking is less than with shunt-peaking. In
some designs, a combination of series and shunt-peaking is used,
as shown in Figure 65, to obtain the required video amplifier
response characteristic.

The gain of an amplifier stage is proportional to its load resistance. If the load resistance is increased, the gain of the amplifier increases. The maximum gain obtainable is limited by the fact that increased load resistance causes a loss in high frequency response. The effect of increased load resistance on

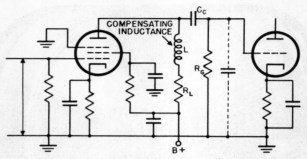

Figure 63. Shunt-peaking frequency compensation.

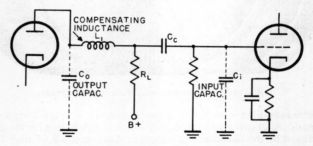

Figure 64. Series-peaking frequency compensation.

the frequency response of an amplifier is shown in Figure 66. Since high frequency response is important in video amplifiers, low values of load resistance, sometimes as little as 1,000 ohms, are often used. As a result, a stage gain of about 20 is obtained. With a gain of this order, a single video amplifier stage is sufficient, providing at least a 2 volt signal is available at the output of the second detector. An output signal of lesser amplitude necessitates an additional stage of video amplification before the picture tube.

3-41 Low Frequency Compensation. At low frequencies, the reactance of the video amplifier output coupling capacitor is

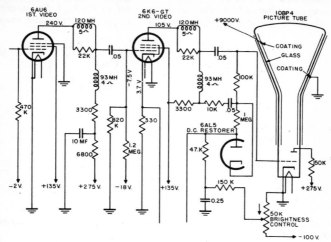

Figure 65. Two stage video amplifier suing shunt and series peaking.

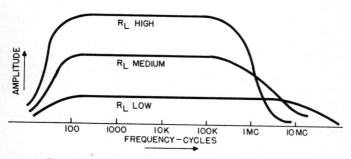

Figure 66. Effect of different load resistances on the response of resistance coupled amplifier.

great enough to cause a loss in low frequency response. This loss occurs because the coupling capacitor forms a voltage divider with the grid resistance of the picture tube. One way to eliminate this effect is by increasing the value of the capacitor to reduce its reactance at low frequencies. While a comparatively high capacitance may be used, a value which entirely eliminates loss of low frequency response will also increase stray capacitance to a value which will effect the high frequency response. Additional reduction in low frequency attenuation may

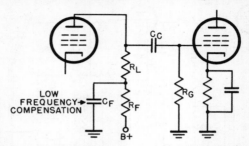

Figure 67. Parallel resistor-capacitor combination for low frequency compensation.

be obtained by making the picture tube grid leak resistor as large as feasible.

After the above precautions have been taken, any remaining low frequency attenuation is removed by a parallel resistor-capacitor combination, placed in series with the plate load resistor of a video amplifier, as shown in Figure 67. The values of the resistor and capacitor are chosen so that they will increase the impedance of the plate circuit at low frequencies. The increased plate circuit impedance results in a greater voltage gain, compensating for low frequency attenuation. The effects of the resistor-capacitor combination are negligible at high frequencies, since the capacitor, Cf, acts as a short circuit across resistor Rf.

Figure 68 shows the circuit of a video amplifier with both low and high frequency compensating elements.

3-42 D-C Restoration. As has already been pointed out, the output of the video detector has a d-c component which determines the average brightness of the scene appearing on the screen of the picture tube. This d-c component is combined with the a-c components of the picture information. Figure 69 shows the video signal at the output of the video detector. When this signal is applied to the grid of the picture tube, all signals which reach or go below the black level drive the grid to cutoff.

Signal levels above the black level extend as high as the white level. Between the black level and the white level are the signal levels which correspond to shades of grey.

In order to reproduce a picture in the proper shades of black, grey, and white, one of the shades must remain fixed, so that it

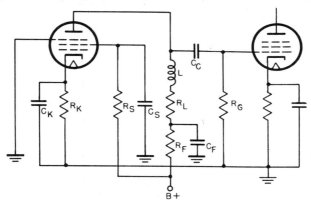

Figure 68. Video amplifier with high and low frequency compensation components.

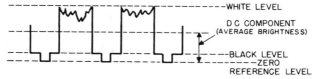

Figure 69. Composite video signal at the output of the video detector.

can serve as a reference for all the other shades. The television signal has one component which is always constant. This is the top of the blanking pulse, which is always equal to the black level. If the tops of the blanking pulses are made to equal the cutoff bias of the picture tube, all signals above the blanking pulse level will swing the picture tube grid more positive and produce shades of grey on the screen.

Consider now what happens when the video signal shown in Figure 69 is passed through an amplifier. The d-c component is blocked by the coupling capacitors of the a-c amplifier. With the d-c component removed, the video signal centers itself above and below the zero reference level, so that as much area of signal is above as is below this level. Under these conditions, the blanking pulses will no longer occur at the black level. Without a fixed black level, some of the blanking pulses occur above

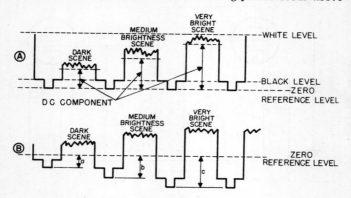

Figure 70. A, video signals of three different screen brightness levels. B, video signals with d-c component removed.

the grid cutoff bias and, therefore, do not blank out the return traces. It is apparent that some means must be provided for reinserting the original d-c level of the signal. Just how much d-c voltage must be reinserted depends upon the original video signal. Figure 70A illustrates several different video signals representing varying levels of average scene brightness. In a dark scene, the d-c component is relatively small. The d-c component is greater for a scene of medium brightness, and rises still further for a very bright scene. When these video signals are passed through an a-c amplifier, they center themselves around the zero reference level, as shown in Figure 70B. In order to hold the blanking pulses of all three signals at the same level, a d-c component equal to "a" volts must be added to the dark scene, "b" volts to the medium brightness scene, and "c" volts to the very bright scene. These d-c components are obtained by feeding the signals to a circuit known as a d-c restorer. A d-c restorer employs a diode which rectifies the portion of the signal below the zero reference axis and derives a d-c signal from the rectified voltage.

3-43 Diode Restorer Circuits. A d-c restoration circuit using a diode is shown in Figure 71. The video signal from the video amplifier is coupled to the grid of the picture tube through C-2. Across the output of the video amplifier is the d-c restoration circuit, consisting of V-2, C-1, R-2, and R-3. At the plate of the video amplifier, there is no d-c component in the signal.

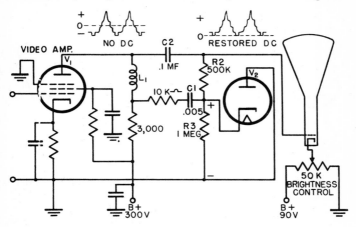

Figure 71. Schematic of diode d-c restorer.

However, at the picture tube grid, the d-c component has been restored by the diode circuit. The operation of the d-c restorer is as follows:

1. When the video signal swings positive, the cathode of the diode is driven positive with respect to its plate, and it does not conduct. On the negative portion of the signal, the cathode becomes negative with respect to the plate, and the diode conducts.

2. Current flows through R-2 and R-3 to C-1, and charges the condenser to a voltage equal to the amount that the sync tips are below the zero reference axis.

3. The d-c voltage built across C-1 is equal to the voltage difference between the sync tips and the desired reference level.

4. The d-c voltage appears across R-2 and R-3 and is applied to the grid of the picture tube.

5. The added d-c component maintains the level of the blanking pulses at the desired reference, or black level.

With this circuit, an increase in the portion of the video signal below the zero reference level causes an increase in the d-c voltage developed across C-1. Thus, as the scene brightness changes, a varying d-c voltage is developed which maintains all blanking pulses at the same level.

It is important to note that the d-c voltage changes each time the video signal varies due to actual changes in scene brightness.

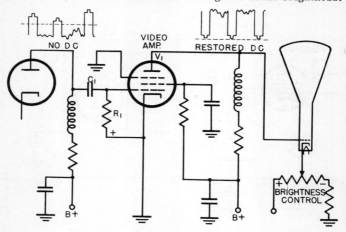

Figure 72. D-C restoration in the video amplifier stage.

The time constant of C-1 and R-2, R-3 is chosen so that C-1 will hold its d-c charge between two successive sync pulses. The time constant is, however, small enough so that when the transmitted scene brightness changes, C-1 is able to charge or discharge to the voltage corresponding to the new brightness level.

3-44 Video Stage Restoration. D-C restoration can take place in the video amplifier itself if the amplifier circuit is arranged as shown in Figure 72. The signal is fed from the video detector to the video amplifier through coupling capacitor C-1. The d-c component cannot pass the coupling capacitor and does not appear on the grid of V-1. When the video signal swings above the zero reference level, the grid becomes positive and draws current which charges C-1. This charge is the d-c component to be reinserted. R-1 is large enough to prevent C-1 from discharging between successive sync pulses. The d-c component which now appears on the grid of V-1 is amplified with the other components of the video signal. The composite signal, including the d-c component appears at the plate and is coupled directly to the grid of the picture tube. No coupling capacitor is used between the video amplifier and that picture tube, because it would block the restored d-c component.

3-45 The Brightness Control. The manner in which the d-c restorer circuit holds all the blanking pulses at a constant level has just been described. In order to blank out the return trace, the beam in the picture tube must be cut off when the blanking pulses reach the black level. If this condition exists, the sync pulses, which are more negative than the blanking pulses, will not appear in the picture. The voltage on the grid of the picture tube must therefore be adjusted so that the grid is biased to cut-off, which corresponds to the black level.

A circuit commonly used to provide for adjustment of the picture tube's grid bias is shown in Figure 73A. A positive voltage is applied to the cathode through the variable resistor R2. Also shown in the circuit is a video amplifier V1, direct coupled to the grid of the picture tube. D-C restoration takes place in the grid circuit of V1 through the action of R1 and C1. The plate voltage on V1 is lower than the voltage on the cathode of the picture tube. Since the grid of the picture tube is directly coupled to the plate of V1, it is negative with respect to the cathode. The negative grid bias can be varied by changing the setting of R2. R2 is adjusted for a negative bias which just cuts off the beam current. This setting corresponds to the black level. Once the bias has been adjusted in this manner, the d-c restoration circuit automatically holds the blanking pulses at the cut-off bias. R2, which initially sets the grid bias, is the brightness control of the receiver.

When this control is properly adjusted, the video signals which are more positive than the black level will permit the beam to pass to the screen and reproduce the shades of the picture being received.

Figure 73B shows how the setting of the brightness control affects the illumination on the picture tube. The bias is adjusted so that all signals to the left of the black level are beyond the cutoff voltage of the picture tube. The video signals to the right of the cutoff bias increase the brightness as they swing toward zero bias voltage.

3-46 Automatic Gain Control. Automatic gain control in a television receiver is similar to automatic volume control in ordinary broadcast receivers. Its purpose is to maintain the intensity of the picture at a constant level despite variations in the average strength of the received signal. The effect on the picture of a fading television signal is more drastic than the effect of a fading audio signal upon the output of a sound re-

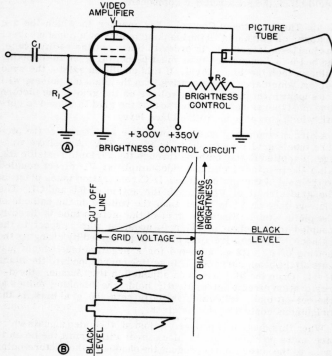

Figure 73. A, circuit for providing adjustment of picture tube bias. B, effect on picture brightness of variations in grid voltage.

ceiver. A fading signal will cause changes in the intensity of the picture, and if of sufficient amplitude, will effect the stability of the picture, because the sync level for which the receiver has been adjusted will not be maintained.

3-47 Automatic Volume Control. While the automatic gain

control system used in television receivers differs considerably from the automatic volume control circuits found in sound receivers, a review of the operation of "a.v.c." will make an excellent background for an understanding of "a.g.c.". Figure 74 is a simplified schematic diagram of the a.v.c. circuit of an

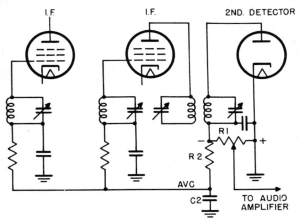

Figure 74. Simplified schematic of a.v.c. circuit of a-m receiver.

ordinary receiver.

The diode detector rectifies the signal at the output of the last i-f transformer. The audio voltage appearing in the output of the detector contains a d-c component whose amplitude is proportional to the strength of the carrier. This d-c component is used to control the gain of the i-f amplifiers. In order to separate the audio and d-c components, capacitor C2 is connected from one side of the decoupling resistor R2 to ground. As a result, only the d-c component is left at the point marked a.v.c. When the carrier strength increases, greater negative voltage is developed across R1, and is fed back to the grids of the i-f amplifiers, where it constitutes negative bias. The i-f amplifier tubes are remote cut-off pentodes whose gain decreases with increased bias. When the carrier strength decreases, the negative bias on the i-f amplifiers decreases, and the gain of the i-f amplifiers increases, compensating for the drop in signal strength. If the by-pass condenser, C-2, were not present in the circuit, the gain of the i-f amplifier would be controlled by the audio signal and not by the average carrier strength, as happens when C2 is in the circuit.

3-48 Automatic Gain Control Circuits. The d-c component of the video signal cannot be used for gain control bias, as is done with the d-c component of the sound signal in ordinary receiv-

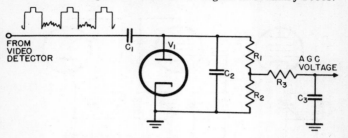

FROM
VIDEO
DETECTOR

A G C
VOLTAGE

Figure 75. Simplified diagram of a.g.c. circuit.

ers. This is so because the average carrier voltage of the television signal represents the brightness of the scene. If the d-c component were used as a gain controlling bias, it would maintain the scene brightness at a constant level, regardless of whether the scene were in daylight or at night. A signal, if used for a.g.c., must be proportional to the maximum carrier strength of the television signal only. It must have no relation to the brightness of the scene. The sync signal fills these requirements. It represents 100% modulation of the carrier and has no relation to the brightness of the scene. When the carrier fades, the level of the sync signal changes, at which time the automatic gain control system increases the gain of the receiver.

A simple a.g.c. circuit is shown in Figure 75. A portion of the video detector output is coupled through C1 to the plate of the a.g.c. rectifier tube V1. The diode conducts because of the positive polarity of the signal applied to its plate. Current flows and charges capacitor C-2 to the peak value of the sync signals. This charge cannot leak off readily because of the long time constant of the circuit formed by C2, R1, and R2. The time constant is set to equal the time duration of about 10 horizontal lines. The voltage across C2 therefore remains constant and equal to the peak value of the sync signals. This voltage is tapped between R1 and R2 and is the a.g.c. signal. When the level of the sync signals decreases for a period of time equal to more than ten horizontal lines, the voltage across C2 drops, and a compensating a.g.c. voltage is applied to the amplifiers under control.

A more complex a.g.c. circuit is shown in Figure 76. The video i-f signal is coupled through C1 to the full-wave video detector V1. The detected signal appears across resistor R2. Rectified voltage appearing at the cathode of V1 is directly

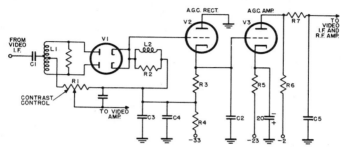

Figure 76. Delayed a.g.c. circuit.

coupled to a.g.c. rectifier V2. When V2 conducts, capacitor C2 charges to the peak value of the sync signals.

As in the previous a.g.c. circuit, the time constant of the network consisting of C2, R3, and R4 is long, and C2 holds its charge for a period equal to several horizontal lines. Since the charge on C2 is equal to the peak value of the sync signals, it serves as the a.g.c. voltage. This voltage is fed to the grid of V3, which amplifies the a.g.c. signal.

The grid of the a.g.c. amplifier is connected to a negative 33 volt source and the cathode to a negative 23 volt source. The grid is therefore 10 volts negative with respect to the cathode. This negative bias is sufficient to cut off the tube when no signal is reaching it from the detector. When signal is present, the amplifier does not conduct unless the signal voltage is high enough to overcome the cutoff bias. Thus, a.g.c. action is delayed. Delayed a.g.c. action is desirable when the signal is weak. The delay permits the i-f amplifiers under control to operate at full gain until the input signal reaches a predetermined level. On very weak signals, there is no a.g.c. action, and the amplifiers operate at full gain.

The plate load resistor of V3, (R6), is connected to a negative 2 volt source. The plate of V3 is therefore 21 volts positive with respect to its cathode. When a sufficiently strong signal appears at the grid of V3, the tube conducts and a potential is developed across resistor R6. This voltage is fed through the isolating network, R7-C5, to the grids of the video and r-f amplifiers.

3-49 A.G.C. vs. Contrast Control. To avoid confusion, the

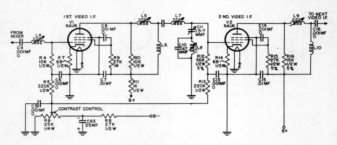

Figure 77. Gain control by varying the grid bias on remote cutoff pentode i-f amplifiers.

functions of a.g.c. and the contrast control should be clearly understood. The contrast control varies the gain of the receiver to obtain the relative brightness of light and dark areas in the picture, as desired by the viewer. Once this control has been adjusted, it remains fixed, and the receiver maintains the same picture contrast as long as its input signal level remains the same.

A change in the amplitude of the signal at the antenna terminals of the receiver will result in a change in contrast. When a change in signal strength takes place, the a.g.c. circuit functions to change the gain of the amplifier circuits and return the contrast to its preset value.

There are several points in a receiver where a variable contrast or gain control can be inserted. In the circuit of Figure 76, the video detector load resistor, R1, is made variable and provides a means for adjusting the input voltage of the video amplifier.

Figure 77 illustrates another method of controlling the gain of a receiver. Here the grid bias of two of the i-f stages is made variable. Since the i-f amplifier tubes are remote cut-off pentodes, variation of their grid bias varies the gain of the tubes.

THE SWEEP CIRCUITS

3-50 So far, those circuits of a television receiver which select and amplify the video signal and bring it up to a level sufficient to drive the grid of the picture tube, have been described.
Not yet covered are those circuits which control the motion of
the electron beam and cause it to trace out a picture in exact

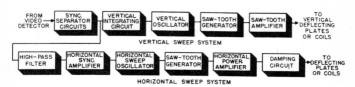

Figure 78. Block diagram of vertical and horizontal sweep
circuits.

Figure 79. Composite video signal.

synchronism with the picture being scanned at the television
station. These circuits are known as sweep circuits.

Figure 78 is a block diagram of the vertical and horizontal
sweep circuits, showing the path of the signal from the video
detector to the deflecting plates or coils. At the output of the
detector, the composite video signal carries both the picture
information and the synchronizing pulses. These parts of the video signal are shown in Figure 79. The picture information is
applied to the grid of the video amplifier, to be passed on to the
picture tube, while the synchronizing pulses must be separated
and directed to the sweep oscillators. This separation of the
sync pulses is known as clipping and is generally accomplished
by a properly biased diode or triode, connected to the output of

the video detector.

The separation of the sync signals may also take place after the video amplifier stage. In this way, the need for a separate sync amplifier is avoided.

3-51 Diode Sync Clippers. A simple diode sync clipper is illustrated in Figure 80. The diode cathode is positive, so that

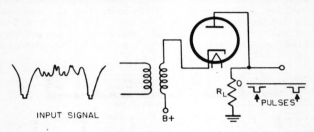

INPUT SIGNAL

Figure 80. Diode sync clipper.

current cannot flow until a negative voltage is applied between cathode and ground. The amplitude of the negative voltage necessary to cause the diode to conduct is determined by the positive cathode voltage. The cathode voltage is positive enough to keep the diode from conducting the picture signal and the blanking pulses. When a sync pulse appears at the cathode of the diode, the diode conducts because the amplitude of the pulse is greater than the bias on the positive cathode of the diode.

The output voltage obtained across the diode's plate resistor contains only the sync pulses as shown in the figure. If the detected signal is of the opposite polarity, the diode is reversed, and a negative voltage applied to the plate to control the voltage level at which the diode conducts.

In the circuit of Figure 81, the diode is self-biased and does not require a separate d-c voltage source. Values of R and C, connected between the cathode of the tube and ground, are chosen to give a time constant equal to the interval between horizontal pulses. The condenser is charged by successive sync pulses, and develops a voltage across the resistor which biases the diode to the level of the blanking pulses. The diode conducts only when the sync pulses, which are of greater amplitude, are applied to the circuit.

3-52 Triode Clippers. The chief advantage of the triode clipper over the diode type is the amplification which takes place in conjunction with the clipping action. A triode clipper and the sync signal in its output are shown in Figure 82. The constants of R and C are chosen so that a negative bias, sufficient to cause cutoff, is developed on the grid. The bias necessary to cause cut-

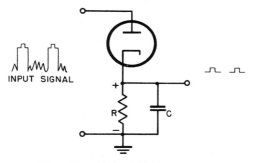

Figure 81. Self-biased diode sync clipper.

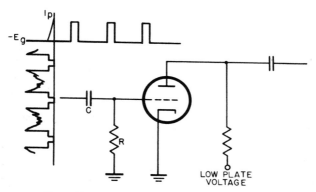

Figure 82. Simplified schematic of triode sync clipper.

off is low, because the tube is operated at a low plate potential.

As shown in Figure 82, the blanking level is equal to the cutoff bias. Signals of lesser amplitude are removed, while the sync pulses, which are of greater amplitude, are amplified and appear inverted in the output of the triode.

In many receivers, a stage of sync amplification follows the separator, and at times a second sync separator is used to remove noise pulses superimposed on the sync signal. Figure 83 shows a circuit using two sync separators. The first sync separator stage clips the video information and reverses the po-

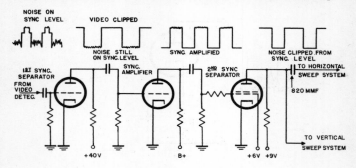

Figure 83. Cascade sync clipper.

larity of the signal. This stage operates at low plate voltage to provide a low cutoff bias which removes all signal information above the blanking level.

The clipped sync signal, appearing in the output of the first separator, is "clean" on one level, but has noise pulses modulating the other level. The signal is then fed to an amplifier which reverses its polarity, so that it is again negative. The operation of the second sync separator should not be confused with that of the first sync separator. The second sync clipping stage is a tetrode operated with a low plate voltage and a relatively high screen voltage. It is grid leak biased. Under these conditions the plate voltage is lower than the screen voltage, and the tube has a dynatron characteristic. It removes the tops and bottoms of the synchronization pulses. Thus, the noise pulses are removed from one level of the sync signal and any remaining picture components are removed from the other level.

3-53 Vertical Sync Segregation. After the sync pulses have been removed from the composite signal, it is necessary to segregate the 60 cycle vertical sync pulses and the 15,750 cycle horizontal sync pulses. Segregation of the vertical sync pulses is accomplished by applying the combined sync signals to a filter network of the type shown in Figure 84. This network is known as an "integrating" circuit. It consists of a series resistance and capacitance, with the output taken from across the capacitance.

Figure 85 shows how an integrating circuit distinguishes the

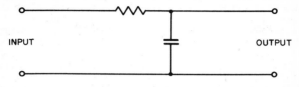

Figure 84. Integrating circuit.

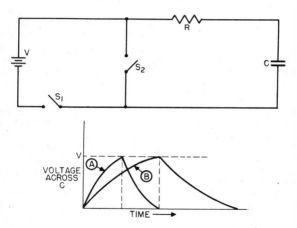

Figure 85. Operation of integrating circuit.

vertical sync pulses from the horizontal sync pulses. In the figure, a battery and switch are connected across an integrating circuit. Operation is as follows:

1. When the battery switch, S1, is closed, a current flows in the circuit and charges the capacitor C through resistor R. The capacitor continues to charge until it reaches the voltage of the battery.

2. If the battery switch, S1, is now opened, and the shunting

switch, S2, closed, the charge on the capacitor will leak off through resistor R.

3. The time that it takes to charge the capacitor is exactly equal to the time it takes to discharge the capacitor. The voltage across C during the "charge" and "discharge" intervals is shown in curve A. The charging and discharging time depends on the values of R and C. The larger the values of R and C, the longer it takes to charge and discharge the capacitor.

4. Suppose now, a capacitor with twice the capacitance is substituted for C in Figure 85. The charge and discharge voltages across the capacitor will now appear as shown in curve B. Note that by doubling the capacitance of C, the charge and discharge time is also doubled. Similarly, if C remains the same and R is doubled, the charging time will be doubled, and the voltage across the capacitor would again appear as in curve B.

The time it takes to charge and discharge a capacitor in series with a resistor, therefore, depends upon the values of each. The time required to charge the capacitor to 63.2% of the voltage applied to the circuit is known as the circuit's "time constant". The value of the time constant, expressed in seconds, is the product of R and C. For example, if a 0.1 microfarad capacitor is placed in series with a 1 megohm resistor, it will take 0.1 of a second for C to reach 63.2% of the applied voltage.

The importance of the time constant (RxC) in the integrating circuit can now be understood. The RC time constant of the circuit is made much longer than the duration of the horizontal sync pulses, which last for about 5 microseconds. When combined synchronizing signals, such as shown in Figure 86, are applied to an integrating network with a time constant of approximately 45 microseconds, the following action takes place:

1. The horizontal sync pulse, which lasts only 5 microseconds, causes the capacitor to charge only slightly (1 and 2 Figure 86B). When the pulse ends, the charge across the capacitor leaks off through resistor R.

2. The equalizing pulses, which last for 2.5 microseconds, create negligible charges (3 in Figure 86B) across C, because the time constant of the circuit is 45 microseconds.

3. When the long duration serrated vertical sync pulse, which lasts for 190.5 microseconds, takes place, the capacitor has sufficient time to charge to the peak value of the applied voltage (in this case, the peak value of the vertical sync pulses).

4. The first serrated pulse charges the capacitor to a much higher level than the horizontal or equalizing pulses.

5. When the pulse ends, the charge starts to leak off through R.

6. Because of the long time constant of the circuit, the charge

leaks off slowly during a short interval (4 in Figure 86) until
the next serrated pulse occurs. The drop in voltage across C is
therefore very small.

7. The second serrated pulse charges the capacitor further.
Again, at the end of the pulse, the charge begins to leak off the

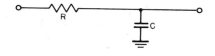

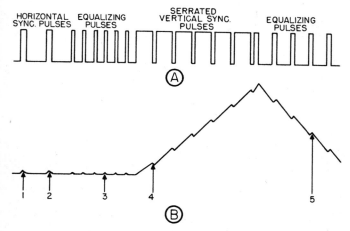

Figure 86. Input and output waveforms of integrating circuit.

capacitor until the third serrated pulse charges it still further.

8. The succession of serrated pulses charges C to the amplitude of the incoming sync pulses.

9. When the serrated pulses are completed, the capacitor begins to discharge.

10. During the discharge period, the six equalizing pulses
occur, but their duration is too short to maintain the voltage on
C. The notches appearing on the discharge portion of the curve
(5 in Figure 86) are due to the slight charging effects of the e-
qualizing pulses.

11. The pulse B of Figure 86 is a segregated vertical sync
pulse which can now be used to synchronize the vertical sweep

circuits.

The net effect of the integrating circuit is to separate the serrated vertical sync pulses from the horizontal sync pulses.

In some receivers, two or three integrating circuits are cascaded for improved integrating action. Such a circuit is shown
in Figure 87.

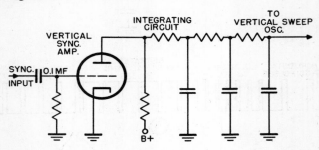

Figure 87. Cascaded integrating circuit.

3-54 Horizontal Sync Segregation. A circuit similar to an integrating network is used to separate the horizontal sync pulses
from the combined sync signal. This circuit is known as a "differentiating" circuit, and is shown in Figure 88A. Two important differences distinguish this circuit from an integrating circuit. First, the RC time constant is much shorter, being about
one fifth (1 microsecond) of the duration of the horizontal sync
pulses. Second, the output is taken from across R rather than
C. The following action takes place when the combined sync
pulses shown in Figure 88B are applied to a differentiating circuit:

1. Since the time constant of the circuit is only 1 microsecond, the horizontal sync pulses, which last for 5 microseconds,
have ample time to charge the capacitor to the peak voltage of
the sync signals. When a horizontal sync pulse occurs, the current charging the capacitor through R rises very rapidly. During the charging period the voltage across R appears as in Figure 88C-1. At the end of the pulse the capacitor discharges very
quickly through R, because of the small time constant of the
circuit. During the discharge period current flows through R
in a direction opposite that during the charge period. The voltage across R during the discharge period is as shown in Figure
88C-2. Hence, the voltage across R appears as a positive pulse

when the capacitor charges during the rise time of the horizontal sync pulse, and then as a negative pulse when the same sync pulse ends. The voltage across R, when the horizontal sync pulses occur, is shown in Figure 88C.

2. The equalizing pulses, which last for 2.5 microseconds,

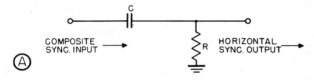

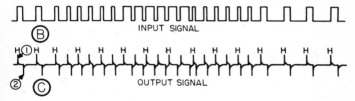

Figure 88. A, differentiating circuit. B, input and output waveforms of circuit in A.

also quickly charge and discharge C. Since the equalizing pulses occur at twice the frequency of the horizontal pulses, they produce positive and negative pulses across R at twice the frequency of those caused by the horizontal sync pulses.

3. When the serrated vertical sync pulse is applied to the differentiating circuit, C charges rapidly, and a positive pulse appears across R during the rise time of the serrated pulse. The long duration serrated pulse holds the charge on C constant until the pulse ends. C then discharges rapidly through R, producing a negative pulse corresponding to the end of the serrated pulse. Each serrated pulse which follows has a similar effect on the differentiating circuit.

The output of the differentiating circuit, shown in Figure 88C, consists of differentiated vertical, horizontal, and equalizing pulses. All of these pulses are fed to the horizontal oscillator, but only those occurring at the horizontal sweep frequency affect the triggering of the horizontal oscillator. These pulses are marked H in the diagram. Note that all of these pulses are the same distance apart and that they occur right through the vertical blanking period. Thus the horizontal oscillator does not lose synchronization during the vertical blanking period.

3-55 Other Differentiating Circuits. Another type of differentiating circuit, which is employed in many receivers, consists
of an inductance placed in the plate circuit of the horizontal sync
amplifier tube. Such a circuit is shown in Figure 89. This circuit's operation takes advantage of the fact that when the cur-

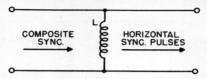

Figure 89. Inductive differentiating circuit.

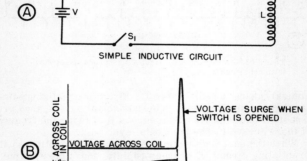

Figure 90. Operation of inductive differentiating circuit.

rent in a coil is suddenly reversed, the voltage across the coil
increases greatly. The principle is illustrated in Figure 90.

When switch S1 is closed, the current in the coil rises slowly,
depending upon the inductance of the coil. The rising current
in the coil builds up a magnetic field around the coil. When
switch S1 is opened, the voltage across the circuit drops to zero.

The magnetic field surrounding the coil collapses suddenly and induces a large voltage in the coil (Figure 90B).

When a composite sync signal, such as shown in B of Figure 88 is applied to a coil type differentiating circuit, the voltage across the coil increases rapidly during the rise time of the

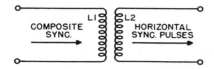

Figure 91. Transformer type differentiating circuit.

horizontal, equalizing, and vertical sync pulses. At the end of a pulse, when its amplitude suddenly falls to zero, the magnetic field surrounding the coil collapses and produces a large voltage across the coil. The polarity of the voltage produced by the collapsing field is opposite that of the voltage produced during the rise period of a pulse. The rise and fall of pulses in the composite sync signal produces positive and negative voltages across the coil, similar to those produced by the RC circuit of Figure 88.

The differentiated sync voltages can be applied directly to the sync terminals of the horizontal oscillator if they are of positive polarity. If not, an amplifier must be provided for pulse reversal.

A two-winding transformer is sometimes used as a differentiating circuit, as shown in Figure 91. The primary acts as the differentiating circuit, while the secondary performs the task of coupling the differentiated pulses to the horizontal generator. With a two-winding transformer, the secondary can be reversed, if need be, to produce positive sync pulses at the horizontal saw-tooth generator.

3-56 Sweep Oscillators. The scanning of the mosaic in the camera pick-up tube was explained in Section 2. It was explained that the television picture is formed by the electron beam sweeping horizontally 15,750, and vertically 60 times per second. This motion of the beam was the result of two sweep voltages which were applied to deflection plates mounted in the tube. The sweep voltages were saw-tooth in shape. At the receiver, similar saw-tooth voltages are generated, which move the picture tube beam in step with that of the camera tube and help compose the final picture.

The saw-tooth voltages in the receiver are generated by charging a condenser with d-c voltage and then rapidly discharging it with a sharp pulse. The voltage across the condenser is the desired sawtooth waveform.

The sweep oscillators provide the sharp discharge pulse at the

Figure 92. Raster pattern.

correct time, determined by the synchronizing pulses which maintain the oscillators at the same frequencies as the television station sync generator.

In the receiver there are two sweep oscillators, each of which is independent of the other. If vertical and horizontal sync pulses are not received to "lock in" the oscillators, they operate at their natural frequencies. Thus, discharge pulses are always provided for the saw-tooth generator circuit to form the pattern on the receiver screen known as the raster. A typical raster is shown in Figure 92. If the oscillators could not operate at their natural frequencies when no sync signal is being received, deflection voltages would not be generated, and the beam would form an intense spot at the center of the screen, causing a screen burn.

The two most common sweep oscillator circuits used in television receivers are the "blocking oscillator" and the "multivibrator"

3-57 The Blocking Oscillator. The circuit of a typical blocking oscillator is shown in Figure 93. It consists of a tube whose

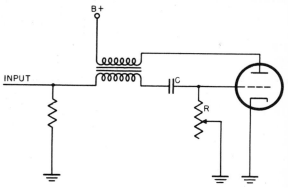

Figure 93. Blocking oscillator circuit.

grid is transformer coupled to its plate. It operates as follows:

1. When the power supply potential is applied to the plate, current flows through the tube.

2. This current passes through the transformer winding which is in the plate circuit, causing a potential to be induced in the grid winding of the transformer.

3. The polarity of the induced voltage is such that the grid is made positive.

4. The positively charged grid causes an increase in the current through the tube and consequently through the plate winding of the transformer.

5. The increased current in the plate winding increases the potential induced into the grid circuit, causing further increases in plate current. The process continues until the tube reaches saturation.

6. During the process of increasing plate current, the capacitor in the grid circuit is charged.

7. When the tube reaches saturation, the current through the

plate winding is no longer increasing and therefore there is no longer any induced voltage across the grid winding.

8. The absence of induced voltage permits the capacitor to discharge through resistor R, placing a negative potential on the grid. The negative potential reduces the current through the tube and through the plate winding.

9. The reduced plate current induces a potential across the grid winding, which increases the negative charge on the grid. The process continues until the tube reaches plate current cut-off.

10. During the decrease in plate current, the condenser C is charged, and when cutoff is reached, it discharges slowly through R, until the grid is no longer below cutoff and the cycle begins again.

The cycle of the grid voltage is shown in Figure 94. If a syn-

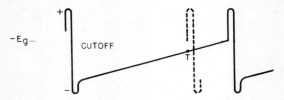

Figure 94. Grid voltage cycle of blocking oscillator.

chronizing pulse, which raises the grid voltage to a point where plate current can flow, is applied to the oscillator, it will "trigger" when the pulse is applied, rather than at its natural frequency as determined by the values of R and C. In Figure 94 a synchronizing pulse is applied at point T, which causes the oscillator to trigger as indicated by the dotted line. In this manner, the synchronizing pulses keep the blocking oscillator in step with the scanning motion occuring at the transmitter. The grid resistance R controls the natural frequency of the oscillator. It is commonly called the hold control, and is usually variable so that it can be adjusted for synchronization.

The blocking oscillator circuits of the vertical and horizontal sweep systems are essentially the same. The only differences are in the values of the resistor and capacitor in the grid circuit, which determine the frequency of oscillation. The oscillator transformers also differ slightly, the horizontal type having a lower capacity between windings to make it possible to obtain a sharp pulse at the horizontal frequency of 15,750 cps.

Several points should be remembered regarding the operation of a blocking oscillator.

1. As illustrated in Figure 94, a blocking oscillator can be triggered before its natural frequency by a positive sync pulse which is sufficient to raise the bias voltage above cutoff value. A negative sync pulse will drive the grid further beyond cutoff and continue to block the tube.

2. When the hold control R sets the natural oscillator fre-

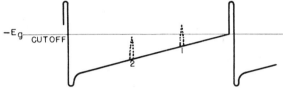

Figure 95. Horizontal sync pulse (1) is of sufficient amplitude to trigger oscillator. Equalizing amplitude at (2) does not trigger oscillator because of position on grid voltage curve.

quency near the sync frequency, only sync pulses can trigger the oscillator. Equalizing pulses occurring between horizontal sync pulses are not of sufficient amplitude to affect the oscillator, since they occur too far down on the grid cutoff, as illustrated in Figure 95.

3. The negative pulses produced by a differentiating circuit cannot affect the operation of a horizontal blocking oscillator because they drive its grid further negative.

4. Positive pulses can be obtained from either the grid or plate circuits of a blocking oscillator.

3-58 The Multivibrator. The multivibrator type of oscillator consists of two triodes and a number of resistances and capacitances. Since no transformer is necessary, this circuit is somewhat cheaper to construct than the blocking oscillator, and is therefore preferred where economy is a factor.

A typical multivibrator circuit is shown in Figure 96. When plate voltage is applied to the oscillator, the following actions occur:

1. The plate voltage of V2 is applied to C1.

2. C1 is charged and causes the grid voltage of V1 to rise.

3. The rise in grid voltage produces an increase in the plate current of V1.

4. The increase in the plate current of V1 increases the voltage across R1 and reduces the voltage on the plate of V1.

5. This permits C2 to discharge through R4, causing the grid of V2 to become negative.

6. The current through V2 diminishes, decreasing the drop across R2 and increasing the voltage on the plate of V2.

7. The increased voltage on the plate of V2 increases the charge on C1, and causes steps 2, 3, 4, 5, and 6 to be repeated.

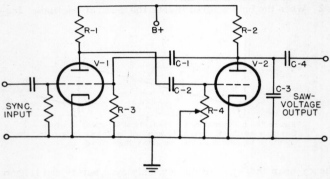

Figure 96. Multivibration circuit.

This action continues until V2 reaches cutoff and current ceases to flow through it.

8. V2 remains cut off until C2, discharging through R4, produces a voltage drop, sufficient to permit V2 to conduct.

9. When no current was flowing through V2, there was no drop across R2 and the plate of V2 was at the full B supply potential. Now, with current flowing, a drop occurs across R2, which reduces V2's plate potential.

10. This reduction is transferred through C1 to the grid of V1, where it produces a negative potential.

11. The negative potential reduces the current through V1, the drop across R1 decreases, and the potential at the plate of V1 increases.

12. Coupled to V2 through C2, the increase in potential on the plate of V1 causes an increase in the voltage on the grid V2.

13. This results in an increase in the current through V2 and a decrease in its plate current. Steps 10, 11, and 12 are repeated. This action continues until V1 is cut off, completing the cycle of operation.

The frequency of operation is determined by the values of resistance and capacitance employed.

3-59 The Cathode-Coupled Multivibrator. A special type of multivibrator, known as the cathode-coupled multivibrator or "Potter" circuit (after its originator) is used in many television receivers which have electrostatically deflected picture tubes. A cathode-coupled multivibrator circuit is shown in Figure 97. The basic difference between this circuit and that of Figure 96 is in the feedback circuit. In addition to the feedback condenser C2, coupling between the two stages takes place through the common cathode resistor Rc.

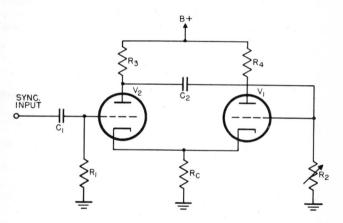

Figure 97. Cathode-coupled multivibration circuit.

The sequence of operation of the cathode-coupled multivibrator is as follows:

1. When the B+ voltage is applied to the plate of V2, capacitor C2 charges through R3 and R2. The B+ voltage is also applied to the plate of V1.

2. Plate current flows through V1 and V2, building up a bias voltage across the common cathode resistor Rc. The flow of plate current in V2 also lowers the plate-to-cathode resistance.

3. The bias voltage built up across Rc reduces the amount of current flowing in V1 and V2.

4. C2 discharges through R2 because of the lowered resistance path of V2.

5. The current flow through R2 places a high negative charge on the grid of V1, driving it to plate current cutoff.

6. As C2 continues to discharge through R2, the grid of V1

becomes less negative. V1 again starts to conduct.

7. When V1 conducts after the grid bias is reduced from cut-off, the sudden flow of current produces a large positive voltage across Rc.

8. The voltage across Rc, which is common to the cathode of V2, drives the grid of V2 negative with respect to its cathode.

9. Less current flows in V2 as a result of the higher negative grid bias. The plate-to-cathode voltage drop is reduced and the plate voltage of V2 rises.

10. The higher plate voltage causes C2 to charge, thereby applying a positive voltage to the grid of V1. This positive voltage increases the flow of plate current through V1, reinforcing the current which began flowing in step 6.

11. The increased bias voltage across Rc, as a result of this increased flow of current, is finally able to stop the flow of plate current through V2.

12. C2 has been charging until V2 stops conducting.

13. With V2 cut off, the current through Rc decreases and the negative bias voltage on the grid of V2 is reduced.

14. As V2 starts to conduct, C2 discharges through V2, R2, and Rc.

15. The current flowing in R2 builds up a negative voltage on the grid of V1, driving it to cutoff.

16. The grid of V1 is now in the same condition as during step 5, and the cycle begins again.

The variable resistor R2 controls the frequency of oscillation of the cathode-coupled multivibrator. It serves as the "hold" control in the sweep circuit.

3-60 Synchronizing the Multivibrator. If a sync signal is fed to one of the grids of the multivibrator circuit shown in Figure 96, and if the frequency of the sync signal is close to the natural oscillating frequency of the multivibrator, the sync signal will control the operating frequency of the multivibrator. A signal consisting of either positive or negative pulses may be injected into either of the grids to obtain synchronization. R4 is variable to permit adjustment of the natural oscillating frequency of the multivibrator.

The cathode-coupled multivibrator of Figure 97 is synchronized by applying negative sync pulses to the grid of V2. The discharge action of a cathode-coupled multivibrator begins with a negative pulse, developed on the grid V2 as a result of feedback voltage across the cathode resistor Rc. Therefore, a negative sync pulse, applied to this grid, will take over the triggering action and controls the frequency of oscillation.

3-61 Noise Effects. In a conventional synchronizing system, each individual synchronizing pulse triggers the blocking oscillator or multivibrator. The manner in which these circuits lock to the frequency of the sync pulses has already been described.

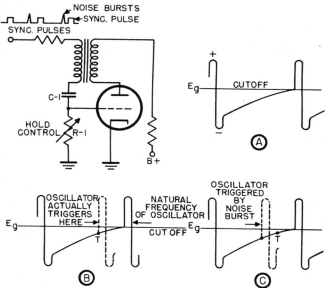

Figure 98. How noise affects the operation of blocking oscillator circuit.

Noise adversely affects the operation of conventional sync circuits. If noise of sufficient amplitude occurs close to the natural frequency of a blocking oscillator, it can trigger the oscillator as shown in Figure 98C. In Figure 98B, T is the time when the sync pulse occurs which triggers the oscillator before the end of its natural period. If a noise pulse occurs just before the sync pulse, as shown in Figure 98C, the noise pulse will trigger the oscillator. As a result, loss of synchronization takes place and the picture on the screen is distorted.

The effect of noise bursts on the stability of synchronization of receiver circuits emphasized the need for changes in the design of sync circuits, the shortcomings of "triggered" sync having become evident under operating conditions. Vertical sync circuits are considerably more immune to noise disturbances than are horizontal sync circuits. Under most conditions, ordinary vertical sync circuits are satisfactory. In areas where the signal-to-noise level is low, or where auto ignition and sim-

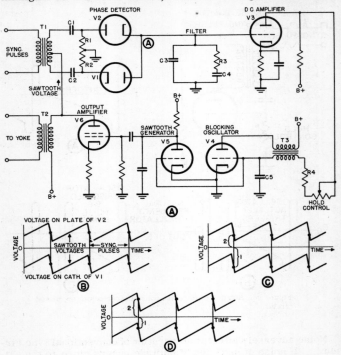

Figure 99. A.F.C. sync circuit and operating waveform.

ilar noise is prevalent, simple horizontal sync systems do not perform sufficiently well.

In order to reduce the effects of noise on horizontal synchronization, a system which provides automatic frequency control of the synchronizing circuits has been developed. The addition of "AFC" results in a significant increase in noise immunity over that of receivers using conventional synchronizing circuits. When it is used, random noise from diathermy, car ignition, and home appliances does not cause tearing of the picture and horizontal resolution is improved.

3-62 AFC Sync Circuits. The shortcomings of a synchronization system in which each sync pulse triggers the oscillator are obvious, since the oscillator cannot distinguish between a sync pulse and a noise pulse. In AFC sync circuits, a d-c control voltage is used, rather than individual sync pulses, to control the frequency of the sweep oscillator.

Figure 99A is a simplified diagram of one type of AFC sync system. As with conventional sync circuits, the sync signal is first clipped from the composite video signal and segregated into vertical and horizontal sync pulses. Instead of feeding the horizontal sync signals directly to the grid of the sync oscillator, they are injected into a phase detector, which compares the relative phase of the incoming sync pulses with that of the saw-tooth voltage in the output of the deflection circuit. If the sync pulses and the saw-tooth voltages are out of phase, the phase detector produces a signal which pulls the sync oscillator to the correct frequency.

The phase detector consists of two diodes, V1 and V2. The sync pulses are applied to the plate of V2 and the cathode of V1 through transformer T1. The saw-tooth voltage, tapped from the output transformer of the deflection amplifier is coupled to the phase detector at the center tap of the secondary of T1. Since the saw-tooth voltage is fed into the secondary of T1, it has the same polarity on the plate of V2 as it has on the cathode of V1. The unidirectional sync pulses, on the other hand, are fed into the primary of T1 and appear 180° out of phase on the plate and cathode. When a positive sync pulse is applied to the plate of V2, the plate voltage is raised above ground by a voltage equal to the amplitude of the pulse. Simultaneously, a negative sync pulse is applied to the cathode of V1, which lowers the cathode voltage by an amount equal to the sync pulse amplitude. Figure 99B shows the signals on the plate of V2 and the cathode of V1.

Point A in Figure 99A is at the average of the potentials on the plate of V2 and the cathode of V1. In Figure 98B, this potential is zero because the saw-tooth voltage on the plate and cathode are of the same amplitude, above and below the zero voltage axis, at the time that the sync pulses occur. However, if a small phase displacement occurs between the sync pulses and the saw-tooth signals, as shown in Figures 99C and 99D, the average potential of the saw-tooth voltages is no longer zero. If the saw-tooth shifts to the left, the average potential at point

A becomes negative. If it shifts to the right, point A becomes positive. The changing voltage at point A is applied to the grid of V4 through an amplifier V3. The oscillator V4 can be either a blocking oscillator or a multivibrator. In the circuit shown, V4 is a blocking oscillator. This oscillator differs slightly from the circuit described previously. In this circuit, d-c voltage, determined by the setting of R4 (the hold control), is applied to the grid. This d-c voltage determines the point at which the oscillator will trigger. If the d-c voltage is raised, the oscillator will trigger sooner; if it is reduced, the oscillator will trigger later. Thus the frequency of the oscillator is controlled by the d-c voltage on its grid. The voltage is the potential at point A after it has been amplified by d-c amplifier V3. V3 is d-c coupled so as not to lose the d-c component at point A, which is necessary to the operation of the circuit.

If the sync pulses and the saw-tooth voltages are in phase, the potential at point A is zero and the scanning oscillator operates at the proper frequency. Should the scanning oscillator suddenly change frequency, the saw-tooth will shift in phase with respect to the incoming sync pulses, and the potential at point A will no longer be zero. The resultant voltage at point A is amplified and applied to the grid of the scanning oscillator to bring it back to the correct frequency. Thus, the frequency of the scanning oscillator is controlled by a d-c potential, rather than recurring sync pulses.

If a noise pulse is fed into the circuit of 99A, it will cause a rapid change in the d-c control signals at point A. The values of R3, C4, and C3 are chosen so that sudden changes are filtered to ground. In other words, only the regularly recurring sync pulses can determine the d-c control voltage, while random noise pulses have little effect. This system is sometimes called flywheel synchronization because of the "flywheel" action of the sync pulses in determining the average d-c control voltage despite sudden variations in the incoming signal.

Another type of AFC circuit is shown in Figure 100. This circuit eliminates the need for a manual hold control. A hold control is normally necessary to permit correction of frequency drift in blocking oscillators and multivibrators, the two types of sweep oscillators most common in television receivers. By using a more stable oscillator, the automatic characteristics of the flywheel system just described, can be greatly improved.

The horizontal oscillator used in the circuit of Figure 100 is a stable Hartley oscillator, operating at the horizontal sweep frequency of 15,750 cycles per second. Coil L1 is the oscillator coil. This coil is coupled to winding L2 and thus feeds a sine wave voltage to V1.

The sync discriminator, V1, produces a d-c voltage proportional to the phase displacement between the incoming sync pulses

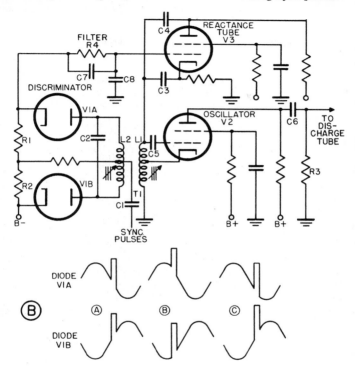

Figure 100. Automatic frequency control circuit which eliminates need for manual hold control.

and the horizontal oscillator signal. The sync pulses are applied to the plate of diodes V1a and b through the center tap of winding L2. The sync pulses appear on both diode plates with the same polarity. Sine wave voltage from the oscillator V2, which appears across L1, is coupled to the plates of the diodes. Because of the transformer coupling, the sine wave voltage on the plate of V1a is 180° out of phase with the sine wave voltage on V1b.

The d-c output of the discriminator is applied to the grid of V3 through the filter network consisting of R4, C7 and C8. V3 is used in a reactance tube circuit which is shunted across the

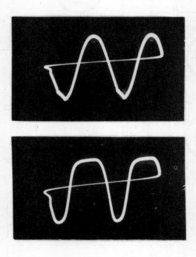

Figure 10i. Signals on grid and plate of Hartley oscillator operating at low plate voltage.

oscillator coil. A change in the d-c voltage applied to its grid causes a change in the mutual conductance of V3, which in turn affects the frequency of the sweep oscillator.

When the sync pulses and the sine wave output of the sweep oscillator are properly phased as in (A) of Figure 100B, both diodes produce equal voltages across their load resistors R1 and R2. These voltages are of opposing polarity; therefore, the sum of the voltages across the load resistors is zero. If the

phase of the pulse changes with respect to the sine wave as in
(B) of Figure 100, V1a will produce more voltage across R1
than V1b produces across R2. Thus, the sum of the voltages across the two will be a positive potential. In (C), the opposite condition exists. It is obvious that the output of the discriminator can swing from positive through zero to negative,

Figure 102. Improvement brought about by incorporating flywheel sync in receiver.

dependent upon the phase relation of the sync signal and the oscillator output. This changing d-c output is applied to the grid
of V3. V3 is a reactance tube connected across the oscillator
coil. A change in the d-c output of the sync discriminator produces a change in the mutual conductance of V3. If the phase
of the oscillator shifts with respect to the synchronizing pulses,
the change in the d-c output of the sync discriminator is applied to V3 to bring the oscillator back into phase.

C7, C8, and R4 form a filter circuit which by-passes rapid
changes in the d-c voltage from the discriminator, such as are
produced by noise bursts.

The output of a Hartley oscillator is normally unsuitable for triggering a sweep circuit. In order to secure a suitable signal, a comparatively low plate voltage is placed on V2 so that, when the tube oscillates, the sine wave voltage on the grid overloads the plate circuit and causes saturation. The signal at the plate appears flat topped. The signals on the grid and plate are shown in Figure 101. The flat-topped signal on the plate is applied to a differentiating network consisting of condenser C6 and resis-

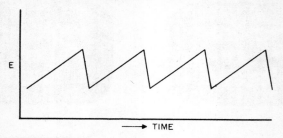

E

⟶ TIME

Figure 103. Waveform of current in deflection coils.

tor R3. This network converts the flat-topped wave into positive and negative triggering pulses in the same manner in which the horizontal sync pulses are formed in a differentiating circuit. The resulting differentiated wave is a pulse sufficiently sharp to trigger a discharge tube.

3-63 Comparison of Sync Systems. Figure 102 illustrates the improvements brought about by incorporation of AFC into a receiver. The photographs on the left were made of a receiver using ordinary triggered sync, while those on the right indicate the results obtained with flywheel sync. A is the screen of a receiver utilizing triggered synchronization. A and B illustrate the improvement obtained with a weak signal received 70 miles from the transmitter. A is without and B is with flywheel sync. In C and D, a doorbell buzzer was sounded near a receiver in the vicinity of a strong local station. The word "Philadelphia" is much clearer in D, which is a receiver using flywheel sync.

3-64 Saw-Tooth Generators. The circuits which separate and segregate the sync pulses, and the methods used to synchronize a receiver's sweep oscillator with the electron beam in the camera tube have been discussed. These circuits all serve to control the frequency of the saw-tooth generator which is the circuit in which the shaping of the deflecting voltage begins. In both electrostatic or magnetic systems, the force which acts upon the beam in the picture tube must increase in a linear fashion, so as to move the beam from left to right at a constant rate. At the end of a scanning line (or field) the beam must return quickly to its initial position. The saw-tooth wave of Figure 103 provides these characteristics. In an electrostatic deflection circuit, this waveform is the voltage impressed upon the deflection plates. With electro-magnetic deflection, a current of the waveform shown in Figure 103 must flow in the coils to set up the proper magnetic lines of force which move the beam. It will be shown later that the voltage across a deflection coil which causes a saw-tooth current to flow, is not of saw-tooth shape.

Although the voltage and current wave shapes ultimately required by the two deflection systems are different, both systems first generate a saw-tooth voltage. A crude method of producing a saw-tooth voltage is shown in Figure 104A. When switch A is closed, a constant d-c voltage, supplied by a battery, sends current through the resistor into the condenser. The condenser charges rapidly when A is closed, and then more slowly as the potential across the condenser approaches the battery voltage. Finally, the potential across the condenser becomes equal to the voltage of the battery and the current flow ceases. The increase in voltage across the condenser from the time when the switch is closed until current stops flowing is shown in Figure 104B. The curve is approximately linear up to point 1.

If switch A is opened and switch B is closed when the condenser has charged to the voltage represented by point 1, the condenser will be short circuited and discharge through the switch (Figure 104C). If, following the discharge period, switch B is opened and switch A is closed, the battery will begin charging the condenser for the next cycle.

By discharging the condenser at point 1, which is the point on the curve at the end of the linear portion of the charging curve, a linear saw-tooth voltage is obtained. Were it possible to open and close the switches very rapidly, at a rate of 60 times per second, this circuit would provide a saw-tooth voltage at the vertical sweep frequency. A similar switching arrangement, operating 15,750 times per second, would generate saw-tooth waves at the horizontal sweep frequency. A mechanical switching system operating at these frequencies is impractical and would be difficult to synchronize. By substituting an electronic switching system for the manual one just described, a method for producing saw-tooth signals for use in the television receiver is available. Before describing the circuits used to generate the sweep signals, a further examination of the properties

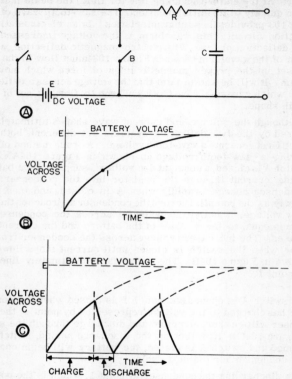

Figure 104. Simple method for producing saw-tooth voltage.

of charging and discharging resistance-capacitance circuits is in order.

If the resistance in series with the capacitor of Figure 104A were variable, and its value changed while the switching rate was maintained at a constant frequency of 60 çycles per second, the following would take place: As the resistance was decreased, the rate at which the capacitance changed would increase. Lowering the resistance would therefore permit the capacitor to charge to a higher potential during the fixed charging time. Figure 105 shows charging curves for different values of R. The larger saw-tooth voltages are generated when the resistance is decreased. Since the frequency remains constant, discharge takes place at the same time regardless of the resist-

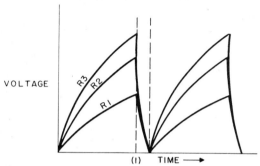

VOLTAGE

R3

R2

R1

(1)   TIME ⟶

Figure 105. Effect on charging curve of different values of R in Figure 104.

ance. Thus, though the frequency is the same, the amplitude of the saw-tooth voltages is greater. R then is an effective amplitude control. If it were located in the vertical sweep circuit of a television receiver, it would determine the height of the picture. If it were located in the horizontal sweep circuit, it would determine the width of the picture.

3-65 Electronic Saw-Tooth Generators. A simple electronic saw-tooth generator is shown in Figure 106A. The resistance R and capacitance C are connected in series with a d-c voltage. Across the condenser is a neon bulb.' A neon bulb acts as an open switch until the voltage across its electrodes reaches the bulb's "ionization potential". When the ionization potential is reached, the neon gas in the bulb ionizes, and current flows through the bulb. The circuit in Figure 106A operates in the following manner:

1. When d-c voltage is initially applied to the circuit, condenser C charges through resistor R.

2. During the charge period the neon bulb acts like an open switch.

3. The condenser continues to charge until the ionization potential of the neon bulb is reached.

4. When its ionization potential is reached, the neon tube conducts and discharges the condenser.

5. The condenser discharges until the voltage across it drops to the "de-ionization potential" of the neon bulb. The de-ionization potential of a neon bulb is considerably less than its ioni-

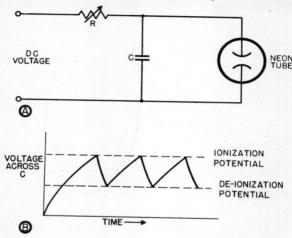

Figure 106. Simple electronic saw-tooth generator.

zation potential. When the de-ionization potential is reached, the neon bulb stops conducting and again acts line an open switch.

6. After the de-ionization potential has been reached, condenser C stops discharging and begins charging again to repeat the cycle.

The charge and discharge voltage across C is shown in Figure 106B.

Another type of discharge tube used in saw-tooth generator circuits is the thyratron. Thyratrons are filled with mercury or argon instead of neon. The potential at which a thyratron conducts is controlled by a grid element between the plate and cathode. For a given plate voltage, there is a corresponding grid voltage value which will cause a thyratron to conduct.

Figure 107 shows a simplified version of a thyratron saw-tooth generator circuit. It operates in the following manner:

1. A d-c potential is applied to the charging condenser C through resistor R. The charging voltage is also applied to the plate of the thyratron, which is in parallel with C.

2. During the charging period, the thyratron does not conduct because a fixed negative voltage is applied to its grid.

3. A positive pulse is applied to the grid of the thyratron.

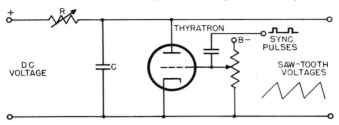

Figure 107. Thyratron saw-tooth generator circuit.

This pulse overcomes the negative bias and permits the thyratron to conduct.

4. The tube continues to conduct until the voltage across condenser C, which is discharging through the thyratron, drops to the de-ionization potential of the tube.

5. When the de-ionization potential is reached, C stops discharging and begins to charge again to repeat the cycle.

Thyratron saw-tooth generator circuits were employed in many pre-war television sets and are still used in cathode-ray oscillograph sweep circuits. Present television receivers use vacuum tubes for sweep oscillators, rather than gas tubes, because their operation is less affected by line voltage and temperature changes.

The vacuum tube oscillators which are commonly used to discharge saw-tooth generating circuits are the blocking oscillator and multivibrator.

3-66 The Multivibrator and Discharge Circuit. A multivibrator and discharge circuit capable of generating a synchronized saw-tooth voltage is shown in Figure 108. The power supply charges capacitor C3 through resistor R2 during the time that tube V2 is not conducting. Sync pulses applied to the grid of tube V1 control the frequency of oscillation of the circuit. When V2 conducts, C3 discharges through the tube. The cycle then repeats as V1 and V2 alternately conduct. The sawtooth voltage developed across C3 is coupled through C4 to the grid of the deflection amplifier tube. The time constant of the discharge circuit is determined by R2 and C3, whose values are chosen for the 60-cycle frequency of the vertical sweep or for the 15,750-cycle frequency of the horizontal sweep.

3-67 The Blocking Oscillator and Discharge Circuit. Two

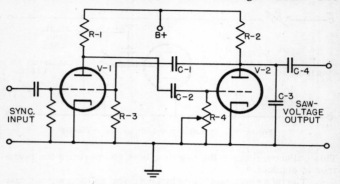

Figure 108. Multivibrator and discharge circuit.

types of blocking oscillator, discharge circuits are commonly employed in television receivers. In one circuit (Figure 109), the charging capacitor and series resistor are incorporated in the plate circuit of the blocking oscillator. During the time that the tube is blocked, C2 charges up. When the positive sync pulse triggers the oscillator, the tube conducts and discharges the capacitor. The plate resistor R2 is made variable to provide amplitude control of the saw-tooth voltage. The variable resistor R1, in combination with C1, determines the time constant of the grid circuit and the frequency of the pulses.

Many receivers use a separate discharge tube to separate the saw-tooth generator from the blocking oscillator and provide greater stability. The principle of operation is the same as in the circuit just described. Figure 110 shows a typical circuit. The grids of the triodes are tied together so that the positive pulse developed during each cycle of the blocking oscillator also appears on the grid of the discharge tube. The charging capacitor C1 and the series "size control" resistor R1 are in the plate circuit of the discharge tube. The sync pulses trigger the oscillator, causing a positive pulse to appear on its grid. The grid is connected directly to the grid of the discharge tube and the pulse causes the discharge tube to conduct and discharge C1. Immediately following the pulse, both grids are cut off and capacitor C1 begins charging again.

3-68 Sweep Amplifiers. The charging condenser across which the saw-tooth sweep signal is generated is not permitted to

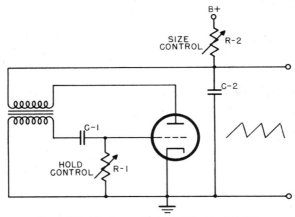

Figure 109. Blocking oscillator and discharge circuit.

charge to the full applied voltage. It is discharged at the end of the linear portion of its charging curve in order to obtain a suitably linear saw-tooth voltage. The resultant saw-tooth signal is not of sufficient amplitude to fully deflect the beam in the picture tube. In order to increase the amplitude of the saw-tooth signal it is fed to a sweep amplifier before it is applied to the deflection plates of an electrostatic tube or to the yoke of a magnetic tube. The sweep amplifier includes a linearity control circuit, which corrects for distortion caused by the slight curvature of the saw-tooth voltage in the charging circuit.

3-69 Sweep Amplifiers for Electrostatic Deflection. A sweep amplifier for use with electrostatic deflection is shown in Figure 111. The saw-tooth signal is fed to the grid of V1. The amplified signal appears across the plate load resistor R2. The signal is coupled through C1 to one of the deflection plates. The other deflection plate is grounded through resistor R3.

The linearity control R1 makes it possible to compensate for non-linearity of the signal at the input of the amplifier. Such non-linearity is a result of the charging characteristics of the saw-tooth voltage generating circuit.

R1 changes the d-c voltage on the cathode of the amplifier and

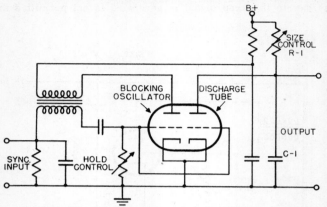

Figure 110. Blocking oscillator discharge circuit using dual triode.

thus changes the grid bias of the stage. Since the triode used in the circuit does not have a linear grid voltage plate current characteristic, the amplifier distorts the saw-tooth signal. By selecting the proper operating point on the characteristic curve, the distortion introduced by the sweep amplifier can be made to compensate for the non-linear quality of the saw-tooth signal fed to its grid.

As illustrated in Figure 112, when a slightly curved saw-tooth voltage A is applied to the triode amplifier, the non-linear amplification property of the tube compensates for the curvature of the saw-tooth. A linear saw-tooth B is obtained at the plate. The cathode resistor R1 determines the d-c grid voltage swing. By changing the position of point P on the curve, R1 can move the saw-tooth voltage to a more linear or a more curved portion of the characteristic curve and achieve different degrees of linearity compensation.

The sweep amplifiers for the vertical and horizontal deflection circuits are essentially the same, except for the values of the resistance and capacitance required for the different sweep frequencies.

The sweep amplifier circuit shown in Figure 111 applies a saw-tooth voltage to only one deflection plate. This circuit is

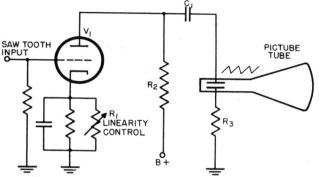

Figure 111. Sweep amplifier for use with electrostatic deflection.

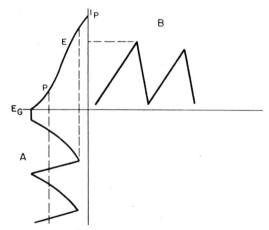

Figure 112. Removal of non-linearity from saw-tooth by operating on curved portion of characteristic curve.

known as a single-ended amplifier and has several disadvantages when used as a sweep amplifier.

One of the most serious disadvantages of single-ended deflection stems from the fact that the average voltage on the deflection plates varies as the saw-tooth voltage swings from zero to

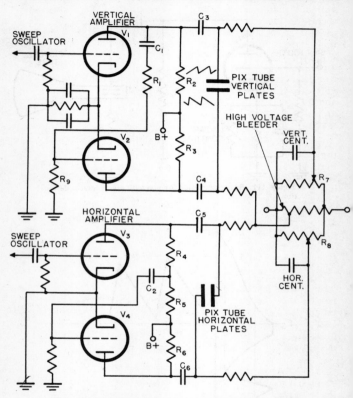

Figure 113. Push-pull vertical and horizontal sync circuits for electrostatic deflection.

maximum. Since the deflection plates are close to the second anode, it is desirable to keep the average voltage on the deflection plates at the same potential as the second anode, in order to keep the electron beam in focus. With single-ended deflection the average voltage on the deflection plates changes during the sweep cycle, and as a result, the picture is slightly out of of focus around its edges.

The shortcomings of the single-ended amplifier can be overcome by using a push-pull sweep amplifier. A typical push-
pull vertical and horizontal sweep amplifier system for electrostatic deflection is shown in Figure 113. Since the operation
of the vertical and horizontal sweep amplifiers is similar, only
the vertical amplifier will be described. The saw-tooth signal
is applied to the grid of V1. R2 is the load resistor of V1. The
amplified saw-tooth signal is applied to one of the vertical deflection plates through C3. A portion of the amplified saw-tooth
voltage is fed from the plate of V1 to the grid of V2 through C1
and R1. R1 and R9 form a voltage divider which reduces the
amplitude of the saw-tooth voltage applied to the grid of V2 to
a value equal to that at the grid of V1.

Because of the 180° phase reversal which takes place in V1,
the saw-tooth signal on the grid of V2 is 180° out of phase with
that on the grid of V1. The saw-tooth signal which is amplified by V2 and applied to the lower deflection plate, is thus 180°
out of phase with the voltage on the upper plate.

As one deflection plate swings positive and attracts the negative electron beam, the other plate swings negative an equal
amount and repels the beam. The average voltage across the
plates is zero. Since the average potential on the plates remains
fixed with respect to the second anode, no defocusing of the beam
occurs.

Push-pull sweep amplifiers do not distort the saw-tooth signal to any appreciable extent and therefore cannot be used to
compensate for non-linearity originating in the circuit generating the signal. By feeding a suitably linear signal to a push-
pull sweep generator, a linear sweep characteristic can be secured without the necessity for a linearity control.

3-70 Electromagnetic Deflection Amplifiers. In receivers with
electrostatic tubes, saw-tooth voltages are required to deflect
the electron beam. In receivers with magnetically deflected
tubes, saw-tooth currents must be passed through the deflection coils. To produce a linear saw-tooth current, such as
shown in Figure 114A, a voltage as shown in Figure 114D must
be impressed across the coils. The need for a voltage of this
waveshape is explained by the theory of magnetic circuits.

The strength of a magnetic field which surrounds a current-
carrying coil is proportional to the amount of current flowing
in the coil. When a voltage is applied to a coil, an induced volt-

age of opposite polarity is generated in the coil. The induced voltage opposes the flow of current. If a square wave voltage, such as shown in Figure 114B, is impressed across a coil which has inductance but no resistance, a saw-tooth current will flow in the coil. The current in the coil does not rise immediately

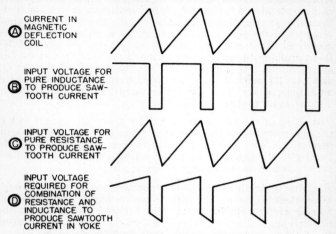

(A) CURRENT IN MAGNETIC DEFLECTION COIL

(B) INPUT VOLTAGE FOR PURE INDUCTANCE TO PRODUCE SAW-TOOTH CURRENT

(C) INPUT VOLTAGE FOR PURE RESISTANCE TO PRODUCE SAW-TOOTH CURRENT

(D) INPUT VOLTAGE REQUIRED FOR COMBINATION OF RESISTANCE AND INDUCTANCE TO PRODUCE SAWTOOTH CURRENT IN YOKE

Figure 114. Waveforms of current and voltage in magnetic deflection systems.

to a maximum when the square wave voltage rises from zero to peak value. As soon as the voltage is applied to the coil, the induced voltage opposes the flow of current. The current rises gradually. At the end of the square wave, the voltage drops to zero, forming a saw-tooth signal. An induced voltage opposes the drop in current, and the saw-tooth current decays gradually.

Since a coil of wire is not a pure inductance, but contains some resistance, a square wave voltage impressed across a coil will not cause a saw-tooth current to flow through the coil.

The voltage required to produce a saw-tooth current in a pure resistance has a saw-tooth shape, as shown in Figure 114C. This follows Ohm's Law, which states that the voltage across a resistor is directly proportional to the resistance of, and the current flowing in, the resistor. A saw-tooth current may be produced in a coil having both inductance and resistance by combining the voltages of Figure 114B and 114C to form the waveshape of Figure 114D. The saw-tooth portion of waveform D produces a saw-tooth current through the resistive component of the coil.

The pulse portion of waveform D plus part of the square wave component (which has reduced the height of the saw-tooth when

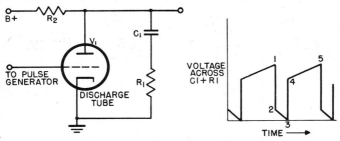

Figure 115. Discharge tube with peaking circuit.

waveform B and C are combined) causes a saw-tooth current to flow through the inductive component of the coil.

3-71 Peaking Circuit. The waveform of Figure 114D is produced in magnetic deflection receivers by a slight modification of the charging circuit. This modification is simply the addition of resistor R1 in series with the charging condenser C1, as shown in Figure 115. With the resistor added, the circuit operates as follows:

1. The condenser C1 is charged by the B supply voltage through R2. During this period, V1 does not conduct. The voltage which builds up across C1 and R1 is a saw-tooth.

2. When a triggering pulse is applied to the grid, the tube conducts, and C1 discharges through the circuit consisting of R1, C1, and the tube resistance.

3. The voltage across C1 does not drop to zero instantly because of the presence of series resistance R1. When the tube conducts, a voltage drop takes place across resistor R2 which causes the voltage across C1 and R1 to drop from point 1 to point 2. Capacitor C1 then begins to discharge gradually from point 2 to 3, at which point the tube stops conducting.

At cutoff, the voltage on the plate of V1 suddenly rises because current no longer flows through R2, and the attendant voltage drop does not take place. The sudden charge causes the voltage on C1 to rise from point 3 to point 4. The capacitor then charges slowly, and the voltage rises in saw-tooth fashion from point 4 to point 5.

The resistor R1 in series with C1 is called a "peaking" resistor, because it adds the pulse to the saw-tooth waveshape. The relative amplitudes of the pulse and the saw-tooth which are

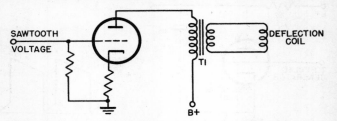

Figure 116. Sweep amplifier for magnetic deflection.

required in a magnetic deflection circuit, depend upon the amount of resistance and inductance in the deflection coils. The amplitude of the pulse and saw-tooth are controlled by the relative values of R1 and C1.

A peaking resistor is used in vertical deflection circuits because the resistive component of vertical deflection coils is usually much greater than their inductance. A typical vertical coil has a resistance of about 700 ohms and an inductance of about 30 millihenrys. At the vertical scanning frequency of 60 cycles, the inductive reactance is therefore quite low. A large saw-tooth voltage plus a peaking pulse is thus required.

The inductive reactance of horizontal deflection coils is much larger than their resistance. A typical coil has an inductance of 8 millihenrys and a resistance of about 15 ohms. At the horizontal scanning frequency of 15,750 cycles, the inductive reactance predominates and the resistance has little effect. A peaking resistor is therefore unnecessary.

3-72 Deflection Circuits. A sweep amplifier for a magnetic deflection circuit is shown in Figure 116. Saw-tooth voltage is applied to the grid. In the vertical deflection system, this saw-tooth voltage has a peaking pulse added to it. The plate of the amplifier is coupled to the deflection coil through step-down transformer T1. This transformer matches the high plate impedance of the amplifier to the low impedance of the deflection coil. Usually a one-ampere peak-to-peak saw-tooth current is needed to set up a sufficiently strong magnetic field in horizontal deflection coils. Since a turns ratio of about 10:1 is used in the coupling transformer, about one tenth as much current flows in the primary. The sweep amplifier tube must therefore be capable of handling about 100 milliamperes of peak-to-peak

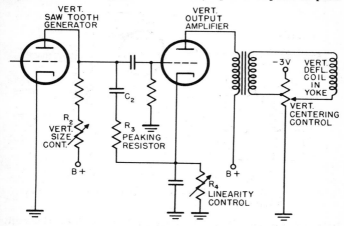

Figure 117. Vertical amplifier circuit.

saw-tooth current. Tubes like the 807 or 6BG6 meet these current requirements and are commonly found in horizontal deflection circuits.

For proper vertical deflection, a saw-tooth current of about 150 ma. peak-to-peak, at 60 cycles, is required. With the step-down transformer having a turns ratio of 10:1, about 15 ma flows in its primary. Tubes such as the 6SN7 (both triode sections operated in parallel) and the 6V6 can handle these currents and are used as vertical sweep amplifiers.

A basic vertical amplifier circuit is shown in Figure 117. The diagram includes the saw-tooth generator, the charging condenser C_2, and the peaking resistor R_3. The B supply voltage is applied to C_2 through R_2. R_2 is made variable and determines the amplitude of the saw-tooth voltage developed across C_2. R_2 therefore serves as a vertical size control.

The peaked saw-tooth voltage is applied to the grid of the vertical amplifier, which is coupled to the vertical deflection coil through a transformer. The variable resistance R4 in the cathode of the amplifier is the linearity control.

3-73 Linearity Control. The saw-tooth voltage fed to the sweep amplifier is not always perfectly linear. Other distortion some-

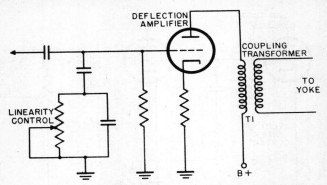

Figure 118. Simplified schematic of deflection amplifier with linearity control.

times takes place in the coupling transformer or deflection coil. To eliminate these effects, the cathode resistor of the sweep amplifier is made variable, just as with electrostatic deflection amplifiers (see R4 in Figure 117). This makes it possible to adjust the bias of the tube so that some distortion can be introduced by operating the sweep amplifier on a suitable section of its characteristic curve. The distortion introduced in this manner tends to cancel the non-linearity present in the signal fed to the grid of the amplifier.

A frequency distortion network is sometimes used rather than the bias control just described. A saw-tooth wave contains many harmonic frequencies. Distortion of the linear leading portion of the wave is caused by the attenuation of some of these frequencies more than others. By placing a resistance-capacitance network in the grid of a sweep amplifier, as shown in Figure 118, it is possible to compensate for the attenuation of the harmonic frequencies. The network acts like a filter across the grid. The filter shunts some frequencies to ground more readily than others, depending upon the values of the resistor and the capacitor. The frequencies which the filter bypasses can be changed by varying the value of the resistor. By setting the resistor correctly, the harmonic frequencies of the saw-tooth which are too strong can be reduced. The variable resistor thus serves as a linearity control.

3-74 Damping Circuits. In receivers using electromatic deflection, a damping diode is connected across the horizontal deflection coil as shown in Figure 119. The damping diode is nec-

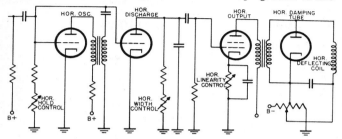

Figure 119. Simplified schematic of horizontal sweep circuit with damping tube.

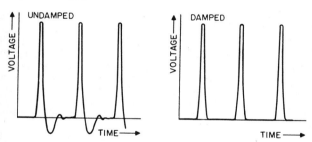

Figure 120. Spurious oscillations which appear across horizontal deflection coil during flyback time.

essary because spurious oscillations appear across the horizontal deflection coil when the saw-tooth current suddenly drops to zero during the flyback time (Figure 120). The sudden drop in current creates a large induced voltage in the coil. This voltage shocks the tuned circuit, consisting of the coil inductance and its distributed capacity, into oscillation. Since the oscillations distort the saw-tooth current, they must be eliminated. The diode effectively damps out oscillations by heavily loading the tuned circuit. It conducts during most of the sweep cycle and acts as a loading resistance across the coils.

The high impedance of the horizontal amplifier tetrode or pentode tubes provides very little damping and necessitates the use of the damping tube. In vertical deflection circuits, triodes are commonly used. Their low plate resistance provides adequate damping of shock-excited oscillations.

A diode is not always used in the damping circuit. In some

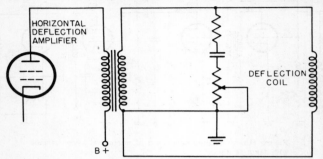

Figure 121. Simplified schematic of damping circuit using resistor and capacitor.

receivers, damping is accomplished by a series resistor and capacitor placed across the deflection coil. Such a circuit is shown in Figure 121. The RC time constant of the circuit is adjusted so that the capacitor readily charges when the high frequency oscillations occur. The charging circuit absorbs energy and by-passes the spurious oscillations occurring in the deflection coil.

It should be noted that there is no need for damping circuits with electrostatically deflected tubes, since deflection coils are not used.

3-75 Positioning Controls. Under ideal conditions, the electron beam in a cathode—ray tube will strike the center of the screen when not subjected to deflection voltages. A perfectly centered picture will then result when deflecting voltages are applied to the plates or coils. Actually, stray magnetic fields or distorted electrostatic fields within the electron gun structure are usually present and displace the beam from its natural position. The distorting influences generally remain fixed so that the displacement of the beam is constant. It is thus possible to introduce other fixed electrostatic or magnetic fields into the cathode ray tube which exactly counterbalance the distortions and bring the beam back to its center position.

In electrostatic tubes, d-c voltages are applied to the vertical and horizontal deflection plates. These d-c voltages set up two mutually perpendicular electrostatic fields. By varying the d-c

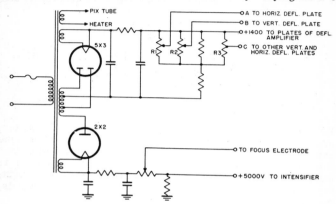

Figure 122. Power supply and positioning controls for electro-static cathode-ray tube.

voltages on the plates, the electrostatic fields can be varied and the beam brought to the center of the screen. When the deflecting voltages are superimposed on these d-c voltages, a centered picture is obtained on the screen. The d-c voltages are normally adjusted using two potentiometers which are connected to the power supply. One potentiometer varies the d-c voltage on the vertical plates and is called the vertical positioning or centering control. The other potentiometer varies the d-c voltage on the horizontal plates and is called the horizontal positioning or centering control. The two positioning controls are adjusted simultaneously to center the picture.

With a magnetically deflected tube, it is necessary to set up fixed magnetic fields to secure proper positioning of the beam. This is accomplished by feeding d-c currents into the vertical and horizontal deflection coils. These d-c currents set up fixed magnetic fields which center the beam. The potentiometers which control the amplitude of d-c current passing through the coils are the vertical and horizontal positioning controls.

The circuit arrangement shown in Figure 122 is used for positioning the beam in electrostatic cathode-ray tubes. A d-c voltage is placed on each set of plates from variable potentiometers R1 and R2 in series with the bleeder located in the high voltage power supply. One vertical plate and one horizontal plate are tied to the midpoint of resistor R3, which is in parallel with the positioning potentiometer. When the movable arms of R1 and

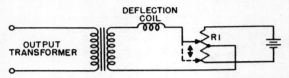

Figure 123. Positioning circuit for electromagnetic picture tube.

R2, which are tied to the other vertical and horizontal plates, are in the center, the d-c voltages at points A, B, and C are the same. As the potentiometers are varied, the potential difference with respect to point C swings from positive, through zero, to negative. The electron beam is thus moved either left or right, up or down, by the horizontal and vertical centering controls, respectively.

The circuit arrangement of Figures 122 has one other important feature. The deflection plates and centering controls must be at a potential near that of the second anode. A large difference in voltage between the deflection plates and the second anode will set up an electrostatic field and cause defocusing of the electron beam. With the bleeder arrangement shown, no appreciable difference of potential exists between the deflection plates and second anode.

The positioning circuits for magnetically deflected tubes are usually located in the secondary circuits of the vertical and horizontal sweep output transformers. Figure 123 shows a typical circuit used to pass a variable current through a vertical or horizontal deflection coil. One end of the output transformer is connected to the center tap of a potentiometer connected across a low d-c voltage point (about 10 volts in most receivers) in the power supply. The movable tap is connected to the deflection coil. When this tap is at the center of the resistor, no d-c current flows through the coil. Moving the tap above or below this point causes a d-c current to flow through the deflection coil in either a positive or negative direction. Identical circuits are used for vertical and horizontal positioning.

THE PICTURE TUBE

3-76 When television was introduced to the public in 1939, one of the serious objections raised by the viewing audience was that the screen was too small and images were not sufficiently bright and sharp. The picture size was limited by the picture tube, the largest magnetic type introduced at the time being the 12AP4, which was capable of producing a picture 8 x 10 inches in size. A few electrostatic tubes of 14- and 20-inch diameter were also built, but the rounded faces of these tubes resulted in distorted images.

These shortcomings have been solved in two ways. The first has been the increasing of the face diameter of direct view tubes while also making them substantially flat. The second has been the use of small projection tubes which produce images bright enough to project onto a screen.

Direct view tubes are manufactured in two types, electrostatic and magnetic. To date, only a seven-inch diameter electrostatic tube has been produced and used in commercial receivers. Magnetic tubes are available with diameters of 7, 10, 12, 15, 16, and 20 inches. The operating voltages and connections for these tubes can be found in Section 12. A picture 13 x 18 inches is obtained on the 20 inch tube, the largest direct view type manufactured. Projection systems employ 3, 4, and 5-inch diameter tubes which, with a suitable optical system, throw images of 19 x 25 inches and larger onto a screen.

3-77 Operating Voltages. Figure 124 illustrates the points at which the various voltages are applied to a picture tube. The tube shown in the diagram is magnetically focused and deflected. The voltages applied to it are as follows:

1. The filaments of modern tubes require 6.3 volts at 600 ma. The supply for the filament is usually 60-cycle a.c. The tube shown in the figure is operated with the cathode at low potential so that the filament winding connected to it does not have to be insulated against high voltage breakdown. At times cathodes are operated several thousand volts ·negative with respect to the grid, in which case the filament winding is insulated accordingly.

2. A positive voltage is applied to the cathode. This is done

in order to maintain the control grid at a negative potential with respect to the cathode, for in some circuits the grid is directly connected to the positive plate of the video amplifier. Thus the cathode must be raised to an even higher positive potential than the grid in order to keep the latter negative with respect to the cathode. The cathode voltage is usually made variable to permit

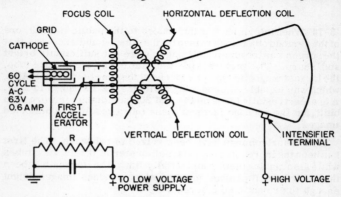

Figure 124. Points at which voltages are applied to electromagnetic picture tube.

changes in the grid bias, and hence the beam current. A variable cathode voltage is obtained from potentiometer, R, connected across the low voltage power supply. This potentiometer is the brightness control of the receiver.

3. Following the grid in the order of elements in the tube is the first accelerating electrode. In magnetic tubes it is operated several hundred volts positive and is connected to a tap on the bleeder of the low voltage power supply.

4. Two types of focus coils are found in receivers today: one of high resistance requiring approximately 30 ma, and another of lower resistance which draws about 250 ma. The higher resistance focus coils contain more turns of wire. Since it is the number of ampere-turns which determines the effectiveness of a focus coil, the greater the number of turns, the less the current required. The low resistance focus coil has fewer turns, which explains why as much as 250 ma is needed to obtain enough ampere-turns for proper focusing.

The low current drain of the high resistance focus coil permits it to be connected directly across the low voltage power supply. If the low resistance type were shunted across the supply, the current drain would be excessive and needlessly increase the size of the power supply. In practice, the low resistance coil is placed in series with the filter network in the same manner as are the field coils of the speakers in many AC-DC radio receivers.

5. The amplitude of the second anode or intensifier voltage which is required by a picture tube depends upon its size. Seven-inch tubes require from 2.5 to 6 kv accelerating potentials. Ten-inch tubes operate at 8 to 10 kv, and the large fifteen and twenty inch tubes are driven at voltages as high as 15 and 18 kv, respectively. Projection tubes generally operate with second anode voltages of from 25 to 30 kv.

The voltage requirements for electrostatic tubes are the same as for magnetic tubes except for those applied to the focusing electrode and the deflection plates. The first anode or focusing electrode is operated at approximately 1000 volts in electrostatic tubes. This voltage is obtained from a tap on the bleeder of the high voltage power supply.

A sawtooth voltage of approximately 50 volts, peak-to-peak, will deflect the electron beam one inch in an electrostatic cathode ray tube, operating at 2,500 volts. This means that a seven inch tube which reproduces a picture approximately 4 x 5 inches will need a 200-volt sawtooth voltage on the vertical deflection plates and a 250-volt saw-tooth voltage on the horizontal deflection plates.

3-78 Seven Inch Tubes. Four types of seven inch diameter tubes are now being manufactured. They are the electrostatic types 7EP4, 7GP4, 7JP4, and the magnetic type 7DP4. The useful picture area of seven-inch tubes is approximately $4 \times 5\frac{1}{2}$ inches. The 7EP4 operates at the lowest accelerating potential, about 2,500 volts. It thus requires the smallest high voltage supply, an important factor determining the cost of a receiver.

The 7GP4 and 7JP4 have similar characteristics. They are operated at accelerating potentials as high as 4,000 volts, have greater light output than the 7EP4, and higher deflection sensitivity.

The 7DP4 is the smallest direct view magnetic tube that is now employed in television receivers. It is electrostatically focused and magnetically deflected and operates at 6,000 volts. At this high voltage, it produces the brightest and sharpest picture of all tubes in the seven-inch series.

3-79 Ten-Inch Tubes. 10-inch tubes give a picture size of approximately 6 x 8 inches. These tubes are used in both table models and consoles. The 10-inch types include the 10BP4, 10EP4, and 10FP4. The 10BP4 and 10EP4 are identical except for their high voltage intensifier terminals. The former has the recessed cavity type, while the latter uses the ball type, as shown in Figure 125.

The electron guns of the 10BP4 and the 10EP4 are similar to

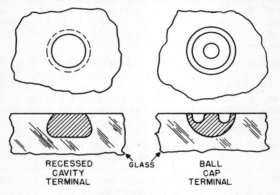

RECESSED   GLASS   BALL
CAVITY   CAP
TERMINAL   TERMINAL

Figure 125. Intensifier terminals.

the 7DP4. They are magnetically deflected and have ion traps, which are described later in this section. They are, however, different from the 7DP4 in that they are magnetically focused. They are normally operated at an accelerating voltage of 9,000 volts.

Some 10BP4 tubes have conductive coatings on the inside and outside of their glass funnels. The inner coating, which is the second anode, is connected to the high voltage supply. The outer coating is grounded by means of two small springs on the deflection yoke support. The capacity between the two coatings is approximately 500 mmf and is used as a filter condenser in the high frequency, high voltage power supplies employed with the tubes. Not all manufacturers of picture tubes provide the double metallic coating, it being claimed that the Q of such a condenser is too low to provide substantial filtering.

3-80 Aluminum Backing. The 10FP4 is the newest 10-inch tube featuring several important developments. These tubes have aluminum-backed screens, which permit greater brilliancy and contrast of image. The aluminum backing consists of a film of microscopic thickness which permits the passage of the fast

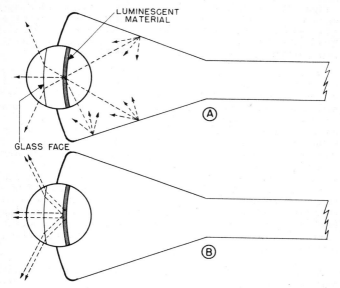

Figure 126. How aluminum backing increases image brightness.

moving electrons to the screen and, by its reflective qualities increases the light output.

In magnetic tubes which are not equipped with an aluminum-backed screen, a small spot appears on the face of the tube after considerable use. The formation of this spot is normally avoided by the use of an ion trap which is described later in this section. When a tube is equipped with an aluminum-backed screen, the ions cannot reach the phosphor coating to form the spot and therefore the need for an ion trap is eliminated.

Figure 126 illustrates how the advantages of the aluminum backing are achieved. The region in the circles represents greatly magnified sections of the faces of a conventional tube and one equipped with aluminum backing. In the conventional tube, A, at least 50 percent of the light generated in the screen is emitted back toward the electron gun. Another 15-25 percent is lost by reflection from the glass on the inside of the tube face. Thus, only 25-35 percent of the total light generated passes through the glass face in the form of useful light output.

Figure 126B shows a tube whose screen is covered with a layer of aluminum which is thin enough to permit the electrons to pass, but sufficiently thick to serve as a good reflecting surface. The light which previously would go toward the electron gun is reflected back toward the viewing position.

Metal-backing is best employed on tubes operating at fairly high voltages. With the addition of the aluminum layer the light output of a tube is actually decreased until the accelerating voltage is made sufficiently high for all the electrons to penetrate the layer. The accelerating voltage at which the light output of an aluminum-backed tube equals that of a conventional tube is called the "cross-over point". Above this voltage, the light output of the aluminum-backed tube increases at a much greater rate because of the elimination of stray light reflections. The cross-over point is governed by the thickness of the aluminum layer. Ten-inch tubes usually cross over between 3 and 6 kilovolts. If the layer is made too thin, it does not serve as an efficient reflecting surface nor fully stop the heavier ions. Too thick a layer raises the cross-over point and requires higher accelerating voltages to achieve more light output than with a conventional tube.

3-81 Twelve-Inch Tubes. The 12JP4 and the 12QP4 are the most widely used 12-inch tubes. They are almost an inch shorter than standard ten-inch tubes and thus can be used in table models as well as consoles. The $8 \times 10\frac{1}{2}$ inch image obtained on a 12-inch tube provides a picture area about 40 percent greater than do ten-inch tubes. The 12JP4 and the 12QP4 operate at an accelerating voltage of 8-10,000 volts and are magnetically focused and deflected. No ion trap is used in the 12JP4. The 12QP4 employs a bent-gun type of ion trap which is described later in this section.

3-82 Fifteen and Twenty-Inch Tubes. Fifteen-inch tubes provide a picture $9\frac{1}{2} \times 13$ inches in size. The only one now in use in television receivers is the 15AP4. This tube is comparatively short for its screen diameter, being only slightly more than twenty inches from face to socket. It is normally operated at 10,000 to 12,000 volts, requiring a power supply slightly larger than the ten and twelve-inch types. No ion trap is necessary with this tube.

The first twenty-inch tube to be used widely is the 20BP4. It is the largest direct view tube found in commercial television receivers and provides a $13\frac{1}{2}$ x 18 inch picture. It operates at an intensifier voltage of 12÷15,000 volts. The overall length of the 20BP4 is 28-3/4 inches so that if the tube were mounted horizontally, too bulky a cabinet would be needed to house it. One novel means of mounting the tube, which overcomes this

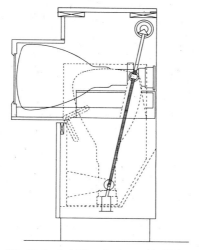

Figure 127. Mechanical lift mechanism used with large picture tubes.

objection, is shown in Figure 127. When the cabinet is closed, the tube is supported vertically (thus the cabinet has to be only a little deeper than the 20-inch diameter of the tube face). By opening the lid of the cabinet, the tube is automatically lifted into the horizontal viewing position.

3-83 Ion Traps. One of the characteristics of magnetic type tubes is the ion burn which forms in the center of the screen after a few hours of operation. This ion burn appears as a brown spot about the size of a half dollar, and is caused by the continuous bombardment of the phosphor screen by the heavier and slower moving ions inside the picture tube. These ions are emitted from the electron gun along with the useful electrons, and are attracted by the high accelerating voltage toward the screen. To avoid the formation of an ion spot, an ion trap electron gun in combination with a magnet has been devised.

As shown in Figure 128A, the first and second anodes are constructed with an oblique gap which causes both electrons and ions to be deflected at right angles to the gap. The ion-trap magnet, placed on the neck of the tube behind the focus coil, as

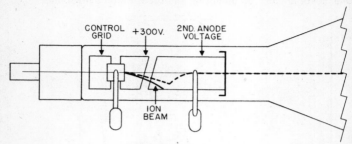

Figure 128A. Ion trap.

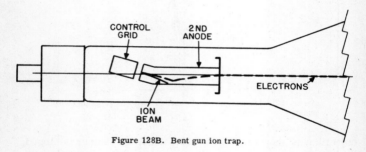

Figure 128B. Bent gun ion trap.

shown in Figure 129, applies a steady magnetic deflecting field to the electrons and bends them back along the axis of the tube. The heavier ions which are not so readily affected by the magnetic field, continue along their original path and are collected by the second anode. In this way, the ions and electrons are separated, and the ions trapped within the gun structure.

A second type of ion trap, known as a "bent-gun", is shown in Figure 128B. In this design, the cathode, grid, and anode are bent toward the wall of the tube. The electrons travel along the axis of the gun, but before they can strike the glass wall, they are deflected back to the axis of the tube by a magnetic field, set up by a bending coil placed over the neck of the tube and adjacent to the bent anode. The bending coil is similar in design to the ion trap magnet described above. The heavier ions, which are part of the electron stream, are not substantially affected by the magnetic field which deflects the electrons. The ions

Figure 129. The ion trap magnet is mounted between the tube base and the focus coil.

Figure 130. Picture tube with metal funnel.

continue to travel in a straight line and strike the anode wall.

3-84 Metal-Funnel Tubes. Picture tubes are now being man-ufactured which use a metal funnel attached to a flat glass plate. This tube is much cheaper to manufacture and is lighter in weight than glass tubes of equivalent size. The type 16AP4 sixteen-inch tube with a metal funnel is shown in Figure 130.

One disadvantage of this type of tube is the fact that the metal portion operates at high potential. In glass tubes, the high voltage intensifier terminal is only a small region covered by an insulating cap. But in metal tubes the entire funnel serves as

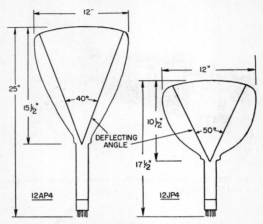

Figure 131. Relative shapes of old and new picture tubes.

the high voltage electrode. Except for this feature, the tube is operated like any other magnetically deflected and focused type.

3-85 Bulb Shape. A notable feature of modern magnetic tubes is the similarity in shape of the bulbs. The older type tubes had a 40 degree funnel angle which meant that the electron beam had to be deflected through this angle for full picture size. The newer magnetic tubes have a 50 degree funnel angle, permitting a shorter funnel and overall tube length. The relative shapes of the old and new type bulbs are shown in Figure 131. Though the new bulbs have the advantage of being shorter, the wider deflecting angle requires greater deflecting currents.

3-86 Deflection Requirements. In Figure 132, the sizes and shapes of the seven, ten, twelve, fifteen and twenty inch magnetic type tubes are compared. Note that the larger picture sizes are obtained by virtue of added bulb length, and that the deflecting angle of all the tubes is the same. In other words, if the accelerating potentials were the same, the deflecting current required for a seven inch tube would be sufficient for a twenty inch tube. Deflection coil current requirements do, however, increase with accelerating voltage. Thus ten and twelve inch tubes, which operate at about the same accelerating potentials, require the same deflecting current, while both require a

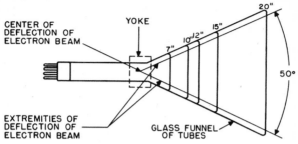

Figure 132. Relative sizes of magnetic picture tubes.

higher deflection current than is needed for seven inch tubes which operate at lower accelerating potentials.

A single 6BG6 (an 807 which has been modified for television sweep circuits) is capable of supplying the deflecting currents for the horizontal sweep in seven, ten and twelve inch tubes. The two sections of a double triode type 6SN7 in parallel (or an equivalent tube) are suitable as a vertical deflection amplifier. The current requirements of the higher voltage fifteen, sixteen, and twenty inch tubes are slightly above the maximum ratings of a single 6BG6; hence, two are often used in parallel for the horizontal sweep. Two sections of a 6SN7 in parallel will provide sufficient vertical sweep current for both fifteen and twenty inch tubes.

3-87 Projection Systems. Projection systems are utilized to magnify a small intensely brilliant picture formed on a special picture tube. Because the transmission efficiency of a lens is low, the light output of the picture tube has to be much higher than that of a direct-view tube. To obtain these brighter pictures, projection tubes are operated at voltages as high as 30,000 volts. Two principle methods of projection have been developed, the refractive system, and the Schmidt reflective system. A refractive projection system is shown in Figure 133. The tube is mounted vertically in the cabinet, and the light is projected by a refractive lens onto a 45 degree angle mirror, which in turn throws the picture onto a translucent screen. Projection systems using refractive lenses have not been employed to any

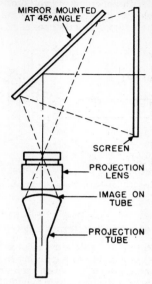

MIRROR MOUNTED AT 45° ANGLE

SCREEN

PROJECTION LENS

IMAGE ON TUBE

PROJECTION TUBE

Figure 133. Refractive projection system.

great extent in home receivers because the cost of suitable lenses is quite high.

3-88 **The Schmidt Projection System.** An efficient low cost projection system, known as the Schmidt optical system, has been used for many years in reflective astronomical telescopes. The Schmidt principle has been applied to projection television system, as illustrated in Figure 134. The projection tube is mounted vertically, facing downward. The picture is projected onto a spherical reflecting mirror. The mirror collects most of the light from the tube and transmits it to a flat inclined mirror, thence to a vertical translucent surface. An intervening lens, molded of lucite, corrects the spherical aberration caused by the reflecting mirror. The light transmission efficiency of this system is much higher than that of refractive lens systems. The center section of the spherical mirror is painted black to prevent the illumination which falls on this sector from being reflected back to the face of the picture tube. Such reflections would reduce the picture contrast by illuminating the dark areas in the picture.

The spherical aberration of the reflecting mirror can be under-

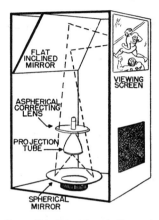

.Figure 134. Schmidt projection system.

stood by studying Figure 135A. Light rays coming from point A on the tube should focus on the screen at the image point E; instead, the reflected rays intersect the axis of the mirror at distances B, C, and D.

A correcting lens is inserted between the spherical mirror and screen to focus these divergent rays to a single point. With a correcting lens of the shape shown in Figure 135B, which has a constantly changing curvature on one side, the rays are bent so that they converge at the screen. The size and shape of the correcting lens depends upon the degree of magnification for which the system is designed.

It is interesting to note that the leads from the deflection yoke and the picture tube socket pass through the optical path directly above the corrector lens. Due to the fact that light from any given point on the tube passes through all parts on the corrector lens, as shown in Figure 136, the leads do not cast a shadow on the picture, but instead reduce the optical efficiency of the system by a small amount, proportional to the percentage of the corrector lens area which they block.

The reflective optical system has a resolution of approximately 1500 lines and an efficiency equivalent to that of an F.8 lens.

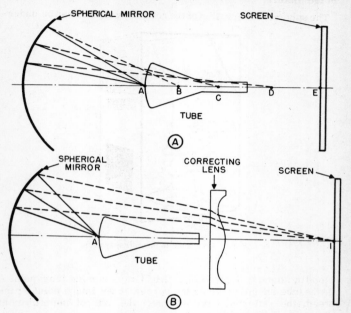

Figure 135. Function of correcting lens in Schmidt projection system.

A refractive projection lens of equivalent efficiency is prohibitive from the standpoint of both cost and size.

The Schmidt system has been used by several manufacturers. In RCA receivers, a type 5TP4 projection tube operates at a second-anode potential of 28,000 volts, and employs an aluminum-backed phosphor screen. The elements of the RCA system are shown in Figure 137. The projected image is reflected from a 45-degree mirror onto a translucent viewing screen of special construction. A pressed plastic coating on the screen gives it a highly directional characteristic, restricting the angle of view to 50 degrees in the horizontal plane and 30 degrees in the vertical plane. This screen reflects only 15 percent of the ambient light and transmits 85 percent of the image illumination. The light output and contrast of such a projection receiver is

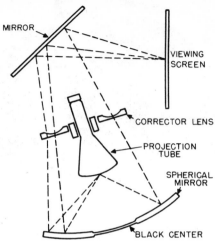

MIRROR

VIEWING SCREEN

CORRECTOR LENS

PROJECTION TUBE

SPHERICAL MIRROR

BLACK CENTER

Figure 136. Light from a single point on the picture tube screen passes through all points of the corrector lens.

nearly equal to that of direct view types.

3-89 The Philco Projection System. A variation of the Schmidt principle is shown in Figure 138. Instead of projecting onto a 45 degree mirror and then through a translucent screen, which adds light loss to the system, the picture is thrown directly onto an opaque beaded screen. As before, a correcting lens is incorporated into the system. In the Philco projection receiver, which uses this principle, a four inch tube is operated at 20,000 volts. The picture is reflected from a plane mirror inside the front of the cabinet, onto an inclined specular screen mounted on the underside of the lifted cabinet lid. This screen is highly directional and the viewer must be seated almost directly in front of the receiver in order to appreciate the maximum light output. A picture 15 x 20 inches in size is obtained by this means, with a highlight brightness of 60 to 80 footlamberts. The optical barrel of the Philco system, shown in Figure 139, contains the projection tube, the yoke, focus coil and correction lens.

3-90 "Protelgram" Projection System. A very small, com-

Figure 137. The tube and barrel of the RCA projection system.

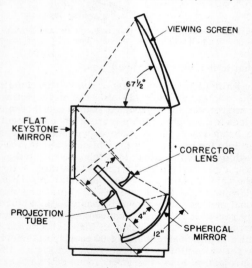

Figure 138. The Philco version of the Schmidt optical system.

pletely packaged version of the Schmidt projection system has been developed by the North American Phillips Co. and is sold to television receiver manufacturers under the trade name

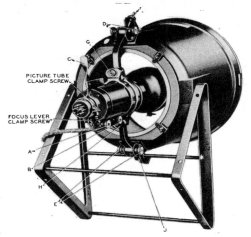

PICTURE TUBE
CLAMP SCREW

FOCUS LEVER
CLAMP SCREW

Figure 139. The optical barrel of the Philco projection system.

"Protelgram". The entire unit is mounted in a metal box $8\frac{1}{2}$ x 9 x $5\frac{1}{2}$ inches, as shown in Figure 140. This compactness is achieved by "folding" the optical system into a triangular arrangement. This is accomplished by placing a plane mirror between the Schmidt mirror and the correction lens which are mounted at right angles to each other.

Contributing further to the small size of the system is the special projection tube which is only 2.5 inches in diameter and 10.5 inches long. A 1.4 x 1.8 inch image on the face of the tube is magnified by the optical system to 12 x 16 inches on the viewing screen.

The tube is operated at 25,000 volts, resulting in an intensely bright image which can be projected with satisfactory brightness under normal lighting conditions. The high voltage is obtained from a self-contained high frequency power supply. The deflection and focusing currents for the tube are the same as for a ten inch magnetic tube operating at 9,000 volts. Thus the same deflection components which are used in direct view receivers are suitable for the "Protelgram" unit.

3-91 Theater Television. Very large pictures are obtained with projection systems designed for use in theaters. Both refractive and reflective systems have been employed, the only difference from those designed for home receivers being that

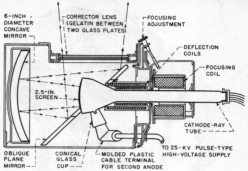

Figure 140. The North American Phillips version of the Schmidt projection system.

Figure 141. Special mirror used in RCA theater projection system.

the projection tubes are operated at higher voltages and are larger in diameter.

RCA's large screen projector employs a fifteen inch tube operating at 80,000 volts. The Schmidt element is accordingly larger, having a 42 inch spherical mirror and a 36 inch correction lens as shown in Figure 141. This projection system is capable of throwing a picture onto a screen 40 feet from it.

3-92 Magnifying Lenses. Another method of obtaining an increased picture size consists of placing a magnifying lens in front of a direct view tube. Magnifying lenses are becoming

Figure 142. Magnifying lens used to enlarge image on screen of picture tube.

increasingly popular with owners of small screen sets. Lenses are produced economically using light weight, transparent plastic, and hollow plastic filled with mineral oil. A typical lens is shown in Figure 142.

Magnifications of about 1.5 to 1 are obtained with commercial lenses. The equivalent of a ten inch tube picture is thereby obtained from a 7 inch tube, a 12 inch picture from a ten inch tube. Some manufacturers are making lenses as large as 15 x 18 inches for use with 15 inch tubes in order to obtain a magnified picture equal to that on a 20 inch tube.

THE POWER SUPPLIES

3-93 Television receiver power supplies are more complex than those found in ordinary radio receivers because they must supply a wide range of voltages. For example, a typical receiver requires 300-400 volts for its r-f, video, audio, and sweep circuits; a negative 10 volts for its beam positioning circuits and grid bias for its video stages. In addition the picture tube requires a driving potential of 12,000 volts.

As a rule two separate supplies are employed as the most

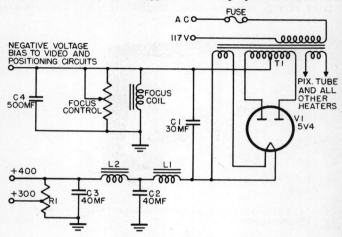

Figure 143. Typical low-voltage power supply.

economical means of producing these voltages. One supply furnishes the high voltage required for the accelerating electrode of the picture tube. The picture tube draws about 200 microamperes from this supply. The sweep circuits of a magnetically deflected tube draw as much as 200 ma at about 400 volts while the rest of the receiver usually consumes an additional 100 to 150 ma at about 300 volts. These high currents are furnished by a second supply, equiped with a bleeder from which the various voltages are tapped.

3-94 Low Voltage Supply. The schematic diagram of a low voltage, high current power supply is shown in Figure 143. The power transformer T1 has a secondary with three windings. One winding steps up the a-c line voltage to about 450 volts and applies this voltage to the plates of a dual diode, V1, a full-wave rectifier. A separate filament winding furnishes heater current for the rectifier. A second filament winding supplies heater current for the picture tube and the other tubes in the receiver.

A two section pi filter is used, consisting of L1, L2, C1, C2 and C3. A bleeder, R1, is connected across the output of the filter. 400 volts is obtained across the full bleeder for the sweep

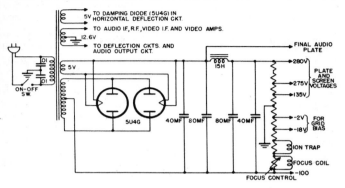

Figure 144. Complete low-voltage supply as used in television receivers.

circuits while a tap provides 300 volts for the r-f, video, and audio circuits.

In the conventional full-wave rectifier circuit, the center tap of the transformer secondary is grounded. In the circuit used here a parallel combination, consisting of the focus control, the focus coil, and capacitor C4, is placed between the center tap and ground. This is a common arrangement employed in television receivers to obtain the 10 to 40 volts negative bias necessary for the positioning circuits and video i-f amplifiers. The negative voltage obtained in this manner is equal to the current drawn through the secondary times the resistance of the parallel combination of the focus coil and focus control. The 500 mf condenser, C4, filters out 60 cycle ripple and sweep voltages which feed back to the power supply.

A low voltage supply, representative of the type found in commercial receivers, is presented in Figure 144.

3-95 High Voltage Power Supplies. Four types of high voltage power supply are being used to furnish the high potential to the picture tubes in television receivers. These are:
    1. The conventional 60 cycle supply.

2. The rectified radio frequency supply, operating at from 50 kc to 300 kc.

3. The pulse type supply which generates pulses at the horizontal scanning frequency of 15,750 cps.

4. The kickback or flyback supply which steps up the voltage pulses generated in the horizontal deflection transformer and converts this normally wasted energy into useful high voltage.

The high voltage supplies must deliver 200 to 300 microamperes. The high voltage required ranges from about 2500 volts for small electrostatic tubes to about 30,000 volts for projection tubes.

3-96 60-Cycle Supplies. The 60-cycle high voltage supply is similar in design and operation to low voltage 60-cycle supplies except that the power transformer and filter components are designed for higher voltages. Half-wave rectifiers are almost always used in 60 cycle high voltage supplies in order to keep the size, cost, and weight to a minimum. Filter capacitors as low as 0.05 mf are effective in smoothing out the ripple because of the low current drawn.

The schematic circuit of a typical 60-cycle high voltage supply appears in Figure 145. The transformer T has two windings on its secondary. One is the step-up winding which furnishes high voltage to the plate of the rectifier tube, while the other winding supplies current for the rectifier filament. Rectifier tubes such as the 2X2, 2V3, or 8013 are used since these types are capable of withstanding high inverse peak voltages. The filter section consists of C1, R1, and C2. A filter choke is ordinarily found in low voltage 60-cycle supplies at the point in the circuit occupied by R1. The resistor is used because for low current drain, the RC combination proves entirely adequate as a filter.

The most serious objection to the 60-cycle supply for television receivers is its danger to human life. The energy stored in the filter capacitors at the high voltage at which these supplies operate is considerable and can cause a severe shock if the body comes in contact with them. Some television tubes require voltages as high as 30,000 volts. If 60-cycle supplies were used to produce such voltages, they would be extremely dangerous.

60-cycle supplies are bulky, heavy, and expensive, and are subject to frequent failure if quality components are not used. The replacement of parts that fail is an expensive proposition. For these reasons, high voltage 60-cycle supplies have been largely superseded by other types.

3-97 Radio Frequency Power Supplies. The radio frequency power supply is essentially a high power r-f oscillator operating at a frequency between 50 and 300 kc. The r-f voltage is

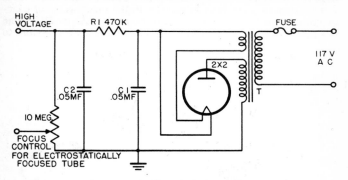

Figure 145. Circuit of a 60-cycle, high-voltage supply.

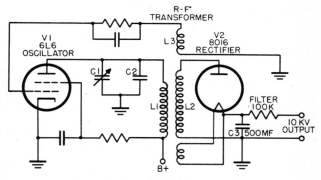

Figure 146. Circuit of an r-f high-voltage power supply.

stepped up to several thousand volts by a transformer, and then rectified. A typical circuit for an r-f supply is shown in Figure 146. The oscillator section consists of tube V1, tuned circuit, C1, C2, and L1, and feedback loop L3. A tube, such as a 6L6 or an 807, capable of supplying a power output of about 15 watts is used. The oscillator frequency is tuned by capacitor C1. The r-f voltage generated in the parallel tuned circuit is stepped up by the secondary coil, L2, which is closely coupled to the primary, L1.

The high voltage developed across the secondary is fed to an 8016 rectifier tube. This rectifier tube requires only one-fourth watt of filament power as compared with the three watts of heater power consumed by such rectifiers as the 2X2 or 2V3. The low power consumption of the 8016 heater makes it possible to

Figure 147. R-F high voltage power supply.

draw this power from the r-f oscillator by looping one or two turns of wire around the high voltage coil, L2, and connecting this loop to the heater. Since the oscillator develops about fifteen watts of power, the one-quarter watt absorbed by the heater is negligible. This method of obtaining the filament power eliminates the need for an expensive fron-core filament transformer which would have to be insulated for 10 kilovolts or more.

The filter required for the rectified r-f voltage is extremely simple, consisting of a 500 mmf 10 kv condenser, and a 100,000 ohm low wattage resistor. The very low value of capacitance is used because, at the high frequency employed, a small amount of capacitance provides a short circuit path to ground for the ripple frequency. The small, inexpensive condensers developed especially for high frequency power supplies have brought about an appreciable saving in cost of high voltage filters.

R-F supplies differ considerably in appearance and size from conventional 60-cycle supplies. Figure 147 shows a side view of a typical r-f supply. Shown in Figure 148 is an r-f transformer. It consists of several universal wound pies on a cylindrical core, usually made of synthane.

The tickler or feedback coil is located at the right, spaced sufficiently far from the high voltage secondary winding to prevent breakdown. The secondary winding consists of seven small pi sections. The primary winding is a single, large pi located to the left of the secondary. The filament winding is a loop of insulated wire, mounted near the left end of the primary.

Rectified radio frequency supplies have been designed for voltages as high as 90 kv, using suitable transformers with high

Figure 148. An r-f supply transformer.

step-up ratios. Rectified r-f supplies have good voltage regulation. Their output varies less than 5% as the beam current in the picture tube changes from zero to 200 microamperes. Such fluctuations in voltage with changes in load are permissible and do not cause observable changes in picture size.

R-F supplies are almost always housed in a completely enclosed metal container to prevent signals from being radiated to the video circuits and modulating the picture signals.

3-98 Pulse Type Supplies. The objectionable effects caused by radiation from rectified r-f supplies are overcome in the pulse-type supply because its generated pulse occurs during the horizontal blanking interval when the beam of the picture tube is cut off. It will be recalled that as the current through the yoke increases, the beam moves across the face of the tube from left to right. The deflecting current then falls rapidly and the beam returns to the left, from which position it starts another cycle. During the time that the beam is retracing from right to left, a blanking pulse is applied to the grid of the tube in order to eliminate the retrace lines on the screen. This blanking pulse lasts for about ten microseconds, during which time the beam is completely cut off.

If a high voltage pulse, less than ten microseconds in duration is generated during the blanking time, it will not be visible even though it is radiated and enters the video channel.

In the pulse-supply circuit of Figure 149, tube V1 is used as a pulse generator. The circuit is a conventional blocking oscillator which generates pulses as shown in Figure

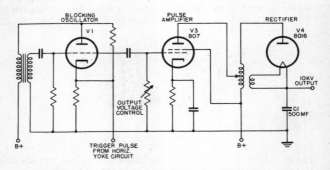

Figure 149. Circuit of a pulse type high-voltage power supply.

150. The blocking oscillator is designed to operate at the horizontal scanning frequency of 15,750 cps, so that a pulse is generated during each horizontal retrace period. The pulses are amplified by tube V3 and impressed on the high voltage autotransformer which steps them up to a 10 kv peak value. In appearance this transformer resembles the r-f transformer shown of Figure 148, except that it does not have a separate secondary winding. A typical transformer can be seen in Figure 151 which shows a complete pulse-type supply.

The amplified pulse is rectified by diode V4. The positive pulse, thus produced, charges filter condenser C1 to almost the full 10 kv pulse peak. The time constant of the filter is such that before the condenser can discharge appreciably, the next pulse comes along to recharge it. In this manner, a constant high d-c voltage is developed across the condenser.

The regulation of a pulse-type supply is about the same as that of an r-f supply. If better regulation is desired, a regulator circuit as shown in Figure 152 may be used.

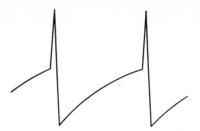

Figure 150. Pulses generated by blocking oscillator.

Figure 151. Pulse type power supply.

The regulator operates in the following manner. A portion of the 10 kv output of the supply is taken from the voltage divider and fed to the grid of the regulator control tube, half of V1. Changes in the magnitude of the high voltage cause voltage variations across the output of the control tube. These variations are applied to the screen of the pulse amplifier tube so as to compensate for the original high voltage change. The VR105 is used to maintain the cathode of the control tube at a constant reference potential with respect to ground.

An important advantage of the pulse-type supply is the fact that when the sweep circuits fail, the high voltage is automatically

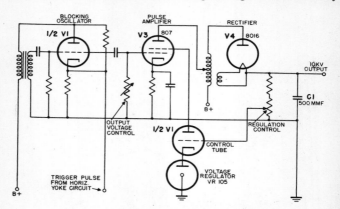

Figure 152. Regulated pulse type supply.

cut off, preventing a spot from being burned on the screen. The supply ceases to operate because the blocking oscillator is bi-ased so that it is cut-off and will not oscillate unless a signal is supplied by the horizontal yoke circuit. The signal raises the cathode bias of the blocking oscillator in the high voltage supply so that it triggers in synchronism with the horizontal sweep circuits. When the horizontal sweep fails, the blocking oscillator ceases to operate and no high voltage pulses are generated. With no high voltage present the beam in the picture tube cuts off.

3-99 The Kickback Supply. The kickback, high voltage supply approaches the ideal for a television receiver. It requires very few components and very little space. The operation of the kickback supply can be understood by referring to the horizontal deflection circuit shown in Figure 153. The pulse produced across the lower half of the transformer, by the horizontal output amplifier, appears across the complete primary. The auto-transformer action of the primary steps up the pulse to a suitable value. The high voltage pulse is then rectified and filtered in the same manner as in the pulse-type circuit. A loop of wire is placed on the output transformer to supply power for the 8016 heater.

A typical kickback high voltage supply circuit is shown in Fig-

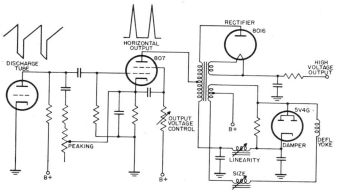

Figure 153. Simplified schematic of kickback high-voltage supply.

ure 154. When the 6BG6 plate current is cut off by the incoming signal, a positive pulse appears on the T1 primary due to the collapsing field in the deflection coil. This pulse of voltage is stepped up, rectified, filtered and applied to the second anode of the picture tube. Since the frequency of the supply voltage is high (15,750 cps), relatively little filtering is necessary - only 500 mmf (C1) in series with a 1 megohm resistor (R1).

The output transformer used in this circuit has a sponge iron powder core which results in lower energy losses at the horizontal frequency than would be the case with a standard laminated core.

There are two disadvantages to the kickback circuit, the most important being that its regulation is poorer than either the r-f or pulse-type supply. The other drawback is the dependence of the high voltage on the setting of the horizontal sweep amplitude. The deflection amplifier screen voltage (or sawtooth voltage amplitude - depending upon which is made the variable in the circuit) is first set for maximum high voltage output. The width control choke, L1 in Figure 154, is then varied to secure correct picture width. Simultaneously, the linearity control is varied. The adjustments of the size and linearity controls may then necessitate the resetting of the screen voltage. This in turn affects the picture size and linearity. By varying all three controls in

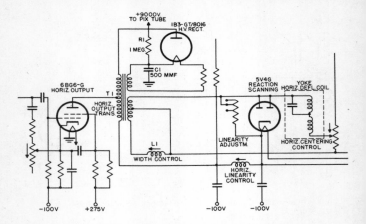

Figure 154. Typical kickback high-voltage supply used in a television receiver.

sequence, maximum output voltage with the best linearity and proper picture size can be obtained.

The kickback supply offers some protection to the picture tube if the horizontal sweep circuit fails. However, if the failure occurs in the yoke circuit, the high voltage will still be generated.

3-100 Kickback Supply for Projection Receivers. A modification of the kickback supply is used in projection receivers which require about 28,000 volts for their projection tubes. The circuit of such a supply is shown in Figure 155. The high voltage pulses are produced during the retrace of the horizontal sweep. An autotransformer winding steps up these pulses to about 9,500 volts. The stepped-up pulses are then applied to a voltage-tripler circuit, consisting of three diode rectifiers. Three windings on the transformer furnish current for the rectifier filaments. When a pulse is fed to the first rectifier, V1, capacitor C3 charges to the peak value of the pulse and the cathode of V1 is raised to 9,500 volts above ground. At the same time, the pulse is also applied to the second rectifier tube V2 through capacitor C1. The pulse charges capacitor C4 9,500 volts. The total voltage across C4 and C3 is approximately 19,000 volts. In like manner, the pulse is applied to the third rectifier, V3, charging capacitor C5 to 9,500 volts. The cathode of V3 is thus

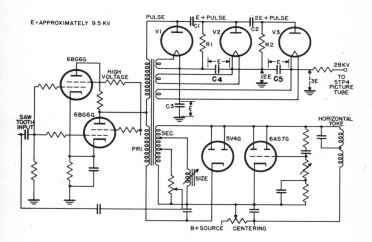

Figure 155. Kickback high-voltage supply for projection receiver.

raised to about three times the peak voltage, or 28,000 volts. The regulation of a voltage tripler is poorer than that of a single rectifier power supply. The tripler circuit will deliver about 50 microamperes with about 10 percent reduction in voltage from the no-load value. This voltage drop is not great enough to cause a perceptible change in picture size.

Because of the higher intensifier voltage used with the projection tube, the horizontal deflection system, of which the tripler kickback supply is a part, requires a greater amount of deflection power. Two type 6BG6 amplifier tubes, in parallel, are therefore used. An additional damper tube, a type 6AS7G, is connected in shunt with the deflection transformer secondary. This tube is connected so that its grid bias controls the linearity of the sweep.

THE SOUND CHANNEL

3-101 Before the war, amplitude modulation (a-m) was used to transmit and receive the sound in the television system. As television broadcasting techniques progressed during the war years, the audio system was switched over to frequency modulation (f-m) and has continued in this manner in accordance with the standards adopted by the FCC in 1945. F-M is not only

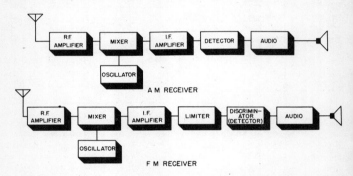

Figure 156. Block diagrams of conventional superhet and f-m receiver.

superior to a-m in fidelity and freedom from noise, but it lessens the possibility of interference from nearby stations. Television stations have two separate transmitters, one for video and the other for audio. The lower audio power required to produce a given signal strength, using f-m, makes this transmission system more desirable.

3-102 F-M vs. A-M Receivers. It is well to examine first the basic differences between receivers used for ordinary broadcast reception and those used for frequency modulated signals. Figure 156 shows a block diagram of a conventional a-m superheterodyne and an f-m receiver. The a-m receiver consists of an r-f stage, local oscillator, mixer, i-f amplifiers, a-m detector, and audio amplifier. Compare this diagram with that of the f-m receiver, and it will be seen that they are quite similar. In fact, if it were not for the f-m detector, which is called a discriminator, it would be very difficult to tell the two receivers apart. Note that the r-f stage, mixer, local oscillator, i-f amplifiers, and audio amplifier are common to both types of receivers. Yet there are some important differences.

Some types of f-m receivers incorporate a limiter stage, which is in fact an additional i-f stage operating under special conditions. The function of this stage is to prevent fluctuations in the strength of the carrier wave from affecting the discriminator output. Other types of f-m circuits do not require limiters.

Detection in f-m receivers is accomplished by different means than in a-m receivers. The detector (discriminator) must reproduce the original audio tones from changes in the frequency of the carrier wave. This differs from the ordinary a-m detector, which must respond only to changes in the amplitude of the applied carrier.

3-103 Advantages of F-M. The important advantages of f-m transmission may be classified as follows:

1. Reduced interference from ignition noises, electrical appliances, and atmospheric conditions. This is probably the greatest single advantage of f-m. Military installations in tanks and other types of vehicles have shown that f-m equipment is able to operate consistently under the most severe noise conditions, where a-m transmission would have been unintelligible. In home installations, where such interference as elevator noises, ignition pickup from cars, and other similar annoyances occur, the overwhelming superiority of f-m has been demonstrated.

2. Greater audio frequency range. In standard broadcast practice today, each station is assigned a channel 10 kc wide, which limits the sidebands to plus and minus 5 kc. This automatically limits the highest audio frequency to 5,000 cycles. Higher audio frequencies are not reproduced and thus most of the brilliance of the music or voice is lost. Good f-m receivers are capable of responding to audio frequencies of 15,000 cycles and even higher. It should be pointed out, however, that were a-m broadcast stations allowed a greater channel width, say 30 kc, wide range transmission would be possible. However, since the a-m sets do not discriminate against noise, the improvement in fidelity would probably be accompanied by an objectionable increase in noise output.

3. Elimination of interference between stations on the same or adjacent channels. For a desired station to "override" an undesired station completely on an a-m receiver, it is necessary that the ratio between their signal strengths be of the order of 100 or 200 to 1. For this reason, it has been necessary that stations operating on the same channels be geographically far apart. F-M receivers encounter no such difficulties since it is only necessary to achieve a ratio of 2 to 1 between the desired and undesired signals in order for the latter to be inaudible.

4. Elimination of fading. This is accomplished partially by the use of high frequencies for f-m transmission (88 - 108 Mc on the f-m band and 54 - 216 Mc when accompanying the video carrier on the television bands). At a-m broadcast frequencies, a phenomenon known as selective fading takes place when a wave propagated directly to the receiver combines with a wave which is reflected from a layer in the ionosphere. At times, the waves are in phase and increase the signal strength, while at other times they are out of phase and lower the signal strength. At the very high frequencies which are used for f-m, practically no ionospheric reflections take place, and selective fading is eliminated. The effects of fading which result from temporary reflections, such as those from airplanes, and the vibrations of the antenna in wind storms, are minimized by the action of the limiter.

The foregoing comparisons between a-m and f-m indicate the advantages of using f-m sound for television broadcasting. Continuing this comparison further, let us examine the technical characteristics of a-m and f-m systems.

3-104 Amplitude Modulation. Amplitude modulation is the process of changing the strength of the carrier wave in accordance with the information to be transmitted. Figure 157A shows a simple circuit which may be used to produce amplitude modulation. It consists of an oscillator tank circuit, L1-C1, which is assumed to have a resonant frequency of 100 Mc. In order to sustain oscillations, a feedback network is added. Across the tank circuit has been placed a high resistance with a sliding tap. A diaphragm which is free to vibrate is connected rigidly through a rod to the sliding tap. The tap connects directly to an antenna. With no modulation present, the diaphragm is at rest and the tap remains at the center point. It is assumed that the voltage Et across the tank circuit is equal to 100 volts. With the tap at the center point, there will be a constant output to the antenna of 50 volts. This corresponds to the amplitude Ec of the carrier wave shown in Figure 157B. If a person speaks very loudly against the diaphragm, the tap moves between the limits of X and

Z. With the tap at position Z, the full output of the oscillator, or 100 volts, is applied to the antenna. When the tap is at Y, the center, only 50 volts is applied, and at position X, there is no output at all. Under these conditions, the shape of the modu-

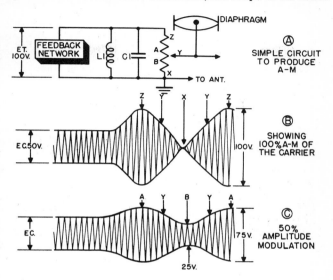

Figure 157. Simple method of amplitude modulation.

lated carrier appears as in Figure 157B. This wave corresponds to 100 percent modulation.

If a person speaks only half as loud as previously, the tap moves only half as much and remains between the limits of A and B. The voltage then varies from 75 volts to 50 volts to 25 volts, and so on. The carrier is now only 50 per cent modulated, as shown in Figure 157C.

This simple system for modulating a carrier illustrates the principle of amplitude modulation, which is defined as follows: Amplitude modulation is the process of changing the strength or amplitude of the carrier wave in accordance with the frequency of the sound signal. The percentage change of the carrier amplitude depends upon the intensity of the modulating signal.

3-105 Frequency Modulation. Frequency modulation is the

process of changing the frequency of the carrier wave in accordance with the information to be transmitted. Figure 158 illustrates a simple circuit for producing frequency modulated waves. As in the previous example, there is a tank circuit and a feedback network to sustain oscillation. The tank circuit con-

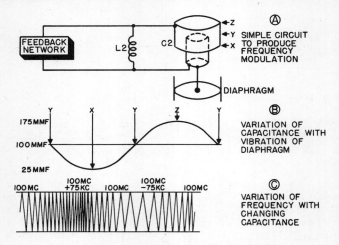

Figure 158. Simple method of frequency modulation.

sists of L2-C2, whose constants determine the frequency of oscillation. However, in this case C2 is a variable condenser which is made up of two metal tubes, one sliding within the other. The movable inner tube, which is insulated from the outer section, is connected rigidly to the diaphragm which vibrates upon the impact of sound waves. Since the capacitance is a function of the surface area between the two conductors, it increases as the inner tube moves up, and decreases as it moves down.

Consider first that the diaphragm is at rest, there being no modulating sound waves present. The inner tubes takes a position halfway into the outer sleeve so that its top rests at point Y. At this halfway position, the capacitance of C2 is assumed to be 100 mmf, and the resonant frequency of the oscillator is, say, 100 Mc. This frequency is known as the carrier frequency of the f-m wave. If sound waves strike the diaphragm, it vibrates, driving the inner tube to the top and bottom of the sleeve between positions X and Z. With the top of the inner tube at position Z, C2 increases, and with the top of the inner tube moving toward position X, C2 decreases. This represents a change of capacitance of plus and minus, say, 75 mmf. The change in capacitance as the diaphragm vibrates varies as a sine wave (Figure 158B).

The instantaneous frequency of the tank circuit is determined by the capacitance of the tank circuit. An increase in capacitance decreases the frequency, and conversely. Referring to Figures 158B and 158C, it is noted that when C2 increases to its maximum, it causes a decrease in oscillator frequency of 75 kc. It follows then that a similar decrease in capacitance will cause an increase in oscillator frequency of 75 kc. Thus, the oscillator frequency varies plus and minus 75 kc.

If weak sound waves strike the diaphragm, it is obvious that a smaller movement of the inner tube will take place above and below point Y, and a smaller change in capacitance will be produced. The frequency does not deviate as much as before and now varies between the limits of, say, plus and minus 10 kc. This sequence of events serves to define the term deviation as used in f-m. Deviation is the change of frequency of the radio frequency from its carrier point, and varies directly with the loudness of the modulating signal. This statement corresponds to the previous definition of amplitude modulation where it was stated that the percentage of amplitude change varied directly with the loudness of the modulating signal. The rate at which the frequency deviates depends upon the pitch or tone of the modulating signal. For example, a low pitch note causes a deviation of 200 cycles per second, and a high pitch note a deviation of 15,000 cycles per second.

The following points summarize the important differences between a-m and f-m signals:

For a-m,
1. The amplitude of the carrier at any instant depends upon the loudness of the modulating signal.
2. The number of changes in amplitude per second depends upon the frequency of the modulating signal.

For f-m,
1. The frequency of the carrier at any instant depends upon the loudness of the modulating signal.
2. The rate at which the frequency of the carrier changes depends upon the frequency of the modulating signal.

3-106 Reactance Tube Modulator. While the preceding example serves to illustrate how an f-m wave can be produced by simple means, the method described is not practical, and actual f-m transmitters make use of reactance tube modulators and frequency multipliers. A reactance tube modulator is an electronic

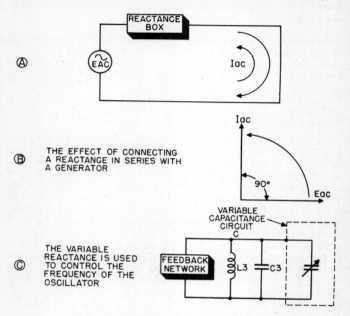

Figure 159. Operation of reactance modulator.

circuit which acts like a variable capacitance when a modulating voltage is fed to it.

Before examining the reactance tube circuit, it is well to review a few fundamentals regarding capacitive reactances. A reactance is a device which causes the voltage and current in a circuit to have a phase difference of 90°. If a generator is hooked up in series with a circuit (Figures 159A and 159B), and if the current leads the voltage by 90°, the circuit is said to have a capacitive reactance. That is, this circuit as a whole acts like a capacitor if it is placed in another circuit. An increase of current in the circuit increases the value of the capacitance, while a decrease in current decreases the circuit capacitance.

If this circuit, which can be made to act like a variable capacitance by changing the current flowing through it, is placed in parallel with the fixed capacitor C3, in the tank circuit of an oscillator (Figure 159C), a means is provided for producing an f-m signal. This is the function of the reactance tube modulator. As the current in the reactance tube circuit is changed, the capacitance across C3 varies, and changes the frequency of the oscillator.

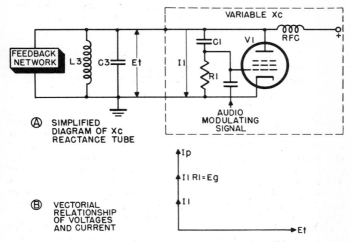

Figure 160. Simplified schematic of a reactance tube modulator.

A simplified diagram in which the reactance tube modulator is used to vary the frequency of an oscillator is shown in Figure 160A. A pentode tube V1 is used as a variable capacitance. The circuit operates as follows: An r-f voltage, Et, is developed across the oscillator tank circuit, L3-C3, and is applied to the series combination C1-R1. The size of C1 is chosen so that it has a reactance about ten times R1 at the operating frequency of the oscillator. Thus the effect of R1 is negligible as compared to the reactance of C1 and for all practical purposes the series combination becomes purely capacitive. Due to Et, a current I1 flows through C1-R1. Since this circuit is capacitive I1 leads Et by 90° (Figure 160B). This leading current produces a voltage drop I1R1 across R1. This voltage drop also leads Et by 90°. It is noted that the voltage I1R1 is applied directly to the grid circuit of reactance tube V1. Therefore, the drop across R1 is Eg, the operating grid voltage for V1. Since this grid voltage is leading by 90°, and because the plate current of a tube is in phase with its grid voltage, it follows then that the plate current is also leading by 90°.

It was previously pointed out that when the current in a device led the voltage by 90°, a capacitance was present. This device is exactly what is represented by the reactance tube V1. The reactance tube is in parallel with the tank circuit of the oscillator and thus affects its frequency. It remains now only to vary

Figure 161. Block diagram of f-m transmitter.

the magnitude of the capacitance in accordance with the modulating signal so that the oscillator frequency follows it. In the circuit of Figure 160A, this is done by applying the audio signal directly to the grid of V1. On the positive half cycle of the applied audio wave, the plate current increases, corresponding to an increase in shunt capacitance, and the oscillator frequency decreases. The negative peak of the modulating signal causes a decrease in plate current, the shunt capacitance represented by V1 also decreases, and the oscillator frequency increases. Thus the amount of frequency deviation depends upon the instantaneous value of the audio signal which is applied to the grid of the reactance tube.

The reactance tube modulator, in common with several other types of frequency modulators, has the disadvantage of not being able to produce sufficient deviation. In order to increase the amount of deviation, use is made of frequency multiplication. As an example, assume a carrier frequency of 105 Mc is desired with a deviation of plus and minus 75 kc at the antenna. If the reactance tube modulator gives a useful deviation at the oscillator of plus and minus 5 kc., then a frequency multiplication of 15 times is needed. As shown in the block diagram of Figure 161, the oscillator frequency starts at 7 Mc and is multiplied 15 times to become 105 Mc. At the same time, the 5 kc deviation is also raised 15 times to 75 kc. Frequency multiplication is necessary whenever the frequency modulator is unable to provide the required deviation directly at the oscillator.

The foregoing sections have dealt with the methods of generating frequency modulated signals. The f-m circuits in the sound channel of a television receiver are discussed in the following paragraphs.

THE TELEVISION SOUND CHANNEL

3-107 In the discussion of the r-f section it was pointed out that the r-f amplifiers of a television receiver have a passband of 6 megacycles to permit the reception of the 4 Mc video channel and its associated sound channel. The local oscillator of the receiver beats with both the video and audio carriers and lowers their frequencies to the intermediate frequencies of 21.9 Mc for the audio and 26.4 Mc for the video. The frequency difference between the audio and video carriers is the same for all stations, namely 4.5 Mc. It is because of this fixed difference in carrier frequencies that correct tuning of a perfectly aligned television receiver is most easily accomplished by tuning for maximum sound.

3-108 Separation of Audio and Video Carriers. The selection of the audio carrier and the rejection of video signals from the sound circuits is accomplished at the first detector by a parallel resonant circuit tuned to 21.9 Mc. It will be recalled that the impedance of such a parallel circuit is greatest at its resonant frequency. Hence, at 21.9 Mc a strong i-f signal voltage is developed across the tuned circuit. This voltage is coupled to the grid of the first sound i-f amplifier tube. The resonant circuit presents a very low impedance to the picture i-f signal voltages which are far off the resonant frequency. Very little video signal voltage is developed across the parallel circuit, and consequently, the video signal is not passed on to the audio i-f amplifier. The succeeding stages are the same as those used in conventional f-m receivers. The number of i-f stages needed depends upon the gain obtained in the r-f section of the particular television receiver. One or more limiters are used depending upon the quality of the receiver.

In the ordinary f-m receiver, designed for use between 88 and 106 Mc., each station is allowed sidebands ranging up to 75 kc on either side of the carrier. Television allocations permit only 25 kc side bands. The narrower band width simplifies the problem of simultaneous reception of the video and audio carriers. Even though the actual frequency deviation of the audio signal is only 50 kc (plus or minus 25 kc about the carrier), the band-pass circuits in the audio i-f amplifiers are generally designed for a width of 200 kc. The extra band width is provided to permit a small amount of frequency drift to occur in the high frequency local oscillator without resultant detuning of the sound.

3-109 Sound I-F Amplifiers. The two most important functions of the sound i-f amplifier are:

1. To build up the signal to sufficient amplitude before demodulation.

2. To provide sufficient selectivity to reject adjacent channel interference.

The maximum gain possible at 21.9 Mc with f-m is much less than that realized at 455 kc with a-m because:

1. Broader bandwidth results in less gain (f-m amplifiers are 20 times as broad as a-m).

2. Stability can only be maintained at high frequencies if the gain is limited.

3. Shunting effects of stray capacitances in tubes become serious at high frequencies. While gains as high as 500 are attainable in 455 kc, a-m stages, single 21.9 Mc f-m, i-f stages are limited to a gain of about 60 at the present stage of development.

At least two i-f amplifier stages must be used to provide sufficient gain (about 3600). With a converter gain of about 5 and an r-f gain of 25, this provides an overall amplification of 450,000 times from antenna to limiter grid. Assuming a two volt signal is needed to saturate the limiter, then the signal at the antenna would have to be about 5 microvolts. Actually this figure is somewhat optimistic and in order to insure proper noise rejection, about 25 to 50 microvolts of signal at the antenna is ordinarily needed.

If the above circuit gains are to be realized at the high frequencies used for the television sound i-f, and stable operation obtained, great care must be taken in the placement of parts and wiring to minimize the possibilities of feedback. Feedback causes regeneration, oscillation, and a reduction in bandpass, which results in distortion.

A typical i-f amplifier response curve is shown in Figure 162. As previously stated, with 100% modulation of the f-m carrier (for television transmission), the frequency deviation is equal to plus and minus 25 kilocycles. It would be expected, therefore, that the overall bandpass would have to be flat for at least 50 kilocycles to insure equal gain for all modulating frequencies. The i-f response curve is not made flat for two reasons. First, the narrower the bandwidth, the greater is the gain of an i-f amplifier. Secondly, a narrowing of the selectivity curve gives better rejection of adjacent channel interference. Such a non-linear characteristic produces little distortion. If the signal is

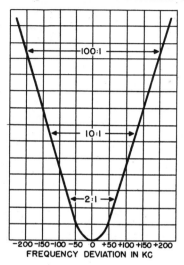

Figure 162. Typical i-f amplifier response curve.

strong enough to saturate the limiter at all modulation levels, the effects of the resultant amplitude variations will be removed.

In some receivers the sound i-f amplifiers have a broadband characteristic and do not depend upon the limiter for the removal of amplitude distortion. Some gain is sacrificed in this way, but less distortion is likely to occur at low signal levels. Figure 163 is an oscillogram of the response of an i-f amplifier tuned for broadband operation.

The schematic arrangement of the i-f amplifiers of an f-m receiver very closely resembles those found in standard broadcast receivers. A typical three stage i-f amplifier of the type used in the sound channels of television receivers is shown in Figure 164. The wideband response of each stage is achieved through the use of overcoupled transformers (Z2, Z3, and Z4).

Both capacitive and inductive tuning are used in f-m i-f stages. There is a slight advantage in inductive tuning at the high frequencies used for f-m circuits in that it can cover a wider tuning range efficiently. To cover an equivalent range, a very large capacitor has to be used. This is undesirable at high fre-

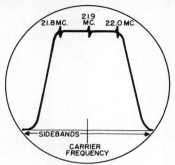

Figure 163. Response curve of a broadband i-f amplifier.

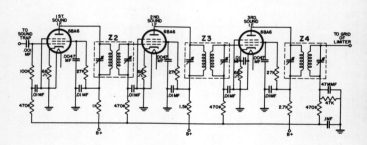

Figure 164. Three-stage sound i-f amplifier.

quencies because the gain of an amplifier depends upon the L/C ratio of the tuned circuit, and increasing the capacitance lowers the gain.

3-110 The Limiter. In order to take advantage of the noise reducing possibilities of f-m broadcasting, it is necessary to use a circuit which removes amplitude variations from the signal, or to provide a discriminator which is not affected by amplitude variations of the received signal. In prewar receivers, the most widely used method for accomplishing this was a limiter stage, still used in many postwar receivers.

A secondary function of the limiter is to restore uniformity to the signal over the pass band. This is necessary due to the peaked response of the i-f selectivity curve, as shown in Figure

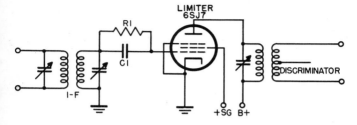

Figure 165. Simplified schematic of limiter circuit.

162. A simplified limiter circuit is shown in Figure 165.

While providing some amplification, the primary function of the limiter is to remove all amplitude variations from the signal. Thus noise pulses and other amplitude variations due to interfering signals are clipped off and not passed on to the detector. In order to accomplish this, the tube used must be of the sharp cut-off variety such as a 6SJ7. Plate and screen voltages must be very low, around 50 to 75 volts. Lowering these voltages reduces the amount of signal input needed to obtain limiting action.

The operation of the limiter stage may be understood by referring to Figure 166. It will be noted that as long as the signal to the limiter remains above a certain amplitude, both positive and negative peaks of the signal are clipped. Noise pulses which ride on top of the positive and negative peaks are also clipped. However, if the input signal is too weak to completely saturate the limiter, only the positive part of the cycle is clipped, and interference signals causing amplitude modulation pass through to the detector on the negative peaks.

The values of the limiter biasing components, C1 and R1 in Figure 165, are quite critical. Capacitor C1 charges up to approximately the peak value of the input signal, thus affording a clamping or d-c restoring action in the grid circuit. This results in a bias at the limiter grid which varies inversely with the input signal, becoming more negative as the signal becomes stronger.

A dual or cascade limiter is sometimes employed to improve the sensitivity of the limiting action. A typical circuit is shown in Figure 167, and a comparison of the effectiveness between single and double limiters is given in Figure 168. It will be noted that in Figure 167 weak signals are not limited on the

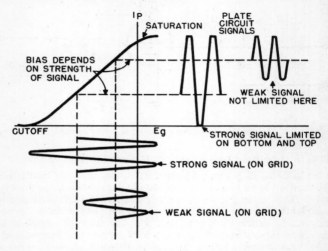

Figure 166. Operation of limiter circuit.

negative half of the input cycle by the first limiter. As a result, the wave shape in the plate shows an unclipped positive wave. This wave is applied to the second stage which operates at zero bias, and is therefore easily saturated. The positive portion of the signal is thus clipped, and practically perfect limiting results. The curves of Figure 168 show that in addition to providing better limiting action, the dual limiter produces a larger signal at its output.

3-111 F-M Detectors. The transforming of the frequency modulated signal into amplitude variations can be performed by several types of detectors. In order to detect a frequency modulated wave, the detecting circuit must have a d-c output voltage which rises when the i-f deviates in one direction, and falls when the deviation is in the other direction. Since the frequency modulated signal of the transmitter deviates in accordance with the audio modulating signal, the variations in the d-c output of the detector are reproductions of the modulating signal.

3-112 Slope Detection. In very low cost television and f-m re-

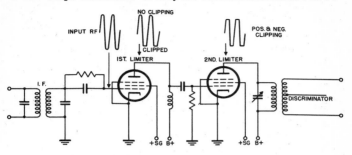

Figure 167. Dual or cascade limiter.

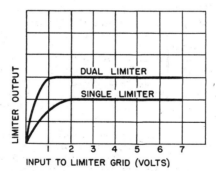

Figure 168. Comparison of single and dual limiter.

ceivers, a standard a-m circuit is sometimes used to receive frequency modulated signals. Refer to Figure 169. The i-f amplifier is detuned so that operation takes place on the slope of the receiver's response curve. This is done by simply tuning the amplifier until the center frequency is located at point A. In this figure, the i-f of the standard television sound channel is used as an example. Let us assume that the i-f amplifier is tuned to the low side of the response curve. As the incoming signal deviates higher in frequency (toward B), the receiver output increases, and as it deviates lower in frequency (toward C), the receiver output decreases. The frequency modulated signal is thus changed to an amplitude signal and the a-m de-

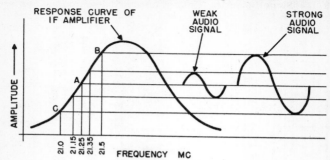

Figure 169. Operation of slope detector.

tector will respond properly.

Slope detection is seldom used for the following reasons:

1. The detector is not balanced and therefore does not reject a-m noise or signals.

2. The side of a response curve can seldom be made linear, and distortion results. This is especially true in connection with standard f-m broadcasts where the deviation is plus and minus 75 kc. The effect is not too serious in the television sound channel where the deviation is only 25 kc on either side of the carrier.

To obtain all the noise-eliminating benefits of f-m, it is necessary to use a circuit in which both limiting and noise canceling actions are provided. This is usually accomplished with the previously discussed limiter and a discriminator.

3-113 The Discriminator. The simple discriminator circuit shown in Figure 170 illustrates the method by which a frequency modulated signal is converted into an audio signal. The frequency modulated signal is inductively coupled from the limiter to the discriminator by a transformer, whose primary, L1, is in the plate circuit of the limiter stage. The secondary of the transformer is made up of two separate windings, L2 and L3, each of which is connected to a diode. Variable capacitors are shunted across coils L2 and L3 to form tuned circuits. The diodes V1 and V2 are connected to load resistors R1 and R2. The output of the discriminator is taken across both resistors.

It will be recalled that a frequency modulated signal deviates in frequency by a certain amount around a fixed or carrier frequency. For standard f-m broadcasting this deviation is plus or minus 75 kc from the carrier, while for television the f-m sound signals deviate plus and minus 25 kc from the carrier. It was pointed out previously that the amount of deviation depends

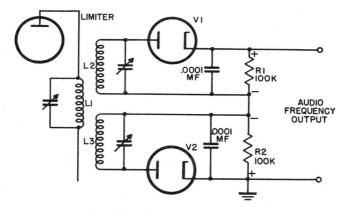

Figure 170. Simple discriminator circuit.

upon the amplitude of the modulating signal. At the receiver it is necessary to convert these frequency deviations back to amplitude variations. This is the function of the tuned circuits of the discriminator. The coils L2 and L3 are tuned to two different frequencies, each of which corresponds to one of the deviation limits. For example, if the carrier frequency of the television sound is 21.9 Mc, one coil is tuned to a frequency of 25 kc above 21.9 Mc, or 21.925 Mc, while the other is tuned to 25 kc below 21.9 Mc, or 21.875 Mc. The response curve of each tuned circuit appears as shown in Figure 171. One response curve appears above the axis and the other below it because of the manner in which the load resistors, R1 and R2, are connected in the circuit. The voltages across the two resistors oppose each other because they are of opposite polarity.

Consider now the voltages which appear at the output of the discriminator when a frequency modulated signal appears across the tuned circuits. Suppose that the frequency of the signal is momentarily at the center or carrier frequency of 21.9 Mc. The same amount of voltage is developed across each circuit and, because R1 and R2 oppose each other, these voltages cancel each other and the output of the discriminator is zero. If the frequency now shifts to 21.91 Mc, the voltage across L3 is greater than the voltage across L2 and the difference between the two voltages appears across R1 and R2 in a negative polarity.

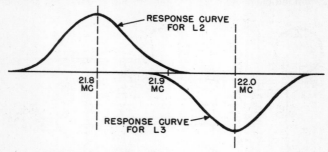

Figure 171. Response curve of tuned circuits of discriminator.

Similarly, when the frequency falls below the carrier, the voltage across L2 is larger, and a positive voltage is obtained at the discriminator output. If the voltage output from the discriminator were measured for all frequencies between the deviation limits, it would be found that they vary with frequency according to the smooth S curve of Figure 172, which is the response characteristic of a discriminator. This curve shows that all frequencies below the carrier produce positive voltages at the output of the discriminator. Conversely, all frequencies above the carrier produce negative voltages. Therefore, as the frequency deviates above and below the carrier, negative and positive voltages appear at the discriminator output to form an audio signal.

Only the straight line portion between the positive and negative peaks of the discriminator curve is used for detecting the f-m signal. If the portion is not linear, distortion of the output signal results. To prevent such distortion, discriminators are generally designed so that the peaks are set farther apart than the frequency deviation limits of the signals to be received. The signals then fluctuate only on the straight line portion of the curve near the carrier frequency.

3-114 Foster-Seeley Discriminator. The operation of the simple discriminator leads to an understanding of the types of discriminator circuits found in television receivers. Figure 173 shows the Foster-Seeley discriminator which is common to many commercial designs. This circuit is very similar to the one in Figure 170, except for two important differences. The secondary, L2, of the transformer is tapped to form two identical

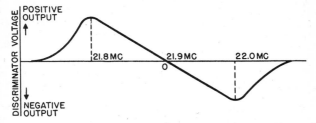

Figure 172. Response curve of typical television receiver discriminator.

coils instead of using separately wound coils. The tapped secondary is tuned by a single condenser, rather than two. This arrangement makes it easier to align the discriminator.

The Foster-Seeley discriminator operates in the following

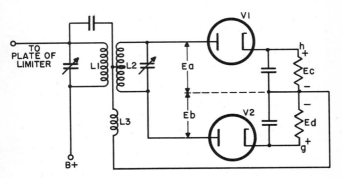

Figure 173. Foster-Seeley discriminator.

manner: Ea and Eb represent the varying frequency voltages which are applied to the discriminator and which are rectified and filtered to produce the d-c voltages Ec and Ed. The d-c voltages are proportional to Ea and Eb, respectively, and have the polarities indicated on the diagram.

The output voltage from the discriminator is the voltage between points g and h. Since Ec and Ed oppose each other, the total voltage is equal to the difference in their magnitude, and has the polarity of the larger voltage. At the carrier frequency, the tuned circuit is in resonance and the voltages at h and g are equal, giving zero output voltage. All frequencies higher than resonance give values of Ec larger than Ed. The total output voltage is then Ec minus Ed, with h positive and g negative. When the signal frequency is lower than resonance, the polarity of the output is reversed, and the output voltage is Ed minus Ec.

Thus, when the frequency of the input signal changes above and below the resonant frequency, an audio voltage is produced which varies in amplitude in accordance with the frequency deviations. In practice, point g is usually grounded. The audio signal is then taken between point h and ground and fed to a conventional audio amplifier.

3-115 Modification of the Foster-Seeley Discriminator. Several minor modifications of the basic Foster-Seeley discriminator have appeared in commercial television receivers. In the circuit of Figure 174A, the limiter is capacitively coupled to the discriminator transformer, rather than through a separate winding. Except for this difference, this circuit operates in the same manner as the circuit of Figure 173.

In the circuit arrangement of Figure 174B, a resistor R replaces the coupling coil, L3, of Figure 173. Another feature of this circuit is the use of 1N34 germanium crystals instead of a dual diode tube. Crystals do not require heater voltage or sockets and require less room than the conventional vacuum tube. The shunting capacities of crystals are lower than the vacuum diode and permit better balance of the discriminator.

Still another modification is shown in Figure 174C. The feedback coil, L3, of Figure 173, is eliminated in this circuit and only one capacitor, C1, is used across the load resistors R1 and R2. The output of the limiter appears across the primary of the transformer. This signal is capacitively coupled to the diode plates through C2 and inductively coupled to the secondary of the transformer. At the resonant frequency, the reactance of C1 is very small and the signal voltages appear across R1 and R2.

3-116 The Ratio Detector. In order to eliminate noise effectively when a conventional discriminator is used, it is necessary to provide a limiter and a high gain i-f system, because the discriminator responds to amplitude variations. A circuit has been developed which demodulates f-m signals without respond-

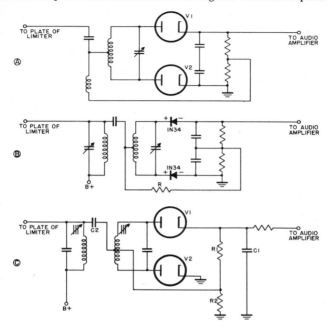

Figure 174. Modifications of the Foster-Seeley discriminator.

ing to amplitude variations. This circuit is known as a ratio detector.

A simple ratio detector circuit is shown in Figure 175. The secondary circuit L2-C2 is similar to that of the Foster-Seeley discriminator. Note that the diodes are connected in series. Assume that Ea is the voltage applied to V1 and Eb the voltage applied to V2. When the f-m signal is at the center or carrier frequency, the potentials applied to both diodes are equal. When the f-m signal deviates above the carrier, Ea is greater than Eb by some ratio, say, 12 volts to 8 volts. When the f-m signal deviates below resonance by the same amount, Ea will be less than Eb by a ratio of 8 volts to 12 volts. Thus, except at resonance, there always exists some ratio between the voltages applied to the two diodes. A detector whose output is made proportional only to this ratio (which is changing at an audio rate),

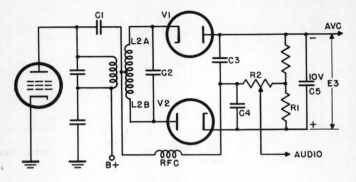

Figure 175. Simple ratio detector.

becomes independent of amplitude variations and does its own limiting. Such a device is the ratio detector.

An equivalent circuit for the ratio detector is given in Figure 176 to simplify the discussion which follows. The RC network, R1-C5 of Figure 175, is connected in series with the two diodes. The direction of electron flow is such that the top of C5 is negative, and the bottom positive. The time constant of R1-C5 is quite long, about 0.2 seconds, so that the potential across R1-C5 remains relatively fixed even for the lowest frequency audio variations. Actually, the charge on C3 is a function of the average carrier strength. This potential is shown in the equivalent circuit as being represented by a 10-volt battery tapped at its center.

To this center point is connected one end of the volume control R2. The other end of the volume control is connected to the junction of C3 and C4. While a fixed potential of 10 volts is shown in the diagram, it must be remembered that this potential may vary slowly with changes in the average carrier strength. L2 is shown in two sections, with generators Ed1 and Ed2 representing the induced voltages for any given deviation of the f-m signal. The following conditions are present in the ratio detector circuit:

1. The ratio of Ed1 to Ed2 always equals the ratio of E1 to E2.
2. The sum of the voltages E1 and E2 on capacitors C3 and C4 must always equal the charge on C5, which is voltage E3,

since C5 is in parallel with C3 plus C4.

At the carrier frequency, Ed1 equals Ed2 and their ratio is 1. Since the ratio of E1 to E2 must also be 1 under this condition, E1 equals E2 and no current can flow through R2. Thus, at the

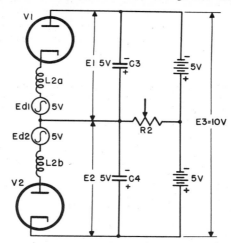

Figure 176. Equivalent circuit of ratio detector.

carrier frequency of the f-m signal, the d-c voltage across R2 is zero.

Going above resonance now, assume that the ratio of Ed1 to Ed2 is 8 to 2, or 4. Under this condition, current flows through R2 and the drop across R2 is positive at the junction of C3 and C4, thus producing the positive half of an audio cycle. If the frequency deviates below resonance by an equal amount, the ratio of Ed1 to Ed2 is 2 to 8, or 1/4. Current now flows in the reverse direction through R2, producing the negative half of an audio cycle. In this manner an audio signal is obtained from the f-m signal.

In the rejection of amplitude modulation due to noise or amplifier distortion, the action of the ratio detector is as follows: Suppose that a sharp increase in the carrier amplitude causes the ratio of Ed1 to Ed2 to become 16/4, or 4. The ratio obviously remains the same as before, but the amplitude is doubled. However, E1 plus E2 remains fixed as determined by E3. The amplitude change cannot take place, for E3 tends to get higher, but the time constant of R1-C5 is made so large that noise pulses or amplitude modulation are too rapid to change this voltage. If the carrier level suddenly drops, the potential E3 is still maintained, and this drop does not appear in the output.

Since the potential across C5 varies with the average carrier strength, it serves as an excellent source of a.v.c. voltage.

An important advantage is the fact that there is no "threshold" effect in the ratio detector, that is, there is no minimum carrier level necessary to cause noise attenuation as with limiter circuits.

3-117 Pre-emphasis and De-emphasis Circuits. A necessary part of the f-m detector output circuit is the de-emphasis circuit, which is required because of the pre-emphasis applied to the signal at the transmitting station.

Pre-emphasis and de-emphasis are used to reduce the effects of noise developed in the transmission and reception of the signal. Although the f-m method of transmission, and the auxiliary circuits used with it, are designed to discriminate against noise, these measures are not perfect, and there is always a threshold of minimum signal strength and modulation degree at which noise starts to become audible. Most of the noise is concentrated in the high frequency audio range from 5,000 to 15,000 cycles. The human ear is more sensitive to high frequency sound and, therefore, high frequency noises are objectionable. The system of pre-emphasis consists of increasing the relative degree of modulation at high frequencies so that at 15,000 cycles modulation is ten times that at 1,000 cycles. At the receiver, a de-emphasis network reduces the high frequency level to normal, at the same time greatly attenuating all high frequency noise.

The operation of pre-emphasis and de-emphasis circuits is as follows:

1. At the transmitting station, the audio frequency component of the signal is passed through an amplifier containing a pre-emphasis filter, such as shown in Figure 177. Its response characteristic is as illustrated in the graph of Figure 178. The high frequency components of the signal are amplified the most.

2. The f-m signal, modulated by the pre-emphasized a-f signal, is transmitted to the receiver and is demodulated in the receiver's f-m detector. The demodulated a-f signal retains the high frequency emphasis given it at the transmitter.

3. During transmission and reception, noise components mix with the signal. The addition of this noise bears no relation to the emphasis on the a-f signal, but a large proportion of the

noise components have frequencies in the emphasized range.

4. At the output of the detector in the receiver, a de-emphasis

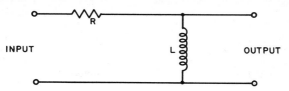

Figure 177. Pre-emphasis filter.

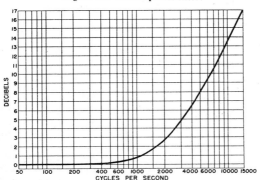

Figure 178. Response characteristic of pre-emphasis filter.

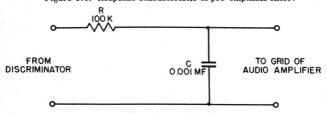

Figure 179. De-emphasis filter.

circuit compensates for the pre-emphasis of the high frequencies in the a-f signal.

The de-emphasis circuit restores the amplitude of the high audio frequencies to their original value. This is accomplished by suppressing the high frequency components so that their amplitude is equal to that of the low frequency components.

5. The noise superimposed on the signal, being mostly in the high frequency range, is suppressed with the high frequencies. Since the noise was not previously emphasized, it is thus reduced to a very low level, while the high frequency a-f components are returned to normal.

The de-emphasis network at the receiver is inserted between the discriminator output and the first audio amplifier. A low-pass filter circuit is used for this purpose, as shown in Figure 179. This type of network attenuates the high frequencies more than the low frequencies.

COMMERCIAL RECEIVER DESIGN

3-118 In the introduction to this chapter it was pointed out that modern, commercial television receivers can be grouped into three categories according to the type of picture tube employed. The basic circuits have been discussed in the preceding paragraphs. In the following paragraphs, an effort will be made to explain how these circuits are combined into the three types of receivers. No attempt will be made to cover all details. This discussion is primarily intended to demonstrate to the reader how the circuits previously described are integrated according to the type of receiver.

A detailed analysis of receiver designs is given in the chapter on modern television receivers.

3-119 Direct View Electrostatic Receivers. The Philco Model 48-700 has been chosen as being typical of the receivers falling into this category. It employs a 7GP4 electrostatic picture tube. A block diagram of the receiver is shown in Figure 180.

Provision is made in the Philco r-f tuner to permit the use of two antennas, one for the low-frequency band and the other for the high frequency band. When the tuner is set to the desired channel, the proper antenna, antenna input coil, r-f coil, mixer coil, and oscillator coil are automatically selected.

The signal from the antenna is coupled to the 6AG5 r-f amplifier stage through the antenna coil. The output of the amplifier is inductively coupled to a 6AG5 mixer stage. The mixer coil and the oscillator coil for each channel are wound on the same coil form. These coils are inductively coupled on channels 1 through 6, and are capacitively coupled on channels 7 through 13, to provide the proper amount of oscillator-injection voltage.

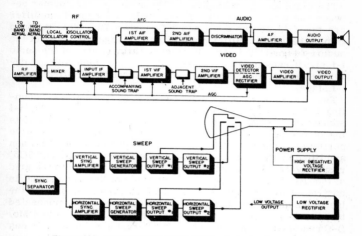

Figure 180. Block diagram of television receiver using seven-inch tube.

The oscillator used in the Philco tuner is of the Colpitts type, employing one section of a 6J6 dual triode. An interesting feature of the design is the automatic frequency control of the oscillator frequency. The oscillator tube is shunted by a reactance tube which utilizes the other section of the 6J6. The reactance tube is controlled by a d-c voltage obtained from the output of the f-m discriminator in the sound channel. When a positive voltage is applied to the grid of the reactance tube, the oscillator frequency is decreased. Conversely, when a negative voltage is applied, the oscillator frequency is increased. The output voltage of the discriminator varies in polarity from negative through zero to positive in accordance with the frequency of the discriminator input signal. Changes in the oscillator frequency change the frequency of the discriminator input signal and produce a change in discriminator output voltage. This voltage is applied to the control tube which in turn brings the frequency of the oscillator back to the correct frequency. Thus, the receiver remains in tune regardless of heating effects, aging of tubes, input signal drift, etc.

The output of the mixer which contains both the video and audio signals is applied to a 6AG5 input i-f amplifier. This is in variance with most receiver designs, in which the two carriers are separated in the plate of the mixer.

The plate and grid windings of the coupling transformer between the input i-f amplifier and the first video i-f amplifier are tuned to accept the video i-f carrier (26.6 Mc). A sound trap in the input amplifier plate circuit is adjusted to reject the audio i-f signal (22.1 Mc). Thus, very little, if any, of the audio i-f signal remains in the video section. The audio voltage developed across the sound trap is transferred to the first audio i-f stage.

Two stages of video i-f amplification, with broad-band coupling between stages, are employed. The amplified video i-f signal is fed to the video detector. The video detector, consisting of one section of a 6AL5 dual-diode, rectifies the negative portion of the video i-f signal. The resultant video signal is then amplified by two video amplifier stages using a 6AG5 and 7C5, respectively. The output of the 7C5 stage is applied to the grid of the 7GP4 picture tube. The amplitude of the video signal is controlled by the contrast control which varies the bias on the last video amplifier stage. Both video stages are compensated to provide a response from approximately 30 cycles to 4 Mc. D-C restoration is provided by a 1N34 crystal which establishes a d-c bias level according to the picture content of the signal on the grid of the picture tube.

Automatic gain control is secured by using one half of the video detector diode to rectify the sync tips. The voltage obtained is used to control the gain of the r-f amplifier, the input i-f amplifier, and the first video i-f amplifier, so that changes in the strength of the incoming signal are compensated for by a change in the gain of these stages.

The audio section consists of two i-f stages (tuned to the sound carrier frequency of 22.1 Mc), a ratio detector, and two stages of audio amplification. The output of the ratio detector is connected through an RC filter to the grid of the oscillator control tube which maintains the oscillator frequency, as previously described.

A portion of the video signal, taken from the screen of the first video amplifier, is applied to the grid of the 7B5 sync-separator tube, and separates the synchronizing pulses from the video signal. The voltages applied to the sync separator tube are such that the video portion of the composite video signal applied to its input is insufficient to operate the tube, and only the sync signals are passed. The output of the sync separator is applied to the 7F8 vertical-sync and horizontal-sync amplifiers through separate RC segregation circuits, each circuit having a different time constant.

The longer time constant circuit accepts both vertical and horizontal sync pulses and applies them to the vertical-sync-amplifier grid. These pulses are amplified and applied to an integrating network and then to the vertical sweep oscillator grid. The horizontal sync pulses, being of short duration, build up very little voltage across the integrating network, whereas the long, serrated, vertical sync pulses have a maximum effect. Thus, they trigger the grid of the vertical blocking oscillator. The pulses derived from the blocking oscillator discharge the sawtooth generator which is the other half of a 6SL7 twin triode. Sixty-cycle sawtooth voltages are thus obtained. The sawtooth voltages are applied to the grid of vertical-sweep amplifier tube No. 1 which operates in push-pull with vertical-sweep amplifier tube No. 2. A portion of the output voltage from tube No. 1 is used to drive the grid of tube No. 2. The output voltages of the amplifiers are coupled to the vertical deflection plates of the picture tube. A linearity control in the plate circuit of the sweep amplifiers determines the amplitude of voltage fed back to control the linearity of the vertical sweep. Vertical centering is achieved by varying the d-c voltage applied to the vertical deflection plates.

In the output of the sync separator tube, there is a differentiating network which changes the short time horizontal synchronizing pulses to sharp negative pips. These pips are amplified and inverted by the horizontal sync amplifier tube and are applied to the grid of the 6SL7 horizontal sweep oscillator. Except for the fact that the horizontal circuits operate at a higher frequency, they are similar to the vertical stages.

The power supply section contains two power supplies: one is a low-voltage high current supply for the receiver circuits, and the other is a negative high-voltage low-current supply for the picture tube. The low-voltage supply employs a 5U4G tube in a full-wave rectifier circuit.

The 60-cycle negative high-voltage supply uses a 1B3GT tube in a half-wave rectifier circuit, the output of which is filtered by a low pass filter. A bank of series resistors makes up the bleeder network, which supplies voltages for the focus and brightness controls. The use of a negative high voltage supply should be noted. This supply furnishes 2900 volts negative to the cathode of the picture tube through a variable resistor. The grid of the picture tube is operated from a point further up on the bleeder at 3050 volts negative. The variable resistor in the cathode circuit varies the potential difference between the grid and cathode from almost zero to 150 volts. This variable resistor permits changing the picture tube beam current and functions as the brightness control. The grid and cathode are run at a high negative voltage so that the second anode may be operated at a relatively low positive voltage. It will be recalled that in order to prevent astigmatism of the beam in an electrostatic picture tube, the deflection plates and second anode should be operated at the same potential. Since the deflection plates are operated at about 250 volts, the second anode must be operated at the same voltage. Were the cathode to be operated near ground potential and the second anode at the high positive potential, there would be as much as 2500 volts between the second anode and deflection plates.

The important point to remember about the operation of electrostatic picture tubes is that the actual potentials on the electrodes are not as important as the potential difference between electrodes. Thus, even though the cathode in this receiver is run at a negative voltage, the second anode is still 3150 volts more positive than the cathode (250 volts positive plus a negative 2900 volts equals 3150 volts).

From this discussion of a seven-inch electrostatic receiver, several conclusions can be drawn regarding the design of receivers in this category.

By using a small picture tube, a relatively low accelerating voltage is needed. This low voltage makes it easier to deflect the electron beam and a 250-volt low voltage power supply is adequate for the sweep amplifiers. The cost of the low and high voltage supplies is therefore reduced. The 7GP4 is one of the lowest cost picture tubes on the market. In addition, a focus coil, a deflection coil, and an ion trap are not required. The important economies in a receiver of this design are in the deflection circuits, power supplies, and the picture tube. Otherwise, receivers in this category contain much the same r-f, video, and audio circuits and components as any other type.

Basically, receivers which fall in the large direct-view and projection categories differ from small tube receivers only in those circuits which deflect the electron beam and supply the operating voltages to the picture tube. To understand these other receiver types, it is therefore necessary to discuss their deflection and power supply circuits.

3-120 Direct View Magnetic Receivers. An excellent example

of a direct-view magnetically deflected receiver is the RCA
Model 630TS. It uses a magnetic type 10BP4 picture tube. This
tube has an ion trap. A complete block diagram is shown in Figure 181.

This receiver has a thirteen channel r-f tuner. It employs

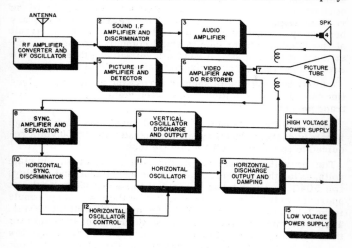

Figure 181. Block diagram of television receiver using ten-inch
tube.

stagger-tuned video i-f amplifiers, and has automatic frequency
control of the horizontal sweep circuit. For this discussion,
attention will be concentrated on the vertical and horizontal
sweep circuits and the high voltage power supply, starting with
the vertical discharge tube circuit in block 9.

A single 6J5 triode with its associated components forms a
blocking oscillator and discharge circuit. The sawtooth voltage
derived from this circuit has a peaking pulse added to it. The
peaked sawtooth voltage is required to produce a sawtooth current
in the deflection coil. The pulse is added to the saw-tooth
by a peaking resistor in series with the charging condenser in
the discharge tube plate circuit.

This voltage is fed to a 6K6GT connected as a triode. A vertical
output transformer matches the resistance of the vertical
deflection coils to the plate impedance of the 6K6GT. A verti-

cal sweep linearity control is obtained by inserting a variable resistor in the cathode of the 6K6GT. Since the grid-voltage, plate-current curve of this tube is not a straight line over its entire range, the effect of varying this resistor is to produce slight variations in shape of the saw-tooth by shifting the operating point of the tube to different points along the curve. The horizontal sweep amplifier stage (block #13) is similar to the vertical except that no peaking of the sawtooth is necessary because the inductive reactance reflected into the plate circuit of the 6BG6 amplifier tube is small compared to the plate resistance of the tetrode. A sawtooth voltage can thus produce a sawtooth current in the horizontal deflection coil.

A 5V4G damping tube is shunted across the horizontal deflection coil to stop oscillation of the sweep voltages during the retrace period.

3-121 The Power Supplies. The picture tube high voltage supply is of the kickback type. It generates the 9,000 volts required to operate the 10BP4 picture tube.

The low voltage power supply provides the filament and plate voltages for the receiver. The unit is conventional, and employs two 5U4G rectifier tubes in parallel to supply 400 volts d-c at approximately 290 ma. Compare it with the low voltage supply in the 7-inch Philco receiver which furnishes 395 volts at 200 ma. The 90 ma more current required in the RCA set is mainly for the sweep amplifiers. In the magnetic receiver, these are low voltage, high current-power amplifiers. For electrostatic deflection, voltage amplifiers are used which have low current drain.

3-122 Electrostatic vs. Electromagnetic Receiver. Two significant variations are apparent in the electrostatic and electromagnetic receivers. First, in the former, saw-tooth voltages are fed to the picture tube deflection plates through voltage amplifiers. In the latter, saw-tooth currents are transformer coupled to the deflection coils from high current amplifiers.

Second, the cathode ray tube is operated at a much higher potential. This voltage is derived in the kickback circuit from the horizontal output transformer. A 9,000 volt supply is thus obtained at little extra cost. Obviously, the kickback circuit cannot be used in the electrostatic receiver which has no sweep output transformer.

3-123 The Projection Receiver. The RCA Model 648 PTK projection receiver employs a projection type 5TP4 cathode-ray tube operating at 29,000 volts. A schmidt optical system provides a 15" x 20" picture on the screen. The similarity between a projection receiver and a direct view magnetic type receiver is emphasized in the RCA Model 648PTK and Model 630 TS designs. The r-f section, video channel, sound channel, synchronizing circuits, and vertical sweep system are identical. The only major differences between the two is in the horizontal sweep amplifier stage and power supply of the projection receiver.

Since the 5TP4 projection tube runs at a much higher potential than the 10BP4, more power is needed to deflect the beam. In the vertical circuit, the 6K6GT sweep output tube is still capable of meeting the power requirements, and so no change has to be made from the Model 630 TS design. The Model 648PTK however, uses a voltage tripler version of the kickback supply to produce 29,000 volts. The increased power thus drawn from the kickback circuit makes it necessary to put another 6BG6 power amplifier tube in parallel with the 6BG6 in the horizontal sweep amplifier circuit. Other than these variations, the circuit of the Model 648PTK projection receiver is almost identical to the Model 630 TS direct view receiver.

THE TELEVISION STATION

Pick-up - Control - Transmission

4-1 A television station consists of a complete sound broadcasting system and a picture transmission system. Electrically, each system operates independently of the other, even though the sound and picture equipment are usually physically located together. The sound equipment is identical to that found in any radio station, except that it generates a frequency modulated signal and operates on a much higher frequency.

The functions of the picture system are, to pick up the scene to be televised, convert it into a suitable electrical signal, and transmit it. The components of a very simple television system which can perform these functions are shown in Figure 1. The first block is the camera containing the pick-up tube for converting light into electricity. The camera also contains circuits for controlling the pick-up tube and amplifying the weak electrical signals which it generates. The output signal from the camera is fed to a picture monitor. In this unit the picture is viewed while adjustments are made on the camera to improve signal quality. A synchronizing generator simultaneously sends keying signals to both the camera and the monitor. These keying signals control the motion of the scanning beams in the pick-up tube and in the monitor receiving tube. The synchronizing generator also feeds the keying signals to the mixing and distribution amplifier. In this unit, the signal from the camera is combined with the keying signals to form what is known as the composite video or television signal. The video signal is then

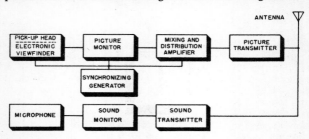

Figure 1. Block diagram of simple television transmitter.

fed to the transmitter where it is further amplified and used to modulate the television radio frequency carrier. The modulated carrier is fed to the antenna to be radiated.

At the same time that the picture signal is being formed, the sound accompanying the picture is picked up by a microphone, amplified, monitored, and fed to the sound transmitter. The modulated sound carrier from the transmitter may be radiated from a separate antenna, or from the video antenna.

In succeeding portions of this section, each of the units in the block diagram is discussed in detail. Since the average television station is considerably more complex than the simple system shown in the diagram, after the simple system has been explained, all the accessory equipment found in the average television station will be discussed. This will be followed by descriptions of commercial equipments whose designs are typical of each unit in the television system. Finally, station operation and maintenance will be covered.

Many of the basic television circuits are common to television transmitters and receivers. The detailed description of some of these circuits was covered in the previous chapter on television receivers. The reader will be referred at times to the receiver chapter for a more complete discussion of a common circuit whenever it is encountered in this description of station equipment.

CAMERA TUBES

4-2 The progress of electronic television transmission can be gaged by the improvements made in the camera pick-up tube. The quality and interest of television programs as well as the design of the station equipment depend, to a great extent, upon the characteristics of the image forming tube used in the camera. In Section 2 a complete description was given of the operation of the iconoscope. The iconoscope was one of the first pick-up tubes which overcame the limitations of the mechanical television scanning system and made possible the all electronic television system. Although the iconoscope is one of the earliest camera tubes, it is still superior to other commercial designs with regard to the detail and sharpness of the image it produces. It also has a number of shortcomings which have made it necessary for the industry to develop other types of pick-up tubes.

The poor light sensitivity of the iconoscope makes it necessary to equip studios with tremendous lighting installations. The cost of operation of such lights can be appreciated by the fact that when one New York station was using iconoscope cameras exclusively, the electric power dissipated by the lights exceeded the power required for running the entire station (including studio equipment and the transmitter). Not only is the cost prohibitive, but the heat given off by the lights causes many difficulties. Actors constantly complain of the difficulty of working under the lights in studios equipped with iconoscope cameras. As a result of the heat generated, expensive air conditioning systems have to be installed.

Even when used with extensive lighting systems, the iconoscope's low sensitivity limits program interest. The lens iris must be run wide open to obtain sufficient picture contrast, thereby reducing the depth of focus and limiting the field of view. Interesting shadows or lighting effects, which have been so highly perfected in motion pictures, cannot be obtained with iconoscope cameras.

The physical shape and size of the iconoscope presented a problem in cameras designed for remote work. Compact, portable equipment is needed for programs televised outside of the studio. The large size of the iconoscope makes a small camera impossible. Outdoor pick-ups often require telephoto lenses. The cost of telephoto lenses large enough to cover the area of the iconoscope mosaic is prohibitive.

To overcome the problem of physical size, the orthicon tube was developed. It is smaller than the iconoscope and has a higher light sensitivity. These characteristics make it more suitable for use in portable cameras. Before the war, the orthicon camera was used for most field work while the iconoscope camera was employed in picking up live talent shows and films in the studio.

One other tube was in common use in studio equipment until recent years. This tube is called the image dissector. Its sensitivity and resolution capabilities are about the same as those of the iconoscope.

The first real post-war advance in camera tubes came with the introduction of the image-orthicon by RCA. This tube is over 100 times as sensitive as the iconoscope and is considerably smaller in size. Unfortunately, it is not capable of producing as sharp and as detailed a picture as is the iconoscope. Nevertheless, because of its high sensitivity, the image-orthicon is now preferred for use in both outdoor and studio camera equipment. A few stations which were equipped with iconoscope cameras and the necessary light installations, continue to use iconoscope equipment for studio programs. The best images are still produced with the iconoscope.

Most new stations are not investing in expensive lighting installations and iconoscope equipment, preferring to compromise on the slightly inferior pictures obtained with the image orthicon. These stations use the image-orthicon camera for outdoor and studio work. In some instances it is also used for film pick-ups, although in the majority of cases a separate iconoscope camera is provided for this purpose.

The television camera tube problem appears to be resolving itself in the following manner. Most stations are buying image-orthicon cameras for studio and outdoor use. If better resolution of picture is desired for studio work, the station must invest in iconoscope cameras and an expensive lighting installation. The iconoscope camera is now used almost exclusively for televising from films. In film pick-up equipment the light concentrated on the mosaic is sufficiently intense for use with the iconoscope.

The operation of the iconoscope was covered in Section 2. The following pages contain descriptions of the other types of camera tubes.

4-3 The Image Dissector.

The image dissector (Figure 2),

Figure 2. The image dissector. (courtesy Farnsworth)

was invented by P. T. Farnsworth and was used extensively in studio and film cameras before the war. Its low sensitivity to light and the advent of more sensitive tubes now limit the use

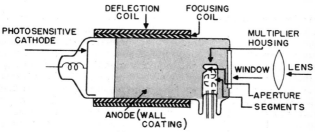

Figure 3. Construction of the image dissector.

of the image dissector to film cameras where the light level is high enough to utilize the excellent resolution capabilities of the tube.

The elements of an image dissector tube are shown in Figure 3. The object to be televised is projected through a window and focused on a photosensitive cathode. The number of electrons released from any point on the photocathode depends upon the intensity of light at that point. These photoelectrons are accelerated as an "image cloud" down the length of the tube toward the aperture. The silver layer on the inner surface of the tube acts as the positive anode which pulls the electrons from the cathode. A focusing coil surrounds the tube and keeps the electrons moving in a straight path. The entire electron image is then moved both horizontally and vertically by means of two deflection coils also surrounding the tube. In this way the image is moved past the aperture, permitting electrons to enter it in a chain of pulses. In other words, instead of moving as a single beam of electrons to scan the image on the mosaic as is done in the iconoscope, the entire electron image in the dissector is moved back and forth past a small opening at the horizontal and vertical scanning frequencies.

Since only a very small fraction of the total image is in front of the scanning aperture at any instant, most of the light (and the photoelectrons released from the photocathode by it) does not contribute to the output signal. To overcome this inherent insensitivity, a "multiplier" section is added near the aperture. The electrons which pass through the aperture excite secondary electrons in the "multiplier", resulting in a signal which is several thousand times stronger. Even with this multiplier section and the large size lenses which are used with the tube to collect as much light as possible, the image dissector remains a very low sensitivity tube in comparison to other types.

4-4 The Orthiconoscope (Orthicon). The orthiconoscope (orthicon for short) is a camera tube of the storage type like the iconoscope. The image is stored on a mosaic until the scanning beam converts it into an electrical signal. The orthicon uses a scanning beam of much lower velocity than does the iconoscope so that no secondary electrons are emitted. This is advantageous, for there are no spurious secondary electrons to fall back on the mosaic as is the case with the iconoscope. This in turn eliminates the necessity for shading signals to correct for spurious secondary emissions. In the absence of secondary electrons in the orthicon, the scanning electrons themselves are collected to form the video signal.

The structure of the orthicon is shown in Figure 4. The image to be televised is focused on a plate which is transparent to light. On one side of this plate is a photosensitive surface or, mosaic. An electron image is stored on this mosaic. The scanning beam, coming from the other direction, moves across the mosaic in the same manner as in the iconoscope. If the scanning beam impinges upon a point on the mosaic which has previously lost its charge (caused by light falling on it), several electrons are collected by the mosaic from the beam to neutralize the point. In this manner, each point on the mosaic is returned to an equilibrium condition by the necessary amount of

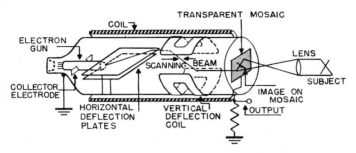

Figure 4. Construction of the orthiconoscope.

electrons. These electrons set up a varying potential on the mosaic and so constitute the video signal.

The orthicon's physical shape gives it several advantages over the iconoscope. The optical image and scanning beam strike the mosaic along the tube's axis. No keystoning distortion takes place as in the iconoscope. The tube is about four inches in diameter and about 20 inches long, and the mosaic is 2 by $2\frac{1}{2}$ inches. The orthicon lends itself to mounting in smaller, more compact cameras for outdoor work. The smaller mosaic enables the use of smaller lenses than are required with the iconoscope.

The orthicon is about 10 to 20 times as sensitive as the iconoscope. Its noise level is higher and its resolution lower. While some stations are still using cameras with orthicon tubes, the newer image orthicon is rapidly making the orthicon obsolete.

4-5 The Image Orthicon. The most sensitive commercial camera tube developed to date is the image orthicon. It is about 100 times as sensitive as the iconoscope and can pick up a scene lighted only with a candle. The images produced by the image orthicon lack the detail of those produced by the iconoscope, and its signal to noise ratio is lower. It is not the best camera tube for operation in the studio where the light level can be made high enough to permit the use of a less sensitive, but less noisy tube like the iconoscope or the image dissector.

The great sensitivity and small size of the image orthicon make it an extremely valuable tube for use in remote pick-up equipment, which must often be operated at very low light levels. The tube is quite small, as shown in Figure 5, and has a target

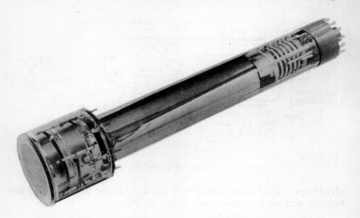

Figure 5. The image orthicon. (courtesy RCA)

area only 1-1/4 inches in diameter. It thus makes possible light, portable cameras and permits the use of turrets carrying lenses of several different focal lengths. This is advantageous in covering outdoor events, such as football games, where it is desirable to switch very quickly from a telephoto lens to a wide angle lens. The tube's high sensitivity also allows the lens to be stopped down to achieve greater depth of focus. An image-orthicon camera used in field pick-up equipment and equipped with a turret lens is shown in Figure 6.

The image-orthicon tube consists of three sections: The image section, the scanning section, and the multiplier section. These are shown in Figure 7.

4-6 The Image Section. The image section is shown in greater detail in Figure 8. It consists of a photocathode, an electron lens system, and a target. The camera lens focuses an optical image on the front of a translucent photocathode which is found on the inside of the large section of the glass envelope. Photo-electrons are emitted from the rear of the photocathode. Their distribution and number correspond to the light rays which fall on the front of the photocathode.

Figure 6. Image orthicon camera. (courtesy RCA)

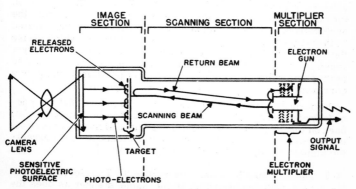

Figure 7. Construction of the image orthicon.

An electrostatic field, set up by the potential difference existing between the photocathode and the target, combines with the longitudinal magnetic field to focus the electron image on the front surface of the target. The target is a very thin glass plate, in front of which is located a fine mesh screen. The photoelectrons traveling toward the target, having been accel-

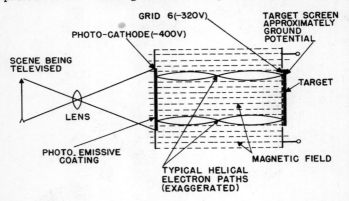

Figure 8. Multiplier section of the image orthicon.

erated by approximately 400 volts, pass through the screen and strike the target, causing secondary electrons to be emitted. These secondary electrons are collected by the fine mesh screen and are returned to ground. This leaves a positive charge on the target which corresponds to the electron emission from the photocathode. Since the number of secondary electrons emitted by the target is greater than the number of electrons which strike the target, a charge configuration is produced on the target which is several times as great as the original charge emitted by the photocathode. This charge is most positive at the points corresponding to the brighter portions of the picture.

The purpose of the fine mesh screen is to insure that the secondary electrons will be collected rather than be allowed to fall back on the target again to produce spurious signals. This effect is common in the iconoscope and requires that external correcting signals be injected into the video signal.

4-7 The Scanning Section. See Figure 9. The electron gun of the image orthicon operates in the same manner as does the electron gun in a conventional cathode-ray tube. The voltage on grid 2 determines the velocity with which electrons leave the gun. The potential on grid 1 limits the beam current. The combination of voltages on grids 2, 4, and 5, and the longitudinal magnetic focusing field, causes the beam to be focused upon the

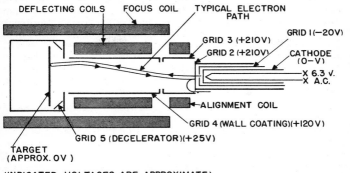

DEFLECTING COILS   FOCUS COIL   TYPICAL ELECTRON PATH

GRID 3 (+210V)   GRID I (−20V)

GRID 2 (+210V)   CATHODE (0−V)

X 6.3 V.
X A.C.

ALIGNMENT COIL

GRID 4 (WALL COATING)(+120V)

GRID 5 (DECELERATOR)(+25V)

TARGET (APPROX. 0V)

(INDICATED VOLTAGES ARE APPROXIMATE)

Figure 9. Scanning section of the image orthicon.

rear surface of the target. Grid 3 has little effect during the forward travel of the electron beam.

Since the target mesh is operated at ground potential, or even slightly negative, the electron beam composed of negative electrons is repelled by the negative charge on the target and never reaches it. The beam actually turns around and travels back toward the electron gun. This returning beam eventually determines the character of the output video signal.

It will be remembered that light from the original scene was focused on the photocathode and caused photo-electrons to be emitted. These electrons were accelerated, and passed through the tube to strike the target. Due to the physical characteristics of the target, each incident photo-electron caused the emission of several secondary electrons which were collected by the target mesh. Thus the final effect was to leave those sections of the target corresponding to the white portions of the picture more positive with respect to the mesh than those corresponding to dark portions of the picture. This charge pattern is transferred substantially unchanged to the rear, or scanned side, of the target.

By correctly setting the potential of the target mesh, the electron beam can be made to approach the target at a velocity which will enable those sections of the target representing black portions of the picture to repel the beam. The beam will only supply electrons to neutralize the charge deficiency on those more positive portions corresponding to whiter sections of the picture. Thus, if the beam is scanned over the target, part of the beam will be collected by the target, and part will reverse its direction and be accelerated back toward the electron gun structure. The amount of current in the return beam at a given instant will depend upon the charge on the portion of the target being scanned at that time. The current variation in the return beam is such that maximum current corresponds to black in the picture, while minimum current corresponds to white in the picture.

Scanning is produced by passing sawtooth scanning currents through the horizontal and vertical deflection coils which surround the tube. These coils are located inside the focus coil. The focus coil provides the longitudinal magnetic field which passes through the scanning and image sections. It is important that the scanning fields do not extend to the target and image section. Any scanning action in the image section will result in picture blurring due to displacement of the photo-electrons. To prevent this loss of resolution, a metal shield is placed around the target end of the image section.

Sections of the target which have been scanned have no positive charge remaining (assuming proper beam current adjustment), and are in the same condition as the portions which correspond to black. The scanning beam can not be permitted to strike the target during sweep retrace times, since this would cause the charge pattern to be neutralized and cause black lines to appear in the picture. Negative pulses are used to repel the beam from the target during horizontal and vertical retrace times. When the pulse inserted in the picture for target blanking is properly set, it provides a definite black picture reference level in the video signal.

4-8 The Electron Multiplier Section. The electron multiplier section is shown in Figure 10. As the return beam from the target enters the region of grid 3, the beam tends to spread. In so doing it strikes the outer surface of grid 2 rather than returning through the hole from which the forward beam came. Grid 2 is also called the 1st dynode. The dynodes are coated with a material which enhances their secondary electron emitting characteristics. For each incident electron in the return beam which strikes the 1st dynode, several secondary electrons are emitted. By passing the secondary electrons to the next dynode, the number of secondary electrons is further increased. For each secondary electron emitted from the first dynode, many more secondary electrons are emitted from the second dynode. Thus each dynode multiplies the number of electrons.

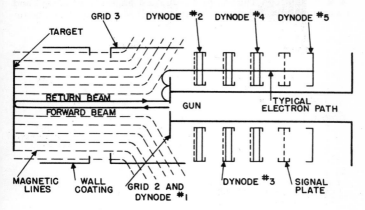

Figure 10. Electron Multiplier Section of the image orthicon.

The combined action of the dynodes results in a considerably stronger signal than that originally produced on the photocathode. It is this multiplier arrangement in the image orthicon which gives the tube its high sensitivity.

When the electrons in the return beam cause the emission of several secondary electrons from the first dynode, the secondary electrons find their way into the space between dynode 1 and grid 3 immediately, or, after falling back to the dynode 1 surface a few times. When they finally do reach the space, they are subjected to an accelerating field produced by dynode 2 which is operated at approximately 500 volts. The accelerating field causes them to pass through a screen into the dynode 2 vanes. The voltage on grid 3 is adjusted for optimum picture quality, and controls the number of electrons landing on dynode 2. The dynode vanes are flat and radiate from the center of the tube near the gun in "wheel" fashion, as shown in Figure 11.

An electron entering the vane structure perpendicularly to its plane must always strike one of the vanes. The electron, in striking the vane, excites further secondary emission. The secondary electrons are then accelerated to dynode 3, then 4 and 5. A typical electron path from one dynode to the next is shown in Figure 10. The final multiplied current is collected by the signal plate. The current is passed through a load resistor and constitutes the output video signal.

4-9 Monoscope Tubes. In tubes such as the iconoscope and image orthicon, the video signal is created by an electron beam

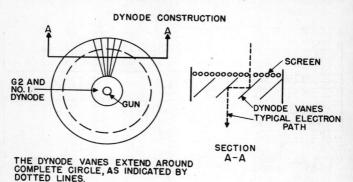

Figure 11. Construction of the dynode vanes in the image orthicon.

bombarding a photosensitive plate. The plate emits secondary electrons in varying numbers as the beam bombards successive points on its photosensitive surface. A photosensitive plate, or any surface which gives off secondary electrons, can be used to generate a television signal.

This principle has been used in another television camera tube of simple construction. This tube is known as a monoscope (also called a phasmajector or a monotron), and is built into a simple camera which produces a fixed image used for testing equipment in the television station. A monoscope camera is sometimes used in receiver manufacturing plants as a source for a test picture when no television signal is otherwise available.

The picture obtained from a monoscope is shown in Figure 12. This pattern is printed on an aluminum plate with ordinary printer's ink. The back of this plate may be seen in Figure 13. The carbon in the ink and the aluminum have different secondary emission characteristics. The aluminum gives off about twice as many secondary electrons as the carbon when bombarded by an electron beam.

The printed plate is mounted in the tube where an electron beam scans the printed half-tone pattern, causing greater secondary emission from the aluminum surfaces (the white portions of the picture) than from the black printed portions. The varying secondary electrons are collected on an electrode which

Figure 12. Pattern obtained from monoscope tube.

Figure 13. Monoscope tube. (courtesy RCA)

consists of a conductive coating on the wall of the monoscope tube. The video signal is developed across a load resistor connected between the coating and ground.

Deflection of the scanning beam is achieved magnetically with horizontal and vertical deflection coils. These coils are mounted in a yoke which fits over the neck of the monoscope tube. The electron gun is similar to that found in conventional cathode-ray tubes. Electrostatic focusing is used.

The monoscope has a much higher efficiency than tubes utilizing photosensitive surfaces. Signals as high as 4 or 5 millivolts are obtained across the output load. The detail of the image is good and is limited only by the cross-sectional area of the scanning beam and the quality of the half-tone used to print the pattern. Most monoscope tubes are capable of 500 line resolution, which is sufficient to test the full capabilities of television equipment as to contrast and resolution. The ruled lines on the pattern of Figure 12 are used to check the linearity of deflection circuits.

The chief advantage of a monoscope camera in a television station or receiver factory is that it offers a standard reproducible image for comparing the performance of equipment over a period of time. No source of lighting is required. Consequently, there are no variations in illumination and an image of constant contrast is obtained.

CAMERA CIRCUITS

4-10 The following description of camera circuits applies to designs using the type 2P23 image-orthicon tube which is used in most of the new television station cameras. Circuit designs differ somewhat in equipment offered by the various manufacturers, but the basic principles are the same. The description of the image orthicon camera circuits covers most of the circuits required for other types of camera pick-up tubes.

The television camera is in reality two units. One is the pick-up head containing the image orthicon and its associated video, sweep, and power supply circuits. The other is the electronic view finder containing a miniature television receiver on which the camera operator watches the scene being televised. These units are shown in Figure 14. In pre-war cameras, optical viewfinders were often used. However, since the human eye and the image orthicon have different color responses, with an optical viewfinder the camera operator sees a picture which does not correspond to the one transmitted. The electronic viewfinder enables him to see the picture exactly as it is sent out over the air.

Some cameras are equipped with a third unit which is housed in a separate case. This unit is known as the camera pick-up auxiliary. When in use it is placed close to the camera. The

Figure 14. Pickup head and electronic viewfinder.
(courtesy DuMont)

camera pick-up auxiliary contains the power supply and synchronizing circuits for the camera which need not be housed in the pick-up head itself. By placing these circuits in an external case, the weight and size of the camera are kept to a minimum.

4-11 The Video Circuits. A video amplifier system is located in the pick-up head, along with the camera tube and the sweep circuits. Figure 15 shows the circuit of a typical video amplifying system for use in a television camera.

The video signals appearing on the final multiplier of the image-orthicon tube are coupled to the grid of the first video amplifier,

V98-2. The video amplifier stages consist of 6AK5s, V98-2 through V98-5, and one 6J6 tube, V98-6, as shown in the block diagram of Figure 16. The first two stages are shunt-peaked to produce a frequency response flat to 8 megacycles (the response

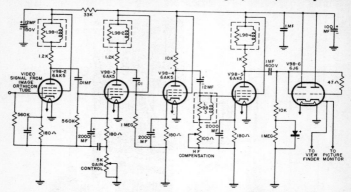

Figure 15. Circuit of video amplifier used in image orthicon camera.

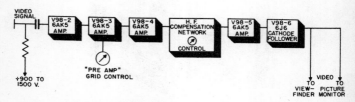

Figure 16. Block diagram of video amplifier used in image orthicon camera.

of the video amplifier in station equipment is generally made greater than the required 4 mc to insure that no loss in picture quality will occur). The third stage is coupled to a high frequency compensation network used to accentuate high frequency response to compensate for high frequency losses which occur in the input coupling network. V98-5 is a voltage amplifier stage feeding V98-6, a 6J6 double triode, connected as a cathode follower output. The cathode follower is used to match the high impedance of the last video amplifier stage to the low impedance of the transmission line which connects it to the picture monitor. A manual gain control is provided in the cathode of V98-3 to accommodate the various signal output levels of different orthicon tubes and/ or different light conditions.

4-12 The Sweep Circuits. The camera tube sweep circuits are similar to those used in a television receiver. A typical camera sweep circuit is shown in Figure 17. Horizontal and vertical

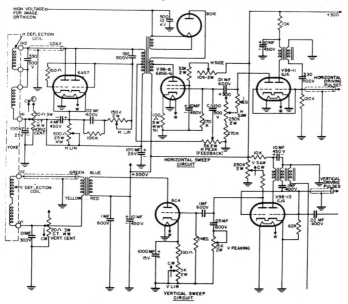

Figure 17. Vertical and horizontal circuits for use with image orthicon.

synchronizing or driving pulses, already separated and shaped, are received from the camera pick-up auxiliary unit. The horizontal pulses trigger one-half of a 6J6 tube (V98-11), used as a blocking oscillator. The blocking oscillator pulses are applied to the second section of the 6J6, which is a discharge tube, producing a sawtooth voltage on discharge condenser C-1. This sawtooth is applied to the grid of the 6BG6-G amplifier tube which amplifies the sweep voltage and feeds it to the camera tube yoke through a coupling transformer. A 6AS7 tube is used as a damper. High voltage for the image-orthicon is derived from a kickback circuit (Section 3) in the horizontal sweep output stage.

The vertical synchronizing pulses trigger one half of a second 6J6 tube (V98-13) also used as a blocking oscillator. The blocking oscillator pulses are applied to the second section of the tube which produces a sawtooth voltage at the vertical frequency. The resultant sawtooth is fed to the grid of a 6C4 sweep amplifier. This stage is transformer coupled to the vertical deflection coils.

4-13 The Electronic Viewfinder. The electronic viewfinder is mounted in the pick-up head. Its purpose is to permit the camera operator to see the scene being televised. The viewfinder is actually a television receiver without radio frequency circuits. A block diagram of the viewfinder is shown in Figure 18.

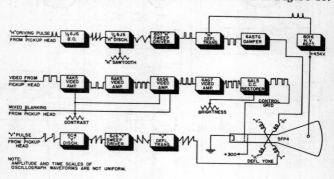

Figure 18. Block diagram of circuits of electronic viewfinder.

It contains the same type of sweep circuits used to deflect the beam in the image-orthicon tube. In the camera viewfinder the beam traces out the picture on a small television receiving tube, usually a 5FP4. The 5FP4 is a five inch magnetic cathode-ray tube identical to those used in television receivers, except for its small size. The picture on the tube is 3 x 4 inches in size. In the viewfinder there is no need for r-f and i-f circuits or a video detector to detect and amplify the video signal in the television receiver. The video signal is fed directly from the camera to the viewfinder. Several video amplifier stages bring the video signal up to a level sufficient to drive the grid of the viewfinder tube.

4-14 The Camera Pick-Up Auxiliary Unit. The camera pick-up auxiliary unit serves as the connecting link between the picture monitor and the camera. Its physical location in the system is such that it is less than 30 feet from the camera, while up to 1,000 feet of cable may be used between the auxiliary and the monitor control. The pick-up auxiliary units serves four functions:

1. It provides regulated positive and negative d-c voltages for the pick-up unit in the camera.

2. It provides adjustable regulated current for the image-orthicon tube focus coil.

3. It provides centering voltages for the pick-up unit and viewfinder.

4. It provides vertical and horizontal synchronizing pulses for the pick-up unit and the viewfinder.

THE SYNCHRONIZING GENERATOR

4-15 In television stations, the synchronizing generator is the "brain center" which furnishes the timing pulses to the studio and film cameras, to the picture monitors, and to the mixing amplifier (which adds the synchronizing pulses from the sync generator to the video signal generated in the camera). Sync generators are also used in laboratories and factories in conjunction with a monoscope camera to furnish a complete video signal which can be used for the development and production testing of television receivers.

The synchronizing generator furnishes all of the timing pulses required in a complete television system. These pulses are accurately timed with relation to each other. Their shape and length is carefully controlled in accordance with the standards set up by the FCC to assure stable operation of television receivers. The waveshape and time relation of these pulses is shown in Figure 19. This is the standard television signal whose components were discussed in Section 2.

Depending upon the commercial design, one or more of the following signals are supplied by the sync generator:

1. Horizontal driving signal - This consists of short-duration, square wave pulses at the horizontal scanning frequency (15,750 cycles). These pulses are used to trigger the sawtooth sweep generator (in the camera), which supplies the horizontal scan-

ning voltage for the pick-up tube.

2. Vertical driving signal - This consists of square wave pulses of longer duration than the horizontal pulses. These pulses occur at the vertical scanning frequency (60 cycles).

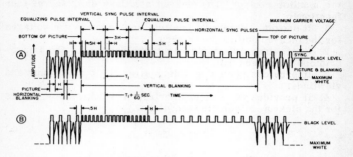

Figure 19. Standard F.C.C. television signal.

They are used to trigger the sawtooth sweep generator (in the camera) which supplies the vertical scanning voltage for the pick-up tube.

3. Mixed driving pulses - Some sync generators combine the vertical and horizontal driving pulses, instead of feeding them separately to the camera. This eliminates one co-axial line which must be run from the generator to the camera. Separator circuits are then employed in the camera, or camera pick-up auxiliary, to separate the vertical and horizontal driving pulses.

4. Synchronizing signal - This is the signal shown in Figure 19, which must be added to the camera picture signal before it is transmitted in order to synchronize the scanning action in the receiver. It is a composite signal consisting of (a) short duration, horizontal synchronizing pulses at 15,750 cycles; (b) longer duration, vertical synchronizing pulses of the "serrated" type at 60 cycles, and (c) a series of six short-duration, equalizing pulses just preceding each vertical pulse interval and six more following it.

5. Blanking signal - This signal is added to the transmitted video signal in order to blank out the return trace in the receiver picture tube. It consists of square wave pulses at the horizontal scanning frequency (15,750 cycles) and the vertical scanning frequency (60 cycles). These pulses are of longer duration than the synchronizing pulses, and their amplitude extends down to the black level of the video signal. They form the "pedestals"

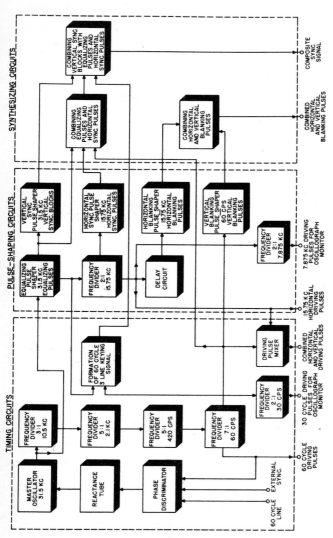

Figure 20. Block diagram of sync generator unit.

on which the synchronizing signals are placed and also blank out the scanning beam during the retrace period.

6. Oscillograph monitor driving signals - These signals are pulses at half the horizontal (7,875 cycles) frequency and half the vertical (30 cycles) frequency. They are used to trigger the sweep circuits in the oscillograph monitors which are located in the picture monitor. Oscillograph patterns which are two lines or two fields in length are thus obtained.

Sync generators are divided into three main sections as shown in the block diagram of Figure 20. The first section contains the timing circuits while the second section contains the pulse-shaping circuits. The third section synthesizes the various pulses into the composite sync and blanking signal. The timing unit generates keying signals which occur at frequencies corresponding to the different pulses in the video signal. The timing unit also provides a means whereby these frequencies (which are all derived from a single master oscillator) may be "locked-in" either with the local 60 cycle power line frequency or with some other external source, such as a remotely generated synchronizing signal. The pulse-shaping unit forms the sync blanking and equalizing pulses. These pulses are then combined into a composite signal by "keying" the shaper circuits with signals from the timing unit.

4-16 The Timing Circuits. The timing of the vertical synchronizing pulses must be very accurately related to the timing of the horizontal synchronizing pulses if accurate interlacing of the two fields of each television frame is to be achieved. In Section 2, the interlaced scanning system was explained. The half-line spacing between fields was achieved by inserting equalizing pulses before and after the vertical sync pulse.

If the vertical and horizontal sync pulses and the equalizing pulses are not properly related to one another a distorted picture results. It is therefore convenient to relate them to one single continuous frequency which is a multiple of their fundamental frequencies. This multiple frequency is generated by the master oscillator in the synchronizing generator. All the signal components of the sync generator are derived from this oscillator by frequency divider and wave-shaping circuits. By relating the timing of all sync signal components to this master oscillator, stable and accurate timing of the pulses is achieved.

4-17 The Master Oscillator. The master oscillator is a stable sine-wave oscillator whose frequency is locked to the 60 cycle power line or to a remotely operated synchronizing generator. Locking the master oscillator to the power line insures synchronization between the television scanning circuits and film cameras which are also locked to the power line by synchronous

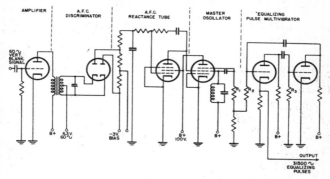

Figure 21. Master oscillator and a-f-c circuits of sync generator.

motors. It also eliminates the possibility of 60 cycle hum patterns drifting through the picture, should this hum originate in the over-all television system. When a program is received from a remote pick-up, the studio sync generator is locked to the remote sync generator. This permits switching from the remote program to the local studio program without disturbing the synchronization of receivers.

The master oscillator frequency is 31.5 kc, which is also the frequency of the equalizing pulses. Half this frequency is the horizontal frequency of 15.75 kc. If 31.5 kc is divided successively by 3, 5, 5, and 7, a 60 cycle frequency results which is the frequency of the vertical synchronizing pulses. Thus, with suitable frequency divider circuits, a timing signal can be obtained from the master oscillator for each type of pulse.

A sine-wave oscillator, such as the Colpitts (Section 3) or the Transitron is used to generate the master oscillator frequency. The drift stability of the oscillator is not as important as the cycle-to-cycle regularity which is required to produce a television picture with straight vertical edges. Oscillator drift is prevented by locking the oscillator to the power line with an automatic frequency control system which will be explained later.

A typical master oscillator circuit using a Transitron oscillator is shown in Figure 21. The Transitron oscillator can be recognized by the fact that a pentode is always used and the positive voltage on the screen is greater than that on the plate. A negative voltage is applied to the suppressor through resistor R-1. Under these conditions, the tube offers a negative resistance to the tuned circuit. In other words, a decrease of screen voltage causes an increase in screen current and vice versa, due to the relative effect of the suppressor and screen grid fields. The advantages of the Transitron are its simplicity, and the ease with which its frequency can be controlled by an injected signal.

Automatic frequency control of the master oscillator is achieved with the discriminator and reactance tube circuits shown in Figure 21. The phase discriminator compares the 60 cycle power line frequency (6.3 volts a-c) with the 60 cycle output of the frequency divider chain in the master oscillator. The discriminator develops a direct-current output whose value depends upon the relative phase of the two input signals to the discriminator. This d-c current is fed to the reactance tube which is connected across the tuned circuit of the Transitron oscillator.

The gain and phase relationships of the reactance tube are such that they produce a current and voltage in the plate circuit, equivalent to an inductive or capacitive reactance. This reactance is capacitive or inductive, dependent upon the amplitude of the fluctuating d-c signal on the grid. The variable reactance, connected across the tuned circuit of the oscillator, causes its frequency to vary accordingly. If the master oscillator and power line are in phase, there is zero output from the discriminator. If the two move out of phase, a d-c control voltage is obtained from the discriminator which changes the reactance across the oscillator tank circuit, pulling the oscillator back to its correct frequency.

4-18 The Frequency Divider Chain. The frequency divider chain consists of a number of stages which divide the master oscillator frequency into submultiples of the vertical and horizontal sync frequencies. Three types of divider circuits are used for this purpose. These are the multivibrator, the blocking oscillator, and the counter circuit.

The multivibrator divider is an oscillator composed of two resistance coupled amplifiers. The output of the second stage is fed back to the input of the first stage to support oscillation.

The oscillator frequency is determined by the time constants
R1-C1 and R2-C2 (Figure 22). If a pulse is fed into the grid of
the first stage, it will synchronize the oscillator on a submultiple

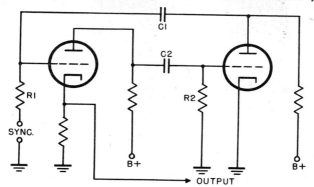

Figure 22. Multivibrator frequency divider.

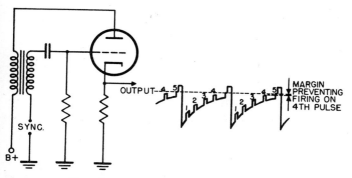

Figure 23. Blocking oscillator frequency divider.

of the pulse frequency. The submultiple at which it operates
depends upon the time constants of R1-C1 and R2-C2.

The blocking oscillator divider is a little more stable than the
multivibrator because it substitutes a stable transformer for
one of the tubes. The blocking oscillator divider is shown in
Figure 23. The voltage on the grid during one cycle of oscil-

lation is also shown in the figure. Frequency division is obtained by applying a signal to the grid of the oscillator and setting
the R-C time constant in the grid circuit to a submultiple of the
incoming signal. The oscillator then operates on a lower frequency than the incoming signal.

As shown on the grid characteristic, only the fifth incoming

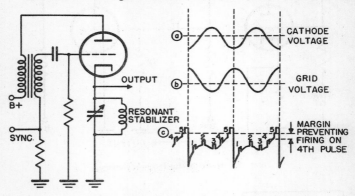

Figure 24. Stabilized blocking oscillator frequency divider.

pulse occurs sufficiently far up on the grid curve to overcome
the cutoff bias on the oscillator and cause it to produce a pulse.
For every five pulses coming into the oscillator, only one pulse
is produced by the oscillator. Note that the fourth pulse is almost sufficient to trigger the oscillator. Incorrect frequency
division occurs if drift in the oscillator stage permits the fourth
pulse to rise above the cutoff voltage. A stabilized blocking oscillator prevents this by providing a greater margin of safety
between the amplitude of the next to the last pulse and the cutoff voltage.

A stabilized blocking oscillator is shown in Figure 24. This
circuit is the same as the blocking oscillator circuit shown in
Figure 23, except that a tuned circuit is placed in the cathode
lead.

The resonant circuit in the cathode is shock excited by the
pulse of grid current that flows through it during the positive
grid portion of the cycle. The voltage that appears on the cathode is a damped oscillation such as shown in Figure 24a. This
damped oscillation appears on the grid 180 degrees out of phase
as shown in Figure 24b. This transient voltage, which occurs

each time the oscillator conducts, is added to the grid characteristic as shown in Figure 24c. The effect is to move the next
to the last sync pulse further below the cutoff voltage, while also
moving the desired pulse further above cutoff. Thus, a greater

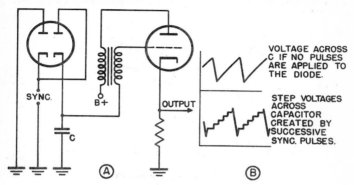

Figure 25. Pulse counting circuit.

margin of voltage is provided between the last and the next to
last pulses.

The transient voltage frequency is set by tuning the cathode-
stabilizing circuit to one and one half times the desired oscillator frequency. This voltage component added to the grid characteristic insures synchronization of the blocking oscillator to
the desired driving pulse despite variations in tube characteristics, power supply voltages, and the amplitude of the driving
pulses.

The third type of circuit used for frequency division is known
as a "pulse-counting" circuit, and is shown in Figure 25a. Two
diodes replace the grid leak resistor of the conventional blocking oscillator. As successive driving pulses are applied to the
diodes, the capacitor C charges in steps, each step corresponding to another pulse. Figure 25b. Finally, the last step has
sufficient amplitude to trigger the oscillator. Thus, for several incoming pulses, only one pulse is produced by the oscillator.

The frequency division from 31.5 kc to 60 cycles is usually
done in four stages in the ratios of 3, 5, 5, and 7. A complete
chain of frequency divider circuits, consisting of four stabilized
blocking oscillators is shown in Figure 26. Note that the stabilizing tuned circuit is put in the grid of the blocking oscillator

to illustrate another version of this type of dividing circuit.

4-19 The Pulse Shaping Circuits. The timing pulses which are generated in the frequency divider chain do not have the correct wave form required for the composite synchronizing signal.

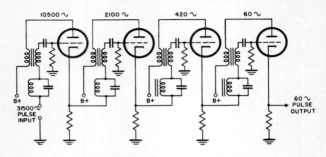

Figure 26. Frequency divider chain.

They are merely used to "key in", at the correct time, the horizontal, vertical, and equalizing pulses which are generated in the shaping circuits. The horizontal and vertical blanking pulses also are formed in the shaping circuits. The blanking pulses must be integrated with the synchronizing pulses to form the standard FCC signal shown in Figure 19.

4-20 The Equalizing Pulses. The equalizing pulses are half as wide as the horizontal sync pulses and are spaced at half-line intervals. Six equalizing pulses occur before the vertical sync signal and six occur after it during each complete field. Although only twelve equalizing pulses are needed per field, it is simpler to generate a continuous train of them and turn them on only when they are needed. If the equalizing pulses were to occur throughout the field, they would have a frequency of 31.5 kc (twice that of the horizontal pulses which occur 15,750 times per second). 31.5 kc is also the frequency of the master oscillator. Therefore, the master oscillator frequency can be used to key the equalizing pulse shaper.

The multivibrator makes an ideal pulse shaper because it generates square wave pulses. The pulse width of the multivibrator can be adjusted by setting R3 in Figure 21. This control can be used to set the width of the equalizing pulses, after which R2 can be set for exact synchronization with the master oscillator signal which is fed into the grid of the first stage.

4-21 The Horizontal Blanking Pulses. The horizontal blanking pulses cut off the television picture in the receiver during

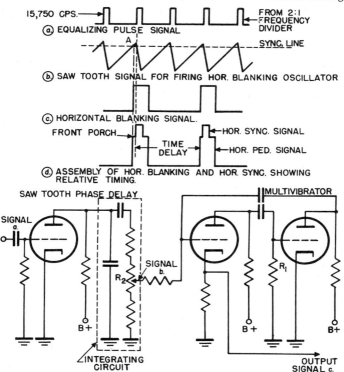

Figure 27. Generation of horizontal blanking pulses.

the time that the spot is returning from the right to the left side of the screen. The blanking signal also provides a "pedestal" on which the horizontal sync pulse is superimposed. The frequency of the blanking pulse is equal to the horizontal scanning rate, which is 15.75 kc. In other words, for each horizontal sync pulse there is one blanking pulse.

The horizontal blanking pulse precedes the horizontal sync pulse by a very short time interval as shown in Figure 27d.

This time interval is often called the "front porch". The front porch may be considered a safety factor to simplify the separation of the sync pulses from the blanking signals at the receiver. Under weak signal conditions, the start of the sync and

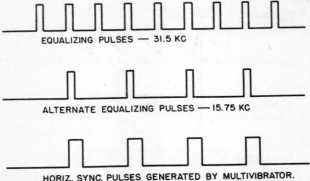

EQUALIZING PULSES — 31.5 KC

ALTERNATE EQUALIZING PULSES — 15.75 KC

HORIZ. SYNC. PULSES GENERATED BY MULTIVIBRATOR.

Figure 28. Relative phase of equalizing and horizontal sync pulses.

blanking pulses would not be distinguishable if the pulses were to occur close together.

Since the horizontal sync pulse must occur in phase with the equalizing pulse as shown in Figure 27a and d, means must be provided for keying the blanking pulse shaper circuit a short time interval before the sync pulse occurs. A method for accomplishing this is shown in Figure 27. The equalizing pulses are fed to a 2:1 frequency divider which produces pulses occurring at 15.75 kc. These pulses are then coupled to an integrating circuit which changes their shape to a sawtooth, as shown in Figure 27b. If a point on this sawtooth voltage such as A, is used to trigger the blanking pulse shaper circuit, the blanking pulse will occur a short time before the equalizing and horizontal sync pulses. A multivibrator is used as the blanking pulse shaper. The pulse width is determined by R-1 and the "front porch" interval is set by the adjustment of the voltage divider R-2. R-2 determines the point on the rising cawtooth at which the multivibrator will trigger.

4-22 The Horizontal Synchronizing Pulse. Horizontal sync pulses occur 15,750 times per second, which is half the frequency of the equalizing pulses. The 2:1 frequency divider which was used to obtain a keying signal for the blanking pulse shaper also feeds a signal to the horizontal pulse shaper. The relative phases of the equalizing and horizontal sync pulses are shown in Figure 28. In the top figure are the equalizing pulses occurring at 31.5 kc. The 2:1 divider circuit produces alternate

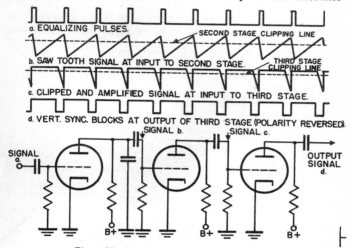

a. EQUALIZING PULSES.

SECOND STAGE CLIPPING LINE

b. SAW TOOTH SIGNAL AT INPUT TO SECOND STAGE.

THIRD STAGE CLIPPING LINE

c. CLIPPED AND AMPLIFIED SIGNAL AT INPUT TO THIRD STAGE.

d. VERT. SYNC. BLOCKS AT OUTPUT OF THIRD STAGE (POLARITY REVERSED).

SIGNAL b.   SIGNAL c.

SIGNAL a.   OUTPUT SIGNAL d.

Figure 29. Formation of the vertical sync signal.

equalizing pulses occurring at 15.75 kc. These key another multivibrator whose output pulse width is set for the wider sync pulses shown in the bottom of the figure.

4-23 The Vertical Synchronizing Signal. The vertical sync signal is made up of a series of six wide pulses. The vertical sync signal is serrated, or divided into these six smaller pulses, so as not to interrupt the regularly timed firing of the horizontal scanning system during the transmission of the vertical sync signal. The serrated vertical sync signal is formed by integrating the equalizing pulses to form a sawtooth voltage as shown in Figure 29. The sawtooth signal is then clipped in two successive amplifier stages to produce the desired wave form.

4-24 The Vertical Blanking Signal. The vertical blanking signal performs a function similar to that of the horizontal blanking pulse. It is often referred to as the vertical pedestal signal. It blanks out the scanning beam during the time that the beam is retracing from the bottom to the top of the picture. The vertical blanking signal is a wide pulse occurring once each field or 60 times per second. A multivibrator, synchronized by the 60 cycle timing signal from the last frequency divider stage, is used to generate the pulse.

4-25 Combining the Sync and Blanking Signals. Two 60 cycle keying signals are required in order to combine the various

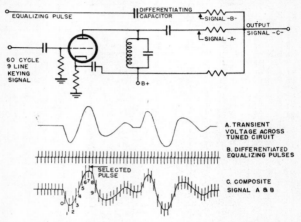

Figure 30. Forming the 60-cycle, three-line keying signal.

pulses produced in the shaper circuits. One keying signal interrupts the train of horizontal sync pulses for a time interval corresponding to nine horizontal sync pulses. During this interval, a group of eighteen equalizing pulses is inserted. The other 60 cycle keying signal adds six serrated vertical sync pulses to the six center equalizing pulses (of the eighteen inserted between the horizontal sync pulses).

The first of the 60 cycle keying signals is the signal obtained from the last frequency divider. It is called a 60 cycle, 9-line keying signal, because it interrupts the horizontal sync pulses for a period of nine lines. The other keying signal is called a 60 cycle 3-line keying signal because it interrupts the equalizing signal for a period of six pulses (corresponding to three lines). The timing of the leading edge of the 60 cycle 3-line keying signal is very critical and must be accurate within a time interval corresponding to the width of an equalizing pulse. This timing accuracy can be obtained by firing the 60 cycle 3-line signal from the leading edge of a particular equalizing pulse. It is difficult, however, to make certain that synchronization occurs on

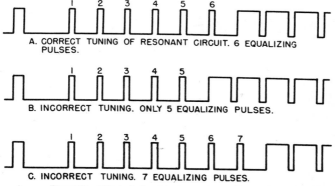

A. CORRECT TUNING OF RESONANT CIRCUIT. 6 EQUALIZING PULSES.

B. INCORRECT TUNING. ONLY 5 EQUALIZING PULSES.

C. INCORRECT TUNING. 7 EQUALIZING PULSES.

Figure 31. Effect of circuit tuning on composite synchronizing signal.

the correct equalizing pulse out of the 525 which are generated during each 60 cycle period.

The method by which the 60 cycle 3-line keying signal is correctly synchronized may be understood by referring to Figure 30. The equalizing pulses are fed to the plate through a differentiating circuit. The differentiated equalizing pulses appear as in Figure 30b. At the same time the 60 cycle 9-line keying signal is fed to the grid. This keying signal shock excites the tuned circuit in the plate and causes transient oscillations as shown in the waveform of Figure 30a. The transient oscillations and the differentiated pulses are combined in the plate circuit. If the resonant circuit is correctly tuned, the 7th equalizing pulse which occurs after the 60 cycle 9-line keying pulse will appear at the top of the transient and becomes the 60 cycle 3-line keying signal. Correct tuning of the resonant circuit enables just 6 equalizing pulses to be keyed in later, as shown in Figure 31a. If the circuit is incorrectly tuned so that an equalizing pulse other than the 7th is at the top of the transient, an incorrect number of equalizing pulses will appear in the final signal as shown in Figure 31b and c.

4-26 Insertion of the Equalizing Pulse into the Horizontal Sync Signal. The horizontal sync pulses are interrupted for an interval of nine lines. This is accomplished by feeding the horizontal sync pulses into a modulator stage (tube D) as shown in

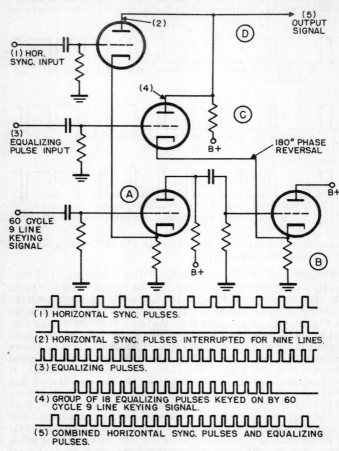

(1) HORIZONTAL SYNC. PULSES.

(2) HORIZONTAL SYNC. PULSES INTERRUPTED FOR NINE LINES.

(3) EQUALIZING PULSES.

(4) GROUP OF 18 EQUALIZING PULSES KEYED ON BY 60 CYCLE 9 LINE KEYING SIGNAL.

(5) COMBINED HORIZONTAL SYNC. PULSES AND EQUALIZING PULSES.

Figure 32. Circuit used to insert equalizing pulses into horizontal sync pulses.

Figure 32. The 60 cycle 9-line keying signal is fed into tube A. The keying signal from tube A is fed to the cathode of tube D and cuts it off for nine horizontal lines. At the same time the

equalizing pulses are fed into another modulator, tube C. The
60 cycle 9-line keying signal is fed into the cathode of tube C,

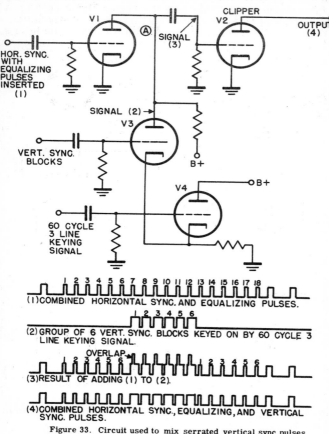

(1) COMBINED HORIZONTAL SYNC. AND EQUALIZING PULSES.

(2) GROUP OF 6 VERT. SYNC. BLOCKS KEYED ON BY 60 CYCLE 3
LINE KEYING SIGNAL.

(3) RESULT OF ADDING (1) TO (2).

(4) COMBINED HORIZONTAL SYNC., EQUALIZING, AND VERTICAL
SYNC. PULSES.

Figure 33. Circuit used to mix serrated vertical sync pulses
with combined horizontal and equalizing pulses.

180° out of phase with the signal that is injected into the cathode
of tube D. This causes tube C to conduct for a period corresponding to 18 equalizing pulses. The plates of the two modulators, C and D, are tied together to form the combined horizontal
and equalizing pulse signal.

4-27 Inserting The Vertical Sync Pulse. The 60 cycle 3-line keying signal is used to select the six vertical sync blocks. It is fed into the grid of tube V4 (Figure 33) whose cathode is tied to the cathode of V3. This puts the keying signal on V3 and causes it to conduct for a period equal to six vertical sync blocks. Therefore, even though a continuous chain of vertical sync blocks

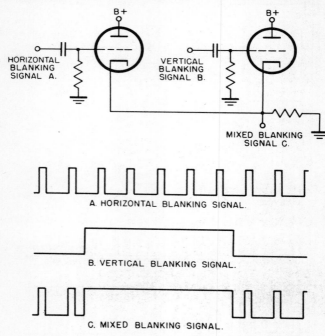

A. HORIZONTAL BLANKING SIGNAL.

B. VERTICAL BLANKING SIGNAL.

C. MIXED BLANKING SIGNAL.

Figure 34. Circuit used to mix horizontal and vertical blanking signals.

are fed to the grid of V3, only six blocks appear at the plate of V3 as shown in waveform 2.

The serrated vertical sync signal consisting of the six blocks is then combined with the horizontal sync and equalizing pulses. The horizontal sync and equalizing pulses which were previously combined are fed to the grid of V1. These are shown as waveform 1 in Figure 33. At point A, where the modulator tubes V1 and V3 are tied together, a combined signal such as shown in waveform 3 of Figure 33 results. The signal is the combination of waveforms 1 and 2. The equalizing pulses which overlap the vertical serrated pulses are clipped off by tube V2, giving the complete synchronizing signal shown in waveform 4 of Figure 33.

4-28 Mixing the Horizontal and Vertical Blanking Signals. The horizontal blanking signal, Figure 34, is modulated by the vertical blanking signal so as to blank it off during the vertical retrace interval. This is accomplished simply by tying the cathodes of the modulator tubes together as shown in the figure, and results in the waveform shown in Figure 34c. The combined blanking signals and sync signals are mixed later in the video mixing amplifiers.

MONITORS

4-29 Picture Monitors. The picture monitor is essentially a television receiver without a radio frequency section. Picture monitors are located at various points in the television station to check the quality of the image.

The sweep circuits of a studio picture monitor, which is used to check the pictures on more than one camera, are synchronized by driving pulses fed directly from the sync generator. In this way, there is no interruption of the scanning while switching the monitor from one camera signal to another. Other types of picture monitors receive both the synchronizing and picture signals together in order that they may provide adequate monitoring of the over-all signals before they are sent to the transmitter. Still other monitors are equipped with shading controls when used with iconoscope cameras.

Monitors use tubes of 5, 7, 10, 12, and 15 inch diameter. The small tubes are convenient for monitors used with portable remote pick-up equipment. The larger monitor tubes are preferable in studio control equipment. They make viewing more comfortable for the video engineer and the program director who must observe the camera picture while directing the program. The larger monitors are also used in the master control equipment, the film camera chains, and in the transmitter room. The picture monitor (Figure 35), used in the studio control room for checking the camera signal, is the most complete monitor found in the station. Its functions are threefold:

1. It contains a picture tube with video and sweep circuits to monitor the outgoing picture signal.

2. It contains a small three or five inch waveform monitor

Figure 35. Picture monitor. (courtesy DuMont)

which allows observation of either the input or output video signal. This monitor may be considered a cathode-ray oscillograph whose sweep is fixed at either of two frequencies: half the horizontal frequency or half the vertical frequency. This permits the viewing of two lines or two fields.

3. Four of the controls of the image-orthicon camera are located in the monitor. These are the beam current, the beam focus, the target voltage and the photocathode focus controls. These controls determine the power supply voltages applied to the camera tube. They are located in the picture monitor because the voltages applied to the camera tube can be most accurately set while observing their effect on the picture.

A block diagram of the picture monitor section is shown in Figure 36. The circuits used are much the same as those found in the 5 inch monitor used as a camera viewfinder.

4-30 Video Waveform Monitor. The video waveform monitor, located in the control room monitor, permits examination of the camera output signal at either the vertical or horizontal frequency. The video waveform monitor is a cathode-ray oscillo-

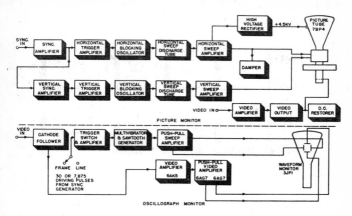

Figure 36. Block diagram of picture and oscillograph monitor.

graph whose sweep frequencies are set at either 30 cycles or 7,875 cycles.

The sweep for the waveform monitor is generated by a multivibrator. The multivibrator is triggered by either 30 cycle vertical or 7,875 cycle horizontal pulses, received from the sync generator. Either frequency is selected by the sweep frequency switch. These pulses are amplified by a trigger amplifier before being applied to the multivibrator. Another section of the sweep frequency switch changes the time constant of the charging circuit in the multivibrator for horizontal and vertical operation. Sawtooth voltages of either line or frame frequency are thereby produced in the plate circuit. Two lines or two fields can thus be observed on the waveform monitor.

The video amplifier of the waveform monitor consists of a 6AK5 amplifier followed by a push-pull stage using two 6AG7s.

MIXING AND DISTRIBUTION AMPLIFIER

4-31 The mixing and distribution amplifier combines the video signal from the camera with the blanking and composite sync signals from the synchronizing generator. Provision is usually made in this unit to distribute the combined signal to several outputs, each of which is isolated from the other. The mixing and distribution amplifier is also used as a distribution ampli-

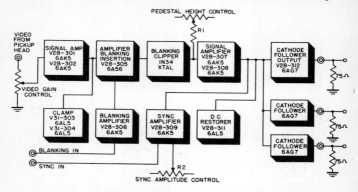

Figure 37. Block diagram of mixing and distribution amplifier.

fier if the video and synchronizing signals from a single source must be fed to several outlets.

4-32 Mixing the Video and Sync Signals. A block diagram of the circuit used for combining the video and sync signals is shown in Figure 37. The video signal from the camera is fed through a co-axial line to the video gain control. The camera signal is amplified in a two-stage video amplifier (tubes V28-301 and V28-302), having a gain of approximately 15. The signal is then fed to the grid of V28-305, which is the mixer stage. Simultaneously, blanking pulses are fed into V28-306 and amplified to a 5 volt peak-to-peak level. These blanking pulses are then applied to the suppressor grid of mixer tube V28-305. The video and blanking signals applied to the grid and suppressor of the mixer, respectively, appear as in Figure 38a and b. In the common plate load of V28-305, the video and blanking signals are mixed and appear as in Figure 38c. A 1N34 crystal rectifier follows the mixing tube to clip any portion of the blanking signal which rises above a d-c level determined by the crystal bias control R-1. This fixes the blanking (or black) level in the video signal.

The signal which now contains blanking pulses is amplified by V28-307 and V28-308 in parallel. The parallel combination is used to provide sufficient voltage swing at the plates without having to drive the grids over a range great enough to cause appreciable non-linearity.

Sync signals at a 1 volt level enter the monitor control from the synchronizing generator and are applied to the grid of

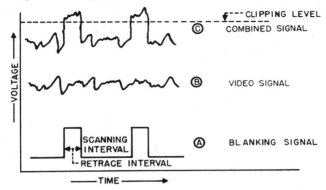

Figure 38. How blanking signal is combined with video signal.

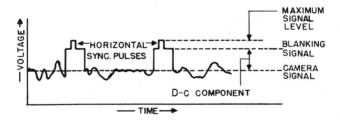

Figure 39. The completed composite video signal.

V28-309. The plate load of V28-309 is common to V28-307 and V28-3-8. Mixing is therefore effected across this common plate load. The combined signal at this point appears as in Figure 39. The sync level is controlled by variation of the grid bias resistor R-2 on V28-309. To meet the requirements of the standard video signal, the sync is adjusted to equal 25% of the peak-to-peak amplitude of the composite signal.

The combined video signal is coupled to the outgoing transmission line through a cathode-follower V28-312. V28-311 is a d-c restorer on the grid of V28-312 which reinserts the d-c level lost in coupling the video signal through the a-c amplifiers. By paralleling several cathode-followers in the output, several isolated output points are obtained.

THE VIDEO TRANSMITTER

4-33 The video or picture transmitter generates an amplitude modulated signal and operates on a carrier frequency in the television band between 50 and 216 megacycles. There are twelve television channels in this band of frequencies, each six megacycles wide. In the 6 Mc channel both picture information and sound information must be transmitted. The picture signals occupy 4.25 megacycles of this channel, while the sound signals use only 25 kilocycles.

4-34 Sideband Suppression. In normal double side band transmission, as used in standard broadcasting, the modulating frequencies appear above and below the carrier frequency. If double side band transmission for television were used, an 8.5 Mc band would be required, since the video signal contains frequencies from about 30 cycles to 4.25 megacycles. To limit the width of the television signal sufficiently so that it will fit into the assigned channel, a special modulating method is used. This method is known as vestigial sideband transmission. In this system only a portion of the lower side band of the picture information is transmitted as shown in Figure 40. The picture carrier is placed 1.25 Mc above the lower edge of the assigned 6 Mc channel. The entire upper sideband of picture information is transmitted in the 4.25 megacycle region above the picture carrier. The sound carrier is located 4.5 megacycles from the picture carrier. This leaves a frequency band of 0.25 megacycles between the picture and sound signals. The last quarter megacycle is used as a guard band between the sound carrier and the picture signals in the next channel.

In the 1.25 megacycle region below the picture carrier it is possible to attenuate or reduce the lower side band energy substantially to zero by the time the lower edge of the 6 Mc channel is reached. Some types of transmitters accomplish this attenuation of the lower side band by tuning out these frequencies in the radio frequency amplifier stages. Other forms of transmitters pass the carrier frequency with the double side band modulation signals up to the final power amplifier stage. A filter for attenuating the lower sideband frequencies is then inserted in the transmission line between the final amplifier stage and the antenna. Whichever method is used, the video trans-

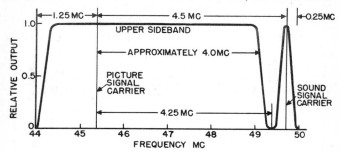

Figure 40. Single sideband television signal.

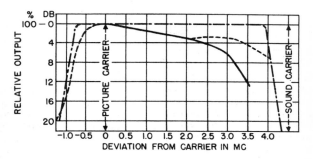

——— FCC SPEC. ANY CURVE PERMITTED BETWEEN O AND 1.25 MC.
- - - - RMA SPEC. ANY CURVE PERMITTED BETWEEN O AND 1.25 MC.
-·-·— IDEAL

Figure 41. RMA and FCC specified transmission channels.

mitter should have a frequency response characteristic represented by the ideal curve shown in Figure 41. Also shown are the practical standards for the response characteristic of a video transmitter as proposed by the FCC and RMA.

4-35 Modulation Methods. There are three basic sections of the television transmitter, namely (1) the radio frequency generator, (2) the modulator, and (3) the power amplifiers. Two methods of modulation are used. One method is high-level modulation used in the television transmitter shown in the block diagram of Figure 42. In this system, the radio frequency is generated at a lower frequency than the carrier, and then multiplied to obtain the carrier frequency. The r-f carrier is then amplified in a series of r-f amplifier stages, sharply tuned to

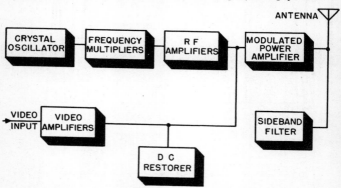

Figure 42. Block diagram of high level modulated transmitter.

the carrier frequency. Simultaneously, the video signal from the studio is successively increased in several video amplifier stages, until a signal level, sufficient to modulate the final amplifier, is reached. The undesired portion of the lower sideband is removed by a high-level filter in the antenna circuit. This system is called high-level modulation because the r-f carrier is modulated in the last high power amplifier stage.

In the low level modulated transmitter (Figure 43), the stages which generate the radio frequency carrier are similar to those used in the high-level type. At the output of the frequency multiplier stages, the carrier level is only a few watts. Video modulation takes place at this point. The modulated r-f carrier is then amplified by a series of wideband stages. The pass band of each stage is so tuned that the unwanted portion of the vestigial sideband is removed.

Both high level and low level modulation are used in commercial transmitters. Each system has advantages and limitations. The wide band video amplifiers capable of supplying a video signal of large amplitude and high power for high level modulation are costly and inefficient. Tubes capable of delivering the modulation power have relatively high interelectrode capacitances and waste much of the energy at the video frequencies. On the other hand, since a large number of wide band r-f amplifiers are needed in low level modulation systems, great care

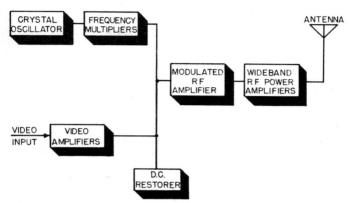

Figure 43. Block diagram of low level modulated transmitter.

must be exercised to keep the transmitter tuned so that the band-pass characteristic is adequate for satisfactory picture resolution. In high level modulation, the picture quality is affected only by the response of the video amplifiers which remain stable over long periods. Only one final r-f power amplifier stage and the vestigial filter need be tuned with high level modulation. In low level modulation, misadjustment of any of the wide-band r-f amplifiers seriously affects the picture quality, and may even reinsert the unwanted portion of the vestigial sideband.

It is apparent from the foregoing discussion that the three important considerations concerning the design of video transmitters are the video power required for modulation, the tuning of the r-f power amplifier, and the use of either a vestigial sideband filter or vestigial sideband tuned amplifiers.

4-36 Generation of the Carrier Frequency. The principal problem encountered in generating the carrier frequency is that of maintaining the required frequency stability. The frequency stability is specified by the FCC as being plus or minus 0.002% of the assigned carrier frequency. A temperature controlled low frequency crystal is usually employed in order to assure this stability. Since it is difficult to grind quarts crystals which will be stable at frequencies above 10 Mc, it is standard practice to start with a crystal frequency of about 5 Mc and use a series

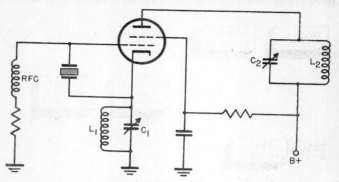

Figure 44. Tri-tet oscillator.

of frequency multiplier stages to reach the desired carrier frequency.

4-37 Tri-Tet Oscillator Circuit. The tri-tet oscillator is commonly employed in television transmitters and is shown in basic form in Figure 44. A quartz crystal is used between the control grid and the cathode of the tube. Tuned circuits are employed in the plate and cathode. When the tuned circuit L1-C1 is tuned to a considerably higher frequency than that of the crystal, oscillations take place. These oscillations occur at the resonant frequency of the crystal. They also cause variations in the control grid potential, causing the r-f signal to appear in amplified form in the plate circuit. The plate resonant circuit L2-C2 may be tuned to the fundamental (crystal) frequency or to a multiple of that frequency.

4-38 Multiplier Stages. The frequency multiplier stages are conventional class "C" amplifiers in the low level stages. A typical two stage frequency multiplier is shown in Figure 45. The tank circuit in the plate is tuned to twice or triple the incoming frequency on the grid, depending upon the degree of multiplication desired. In the multiplier stages, the tuned circuits are made up of conventional capacitors and inductors. The frequency multiplying stages are generally of the pentode type since they are more efficient for this purpose. In high-level modulation transmitters, the desired carrier frequency is generally obtained in the stage preceding the final power output

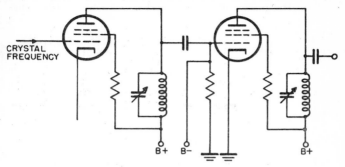

Figure 45. Simplified schematic of frequency multiplying stages.

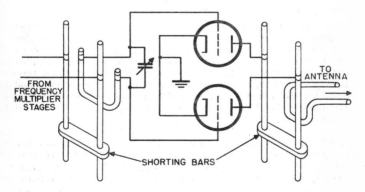

Figure 46. Transmission line tuned push-pull r-f amplifier stage.

amplifier, which acts as a non-multiplying stage. The required r-f power is gradually built up in the multiplying stages.

4-39 High Level Modulation of Power Amplifier. In a high level modulation transmitter only the final power amplifier is modulated by the video signal. Figure 46 shows a typical power amplifier. The tuned circuits used in this final stage are generally made up of transmission line conductors rather than conventional capacitors and inductors. The distributed capacitance and inductance of the transmission lines are tuned by cutting the lines to the proper length, determined by the carrier frequency. The push-pull arrangement is used with triode tubes

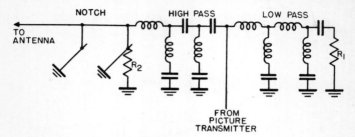

Figure 47. Vestigial sideband filter.

to simplify the problem of neutralization. Small air condensers for neutralizing are built into the transmission lines.

The grid circuit of the final power amplifier is tuned to the frequency of the r-f carrier. The video modulator is also coupled into the grid and modulates the carrier frequency. The modulation of the carrier by the 4.5 Mc video signal produces sidebands extending for 4.5 Mc above and below the carrier frequency. The plate circuit of the final stage must be broad-band tuned for the carrier and the sidebands which are generated. The amplified wideband signal is coupled from the plate circuit to the antenna.

4-40 Vestigial Sideband Filter. The vestigial sideband filter is a permanently tuned r-f filter which is inserted into the output circuit of the final power amplifier of a high-level modulated transmitter. The filter removes a portion of the lower sideband of the modulated carrier and passes on to the antenna a signal which occupies a bandwidth of less than 6 megacycles.

A schematic diagram of the vestigial sideband filter is shown in Figure 47. It consists of three filter sections. A low-pass filter absorbs the undesired energy in the lower sideband and dissipates it in resistor R1. The desired signals are then passed through a high pass filter. A notch filter is located between the antenna and high pass filter. The notch filter is tuned so that the load resistor R2 dissipates all energy at a frequency which is 0.25 megacycles below the lower limit of the channel.

The effects of the three filters on the transmission characteristic of the system is shown in Figure 48. Curve A is the transmission characteristic of the low pass filter. The frequencies below the picture carrier are readily passed by this

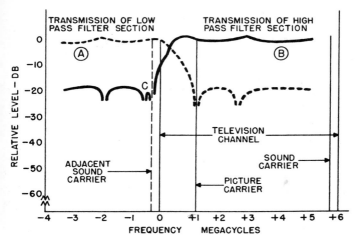

Figure 48. Transmission characteristics of vestigial sideband filter.

filter. These frequencies are then dissipated in the resistor R1. The high pass filter is tuned to accept the frequencies above the picture carrier (curve B) and pass them on to the antenna. The notching filter absorbs energy at the adjacent sound carrier frequency (point C) and dissipates it in resistor R2. The purpose of the notching filter is to eliminate all possible interference with the adjacent sound channel.

4-41 Low Level Modulation R-F Amplifiers. The r-f amplifiers used with the low level modulation system must meet a number of special requirements. Instead of being tuned to a single resonant frequency, as they are with high level modulation, each stage must have a wide band response and linear output between the limits of modulation. In addition to this, suppression of the lower sideband must take place in the r-f amplifiers.

Adequate bandwidth for the video signals — about 4 Mc — is attained through the use of overcoupled circuits. The response

characteristic of an overcoupled circuit is shown in Figure 49.
Figure 50 shows the circuit arrangement of a wide band amplifier as used in r-f power stages. Tuned transmission lines are

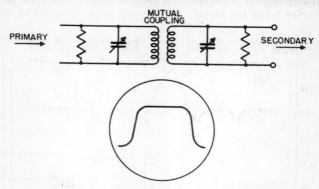

Figure 49. Overcoupled circuit and its response characteristic.

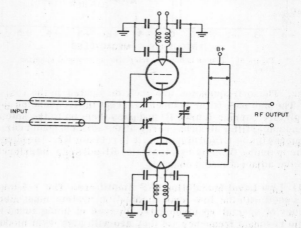

Figure 50. Wideband r-f amplifier circuit.

employed in the grid and plate circuits. The coupling and loading may be varied in order to produce a wideband response
characteristic.

Variation in coupling is accomplished by changing the physical position of the secondary with respect to the primary. This is usually done by means of a worm drive gear system. Figure 51 shows the physical arrangement of the r-f power tubes and

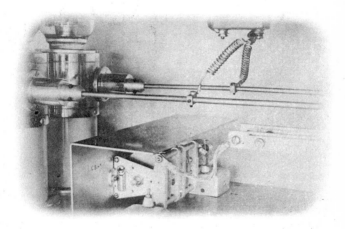

Figure 51. Worm drive mechanism for changing coupling in r-f amplifier.

transmission line elements. On the right is the gear drive which changes the coupling between the tuned lines.

The wideband r-f amplifier stages are tuned so that the upper sideband of the television information is included in the passband characteristic of the tuned circuits. The carrier is positioned on the edge of the low frequency end of the passband and the circuits are adjusted to give a smooth frequency response characteristic over the 4 Mc upper sideband. This adjustment produces a single sideband transmission system, since the tuned circuits reject the lower sideband. The tuned circuit in each amplifier stage contributes to the overall attenuation of the unwanted frequencies.

4-42 Modulators. The modulator section of the transmitter consists of several stages of video amplification, a sync expander, and a circuit for reinserting the d-c component which is lost in the capacitive coupling between amplifiers. In high level modulated transmitters, about 600 volts of peak-to-peak video signal is required to modulate the grid of the final power

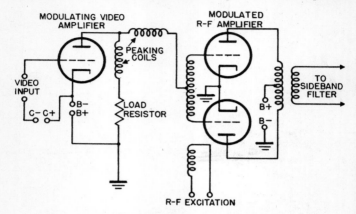

Figure 52. Modulated Class B amplifier.

amplifier stage. 150 volts or less is necessary to properly modulate a transmitter using the low level system.

All video amplifier stages must have a frequency response of 30 kc to above 4 megacycles. Standard practice is to feed 1 volt of video signal from the studio to the video amplifiers. The required video gain then depends on the power level at which modulation takes place.

4-43 Modulating the R-F Signal. When the video signal has been increased to the voltage level required, it is coupled to the r-f carrier through the grid of the modulated stage. Fundamentally, the modulator stage is a class "B" amplifier, as shown in Figure 52. The tube is biased in the vicinity of cutoff. Figure 53 shows the ideal case where the grid bias is adjusted so that the signal excursions on the grid maintain the output waveform over the linear portion of the grid plate transfer characteristic. Should the bias be excessive, operation will take place on the lower knee of the curve, and the resulting non-linearity will cause compression in that part of the signal which represents the white picture area. When the bias is not as great as the tube linearity will permit, sync compression may take place. Sync compression is the result of operation on the upper knee of the transfer characteristic, and when present the sync

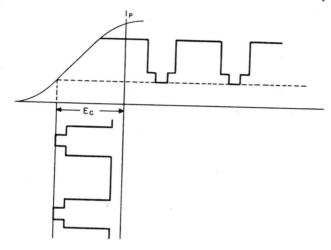

Figure 53. Grid characteristic of Class B modulated amplifier.

level will occupy less than 25% of the composite video signal.

The video signal amplitude at the modulator stage is of prime importance since upon this factor depends the modulation percentage level of the television carrier. The FCC standards state that the sync pulses must occupy 25% of the total r-f signal amplitude, and that the transmitter be modulated to at least 15% of the peak level of a white picture. These modulation limits are shown in Figure 54 for a black picture with a white line. In order to operate within these prescribed limits, which permit an effective modulation capability of only 85%, it is necessary to drive the transmitter with a greater sync-to-picture ratio. Analysis of the proportions of Figure 54 shows that the input video signal must consist of 29.5% sync with respect to the peak-to-peak video signal. A sync stretcher, such as described elsewhere in this section is incorporated in the circuit between the video amplifier and modulator to expand the sync and compensate for the loss in sync-pulse amplitude in the succeeding modulator and power amplifier stages.

4-44 D-C Restoration. The d-c component of the video signal which represents the average brightness of the televised scene is lost when the signal is passed through the video amplifier

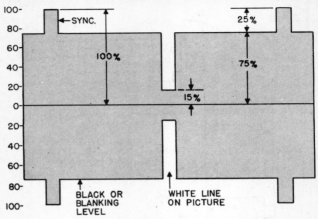

Figure 54. Modulation limits of transmitter.

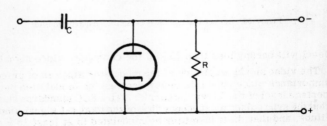

Figure 55. Circuit of diode d-c restoration circuit.

stages to the modulator stage. The d-c level of a television signal can be reinserted by using a d-c restoration circuit, such as shown in Figure 55. By making the RC time constant of the circuit much greater that the time interval of one line of the television picture, a voltage is built up across the diode load resistor which is about equal to the peak value of the video signal (the level of the tips of the sync signal). This voltage is applied to the grid of the modulator as an additional biasing potential. As shown in Figure 56, the effect of the d-c restorer is to refer the tips of the sync signals to the same level. Without d-c reinsertion, the video signal would center itself about the bias level and the sync tips would assume different levels.

The d-c restorer brings all the sync pulses to the same bias

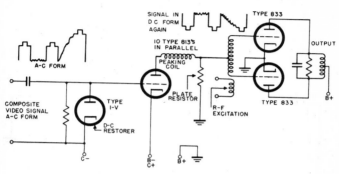

Figure 56. D-C reinsertion in grid circuit of video modulator

level at the grid of the modulator. The tips of the sync pulses thus serve as a reference level for the black and white portions of the video signal. The reference level must be preserved from

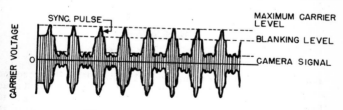

Figure 57. Modulated television carrier.

this point on in the transmitter. The modulator is therefore direct coupled to the grid of the r-f power amplifier. Once the r-f signal has been modulated by the video signal with the d-c level properly restored, the sync and blanking levels remain fixed. Any variation in the modulation envelop, caused by the video signal, will correspond to changes in the d-c background brightness of the picture (Figure 57).

In addition to restoring the d-c signal, the d-c restorer, by holding the sync tips at a fixed level, maintains the modulated r-f signal at a constant peak power level.

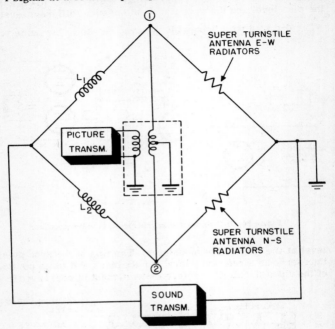

Figure 58. Circuit of diplexer.

4-45 Coupling the Transmitter to the Antenna. It is common practice to use the same antenna for both the picture and sound transmitters. If both of these signals are fed directly to the antenna, sound signals would enter the picture circuits of the transmitter, and the picture signal into the sound circuits. Cross-coupling of the signals is prevented by using a network known as a "diplexer".

The diplexer has two reactors which form two arms of a bridge circuit. Figure 58. The other two arms of the bridge are formed by the elements of the antenna radiators. The picture transmitter is push-pull coupled to points 1 and 2 of the bridge. The impedance of L-1 is made equal to L-2. The impedances of the elements of the radiators are also equal. The bridge is therefor in balance and the potential at point 1 equals the potential at point 2. Since the picture transmitter feeds two points of equal potential with respect to the sound transmitter, no sound signal can feed back into the picture circuits.

The sound transmitter is fed into the circuit across the mid-

Figure 59. Interior of diplexer. (courtesy RCA)

points of the antenna and the inductances L-1 and L-2. Since the potentials at points 1 and 2 are equal, no picture signal can pass into the sound circuits. Thus, while the signals from the two transmitters are fed simultaneously to the same antenna, the output circuits are effectively isolated from each other. A view of the transmission lines elements (L-1 and L-2) of a diplexer is shown in Figure 59.

THE SOUND EQUIPMENT

4-46 The sound equipment used in a television station is very similar to that used in a broadcasting station, and therefore will only be treated briefly here.

The sound pick-up equipment consists of microphones, phonograph turntables, and motion picture film sound track recorders.

Figure 60. Sound control unit. (courtesy RCA)

Generally, the phonograph equipment is located in the studio control room where the program director and the technical operators coordinate the recorded sound with the television pick-up. Additional transcription turntables are located in the master control room for use when inserting background music into those programs where close synchronization is not required between the audio and the video. The sound track equipment used to reproduce audio signals recorded on film are also located in the master control room. Figure 60 shows a sound control unit with station announcement microphone and pick-up turntables located in the master control room.

4-47 Handling Sound Equipment. The sound pick-up equipment used on the studio floor requires special handling, since it is important that the microphones do not appear in the picture. The microphone is generally mounted on a long boom (Figure 61) and adjusted so as to be over the heads of the actors out of range of the camera. A number of microphones connected to amplifiers, adjusted for different gains can be coordinated with the perspective of the pick-up cameras to produce realistic sight and sound combinations. For example, when a switch is made from a close-up camera to a distant camera, a corresponding change in the sound level and quality must occur simultaneously with the change in cameras. Suitable frequency-

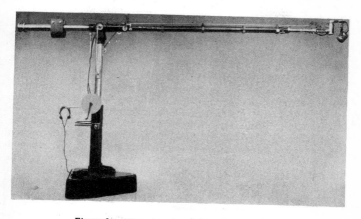

Figure 61. Microphone boom. (courtesy DuMont)

response filters are incorporated in the amplifier circuits to give the impression of a shift in distance from the scene.

4-48 Microphones. Three types of microphones are used with the "mike" boom in the studio and on remote pickups. These are called uni-directional, bi-directional, and non-directional. The uni-directional microphone is sensitive only to sound coming from a single direction. The speaker must talk into the sensitive side of the microphone. Any noise or voices coming from other directions are greatly attenuated. The bi-directional microphone has equal sensitivity at the front and back, but attenuates sounds coming from the sides. Two people can conveniently talk into one microphone of this type. The non-directional microphone is equally sensitive to sound from all directions.

The microphone converts sound energy into electrical signals. The electrical output from the microphone is fed to the sound control desk inside the control room. Each microphone is connected to a separate amplifier whose gain and frequency response can be controlled by the audio engineer. Since several microphones may be used in the studio, the engineer must maintain a volume balance between them by adjusting the gain of each amplifier. On the sound control board, the engineer has a series of switches by means of which he may turn on any combination of microphones and blend their outputs. He may also switch in the sound from phonograph of film pick-ups.

After the sound signal has been properly adjusted at the monitor desk, it is sent, via a separate line, to the audio transmitter.

4-49 The Sound Transmitter. The carrier frequency of the sound transmitter is 4.5 megacycles higher than the video frequency carrier. The sound accompanying television pictures is transmitted by frequency modulation.

The maximum frequency deviation permitted by the allocation for television sound is plus or minus 25 kc as compared to plus or minus 75 kc for standard FM broadcasting. The frequency deviation of the television sound is purposely limited to 25 kc to allow as much room as possible in the 6 megacycle television channel for the video signals. The fidelity of the television sound signal is as good as that of the standard FM signal, even though its frequency deviation is less. The frequency deviation is determined only by the loudness of the audio signal at the transmitter and not its frequency response.

The lineup of sections of the FM transmitter differs considerably from those in the AM transmitter. A block diagram of an FM transmitter is shown in Figure 62. The heart of the FM system is the reactance tube. This tube converts the audio signal coming from the studio into a frequency modulated signal. The reactance tube and its circuits are connected across the tank coil of an oscillator (such as a Hartley or Colpitts). If no audio signal is fed to the reactance tube, the oscillator generates its carrier frequency. When a signal of varying frequency and amplitude is applied to the grid of the reactance tube, variations in the reactance tube plate current occur. The plate current also flows through the oscillator tank circuit. The reactance tube circuit is so designed that the changing plate current effectively changes the value of inductance or capacity across the oscillator tank circuit. As this reactance changes with variations in the audio signal, the oscillator frequency continuously varies above and below the carrier frequency. The stronger the audio signal, the greater is the frequency deviation. The rapidity with which the signal deviates from the carrier frequency is determined by the frequency of the audio signal. High frequency sounds cause the frequency modulated signals to vary more rapidly.

The mean or carrier frequency of the oscillator is not the final carrier frequency of the transmitter, nor are the frequency deviations at this point in the transmitter as high as the allowable 25 kc. For example, the mean frequency of the oscillator

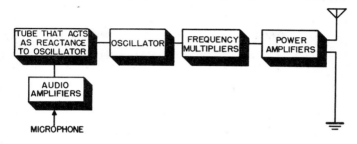

Figure 62. Block diagram of f-m sound transmitter.

may be only 2 Mc. At this point in the circuit the volume of the audio signal may be controlled so that the 2 Mc carrier deviates plus or minus 5 kc. If this signal is fed into a frequency doubler stage, the carrier frequency will be 4 Mc and the frequency deviation 10 kc. Successive frequency multiplier stages bring the carrier frequency up to the desired sound carrier with a frequency deviation of 25 kc.

Except for the reactance tube circuit which converts the audio signal into a frequency modulated signal, the components of the FM transmitter are the same as those described for the video transmitter. The frequency multiplying stages and the power amplifiers are similar in the sound and picture transmitters.

MASTER CONTROL

4-50 A simple television station system was shown in Figure 1. It consisted of a single camera and associated control equipment which fed the signal to the transmitter. Large-scale television station operation requires a far more complex arrangement of equipment than shown in this simple system. To handle a full day of programming, more than one studio is required, each equipped with several cameras. A great deal of television program material comes from movie film, so that provision must be made for extra film cameras. Other programs are televised remotely and transmitted to a control room at the station before being put on the air. Many stations use network programs to fill some of their broadcast time. The integration of all of these facilities requires a central monitoring point through which programs pass before transmission. This centrally located point in the television station is called the master control room. The complexity of the master control depends upon the number of studios, film cameras, and remote facilities which the station has available.

A typical small television station installation is shown in Figure 63. Here three studios A, B, and C, are available, two for live talent operations, and a third for film pick-up. Shown in dotted lines are two remote program sources, typically used for sports pickup and similar field activities. Also indicated is a source and output for network programs. Finally, the output to the transmitter is shown.

The master control shown in Figure 63 must accept signals from as many as six sources and furnish signals to either the transmitter, the network outlet, or both. While all of these facilities will seldom be in use at one time, situations will arise when all of the master control equipment is necessary. The control room must be designed to meet such an emergency.

An example of how all the station facilities shown in Figure 63 could be used simultaneously is as follows. A live talent program could originate in Studio A, which would require the output of Studio C (the film studio) for portions of the program. An advertiser could be viewing the rehearsal of a new program, scheduled for subsequent use, emanating from Studio B. Remote source 1 could be feeding a sports event to the network. The rehearsal of a new remote program could also be in progress, requiring transmission of signals from remote pickup 2 to master control for distribution to viewing rooms, where the possibilities of the program can be evaluated.

It is easy to see that the master control room which is adequate to cope with such a typical situation will call for a relatively large complement of complex equipment. A listing of the functions that such a master control room must perform gives some idea of the type and amount of equipment necessary.

4-51 Master Control Functions. The following is a list of functions that must be performed by master control.

1. From the synchronizing generator, usually located in the master control room, driving and blanking pulses must be fed to all local studios.

2. Picture signals derived from local studios must have synchronizing information added to them at master control before

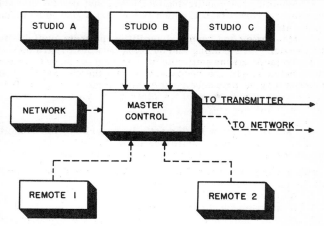

Figure 63. Block diagram of facilities of a small television station.

they are fed to a network or to the transmitter. Remote and incoming network programs which are furnished complete with synchronizing information must pass through master control without any additional synchronizing information being added. However, if the incoming sync signal is distorted, provision must be made to "clean it up".

3. Provision for phasing the synchronizing generator pulses to suit the needs of film projectors must be included.

4. When remote or network programs are contemplated, the vertical synchronizing information from these remote sources must be properly related in phase and frequency to those of the local synchronizing generator, so that switching from local to remote and from remote to local generators may be accomplished without affecting receivers tuned to the station.

5. Facilities for the monitoring and selecting of the proper video channel must be incorporated so that the transmitter or network outlet may be given the required program at the correct signal level and at the proper time. In other words, master control must have a picture monitor for each source of signal. If,

for example, the program on the air combines signals from two sources (say, live talent and film), a picture coming from each source must appear on a separate monitor at master control. At the cue of the director, the master control operator can switch one or the other picture on the air.

6. Selecting and monitoring facilities must also be available for the "preview" signal, which is the next signal to be placed on the air.

7. Monitoring and terminal facilities must be available for the servicing of incoming and outgoing network programs.

8. To facilitate the setting up of the foregoing three functions, video patch panels are necessary so that the several program sources may be properly routed through monitoring facilities to the transmitter, as well as directed to viewing rooms and executive offices.

4-52 Master Control Equipment. In describing the complex master control room facilities, it is convenient to follow a hypothetical signal from its source to its final destination.

Nine major units and two control desks are required to handle all the master control operations.

1. A standard synchronizing generator.
2. A stand-by synchronizing generator.
3. A rack containing power supplies for the synchronizing distribution amplifiers.
4. Sync distribution amplifiers.
5. Remote facilities. This includes a bridging amplifier, sync phasing unit, and sync stretching unit which removes distortion from the sync signal.
6. On-The-Air amplifier distribution system.
7. Preview amplifier distribution system.
8. A trouble-shooting monitor which can be patched into any point in the master control system.
9. Power supplies for the video distribution system.

The block diagram of Figure 64 shows how these nine pieces of equipment are arranged in rack-form. Figure 65 shows the On-The-Air and Preview desks which are located at master control.

The equipment listed above is sufficient to handle as many as six local studio and six remote or network programs, and provides suitable output to the transmitter, outgoing network program, on-the-air, preview, and rehearsal feeds to client rooms, executive offices, and return feeds to all studios. Each studio is arranged to have three video coaxial lines between the studio and the master control room. One coaxial line is used to provide the studio camera output to master control, and the other two coaxial lines are used to provide return feeds from master

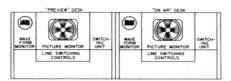

SYNC. DISTRIBUTION POWER	#1 SYNC GENERATOR	SYNC DISTRIBUTION	#2 SYNC GENERATOR	REMOTE FACILITIES	"ON AIR" PICTURE	"PREVIEW" PICTURE	TEST MONITOR	PICTURE DISTRIBUTION POWER
SYNC EQUIPMENT POWER PANEL	HIGH VOLTAGE SUPPLY (TIMING UNIT)	SYNC SWITCHING UNIT	HIGH VOLTAGE SUPPLY (TIMING UNIT)	BRIDGING AMPLIFIER	LINE AMPLIFIER	LINE AMPLIFIER	HIGH VOLTAGE SUPPLY (W.F. MONITOR)	PICTURE EQUIPMENT POWER PANEL
BIAS SUPPLY (SYNC DIST. AMP #1)	TIMING UNIT	SYNC DISTRIBUTION AMPLIFIER #1	TIMING UNIT	REMOTE SYNC PHASING UNIT	PICTURE DISTRIBUTION AMPLIFIER	PICTURE DISTRIBUTION AMPLIFIER	PICTURE MONITOR	LOW VOLTAGE SUPPLY (ON AIR BRIDG AMP)
BIAS SUPPLY (SYNC DIST. AMP #2)	BLANKING UNIT	SYNC PATCH PANEL	BLANKING UNIT	PATCH PANEL	PATCH PANEL	PATCH PANEL		LOW VOLTAGE SUPPLY (ON AIR PICT. MONITOR)
				SYNC STRETCHING UNIT	BRIDGING AMPLIFIER	BRIDGING AMPLIFIER	WAVEFORM MONITOR	LOW VOLTAGE SUPPLY (PREVIEW BRIDG AMP)
LOW VOLTAGE SUPPLY (SYNC. DIST AMP #1)	SHAPING UNIT	SYNC DISTRIBUTION AMPLIFIER #2	SHAPING UNIT	SYNC STRETCHING UNIT	BIAS SUPPLY (LINE AMP)	BIAS SUPPLY (LINE AMP)	LOW VOLTAGE SUPPLY (PICTURE MONITOR)	LOW VOLTAGE SUPPLY (PREVIEW PICT. MONITOR)
LOW VOLTAGE SUPPLY (SYNC DIST AMP #2)	LOW VOLTAGE SUPPLY	SWEEP AUXILIARY	LOW VOLTAGE SUPPLY	LOW VOLTAGE SUPPLY (BRIDGING AMP)	LOW VOLTAGE SUPPLY (LINE AMP & W.F. MONITOR)	LOW VOLTAGE SUPPLY (LINE AMP & W.F. MONITOR)	LOW VOLTAGE SUPPLY (W.F. MONITOR)	HIGH VOLTAGE SUPPLY ON AIR PREVIEW W.F. MONITORS
					LOW VOLTAGE SUPPLY (DISTRIB. AMP)	LOW VOLTAGE SUPPLY (DISTRIB. AMP)		

Figure 64. Master control desk and equipment layout.

Figure 65. Preview and On-the-Air desks used in master control. (courtesy DuMont)

controls, to the studio of both the on-the-air program as well as that of a rehearsal or preview program.

In this way the director of a television show can view the picture which is sent to master control for broadcast purposes, as well as the return feed of this program showing the signal that is sent to the transmitter.

The return signal may be considerably different from the signal which originally left the studio, since the output of a film

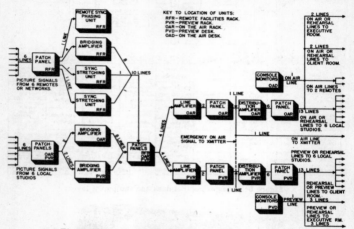

Figure 66. Block diagram of signal paths through station facilities.

camera, or material from a remote source may have been integrated, in the master control room, with the signal that the director is sending from the studio. The second return feed from master control may be used to show the program director the next program to be selected, should program continuity call for the outputs of two studios to be used in conjunction with one another.

Figure 66 shows a functional block diagram which illustrates the path of the picture signal through the various equipment components.

Twelve sources of program channels are available, six from local studios and six from remote or network programs. The signals from these sources appear on the patch panels associated with the on-the-air rack and the remote facilities rack. The following paragraphs will trace the signals for a hypothetical case, starting from the studios.

Of the six studios, four are ready for immediate use. Two of

these go to the bridging amplifier in the on-the-air rack (OAR),
and two to the bridging amplifier in the preview rack (PVR).
A bridging amplifier usually provides two inputs and four multiple outputs for each input. Having passed through the bridging
amplifier, there now exist four lines for each of four selected
video channels. These outputs also appear on the OAR patch
panel (Figure 67) and the PVR patch panel, where they are

Figure 67. On-the-Air patch panel. (courtesy DuMont)

labeled OAR bridging amplifier outputs and PVR bridging amplifier outputs, the total consisting of 16 lines.

One four-channel line amplifier is situated in the OAR rack
and another in the PVR. These amplifiers are controlled by
push-button switches located in the on-the-air and preview
desks. If remote programs are not used, four signal lines, two
from each bridging amplifier, are patched through to the line
amplifier in the OAR and the line amplifier in the PVR. The
output of the on-the-air line amplifier consists of two lines, each
carrying the same signal. This signal can be any one of the
four at the input.

The two outputs again appear on the OAR patch panel. One is
permanently tied to the transmitter input, the other is connected
to a studio distribution amplifier. The studio distribution amplifier is identical to the bridging amplifier except that its inputs
and outputs are multiplied in a different manner. It is arranged
to have but one input line and six output lines. Each of these
six output lines appears on the OAR patch panel and together

they represent the on-the-air program. One output is returned to the on-the-air desk, where it appears on the console monitor, and another is returned to the selected studio to indicate what material is on the air. The remaining four lines are set up on the OAR patch panel to feed the signal to client rooms, network outlets, or executive offices, as required.

Returning to the preview line amplifier, its two outputs are fed to the PVR patch panel where one is reserved as a standby for transmitter feed, and the other is sent to the PVR distribution amplifier. The six output lines, from the distribution amplifier appearing on the PVR patch panel, are divided in a similar manner as those on the OAR patch panel. One is fed to the preview desk to be displayed on the console monitor, and another is returned to the studio as a preview return feed. The four remaining lines can be distributed as required.

The above analysis has been predicated on the absence of remote or network programs. Since these constitute a major source of programming material, most stations make extensive use of them.

4-53 Network Programs. Tracing the signals through the block diagram of Figure 66, it will be found that six remote sources appear on the Remote Facilities Rack (RFR) patch panel. If the video signal is stable enough and does not require modification, it may be patched directly to one of the four remote bridging amplifier inputs, appearing as eight output lines on the RFR patch panel. Alternatively, two of the remote program sources may require sync modification, in which case they are fed through sync stretchers on the RFR patch panel.

In the sync stretcher units, the correct sync-to-picture ratio is restored. The outputs appear on the RFR patch panel. By means of the latter facility, it is possible for two sync stretchers to service a number of successive remote programs. A maximum of ten signal lines appear as outputs on the RFR patch panel. These are selected as required for the line amplifiers in both the OAR and PVR, and are directed to the transmitter network outputs or to other points.

By way of summary, these operations may be grouped as follows: Of a total of six local studio signals and six remote network programs, four may be selected for immediate use. They are selected by push-buttons in the line amplifier and the output fed to the transmitter and other points that require the on-the-air signal.

The four selected channels are normally fed to the line amplifier in the PVR and dispatched from this point as preview return feeds to whatever locations require the signal. It is of course possible to re-route other program channels for subsequent operations while one channel is being continually fed to the transmitter. Numerous combinations of facilities can be made by patching. For example, the output of the preview line amplifier may be used to feed a program to the network different from the program fed to the local transmitter. For such portions of the network program as might be carried by the local transmitter, an arrangement could be made through the use of switching circuits in the on-the-air line amplifier.

4-54 Synchronizing Problems. When switching from studio to remote pick-up, two synchronizing generators are involved; one associated with the remote program and the other with the local studio. While it has not been found necessary to lock the synchronizing generators together at the horizontal sweep frequency when remote and local programs follow each other, it is important that they be locked together at the vertical sweep frequency rate so as to prevent loss of vertical synchronization at the receivers in the field.

This synchronization may be secured in either of two ways. If the remote program emanates from a location within the same power line district as that of a master control installation, and if both synchronizing generators are locked with the 60 cycle line, they may differ in phase but they will be of the same frequency. If the remote operations crew can receive an off-the-air signal from the main transmitter, it can adjust the phase of the remote synchronizing generator with respect to that in master control. Alternatively, the master control sync generator may be phased to meet the requirements of the remote sync generator.

4-55 Sync Phasing. When the remote program is derived from a location in another power line district, the synchronizing generators may differ in both phase and frequency of the vertical synchronizing signal. In this case, if vertical synchronizing continuity is to be maintained, it is essential that the synchronizing generator in the master control installation be locked to the sync generator frequency of the remote or network program.

To accomplish this, a sync phasing unit is incorporated in the master control remote facilities rack. Its input appears on the RFR patch panel. The output of the sync phasing unit is fed as a 60 cycle signal to the master control sync generator, and serves to lock it with respect to the remote or network program in both phase and frequency.

A block diagram of a circuit used for phasing remote and master control sync generators which are on different power lines is shown in Figure 68.

The remote video signal is fed into V-1 and amplified. The next stage clips the video portion and leaves the sync signals.

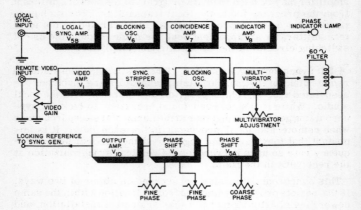

Figure 68. Block diagram of sync phasing unit.

The vertical sync is separated and triggers V-3, which is a blocking oscillator. The output pulse of the blocking oscillator triggers V-4, a multivibrator, whose output circuit includes a 60 cycle resonant filter. V-4 thus generates a sine wave at the vertical frequency of the remote sync with a fixed phase relationship to the vertical sync interval. This sine wave is applied to a phase shifter, V-5a, whose output is applied to two more phase shifting stages in V-9. The output of the phase shifter is applied to V-10 whose plate circuit includes an output transformer which supplies a 60 cycle locking signal to the master control sync generator.

Returning now to the local sync input, negative sync pulses from the master control sync generator are amplified by V-5b. After the vertical sync signal is separated, it is used to trigger another blocking oscillator, V-6. Thus a pulse is obtained, occurring at the vertical interval of the master control sync generator, and of the same shape and relative timing as that generated by V-3. The pulses from V-6 and V-3 are fed to a coincidence amplifier, V-7. In such an amplifier, the grids are biased so that the tube will conduct only if the two input signals coincide within certain time limits. If so, the addition of the two voltages is sufficient to overcome the cutoff bias. If the two signals do not coincide, neither is able to make the tube conduct.

The phasing controls in the phase shift circuit are adjusted until the two signals coincide. This is indicated by a lamp which

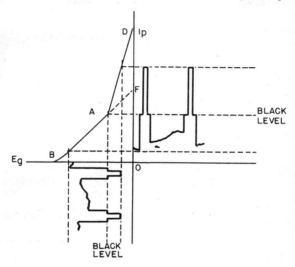

Figure 69. Grid-voltage, plate-current curves of non-linear amplifier stage.

lights up when the coincidence amplifier conducts and sends a signal to V-8. V-8 amplifies the indicating signal, causing the lamp to light. Under this condition a correctly phased signal is obtained from V10 for locking the master control sync generator.

4-56 Stabilizing Amplifiers. If the signal from the remote source contains spurious signals, such as hum, thermal noises, and other random disturbances, it must first be stabilized at master control before being fed to the transmitter. This is done in a sync stretcher or stabilizing amplifier. In such a unit, the signal is first amplified by several video amplifier stages.

The signal is then fed to three non-linear amplifiers so that the sync pulses are amplified by a larger factor than the other parts of the signal. Figure 69 shows how the three non-linear amplifier stages function. One of the three tubes operates as a normal amplifier, and contributes signal through that part of the characteristic curve between B and F. At grid voltages above the

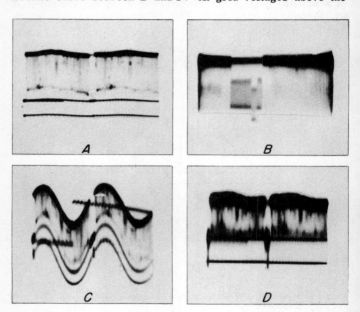

Figure 70. Effect of sync stretching unit on video signal.

black level (point A), the remaining two tubes begin to amplify the signal, giving the increased slope between A and D. This stage, therefore, automatically stretches the sync pulses, thereby increasing the sync-to-picture ratio without adversely affecting the picture signal.

The black level, or peaks of blanking are held at A by a clamping or d-c restoration circuit which functions independently of the picture signal in the amplifier. It holds the peak of each blanking pulse to the correct point on the amplifier curve. Clamping action is independent of the signal, so that spurious additive components are eliminated from this sync-amplifying stage. Amplified sync thus passes on to the clipping stage which clips off part of the sync to restore the correct sync-to-picture ratio.

The oscillograms shown in Figure 70 indicate how effectively a stabilizing amplifier corrects extremely defective video signals. Figure 70a shows an essentially noise-free signal. The signal is not perfect since it contains a small amount of hum which can be observed as a wavy bottom line (sync peaks). To this signal two types of spurious signals were deliberately added separately, a high frequency hiss and 60 cycle hum. The signal after the addition of the hiss is shown in Figure 70b. As can be seen, the amplitude of the hiss is about 50% of the total signal amplitude, and almost obliterates the horizontal sync pulses. Figure 70c shows the signal after the addition of 60 cycle hum equal to about 75% of the total signal. Both these signals were then combined and fed to a stabilizing amplifier. The resultant signal is shown in Figure 70d. It will be noted that the hum has been completely eliminated, and an increase in the sync-to-picture ratio has been effected. In addition, there is a considerable improvement in the signal-to-noise ratio.

REMOTE CAMERA CHAIN

4-57 The remote camera equipment used for field pick-up is essentially the same as the studio equipment. The remote equipment is capable of televising a program and generating the standard video signal. It operates completely independent of the station, except when it is desirable to lock the frequency of the remote sync generator to the frequency of the station sync generator. Other than the fact that the remote facilities are designed for portable use, they incorporate the same basic components as studio facilities. A typical remote camera chain is shown in the block diagram of Figure 71.

The following paragraphs describe a dual camera chain, rather than a single camera chain as was described in the very simple television system. Remote chains usually employ from two to four cameras.

Figure 71 shows the thirteen units of equipment used in a dual camera chain. The pick-up head and the Electronic Viewfinder are embodied in the camera so that actually only eleven individual pieces of equipment make up the remote facilities.

4-58 Equipment Design. The circuits of the units in the remote camera chain are the same as described for studio equip-

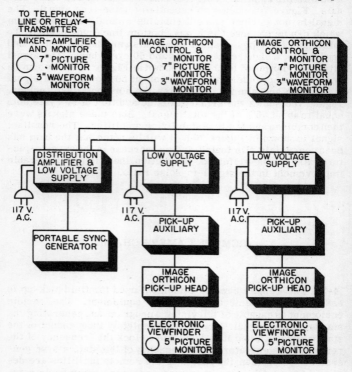

Figure 71. Block diagram of dual image-orthicon camera chain.

ment. The distinguishing feature of remote equipment is its mechanical design. Remote equipment is portable and compact. The following comparisons with studio equipment indicate the major differences between studio and remote equipment.

4-59 The Pick-Up Head. The pick-up head uses an image-orthicon tube similar to that used in the studio. The major difference between the image orthicon tubes used for remote and studio use is their color response. Blue sensitive image-orthicon tubes are best for televising outdoor scenes, while red sensitive tubes perform better under artificial lighting in stu-

Figure 72. Pickup head mounted on tripod for remote pickup use. (courtesy Raytheon)

dios. For field work the pick-up head is mounted on a tripod rather than a dolly (Figure 72).

4-60 The Electronic Viewfinder. The electronic viewfinder is the camera operator's picture monitor. It is located on top of the pick-up head and is identically the same as the unit used in the studio camera.

4-61 The Pick-Up Auxiliary. The pick-up auxiliary is usually mounted in a box located close to the camera (Figure 73). It contains the voltage regulator circuits for the camera circuits which separate the vertical and horizontal sweep driving pulses coming from the sync generator. By locating these circuits in the pick-up auxiliary, the camera head is made smaller and

Figure 73. Pickup amplifier. (courtesy DuMont)

lighter. In studio equipment, the auxiliary circuits are usually located in the dolly or in the camera head.

4-62 Low Voltage Supply. This unit supplies filament voltage and unregulated d-c voltages to the camera, pick-up auxiliary, and the camera control monitor. It is mounted in a box, (Figure 74), whereas in the studio the low voltage supplies are rack-mounted.

4-63 Camera Control Monitor. The camera control monitor in remote equipment assumes the functions performed by both the picture monitor and the mixing amplifier in the studio. Each camera has a separate control monitor containing a picture monitor and an oscillograph monitor (Figure 75). In field equipment the picture tube is 7'' in diameter, and the oscillograph monitor tube is 3'' in diameter. The video signal from the camera is combined with the sync and blanking signals from the portable sync generator in the mixing amplifier section of the

camera control monitor. If only one camera is used in the remote system, the composite video signal from the control monitor is fed directly to the relay transmitter or telephone line.

Figure 74. Low-voltage supply. (courtesy DuMont)

When more than one camera is used, an additional mixing amplifier and monitor is necessary.

4-64 The Mixer-Amplifier and Monitor. In both studio and
remote equipment, a mixer-amplifier and monitor must be added
to the system, when more than one camera is used, to combine
the camera outputs and switch any one of them on the air. A
picture monitor and oscillograph monitor are incorporated into
the unit so that the video operator may observe the particular
camera signal which he has selected (Figure 76).

A system of "on-the-air" lights, located on the monitor panel,
indicates which channel is in use. By means of push-buttons,
the operator may instantaneously switch from one camera to

another. A "fade rate control" is also generally provided so that when the cameras are switched, one picture fades out and the other fades in. The fade rate can be controlled in steps for

Figure 75. Camera control monitor. (courtesy DuMont)

slow, medium, fast, and instantaneous changes.

4-65 The Mixer-Amplifier Circuits. A block diagram of this section is shown in Figure 77. Each of the video channels consists of a cathode follower coupled to a video amplifier which has a voltage gain sufficient to overcome the attenuation of the cathode follower. Gain controls are located at the input of each stage for equalizing the signal level from each camera.

Switching between channels is accomplished by variation of the grid bias on the amplifier stages, and the rate of fade is controlled by the variation of time constants of bias networks, located in the cathode-follower inputs.

If a signal from channel 1 is being delivered to the transmitter, and it is desired to fade out this picture slowly, and at the same time bring in a picture from channel 2, the grid bias on the video amplifiers in the two channels should vary as shown in Figure 78 to accomplish this. This represents the ideal case, for the rate at which the amplifier in channel 2 reaches full conduction

Figure 76. Mixer amplifier and monitor. (courtesy DuMont)

is the same as the rate at which the amplifier in channel 1 is being cut off. The cross-over point of the two curves is at the cutoff voltage of the amplifiers and one picture disappears just as the other one appears.

The arrangement of Figure 79 is a means of approximating the conditions of Figure 78. Initially, switch SW-1A is closed, the amplifier grid for channel 1 is at ground potential, and signals from this channel pass to the output. Switch SW-1B is open, leaving the amplifier grid of channel 2 at a potential well beyond cutoff. If SW-1A is opened and, simultaneously, SW-1B is closed, the voltage on the grid of amplifier 1 will fall to the potential at point B at rate determined by the double time constant R1-C1 and R2-C2. At the same time the potential on the grid of amplifier 2 will rise to ground potential at a rate determined by the single time constant R3-C3.

If the potentiometers R-1, R-2, R-3, and R-4 are ganged, it will be possible to vary the slope of the two curves and therefore the rate of fade. The cross-over point, which determines whether or not the signals are mixed as they are faded, is es-

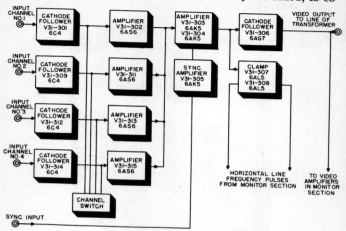

Figure 77. Block diagram of mixer amplifier.

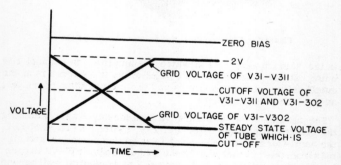

Figure 78. Curve of bias changes which occur in switching amplifiers.

tablished by the position of switch SW-2, which sets the cutoff voltage. In actual practice, more than two channels are employed, and it is possible to select any channel or combination or channels by depressing the correct push-buttons. A selector-switch (rather than ganged potentiometers) controls fade

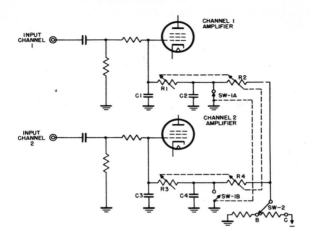

Figure 79. Simplified schematic of input switching circuits.

Figure 80. Portable sync generator. (courtesy DuMont)

rate with positions indicated as "Slow", "Medium", "Fast", and "Instantaneous".

4-66 Distribution Amplifier and Low Voltage Supply. This unit contains the low voltage supplies for the Mixer-Amplifier and Monitor, and also several cathode follower stages which distribute sync and blanking signals from the sync generator to the cameras in operation. In the studio, the distribution amplifiers and power supplies are located on separate chassis mounted in racks.

4-67 The Sync Generator. This unit (Figure 80) is similar to the studio sync generator. It supplies standard RMA blanking and sync pulses for all units of the camera chain. At the station, the studio sync generator is locked to the remote sync generator so that the two operate in phase. This permits switching from studio programs to remote programs without loss of synchronization of receivers in the field.

MICROWAVE RELAYS

4-68 Since remote pickup equipment is used in widely different locations on short notice, it is desirable to provide a number of relay methods whereby the remote pickup signals can be fed back to the main transmitter location. When a regular schedule of pick-ups is planned, as for example, from a sporting arena, it is possible to install coaxial cable facilities to the transmitter. Carefully chosen telephone lines with suitable line amplifier terminal equipment can also be used. Using such facilities, the television signal may be fed by line from the remote pick-up equipment line amplifier to the master control room at the transmitter.

For special pick-ups, it is often desirable to use a wireless relay link. Relay transmitters are of relatively low power since the transmission takes place between two specific points, permitting the use of highly directional transmitting and receiving antennas. Power outputs of 500 watts permit transmission over distances up to 15 miles, with equipment operating in the vicinity of 7000 Mc. At the transmitter, a high-frequency receiver is used to pick up and detect the video signal and feed it to the master control room.

Radio relays are also being set up between cities to provide links between television stations. Because the range of television signals is limited to about 50 miles, a great many of these relay stations are necessary to provide television network facilities, comparable to those used for radio broadcasting. Television networks are being made up by linking stations with radio relays or a combination of radio relays and coaxial lines. Another method of transmitting television signals over long distances is "stratovision". In the stratovision system a television transmitter in a plane beams the signal down on the earth, covering a very large area. Stratovision is still in its experimental stages and has not yet been used for commercial operation.

4-69 Television Relay Transmitters. Television relay transmitters are complete portable transmitting systems consisting of a transmitter and a highly directional antenna which may be rotated on a mounting unit. The transmitter may operate on one of several television relay bands assigned by the F.C.C. The bands presently assigned for relay work are in the 2,000, 4,000, and 7,000 megacycle regions. The parabolic antennas used at these frequencies provide a high gain and limit the output signal to a line of sight path.

4-70 Transmitter Circuits. Other than the fact that the relay transmitter operates at a much higher frequency than the station video transmitter previously described, its basic sections are the same. The principal difference in the relay transmitter design is in the method of generating the ultra-high frequency r-f carrier. Conventional vacuum tubes are incapable of oscillating at these high frequencies. Tubes such as the klystron and magnetron which were developed during the last war for use in radar equipment are used in the relay transmitter oscillator. At these frequencies, capacitors, inductors, and even coaxial lines are not suitable for the tuned circuit elements of the oscillator. Instead, cavity resonators are employed.

A discussion of ultra-high frequency oscillators and cavity resonators is beyond the scope of this book. There are many excellent references on this subject which the reader will find in the bibliography if he wishes to pursue this subject further. Suffice to say here that the relay transmitter consists of an ultra high frequency r-f generator, a video modulator, and a highly directional antenna which confines the radiated television signal to a very narrow beam.

4-71 Relay Receivers. At the relay receiver, a second directional antenna receives the narrow television beam. A klystron or magnetron ultra-high frequency oscillator is again employed to heterodyne the incoming signal. This produces a video i-f frequency. From this point on the relay receiver is identical to conventional superheterodyne receivers. The i-f signal is

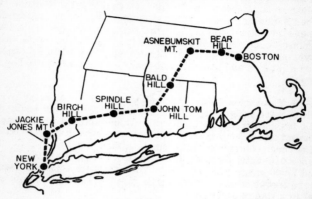

Figure 81. Microwave relay link between New York and Boston.

amplified and detected. The detected signal is the 4 megacycle video signal which was used to modulate the transmitter. In the relay receiver, the detected signal is amplified by one or more video amplifier stages to bring it up to approximately 1 volt, at which level it is fed by co-axial line to the master control room. After being monitored at master control, the relayed signal is fed to the station's transmitter.

4-72 Television Networks. Two methods are being used to distribute television programs, namely co-axial cables and radio relay stations. Coaxial cables are now being installed which will link the major cities from coast to coast some time between 1950 and 1953. The cost of laying coaxial cable is several dollars per foot, bringing the cost of co-axial links to many millions of dollars when they are extended across the country. As a result rental fees for using these lines are high. Many stations are therefore building or renting radio relay links which they believe will eventually prove cheaper to operate.

A radio relay link now exists between New York and Boston, a distance of 220 miles. Relay stations are located at the points shown on the map of Figure 81. This system is equipped with four different relay frequencies in the 3,700 to 4,200 Mc band. The carrier frequencies are at least 40 Mc apart to avoid cross-talk between incoming and outgoing signals. The antennas used at the relay points are designed for operation at two frequencies, the regular channel and a standby channel.

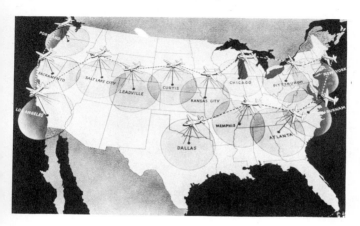

Figure 82. How coverage of United States would be secured using stratovision. (courtesy Westinghouse)

All of the seven relay stations of Figure 81 are identical, each having a receiver and a repeater transmitter.

4-73 Stratovision. This transmitting system is being developed by Westinghouse. The television transmitter is placed in an airplane and the television program broadcast from the airplane while it is in flight. The transmitter's coverage area is increased by virtue of the increased line-of-sight distance to the horizon. At an altitude of 20,000 feet, a coverage radius of 50 miles is possible, which is about the distance reached by the average transmitter on the ground. At an altitude of 30,000 feet, a coverage radius of 210 miles is possible, and at 50,000 feet, about 300 miles is possible.

Approximately 20 kilowatts of power are needed at a ground station to transmit a usable signal a distance of approximately 50 miles, whereas only one kilowatt of power will deliver the same usable signal 200 miles from a transmitter located in a plane flying at 30,000 feet.

A stratovision network of 8 planes could link New York and California, as compared to the 100 ground relays necessary to fulfill the same purpose. Fourteen planes carrying transmitters could supply television programs to 78% of the population of the United States as shown in Figure 82.

The designers of stratovision envision a system operated in the following manner. Airplanes would take off at staggered

Figure 83. An airplane equipped to broadcast television programs. (courtesy Westinghouse)

four hour intervals, remaining at 30,000 feet for eight hours each. This will keep a plane in the air at all times. A standby plane would always accompany the one in use and be ready to take over in case of airplane or transmitter trouble. At each stratovision area, four planes would be required so that while two were flying the other two would be undergoing maintenance or repairs. A completely equipped plane with transmitting and receiving antennas is shown in Figure 83.

The transmitting plane would fly in circles at about 30,000 feet. The program originating in the studio would be transmitted to the plane by a small ground transmitter and directional antenna system. To make the system economical to operate, large planes, capable of carrying two or more transmitters, thereby splitting the operating costs among several stations, could be used.

Stratovision is one of many systems conceived by engineers to extend the boundaries of line of sight transmission. Many schemes, which today seem fantastic, may some day be made entirely practical. A typical suggestion is that of putting an artificial satellite or moon out in space, made of metal and shaped like a spherical mirror. Television signals beamed at this mirror would be reflected over a very large portion of the earth. Proponents of this idea point out that once this satellite is shot from the earth's atmosphere (say, by an atomic rocket), it would circle indefinitely in the free space surrounding the earth.

COMMERCIAL STATION EQUIPMENT

4-74 The average size television station consists of studio facilities for picking up live talent programs, film cameras, one or more remote camera chains, and a video and audio transmitter. In very small stations, portable camera chains can be used for both studio and remote work to keep equipment to a minimum. A floor plan, showing a typical grouping of the above equipment in a small station, is shown in Figure 84.

The station shown has one live talent studio with a control room for local monitoring of the cameras. The film room has one film projector which is focused on an iconoscope camera. The iconoscope picture is monitored at the master control console which has switching facilities for integrating programs from the film pick-up and the studio. At this master control console, programs may be fed in from a network. The transmitter racks are mounted in the same room. This eliminates the need for a separate picture monitor for the transmitter. An announcer's booth, a client's room for viewing programs, and a garage for housing the mobile unit complete the station's facilities.

This small station is typical of many that will appear in small communities about the country. Larger stations located in the big cities are basically the same, but contain several studios, and the added equipment necessary for these studios.

4-75 Studio Equipment. At present, manufacturers are making

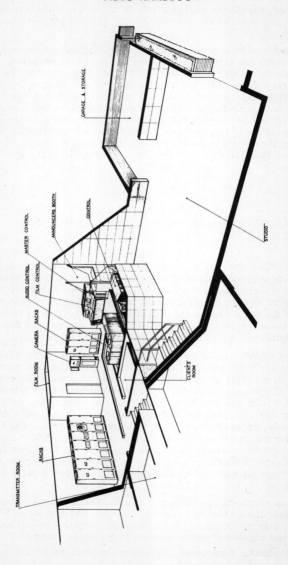

Figure 84. Layout of small television station.

only image orthicon cameras for live talent studio pick-ups. A few of the older stations still use iconoscope cameras made before the war. The studio camera equipment consists of the camera itself, a camera control monitor, mixing and distribution amplifiers, and a synchronizing generator. Usually, only the cameras and control monitors are located in the studio con-

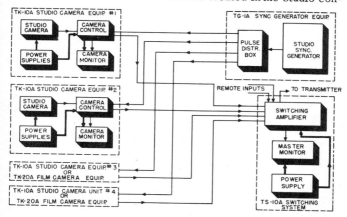

Figure 85. Block diagram of RCA studio camera equipment.

trol booth. The sync generator and the distribution amplifiers are located in master control so that signals can be fed to several studios.

4-76 RCA Studio Camera Chain. The arrangement of studio equipment provided by RCA is shown in Figure 85. A brief description of each unit follows.

The camera can be put on a dolly as shown in Figure 86, or on a boom structure as shown in Figure 87. The boom structure makes it possible to take interesting overhead shots.

The camera consists of image orthicon deflection circuits, a preamplifier, and an electronic viewfinder, all mounted in one unit. Camera circuits are arranged to either side of the image orthicon tube (Figure 88). Hinged doors on either side of the camera swing down to provide easy access to the camera circuits.

Four lenses are mounted on a lens turret, which can be rotated by a handle at the rear of the camera. These lenses are relatively small, due to the small size of the photo-cathode in the pickup tube. They are available in sizes from 35 mm f2.8 to 135 mm f3.8. Optical focusing is accomplished by adjustment of a knob on the side of the camera. This knob moves the pickup tube, and its focus and deflection coil assembly with respect

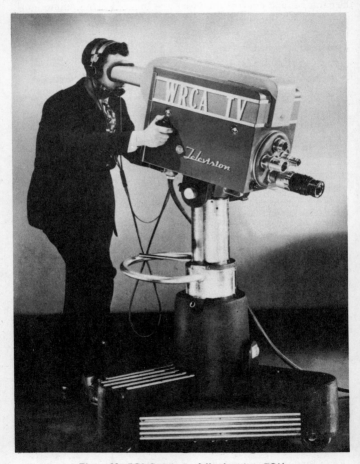

Figure 86. RCA Camera on dolly. (courtesy RCA)

Figure 87. Studio set and boom camera. (courtesy WFIL-TV)

Figure 88. Interior of image-orthicon camera. (courtesy RCA)

to the lens.

Controls for the studio camera circuits are located at the rear of the camera in two rows behind hinged covers, as shown in Figure 89. These controls are normally preset and do not require adjustment during the program.

Figure 89. Rear of RCA camera with doors open to show controls. (courtesy RCA)

4-77 Studio Picture Monitor. The studio picture monitor enables the video operator to monitor and control the quality of the picture signal produced by the studio camera. It is a desk-type console section with a 10-inch picture tube monitor mounted in the upper section (Figure 90). A 5-inch oscillograph tube, which reproduces the video signal waveform, is located below the picture tube. Controls for setting the camera signal gain, and black level, are brought out on the monitor front panel.

The control chassis below the monitor contains the necessary circuits for amplifying the video signal, establishing the black level, adding picture blanking to the picture signal, adding the synchronizing signal, and providing 3 separate outputs. Four commonly used controls are located on the monitor. These are:

1. orthicon focus
2. beam current
3. target voltage
4. image focus

4-78 Studio Camera Switching System. Picture monitors can be installed together in the studio control room to handle several cameras. The RCA desk type sections are fastened together to form an operating console which provides a control center for camera switching, monitoring and other technical aspects of programming. In stations where live talent pro-

Figure 90. Studio picture monitor. (courtesy RCA)

gramming is not planned, but where facilities are employed for film projection, broadcast of network programs and relay pickups, the switching console can be located in the transmitter room or in the projection control room together with the film equipment. If both film and live studio pickups are to be integrated, the studio console can also contain a film monitor.

The studio camera switching equipment enables a single video operator to do the following: (1) Select any signal from six input lines; (2) switch or fade the desired signal into the program line; (3) fade out the previously selected signal and fade in another, simultaneously and at any speed; (4) switch instantly from one signal to another; and (5) superimpose two signals with any desired degree of brightness for each signal. Figure 91 shows a close-up view of the switching console monitor.

Electrically, the studio camera switching console includes all the circuits necessary to accomplish four operations, namely:

1. Video switching - a six pushbutton selector provides for selecting any one of six input signals for transmission to a master control room or to the transmitter.

2. Sync addition - Amplifier circuits combine sync from the

Figure 91. Camera switching monitor controls. (courtesy RCA)

studio sync generator with the camera video signals to form the composite video signal.

3. Monitor switching - A three position switch provides for selection of either of two remote (network or relay pickup) signals for preview, or the signal being sent to the transmitter or master control room.

4. A communication system permits the technical director and program director to converse with all engineering and production personnel.

4-79 Synchronizing Generator. The studio synchronizing generator is an integral unit complete with power supply. It is assembled in a standard cabinet-type rack, as shown in Figure 92.

The sync generator is generally located in the master control room. Its signals are fed to several studios through distribution amplifiers.

Some studio synchronizing generators have self-contained oscillograph monitors for checking the frequency of the divider

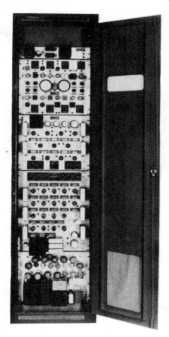

Figure 92. Studio type synchronizing generator.
(courtesy DuMont)

circuit. Figure 93 shows the presentation on the screen of the cathode ray tubes. This type of pattern is obtained on the Du-Mont studio synchronizing generator which has a master oscillator frequency of 157.5 kc. This is five times higher than the 31.5 kc. master oscillator frequency used in most sync generators. The higher frequency is used in the DuMont design to provide 157.5 kc. pulses for checking the horizontal linearity of sweep circuits.

The left hand screen is that of the high frequency monitor whose time base is 900 cycles. The dots represent the master oscillator frequency of 157.5 kc. There are five dots along each line or step in the vertical "ladder", indicating division from 157.5 kc. to 31.5 kc. The bright dots on the high frequency monitor correspond to the 15.75 cycle horizontal repetition rate. There are seven steps in each of the "ladders", indicating a frequency division from 51.5 kc. to 4,500 cycles. In other words

Figure 93. Screens of cathode-ray tube indicators for monitoring synchronizing generator. (courtesy DuMont)

each "ladder" represents 4,500 cycles. The presence of five "ladders" for each cycle of the time base points to a frequency division from 4,500 cycles to the time base frequency of 900 cycles.

At the right on the low frequency monitor, the "ladder" steps represent 900 cycles. Since there are five of them to each "ladder", the indication is frequency division from 900 cycles to 180 cycles. The three "ladders" per cycle of the time base indicate a frequency division from 180 cycles to 60 cycles. The blanked-out section in the middle of the low frequency scan is derived from the 60 cycle power line and confirms the time base of 60 cycles. It also indicates synchronism with the line. When the generator is not locked to the 60 cycle power line, the blanked-out section moves across the time base. This presentation has been found highly useful in the analysis at a glance of synchronizing generator failures due to improper timing.

4-80 Distribution Amplifier. The distribution amplifier shown in Figure 94 may be used in any one of the three following applications: (a) to feed video or synchronizing signals from a single source, such as a sync generator, to several outlets; (b) to mix video signals from several sources in order that they may be fed to a single output line; and (c) as a straightforward line

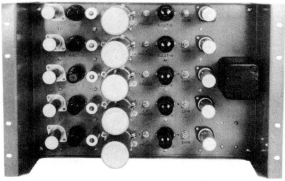

Figure 94. Distribution Amplifier. (courtesy RCA)

amplifier to bring the video signal up to required levels between different points in the television system.

4-81 Film Pickup Equipment. Specially built iconoscope cameras are used almost exclusively for film pickups in a television station. The iconoscope gives a higher quality picture than the image orthicon and is used for film work because all the light from the film is concentrated on the iconoscope mosaic and is thus sufficient to obtain pictures of good contrast. The iconoscope camera used for a film pick-up is stripped of superfluous accessories such as lenses, optical focus controls, and viewfinder. In a typical arrangement, shown in Figure 95, the motion picture projector is permanently mounted opposite the iconoscope camera. The picture is focused directly on the iconoscope mosaic.

Because standard motion picture films must be projected at a rate of 24 frames per second and television images are shown at a rate of 30 frames per second, a system of scanning had to be developed to compensate for the difference in frame frequencies.

The projector mechanism is so designed that three fields of the television picture are secured during the time that one film frame is held before the open shutter. The film is then pulled to the next frame, and two more field scans of the picture are secured. In this way, two frames of film occur for five field scans of the television picture. Therefore, two film frames running through the projector at the standard rate of 24 frames per second will consume 2 x 1/24 seconds or 1/12 seconds.

Figure 95. Typical arrangement of film camera and 16mm film projector. (courtesy RCA)

These two film frames have been utilized in the interval in which 5/60 of a second (or 1/12 of a second) has been consumed for five flashes (or fields) of picture. Synchronization is thus maintained between the 60 fields per second of television scanning, and the 24 frames per second of film motion.

The projector must be driven by a synchronous motor so that it is locked to the power line frequency. The motor is phased with respect to the frequency of the synchronizing generator which drives the entire television system. Since both the synchronous motor and sync generator are locked to the same 60 cycle line, synchronization is maintained once the two units are phased with respect to each other.

4-82 Film Pickup System. The DuMont iconoscope film pick-up system is typical of film systems utilizing a 16mm projector, an iconoscope camera, and a monitoring console.

An interior view of the iconoscope camera is shown in Figure 96. This unit contains the pickup tube, the sweep circuits, a five stage video preamplifier, regulator circuits for the video amplifier voltages, a blanking amplifier for cutting off the beam

Figure 96. Iconoscope film pickup camera without shield covers. (courtesy DuMont)

during return trace periods, and a protection circuit which removes the accelerating voltage from the pickup tube in the event of sweep failure.

The video signal is fed to a monitoring console, Figure 97. This monitor contains both a picture and an oscillograph monitor. The operating controls include iconoscope sweep amplitude, sweep position, focus, and intensity. The shading of the picture is also accomplished at this console.

The picture obtained with an iconoscope camera must be shaded to correct for the spurious effects of secondary emission that occur in this type of pickup tube. The high velocity beam striking the elements of the mosaic causes secondary electrons to be emitted. Those elements near the center of the mosaic sometimes release their secondary electrons to nearby elements, as well as to the wall coatings of the tube. Elements near the edges of the mosaic release their secondary electrons largely to the conducting areas around the mosaic. Thus central

Figure 97. Iconoscope film camera monitor showing shading controls. (courtesy DuMont)

elements may deliver different amounts of secondaries than do edge elements, even when there is no light falling on the mosaic. This difference appears as a video signal, and as such causes the receiving tube to show a variation in illumination over the scanned area.

When a scene is focused on the mosaic, the video signal which it produces is distorted by this spurious signal distribution. For example, a picture which would otherwise have uniform illumination would appear bright in the center and gradually become darker toward the edges.

In the early stages of the video pre-amplifier, a sine wave voltage of proper amplitude and phase can be introduced which distorts the video signal in a manner which compensates for the uneven illumination. The sine wave is one form of shading signal. In practice, the video operator has a choice of three types of shading signal voltages which he can inject into the pre-amplifier stages to produce even illumination. These are the sine wave, saw-tooth, and parabola shaped voltages of Figure 98. There are two controls for each waveshape, making six in all.

One of the two controls operates a shading signal at the line frequency, the other at the frame frequency. With a little practice, the video operator can learn to use any combination of shading signals to provide uniform illumination of the picture. He must constantly manipulate these controls, for the spurious secondary emission will change with changes in picture content.

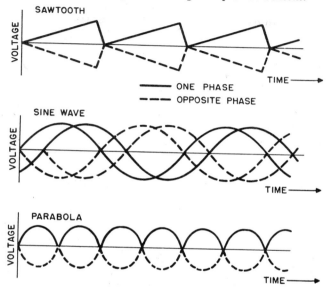

Figure 98. Waveshape used to shade picture.

Some studios use more than one film camera, in which case console units are combined as was done in making up a console desk for several studio floor cameras.

RCA offers a film "multiplexer" unit which eliminates the need for a separate iconoscope camera for each projector. The film multiplexer is an image reflecting device fitted with a standard slide projector. Images can be picked up from the slide projector or from either film projector without moving the film camera or any of the projection units; therefore, all three units can be fastened permanently to the projection room floor at the time of installation.

The film multiplexer mirrors reflect the image from either

of the two film cameras onto the pickup tube in the iconoscope camera. The equipment is mounted as shown in Figure 99. The slide projector, which is focused directly on the pickup tube in the camera provides a means for picking up the station test pattern or for projecting still shots during the program.

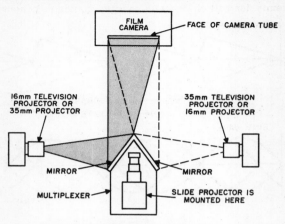

Figure 99. Physical layout of film multiplexer.

4-83 Monoscope Camera. The monoscope camera is used for obtaining a test pattern image for testing of the television system. If the monoscope pattern is put on the air during stand-by periods, the station call letters may be made part of the pattern, if the tube is custom made. A block diagram of a monoscope camera is shown in Figure 100. The circuit is much the same as a picture monitor. It contains a video amplifier to strengthen the monoscope signal, and vertical and horizontal deflection circuits which control the scanning beam in the monoscope tube. These circuits are synchronized by driving pulses from the sync generator. A blanking amplifier is used to control the level and polarity of the blanking pulses received from the synchronizing generator before the pulses are fed into the video amplifier and mixed with the video signal. The output signal obtained from the monoscope contains only blanking and video signals, as shown in the figure. Sync signals are added in a mixing and distribution amplifier in the master control room.

4-84 Flying Spot Scanners. Another type of camera, known as a "flying spot scanner", is useful for presenting test patterns, program titles, and films. A common method of televising test patterns or program announcements is to set up a card in front of a studio camera or use a slide with a film camera. This ties up operating personnel and a camera. The monoscope camera is not flexible enough to perform this function because it has a fixed pattern. The flying spot scanner offers a solution to this

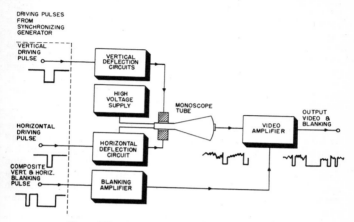

Figure 100. Block diagram of monoscope camera circuit.

problem because it is a relatively inexpensive type of camera.

The principle of the flying spot scanner may be explained by referring to the block diagram shown in Figure 101. A scanning raster is formed on an electrostatic or magnetic cathode ray tube having a screen of very short persistency. To form a raster requires the use of vertical and horizontal sweep circuits and a power supply. A film slide is interposed between the cathode ray tube and a lens and phototube. As the spot on the cathode ray tube moves across the raster it illuminates successive points on the slide. The variations in the transparency of the slide film determine the amount of light which passes through to the phototube. The current given off by the phototube is the video signal. Blanking and synchronizing pulses are added to the video signal in a mixing amplifier, resulting in a composite video signal.

RCA uses a five inch tube in its flying spot scanner, whereas DuMont employs a 10-inch tube. The tubes are operated at 10 to 20 thousand volts to obtain sufficient light output from the flying spot. Deflection circuits, video amplifiers, and power supplies are incorporated. A slide holder and phototube complete the camera.

The flying spot scanner principle is not new. It was used in early mechanical disc television systems in which a light source was located behind a scanning disc and emitted successive pulses of light toward the subject through the holes in the disc. Light reflections from the subject fell on a photocell to form the video signal. Electronic flying spot scanners were tried in the early development stages of electronic television. These experiments were not successful because the phosphorescence of the screen persisted too long between successive excursions of the spot over the same point. This problem has been overcome in the new scanners by the development of the type P 15 phosphor coating which has a very short phosphorescent decay time.

4-85 Remote Camera Chains. Both RCA and DuMont manufacture image orthicon remote camera chains. The cameras are the same as the studio type. Camera control monitors, a switching monitor (when more than one camera is used), a sync generator, and power supplies are similar to the studio type offered by these companies, except that they are packaged in small, portable, self-contained units. An RCA field pickup camera chain is shown in Figure 102.

4-86 Microwave Relay Equipment. RCA's microwave relay equipment operates in the 6,800 to 7,050 Mc. band. The general arrangement of the transmitter and antenna is shown in Figure 103. The antenna is a four foot metal parabola which focuses the power, fed to it by a hook shaped waveguide, into a narrow beam. The transmitter is enclosed in a cylindrical weatherproof housing which is rigidly attached to the back of the parabola. This arrangement requires a very short transmission line between the transmitter and the antenna and eliminates the matching and loss problems which are encountered when a transmitter and antenna are located at different points.

The combined transmitter-antenna assembly is provided with either of two types of mountings. One of these, shown in Figure 103, is a rotatable type which allows the parabola to be moved through a wide arc, either horizontally or vertically. When the equipment is used in portable form for field pickups, the assembly may be mounted on a heavy tripod as shown here. For fixed use, a more permanent mounting, such as that shown in Figure 104 may be used. This type of permanent installation can be used between a studio and transmitter which are not located in

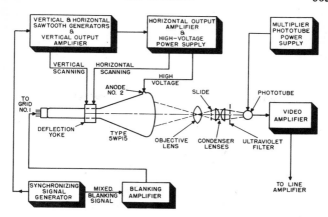

Figure 101. Block diagram of flying spot signal generator.

Figure 102. Field pickup camera chain. (courtesy RCA)

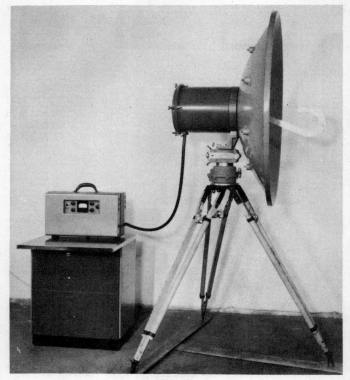

Figure 103. Microwave relay transmitter. (courtesy RCA)

the same building, as shown in Figure 105.

The power supply and operating controls of the transmitter are contained in a small case which may be located as much as 400 feet from the transmitter-antenna unit. Thus, for field use, the transmitter-antenna assembly can be placed on a high point, such as the top of a stadium, while the control unit is located at a more convenient point (with the camera control and switching units). Such an arrangement is shown in Figure 106.

The arrangement of the receiving components, is similar to that of the transmitter. The antenna is identical, except that the parabolic reflector picks up the signal and the waveguide feeds

Figure 104. Permanent installation of microwave relay antenna.

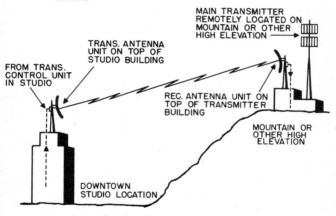

Figure 105. Typical use of microwave relay equipment between studio and transmitter.

it to the receiver unit mounted on the rear of the parabola. The receiver unit includes the heterodyne oscillator, first detector, and four i-f stages. The signal, at the i-f frequency, is fed from this "pre-amplifier" to the remaining stages of the receiver which, along with the receiver operating controls, is located in the receiver control unit. This unit, like the transmitter control unit, is a separate case which can be located as much as 200 feet away. The receiver control unit utilizes a separate power supply, which is mounted in a similar sized case.

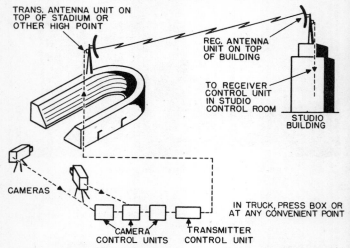

Figure 106. Microwave relay from remote pickup point to studio.

The control unit receives the signal at i-f frequency, detects and amplifies it, and feeds the video signal to the master control room.

4-87 Mobile Television Unit. The RCA mobile television unit is virtually a complete television studio on wheels. It carries a complete image orthicon camera chain and microwave relay equipment. The floor plan shown in Figure 107a, illustrates how this mobile unit stores the equipment and serves as a studio control room.

In action, the mobile unit appears as in Figure 107b. The camera and relay antenna may be mounted on its roof. The camera may also be located as much as 1,000 feet away. The director usually monitors the camera in the mobile unit and sends instructions to the camera operator over a telephone line.

4-88 The Video Transmitter. The RCA Model TT-5A transmitter utilizes high level modulation. It generates 5 kw. of peak video power. In the RCA design, the undesired portion of the lower sideband is removed by a filter in the antenna circuit.

A block diagram of the RCA transmitter is shown in Figure

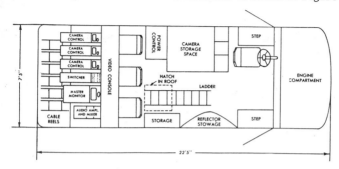

Figure·107. (A) Floor plan and (B) exterior appearance of mobile television unit. (courtesy RCA)

108. The r-f section consists of a crystal oscillator, doubler, tripler, buffer (or tripler when used for the upper television band of 174-216 Mc.) and power amplifier. These stages employ conventional tank circuits, and all but the power amplifier

stage are condenser tuned.

An RCA 1614 tube is employed as a crystal oscillator with its plate circuit tuned to twice the crystal frequency. A 4E27 doubler with tuned input and output circuits follows the oscillator. This doubler feeds a 4E27 tripler, which is in turn inductively

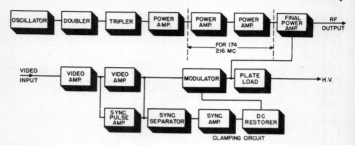

Figure 108. Block diagram of TT-5A transmitter.

coupled to the tuned grids of two 4-125/4D21 tubes operating in push-pull. For the frequency range of 54-88 Mc. (channel 2 to 6), the push-pull stage drives a 8D21 final power amplifier tube. However, for channel 7 to 13 it becomes a tripler, and two additional r-f stages are inserted to provide adequate drive for the power amplifier. The additional r-f unit utilizes two 4-125/4D21 tubes in push-pull, driving a pair of 4C33 tubes, also in push-pull. Sufficient shielding within the 8D21 final power amplifier tube and between the input and output circuits of the amplifier stage eliminates the need for neutralization.

Power is coupled from the power amplifier plate tank to the series-tuned output tank, and from there it is fed to the transmission line.

The picture amplifier and modulator unit consists of two video amplifier stages, the modulator stage, sync expander, sync separator, sync amplifier, and a d-c insertion diode. The gain of the video amplifier is very high (about 600). This high video voltage is necessary in a high level modulation system.

Three 6AG7 tubes in parallel comprise the first video amplifier stage. From this amplifier, video signals pass through a high-frequency compensating network to the second video amplifier which consists of two 807 tubes connected in parallel. To compensate for loss in sync pulse amplitude occurring in the succeeding modulator and power amplifier stages, a 6AG7 tube is connected in parallel with these 807s. As the 6AG7 has a high transconductance (and sharp cutoff), it expands the synchronizing pulse without increasing the amplitude of the picture signal.

Six RCA 4E27 tubes in parallel modulate the grids of the power amplifier. A "clamp" type d-c restorer circuit is used in the modulator stage. This clamping circuit reduces spurious low-frequency signals such as microphonics, power supply surges,

Figure 109. RCA TT-5A transmitter. (courtesy RCA)

and 60 cycle hum introduced in preceding stages to negligible values. Modulator bias is automatically brought to the same predetermined value for each blanking pulse, and in effect, the d-c component is restored.

Plate and screen voltages for the picture r-f portion of the transmitter are furnished by power supplies located in three racks. These power supplies include a 5,000 volt d-c supply for the plates of the power amplifier, a regulated 800 volt d-c supply which furnishes screen voltages to the power amplifier, and a 1,500 volt supply for the plates and screens of the oscillator stage, the frequency multipliers and drivers. Modulator plate voltage is supplied from a 1,000 volt supply using six 8008 rectifiers.

The r-f stages and the modulator occupy the last six racks of the complete TT-5A transmitter shown in Figure 109. The first two racks contain the sound transmitter which will be described later.

A vestigial sideband filter, which is a permanently tuned r-f filter that clips off a portion of the lower sideband of the 9-megacycle television signal (after modulation), and passes on to the antenna a signal which will occupy a bandwidth of no more than 6 megacycles, is used with the transmitter. The filter is contained in a completely enclosed metal cabinet. Since filter com-

ponents of the common coil and condenser type would be difficult to manufacture and uneconomical to use because of the currents, voltages and reactances involved, the sideband filter has
been designed with low loss coaxial transmission line elements.
(Figure 110). Water, flowing through the filter, dissipates the

Figure 110. Vestigial sideband filter. (courtesy RCA)

power absorbed from the lower sideband.

A dummy load is supplied with the TT-5A transmitter to terminate the output of either the picture or sound transmitter and
allow absolute measurement of the power output of either transmitter.

The dummy load is a high attenuation coaxial line which is
matched to the 72 ohm transmission line. The inner conductor
of the load is a water cooled resistor. Power output is measured
by the calorimeter method (described under Operation and Main-

tenance at the end of this section), making use of two thermometers and a flowmeter.

The load, power measuring equipment, and flowmeter are housed in a single cabinet. (Figure 111). When the load is to be used, it is taken from the cabinet and connected to the transmission line. Utilizing the transmitter water-cooling system,

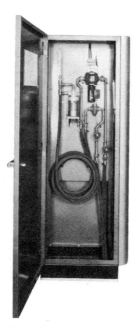

Figure 111. Power output measuring equipment. (courtesy RCA)

two 15 foot water hoses carry the water between the cabinet and load. The flowmeter is provided with an interlock to shut off the transmitter if water fails to circulate. The transmission line is equipped with quick disconnect fittings, allowing the load to be placed in operation in a few minutes.

4-89 The Sound Transmitter. The tube complement and circuits of the sound driver and power amplifier are identical to those of the picture driver and power amplifier. The exciter circuits for the frequency modulation sound, of course, differ. The carrier frequency for the sound channel is higher by 4.5 Mc.

A simplified diagram of the FM exciter appears in the lower portion of Figure 112. Audio signals are fed to the primary winding of an input transformer and passed to the push-pull grids of two 6V6 reactance modulator tubes. The plates of these

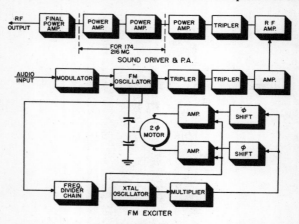

Figure 112. Block diagram of RCA sound transmitter.

tubes are connected in parallel to the tank circuit of a 6V6 Hartley oscillator employing a tuned tank coil. Energy from this tank coil is link-coupled to the tuned grids of the reactance modulator, one of which functions as a capacitive reactance and the other as an inductive reactance across the oscillator tank circuit. Since the amplitude of the reactive plate current of the tubes is proportional to the amplitude of the signal on their grids, application of an audio signal shifts the frequency of the oscillator at an audio rate.

The frequency modulated signal then passes through two frequency multipliers (triplers) and an amplifier which is coupled to the first amplifier in the driver stages of the transmitter.

The FM exciter unit obtains its operating voltages from a regulated power supply. Plate and screen voltages for the r-f driver are furnished by a 1,500 volt supply identical to that of the video r-f driver. The power amplifier plate voltage is furnished by a 5,000 volt supply, which is identical to that used for the video power amplifier. The FM exciter, driver and power amplifier shown in Figure 112 occupy the first two racks in the TT-5A transmitter.

The video and audio transmitter are coupled to the same super turnstile antenna through a diplexer. This unit was described previously in this section.

STATION OPERATION AND MAINTENANCE

4-90 Operating and maintaining the station studio equipment and transmitter is a task requiring careful coordination of the activities of the program department and engineering staff. The crew and equipment used in rehearsals is, in most cases, the same used to put the show on the air. Few stations can yet afford extra rehearsal crews, cameras, and equipment. Little time is left, therefore, for actual maintenance and adjustment, and maintenance procedures must be carefully carried out between rehearsals and on-the-air periods.

Station maintenance procedures can be broken down into two main jobs. One is the adjustment of the studio equipment, including cameras, lighting, sound system, control monitors, and synchronizing generator. The other is maintaining the transmitter and antenna in proper working order. The manner in which station maintenance and operation is carried out by the personnel of a television station may be appreciated by a brief examination of a typical day's operation.

The early part of the day is usually consumed by rehearsals and perhaps a few morning or afternoon shows. During rehearsals, the program director works out the proper placement of microphones with the technical director, the sound man, and the mike man, so that each scene is planned to give the best audio pick-up with the least amount of studio noise. The program director also plans the placement of lights with the performers, technical director, the light man, the camera operator, and the video engineer (who watches the studio scene on the control room monitor while lighting variations are tried). The planning of a set arrangement by the director during a rehearsal is shown in Figure 113.

The studio stage manager sees that the performers are properly guided on and off stage at the correct time and that props are in their right places. He must also plan scenery shifts without disturbing the cameras and mikes which are in use.

While this activity is taking place on the set, the cameras must be ON and ready to move at the director's command, in order to try out various combinations of lighting, set arrangement, and

Figure 113. Planning set arrangement during rehearsal.
(courtesy RCA)

placement and appearance of performers. There are also intervals when the cameras are idle, as for example, during scene shifts or breaks in the performers' rehearsal of lines and action sequences. During these periods lens caps are placed over the lenses to protect the pick-up tubes from damage. A concentrated light beam, such as a spotlight, shining directly into the lens for a period of time will burn the photosensitive surface. To avoid unnecessary use of equipment, the video engineer must find out beforehand from the director how much of the rehearsal is to be utilized as a camera rehearsal and how much for routine study of lines by the actors.

Since the light man, camera operators, mike man, and stage hands are moving about the set when a show is on the air, rehearsals must include arrangements for moving props and equipment quietly without fouling camera, mike, or light cables. To be ready for this activity, the video engineer tests and adjusts the cameras and equipment at least an hour before rehearsal or air time.

4-91 The Studio Control Room. Each studio has its own control room, which is responsible for the proper operation and control of the cameras and microphones. The studio control room feeds video and audio signals to the master control room where they are coordinated with signals from other points. Master control sends driving signals to all local studios for use in synchronizing cameras to the same sweep frequency, so that they may be switched on or off the air at will. The driving signals are fed to each camera in a studio through the studio control room.

There is one picture monitor in the studio control room for each camera in the studio. Each monitor is operated by a video engineer who works with the camera man to obtain a picture with proper focus, contrast, and brightness. As a rule two or three cameras are operated simultaneously from different locations. The program director, sitting behind the video engineers, observes all the monitors and chooses the picture which best suits the action at any given moment. The picture chosen is switched by the technical director onto the line to master control. A few moments later, as the action on the set changes, this camera may be switched off the air and another switched on. All cameras must, therefore, be in readiness at all times during a program, and the video engineers in the control room must constantly adjust the camera signals to produce the best possible pictures on their monitors.

The video engineers in the studio control room have access to four camera controls which affect the picture quality: the electrical focus, the sweep linearity, the signal level, and the shading when iconoscope cameras are used. The electrical focus and sweep linearity adjustments are made before going on the air. The signal level and shading must be constantly varied during operation.

4-92 Electrical Focus. The electrical focus is adjusted by first optically focusing the camera on a uniformly illuminated test pattern (this pattern is usually printed on a large card which is mounted on an easel and kept in a convenient place on the studio floor.) The video engineer adjusts the electrical focus by watching the pattern obtained on the picture monitor.

In order to obtain the best camera tube beam focus for highest resolution, it is frequently desirable to expand the picture monitor tube scanning considerably so that the wedge which runs vertically is spread out to a point where the spot size of the monitor cathode-ray tube is no longer an important factor. Another way of achieving the same result is to decrease the cam-

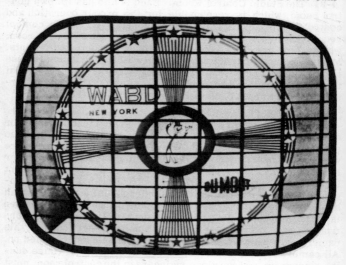

Figure 114. Linearity bars for adjustment of monitor sweep linearity. (courtesy DuMont)

era tube scanning to one half amplitude. In either case, a wedge designed to give 500 line resolution for a fully scanned picture will be, effectively, a thousand line wedge. With reduced scanning in the camera or with an expanded monitor picture, it is possible to precisely adjust the camera tube focus.

4-93 Sweep Linearity. The sweep signals controlling the motion of the scanning beam in the camera pick-up tube must be adjusted for best linearity. If a camera's sweep is not linear, moving objects in the picture will be foreshortened or stretched as they move across the screen. The linearity is checked with special calibration pulses which are received from the master control sync generator and are switched into the video amplifier circuits when needed. These pulses are derived from the divider stages in the sync generator and are called linearity test bars. They appear on the picture monitor as shown in Figure 114. The pulses are fed to the studio monitors from master control in order to obtain uniform linearity on all cameras in the station.

The picture monitor is first checked for absolute linearity by measuring the distance between linearity bars with a calipers or scale, and then making necessary adjustments of the sweep linearity controls. When the monitor sweep is linear, both vertically and horizontally, the camera test pattern is switched onto the monitor. If the pattern appears non-linear, the camera scanning circuits are adjusted.

Without linearity bars, it is difficult to determine whether poor linearity of the picture, as observed on the monitor, is caused by faulty scanning in the camera, or in the monitor, or by a combination of both. It is entirely possible to obtain a linear test pattern on the monitor if the non-linear scanning of the monitor cancels the non-linearity of the camera sweep. Such a pattern would appear non-linear at the receiver. The test bars insure that the picture being transmitted is always linear.

4-94 Adjusting the Signal Level. Because of variations in camera tubes and amplifier circuits, the output signals of all cameras are not of the same amplitude. The picture contrast will therefore change as different cameras are switched on the air, even though all the cameras are focused on the same scene. This undesirable condition is avoided by adjusting the amplitude of the signals from each camera until all the monitors have pictures of equal contrast.

Sometimes it is desirable to create special effects in the picture electronically. For example, a night scene may be "faked" with the studio fully illuminated to obtain maximum contrast in the picture. In the studio control room the video engineer adjusts the d-c level of the video signals so that it drops down near the sync, or black, level. The picture then appears on the monitor as though it were picked up at night.

Another special effect requiring adjustment of the signal level by the video engineer is the superimposing of the picture from one camera on the picture received from another camera. An example of this effect is the portrayal of a person having a dream. One camera is focused on the person while another picks up the scene about which he is supposedly dreaming. When the two signals are combined in the control room, the picture shows the scene superimposed on the performer. To accomplish this effect, the signal from each camera must be reduced in amplitude so that the total signal from the two cameras adds up to the signal level of a single camera adjusted for proper contrast. If this level is exceeded, too strong a signal will be fed to the transmitter. The proper signal levels are adjusted in rehearsal to secure the desired effect as observed on a picture monitor. The signal amplitude of the combined camera signals is then noted on the oscillograph monitor. If the maximum level has not been exceeded, the video engineer notes the setting of

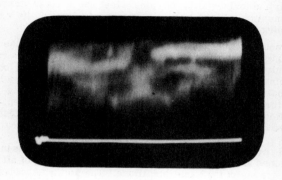

Figure 115. Waveform of properly shaded video signal as it appears on waveform monitor with 30-cycle sweep.

each camera. When the show is on the air and the program director calls for the special effect, the gain controls are set to the previously calibrated positions, and the combined signals fed to the same line.

4-95 Shading the Picture. Shading of the picture is necessary only when iconoscope cameras are used. Each video engineer has a set of shading controls for his camera. These controls are usually located below the picture monitor so that he can watch the picture while making adjustments. The shading signals are sawtooth, parabolic, and sine wave voltages which occur at the vertical and horizontal frequencies. They are injected into the video signal to compensate for spurious secondary emission from the iconoscope mosaic. Since this emission changes the light patterns which fall on the mosaic, the video engineer must constantly adjust the shading signals as the action on the set progresses. To enable him to determine the correct amount of shading signal to inject into the circuit, the engineer must watch two oscillograph monitors located below or on each side of the picture monitor. The time base frequency of one of the oscillograph monitors is set at 30 cycles per second and is so phased that a complete field appears in the middle of the screen as shown in Figure 115. The fact that the tops of the video signals reach approximately the same level indicates that a uni-

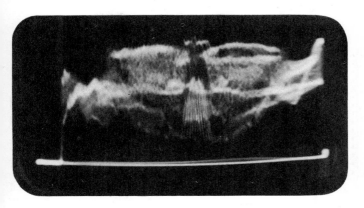

Figure 116. Waveform of properly shaded video signal as it appears on waveform monitor with 7,875-cycle sweep.

formly illuminated picture will be produced on the picture monitor. The time base frequency of the other oscillograph is run at half the horizontal scanning rate, or 7,875 cycles per second. The video signals of successive horizontal lines appear on this monitor as shown in Figure 116.

These oscillograph patterns are very useful in shading the picture. For example, if the engineer inserts a sawtooth shading voltage at horizontal frequency into the video amplifier, the top of the pattern shown in Figure 116 slopes downward from left to right, instead of being relatively flat. This darkens the right hand side of the picture since the video signals occurring near the end of each line have an additional sawtooth component which moves them toward the black level. By inserting a horizontal frequency sawtooth voltage of opposite phase, the engineer can darken the left side of the picture. Or he may use a sine wave, a parabola, or any combination of these signals to compensate for spurious secondary emission, and thus obtain uniform distribution of light across the picture. This condition is indicated by a relatively flat-topped pattern on the oscillograph monitor.

Correct shading is indicated on the vertical frequency oscillograph monitor which shows a complete field. When the top of the video signal pattern appearing on this monitor is substantially flat, the distribution of light in the picture from top to bottom is uniform.

The shading controls are generally arranged in two groups. The engineer manipulates all the vertical controls with one hand and the horizontal controls with the other hand.

Two oscillograph monitors are used with each picture monitor for shading, one for vertical shading, the other for horizontal shading. When image-orthicon cameras, which do not require continuous shading, are used in the studio, only one picture monitor and one oscillograph monitor are employed with each camera.

4-96 The Sound Pickup. The studio control room is equipped with a sound monitoring console and switching system for putting one or more microphones on the air. A record turntable is generally found in the studio control room for working in musical backgrounds or recorded sound effects with the action on the studio floor. The sound equipment is handled by the sound engineer who works closely with the video engineers and program director to coordinate the sound and video pickups. The sound signals which emanate from the studio control room are fed over a separate line to master control.

4-97 The Master Control Room. The master control room staff coordinates and checks the video and audio signals coming from each studio, from remote pickups, film pickups, and from other network stations. The personnel in this control room are responsible for the quality of the pictures and sound transmitted by the station, as well as the maintaining of the standards of transmission required by FCC regulations. The responsibility of maintaining close coordination between studios, film room, and field engineers is that of the master control supervisor.

The number of picture monitors in master control depends upon the size of the station. One monitor is used to check the quality of the "on-the-air" picture. Another monitor is employed to preview the picture coming from the pickup point before putting it on the air. Sometimes two or more preview monitors are used in stations having many studios and remote pickup facilities.

In addition to giving the program its final check before it is placed on the air, master control periodically checks the operation of the sync generator and makes quantitative measurements on the video signal to assure that it conforms with FCC standards. These maintenance procedures include the checking of interlace and the amplitude and shape of the sync and blanking pulses.

4-98 Checking Interlace. The picture monitor is used for checking interlace. The vertical height of the picture appear-

Figure 117. Vertical sweep extremely expanded.

ing on the monitor is increased about three to four times normal, as shown in Figure 117. Expanding the picture makes it possible to see the spacing between lines. The center portion of the picture is then resolved into individual scanning lines between which the interlace can be observed. If the spacing of the lines is uniform, the interlace is correct. Poor interlace is evident when the spacing between lines slowly changes.

4-99 Checking Percent Amplitude of Sync and Blanking Signals. The standard television signal consists of 75% picture signal and 25% sync signal when radiated from the transmitter. Generally, the transmitter modulating characteristics will compress the sync level and, to compensate for this, more than 25% sync must be fed into the mixing amplifiers. The exact percentage that is required at the master control line amplifier which feeds the transmitter is determined periodically by adjusting the sync level until an observer at the transmitter indicates that the percentages of sync and picture signal are correct. The limits of swing of the video signal, as well as the sync and blanking levels, are marked on the master control oscillograph monitor screen to correspond to the limits of swing of the radio frequency carrier and the correct percentage levels.

4-100 Checking Duration of Sync and Blanking Signals. The duration of the sync and blanking pulses is checked on the picture monitor or with a cathode-ray oscillograph. Since the sync generator can be relied upon to produce stable signals over a period of several days, only qualitative measurements are made

Figure 118. Test pattern with sweep at half horizontal frequency.

each day before broadcasting. Experience with the equipment enables the master control supervisor to determine how often quantitative measurements and readjustment of the sync generator are necessary.

The duration of the horizontal sync and blanking pulses is checked by adjusting the horizontal sweep speed of the master control monitor to one half its normal frequency. Two pictures then appear side by side as shown in Figure 118. In the center of the pattern a dark vertical bar appears, which contains the horizontal sync and blanking pulses occurring between lines. With adjustment of the contrast and brightness controls of the monitor, the blanking and sync pulses appear in different shades of grey. The sync pulses will appear slightly darker since they occur in the "blacker than black" level. The horizontal front porch, sync pulses, and back porch are then clearly visible.

The horizontal blanking region may be shown in its entirety only by this half speed scanning process. With the normal scanning pattern, a portion of the blanking occurs at the right side of the picture and a portion at the left side, making measurement of the porches and sync pulses difficult. To measure the duration of the sync and blanking signals in terms of percent of H (the FCC standards are expressed in this manner), the width of the pulse is measured with a calipers. This dimension is divided by the width of a horizontal line (the width of both half-speed pictures plus the blanking interval), and multiplied by 100 to give the percent width of the pulse.

The duration of the vertical sync and blanking pulses is check-

Figure 119. Test pattern with sweep set at half vertical frequency.

ed on the same picture monitor in a similar manner. While making the vertical sync and blanking pulse measurements, the vertical scanning frequency of the monitor is set at half normal, cr 30 cycles per second. Two pictures, one above the other, as shown in Figure 119, appear on the monitor tube. The duration of pulses in the vertical blanking interval in terms of percent of V is measured by dividing the width of the pulse by the total height (the two half-speed pictures plus the vertical blanking interval), and multiplying by 100.

4-101 Video Signal Measurements with an Oscillograph. The measurement of the front and back porches and the duration of the sync pulses by the above method is satisfactory for day to day routine operation. However, periodically the rise time as well as the duration of these pulses must be accurately checked. These measurements can be made precisely on an oscillograph whose sweep speed is sufficient to spread the pulse out over a large portion of the cathode ray screen.

A method for making these measurements, using a standard cathode ray oscillograph, is known as the sine wave sweep method. A 15,750 cycle sine wave which is synchronous to the pulse to be measured provides the horizontal deflection of the oscillograph. The pulse is applied to the vertical amplifier. The pattern on the oscillograph appears as in Figure 120. With

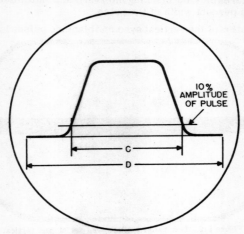

Figure 120. Sine wave sweep method of measuring pulse duration.

a sine wave sweep, the following relationship exists between the pulse width and the dimensions of the pulse on the pattern:

$$\% \text{ width} = \frac{\sin^{-1} \frac{C}{D}}{1.8}$$

where c and d are distances measured on the oscillograph pattern.

This method of using sine wave sweep for measuring the horizontal sync pulses can be applied to the measurement of the vertical blanking interval pulses when the sine wave sweep is 60 cycles and locked to the power line.

The sine wave sweep method is tedious since it requires calculation of the final result, but is one of the few ways at the disposal of the engineer of making measurements accurately in the absence of adequate commercial test equipment. A special cathode ray oscillograph, the DuMont Type 280, is specifically designed for the measurement of all the components of the television signal. This instrument is shown in Figure 121. It permits the direct reading of the rise time and duration of the sync, blanking, and equalizing pulses within the requirements specified by the FCC.

By feeding the composite video signal from the output of the

Figure 121. DuMont type 280 oscillograph. (courtesy DuMont)

line amplifier or transmitter (picked off by a demodulating diode probe) to the input of the oscillograph, and adjusting the oscillograph sweep speed, any portion of the video signal may be examined. For example, in Figure 122 the sweep speeds have been adjusted to show the vertical blanking interval. The number of equalizing pulses may be counted to check the operation of the sync generator. By turning a calibrated dial on the oscillograph, which moves the pulse past a fixed reference point on the screen, the time duration of the pulse may be read directly.

In Figure 123 the sweep speed has been increased to select a horizontal blanking pulse. The front and back porches and sync pulse are clearly visible. The duration of each of these signals can again be read directly in microseconds by rotating the calibrated sweep dial on the oscillograph.

By increasing the sweep speed of the oscillograph still further, the leading edge of a horizontal synchronizing pulse can be expanded so as to appear as in Figure 124. With the rise time of the pulse expanded in this manner, the calibrated sweep dial may again be used to accurately measure its duration.

Precise measurements of the degree of interlace may be made with this instrument. The oscillograph is set so that it triggers on two successive fields. The patterns of both fields are then

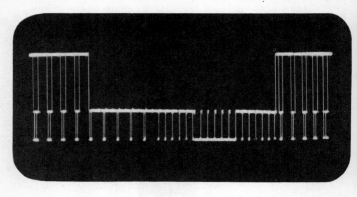

Figure 122. Vertical blanking interval. (courtesy DuMont)

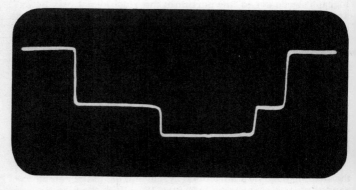

Figure 123. Horizontal blanking and sync pulse.

superimposed upon each other, and when the sweep speed is set to examine a horizontal sync pulse, a pattern is obtained as shown in Figure 125. This shows a horizontal sync pulse in one field superimposed on an equalizing pulse occurring in the next

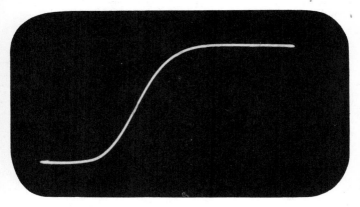

Figure 124. Leading edge of horizontal pulse.

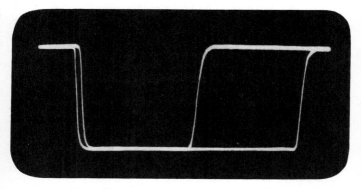

Figure 125. Superimposed horizontal sync pulse and equalizing pulse used to check interlace.

field. If the interlace were perfect, the two pulses would overlap. The displacement between the two is measured in microseconds on the oscillograph, and is an accurate measure of the degree of interlace of the sync signals.

4-102 Checking Resolution. The DuMont Type 280 oscillograph may also be used to accurately measure the resolution of a television signal. It is capable of feeding a marker signal to a standard picture monitor. This marker signal is an exact indication of the portion of the video signal which appears on the oscillograph. On the picture monitor the marker appears as a

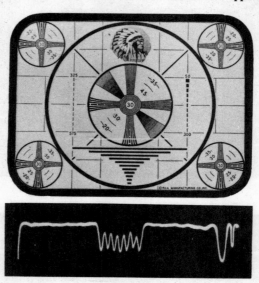

Figure 126. Oscillogram and test pattern used to measure resolution.

white horizontal line as shown in Figure 126. The corresponding video signal appears on the oscillograph screen as shown in the same figure. By adjusting the oscillograph sweep circuits, the marker may be moved to any portion of the picture to examine it in detail. A group of lines may be observed as well, in which case the sweep speed is lower and the marker appears as in Figure 127. To check resolution, the operator moves the marker to the vertical wedge as shown in Figure 126. Ideally, these wedges should appear as square waves in signal form because of the alternate black and white lines. The signal actually appears as a sine wave because a 525 line television system cannot fully resolve the fine lines at the bottom of the wedge. The amplitude of this sine wave is a measure of the degradation from the ideal square wave which would extend from the black level to the white level. Resolution is proportional to the amplitude of the sine wave.

4-103 Audio Facilities. Master control has the same audio facilities as the studio control room. The sound engineer monitors the sound signals coming from the studio to the transmitter.

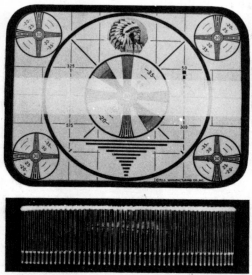

Figure 127. Oscillogram of several horizontal lines and test pattern with marker to indicate portion of pattern used.

A turntable is available for "dubbing" in music, commercial recordings, and station breaks. The audio signal is fed on a separate line to the sound transmitter.

4-104 Operation and Maintenance of the Transmitter. After the video and audio signals are monitored in master control, they are fed to the picture and sound transmitters. Operation and maintenance procedures for the transmitters include checking of the following:

1. Carrier frequency
2. Power output
3. Amplifier bandwidth
4. Transmitter regulation
5. D-C restoration

In order to observe the video signal at different points in the picture transmitter, the modulated carrier must be detected and fed to oscillograph and picture monitors. Use is made of conveniently located pickoff diodes, beginning at the first modulated radio frequency stage and going up through the intermediate power amplifier stages and the final output stage to the antenna

Figure 128. Monitor facilities for checking video transmitter.
(courtesy RCA)

coupling. The diodes pick off small amounts of energy from the various stages, rectify the envelope of the signal, and deliver the video signal over coaxial cables to the main monitor unit in the transmitter room. Figure 128 shows a view of the transmitter monitor rack. The monitor picture tube and the monitor oscillograph are shown. Also illustrated are the facilities for switching to appropriate circuits throughout the transmitter so as to view the pictures as they progress through the transmitter. Such monitor facilities assist greatly in tuning up the transmitter and in determining whether or not the stages are in proper tune during normal operation.

It is important that a good picture be obtained when checking each monitor stage to assure that the overall fidelity of the transmitter is good. For example, the shape of the front and back porches and the sync pulses must be carefully maintained if proper synchronism is to be achieved at the receiver. If, however, one stage of the transmitter is so tuned that it accentuates certain frequencies, the sync and blanking pulses may have sharp tails produced by the improper tuning. Once these tails have been introduced in one part of the transmitter, they may become saturated in later stages. It is thus impossible to equalize certain signals back to the proper wave shape. The successive monitor diodes, therefore, are quite important in the initial adjustment of the transmitter and in observing its operation.

4-105 R-F Passband Characteristic. The r-f passband characteristic is measured by means of a built-in or external wobbulator, whose frequency range is plus or minus 5 Mc. about the carrier frequency. Diode pickup sampling circuits are usually installed in the plate circuit of the modulated amplifier, the cathode circuit of the intermediate power amplifier, the cathode circuit of the power amplifier, the plate circuit of the power amplifier, and in the transmission line output. An oscillograph connected to any one of these diode pickup points when the wobbulator signal is being fed through the transmitter will indicate the response characteristic of the amplifier stage.

4-106 Video Amplifier Frequency Response. The video amplifier must be capable of essentially flat response from 30 cycles to 5 or 6 Mc. The low frequencies response may be checked by feeding a 60 cycle square wave to the video amplifier and observing its output on the oscillograph monitor. Low frequency distortion is manifested by a tilting of the top of the square wave. The allowable tilt in a video amplifier is about 2 percent for a 60 cycle square wave. Excessive low frequency compensation of the video amplifier stage is observed on the oscillograph as a rise in the trailing edge of the square wave, while insufficient compensation results in a rise of the leading edge. Each amplifier stage must be adjusted separately so that it is flat. Staggering the response a number of stages to give an overall flat characteristic may result in objectionable phase shift in the transmitter and is therefore avoided wherever possible.

The high frequency response of video amplifiers is checked by means of an oscillograph and wobbulator whose output is linear from about 200 kc to 8 Mc. The high frequency peaking coils are adjusted until a frequency response characteristic is obtained which is flat to at least 5 Mc.

4-107 Checking the D-C Restorer. The purpose of the d-c restorer in a transmitter is to refer all sync tips of the video signal to the same bias level in the modulator. The restoring characteristic is measured at the plate of the modulator. Figure 129 shows how the oscillograph is connected for this measurement. The signal must be connected directly to the deflec-

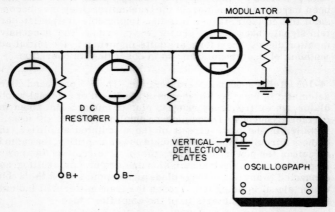

Figure 129. Method used to measure d-c restoration in transmitter.

tion plates of the oscillograph in order to observe the d-c component.

With no video signal fed to the oscillograph, the beam on the oscillograph is adjusted to the center of the screen. The video signal is then fed to the oscillograph. The peaks of the signals which represent zero level should remain at essentially the original center position of the tube if the d-c restoration is correct.

4-108 Measurement of Transmitter Power Output. Measurement of power at high frequencies presents problems not present at lower frequencies since instruments for voltage and current measurements at high frequencies are not yet available. In addition it is difficult to connect measuring instruments to a transmitter without upsetting its tuning.

A satisfactory method for measuring the transmitter power output without disturbing the amplifiers is known as the calorimeter method. The transmission line to the antenna is disconnected and terminated with a pure resistance equal to the characteristic impedance of the line. This dummy load is geometrically designed so that it may be coaxially installed in the transmission line. (See Figure 111) A coolant, such as water, is passed over the resistance element. The initial temperature of the coolant is first measured with a thermometer before it flows over the dummy load. It is measured again after it has been heated by the power dissipated in the dummy load. The temperature difference is a measure of the power fed to the dummy load, or the output power of the transmitter. The actual average power output is calculated from the temperature difference, the rate of flow of the coolant (measured in volume per unit time), and the specific heat of the cooling fluid. A nomograph, which relates power, temperature difference, and specific heat is then used to determine the average power output.

To determine peak power output, the above measurements are made when the standard video signal (25% sync and 75% video) is fed from the transmitter to the dummy load. The peak power is then 1.68 times the average power output as determined by the calorimeter method.

4-109 Measurement of Transmitter Regulation. The term transmitter regulation refers to the change in r-f peak signal amplitude which takes place when the video content of the signal is changed from an all white to an all black picture. It gives an overall indication of the operation of the d-c restorer, the regulation of the power supplies, the stability of the a-c line, and, in general, all the equipment in the transmitter. The r-f signal is observed on an oscillograph during the measurement. The oscillograph is coupled to the antenna transmission line by a loop.

To measure the transmitter regulation, the ratio of sync signal to video signal is first adjusted to be 30 to 70 for a totally white picture. Modulation of the r-f carrier is then set to give sync down to 75% of peak and white down to 15% of peak. The video signal is then changed to a totally black picture (consisting of sync and blanking only), whose amplitude is the same as for the white picture. The decrease in peak to peak r-f modulation is a measure of the overall regulation. The change in peak signal amplitude from an all black to an all white picture should not exceed 10% of the signal amplitude with an all black picture.

The regulation is always measured with the transmitter operating under conditions of rated peak power output.

4-110 Transient Response. The fact that the transmitter amplifiers appear to have the correct frequency response when viewed with a wobbulator does not assure that they will respond correctly to steep fronted pulses. The measure of the ability of an amplifier to respond to a sharply rising pulse without introducing overshoot or sudden oscillation is referred to as its "transient response". Standards for measuring the transient

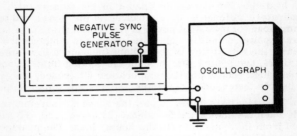

Figure 130. Method used to check antenna impedance match.

response of a transmitter have not yet been established, but techniques for their measurement are being developed.

A transient response check can be obtained by feeding a symmetrical 100 kc square wave into an amplifier. The square wave must have a rise time of less than 0.03 microseconds. To view this transmitted signal, an ideal television receiver is required, whose r-f and i-f amplifier characteristics will not distort the 0.03 microsecond rising square wave. Instead of viewing the detected signal on the picture tube, it is fed to a cathode ray oscillograph whose video amplifiers can pass the square wave without distortion. Degradation of the square wave, showing effects of overshoot, ringing, and sloping of the top of the wave, give an indication of the transient response.

4-111 Checking the Carrier Frequency. A frequency monitor is used in the television transmitter to insure that the carrier is operating on its correct frequency. The monitor is coupled into the final amplifier stage. A crystal controlled oscillator generates the exact frequency on which the transmitter channel is to operate. This signal beats against the signal from the transmitter, producing an audio difference frequency which is amplified and applied to a frequency deviation meter.

4-112 Checking the Antenna Impedance Match to the Trans-

mission Line. Since an antenna may be considered as a wide-band tuned circuit, it should have a broadband frequency characteristic. When coupled to the transmission line coming from the transmitter, it should present a resistive load to the transmission line in order not to set up signal reflections in the line. The impedance which the antenna presents to the transmission

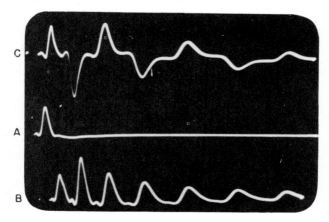

Figure 131. Oscillograms showing patterns obtained for properly and improperly matched transmission line.

line is analyzed by means of a short-duration pulse generator and a high frequency, driven-sweep cathode ray oscillograph. The connections are as shown in Figure 130. A negative trigger pulse synchronizes the oscillograph sweep and also supplies the pulse to be observed to the vertical amplifier of the oscillograph. The transmission line (at a point near the transmitter) is paralleled across the vertical amplifier input of the oscillograph. The pulse travels down the transmission line to the antenna and back to the oscillograph if the line is not properly terminated. Figure 131a shows the pattern produced when the antenna is correctly matched to the transmission line. It will be noted that only the original pulse is visible, since no reflections have taken place. Figure 131b and 131c illustrate the patterns which result when the terminating impedance is not equal to the transmission line characteristic impedance. In Figure 131b the pulse is reflected in phase and the impedance is greater. In Figure 131c the pulse reflections are out of phase and the impedance is less. The antenna coupling is adjusted until these reflections disappear, as indicated by the oscillograph.

TELEVISION ANTENNA SYSTEMS

All types of radio broadcasting are dependent upon the wire-less transmission of speech, music, pictures or some other signal, through the air. The final link between the individual transmitting station and the multitude of widely displaced receivers is the antenna. The antenna may exist in many forms, but in any form its purpose is to radiate or receive signal-bearing radio frequency energy.

5-1 The Transmitting Antenna. The transmitting antenna is designed to meet the particular requirements of the television broadcast station. Such stations operate on frequencies which are characteristically different from those of AM stations, and, moreover, they must transmit with good uniformity a wide band of frequencies. Care must also be taken to achieve radiation that will be substantially equal in all directions along the earth's surface.

In the early days of television, separate antennas were employed to radiate the picture signal and its accompanying sound signal. Today, the transmitting antenna is designed and constructed so that its effective bandwidth is adequate for the faithful transmission of both the picture and sound signals, which together occupy a band of frequencies six megacycles wide.

5-2 The Receiving Antenna. The finest television receiver may be said to be only as good as the antenna to which it is connected.

The considerations involved in the design of a television receiving antenna are different from those of the broadcast receiving antenna, which is usually short compared with the received wavelength. Because of the higher frequencies employed for television broadcasting, a receiving antenna one-half or more wavelengths long is generally used and constitutes in itself a tuned circuit.

Another unusual characteristic of the television receiving antenna is the wide band of frequencies over which it must perform. An efficient antenna must be capable of providing adequate reception — free from ghosts and other interference — on all the television channels serving the area. In order to be able to select the proper antenna for a given installation, a thorough knowledge of the basic antenna elements which are combined to achieve the desired television reception, is of paramount importance.

5-3 Behavior of Radio Waves. The answers to many of the questions as to why one type of antenna is better than another are to be found in the nature of radio waves and the ways in which they travel. The behavior of waves of different frequencies gives the clue to important points in antenna design. An elementary knowledge of wave propagation will lead to a reasonable explanation of what to expect.

5-4 Wavelength vs Frequency. Radio waves, unlike the transmitting apparatus which produces them and the receiving apparatus which converts them to useful information, cannot be seen or touched. We know that they travel with the speed of light (300,000,000 meters, or 186,000 miles, per second in vacuum), that they are electromagnetic, and that they can be refracted and reflected.

The relation between wavelength and frequency is expressed by the equation:

$$\lambda = \frac{300,000,000}{f}$$

where λ is the wavelength in meters (39.38 inches), and
 f   is the frequency in cycles per second.

5-5 Classification of Frequency Bands. Practical limitations on the size of a radio antenna result in very little power being radiated at frequencies less than 15,000 cycles per second, so that only frequencies greater than that are used in radio communication. The frequencies used in radio communication are classified as follows:

Frequency Range	Nature of Range	Abbreviation
Below 30 KC	Very low frequencies	VLF
30-300 KC	Low frequencies	LF
300-3000 KC	Medium frequencies	MF
3000-30,000 KC	High frequencies	HF
30-300 MC	Very high frequencies	VHF
300-3000 MC	Ultra high frequencies	UHF
3000-30,000 MC	Super high frequencies	SHF

5-6 Television Frequency Allocation. The channels used for television are between 44 and 88 megacycles, and between 174 and 216 megacycles and are in the VHF band.

Channel No.	Megacycles	Channel No.	Megacycles
1	44-50	7	174-180
2	54-60	8	180-186
3	60-66	9	186-192
4	66-72	10	192-198
5	76-82	11	198-204
6	82-88	12	204-210
		13	210-216

In addition to the above channels, which have been assigned to commercial television broadcasting, a group of frequencies in the UHF band, 2000 and 6800-7050 mc, have been assigned to mobile relay television broadcasts and STL's (studio to transmitter links).

5-7 Electric and Magnetic Fields. The radio wave energy which is emitted from a transmitting antenna is divided equally between an electric field and a magnetic field. This radio wave energy may be represented by a latticework of horizontal and vertical lines as shown in Figure 1. If the horizontal lines represent the electric field, the vertical lines are the magnetic field. The plane containing the latticework represents the wave front, and the direction of the wave's travel is always perpendicular to the wave front.

5-8 Intensity of the Wave. The intensity of the wave is usually expressed in microvolts or millivolts per meter, which is a measure of the dielectric stress produced by the electric field,

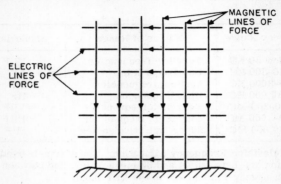

Figure 1. Representation of the magnetic and electric fields of horizontally polarized wave.

or the voltage induced in a conductor 1 meter long held at right angles to the magnetic field and the wave front.

5-9 Wave Polarization. The polarization of the radio wave is determined by the direction of the electric lines of force. A radio wave with its electric field horizontal is said to be horizontally polarized, and one with its electric field vertical is said to be vertically polarized. A horizontal antenna generates a horizontally polarized wave, and a vertical antenna generates a vertically polarized wave.

A horizontally polarized wave traveling in contact with conducting ground falls off very rapidly as it progresses from the antenna, because the electric field is in effect short-circuited by the ground. The electric field of a vertically polarized wave, being perpendicular to the earth's surface, does not fall off nearly so rapidly. The ground acts like a conductor at frequencies up to about five megacycles, but more like a dielectric at higher frequencies.

5-10 Receiving Antenna Orientation. The energy taken from the radio wave by the receiving antenna is greatest when the antenna orientation is the same as the direction of the transmission path of the arriving wave, and has the same polarization. Because of the directive feature of television receiving antennas, it is highly advantageous to point the antenna as accurately as possible in the direction of the transmitter. Note that pointing a receiving antenna involves pointing the broad side of the antenna, and not the ends, toward the transmitter.

5-11 Wave Reflection. Radio waves are reflected by a process very similar to that by which light waves are reflected by a mirror. The efficiency with which the reflection of radio waves occurs depends upon the frequency of the wave energy and the nature of the reflecting surface or object. Size, smoothness and electrical conductivity are factors determining the reflective efficiency of objects in the path of radio waves.

The surface of the earth is a good reflector, particularly of those waves which are incident to it at small angles from the vertical. Layers of the ionosphere which exist from 30 to 200 miles above the earth's surface, also reflect radio waves in the frequency bands below 40 mc.

5-12 Wave Refraction and Diffraction. The gaseous nature of the earth's atmosphere results in a changing dielectric constant. This variation in the dielectric density of the atmosphere causes radio waves passing through the air to be refracted downward toward the earth. Likewise, radio waves grazing the edge of the earth's surface in passing, will deviate from their straight path, resulting in a bending or diffractive effect.

Refraction and diffraction are of interest because their effect enables the television frequency wave to follow the earth's curvature, giving propagation conditions approaching that for a plane earth for some distance beyond the horizon.

5-13 Modes of Propagation. The waves radiated from an antenna may travel either along the surface of the ground, or in the atmosphere above the earth's surface. The ground wave is useful only for short distances at the higher frequencies, but the useful range increases as the frequencies are lowered. Long distance radio transmission takes place by means of the sky wave, radio energy which travels from the earth to the upper atmosphere and is there reflected back to the earth's surface some distance beyond the transmitter. Both modes of wave propagation are shown in Figure 2.

5-14 Low Frequency and Medium Frequency Propagation.

Waves of low frequencies between 15 and 300 KC and medium frequencies between 300 and 3000 KC are transmitted by ground wave with less energy loss than are high frequencies. At these low frequencies, conductivity of the underlying terrain is more important than the dielectric constant.

Because of the long wave lengths involved, antennas for trans-

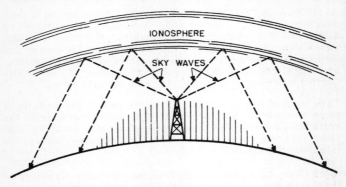

Figure 2. The two principal modes of wave propagation.

mission of these frequencies are physically and electrically close to ground. The radio waves are long enough to be propagated around small obstacles and gentle curves, such as the earth's surface, with little obstruction. At low frequencies, radio transmission over long distances takes place by a combination of the ground wave and sky wave. Propagation of waves at these low frequencies has the characteristic of being guided between the concentric conducting surfaces of the ionosphere and the earth. The ground wave and sky wave are not as easily distinguishable at low frequencies as at medium frequencies. The polarization of radio waves at these frequencies is vertical.

5-15 High Frequency Propagation. The range of the ground wave decreases with increase of frequency in the high frequency band between 3 and 30 mc. In this band, the dielectric constant plays a greater role in the decrease of the ground wave field with distance.

At night, there may be sky wave propagation for frequencies as low as 3 mc, and frequencies above 8 and 10 mc will penetrate the ionosphere at all angles. However, in the daytime, frequencies of about 3 mc are strictly confined to ground wave propagation. Frequencies between 5 and 10 megacycles will produce sky waves in the daytime.

In general, the higher frequencies in this band are favorable for long distance day propagation, dependent on the conditions of the ionosphere.

5-16 Propagation at Frequencies Above 30 MC. At frequencies above 30 mc the decrease of the ground wave field intensity is much more rapid than for lower frequencies. For antennas close to the ground, the field intensity varies roughly inversely as the square of the distance. However, this rapid ground wave attenuation can be overcome in part by the elevation of both the transmitting and receiving antennas a number of wavelengths above ground. This is practical at these frequencies because the physical equivalent of the electrical wavelength is comparatively small. All frequencies in this band are heavily absorbed by the ionosphere, and sky wave transmission is sporadic, if it exists at all.

5-17 Characteristics of Very High Frequencies. Very high frequency waves used for television purposes are not regularly returned to the earth at great distances. Normal transmission at television frequencies is due chiefly to the direct and ground-reflected wave components of the surface wave. Transmission over long distances far beyond the horizon is occasionally possible as a result of unusual atmospheric or ionospheric conditions. However, the reliable transmission range of the television transmitter is generally taken to be at the horizon.

5-18 Line of Sight Propagation. At television frequencies the surface wave is absorbed very rapidly as the distance from the transmitter is increased. If the transmitting location is visible from the receiver, the very-high-frequency signals can usually be transmitted reliably both day and night, with very little fading or other irregularities from atmospheric causes.

The optical line of sight distance may be calculated by the following equation:

$$D = 1.23 \left(\sqrt{H_T} + \sqrt{H_R} \right)$$

where D is line of sight distance in miles.

H_T is height of transmitting antenna in feet.

H_R is height of receiving antenna in feet.

5-19 Radio Horizon. For very high frequencies an extension of the transmitting range is achieved by refraction. This modification to line of sight propagation is known as the quasi-optical, or radio horizon, distance.

The radio horizon is expressed by the equation:

$$D = 1.42 \left(\sqrt{H_T} + \sqrt{H_R} \right)$$

where D is radio horizon distance in miles.

H_T is height of transmitting antenna in feet.

H_R is height of receiving antenna in feet.

This equation includes the effect of a gradual change in the dielectric constant of the earth's atmosphere which, for standard conditions, causes a refracting effect equivalent to increasing the earth's radius by one-third. Figure 3 shows the rela-

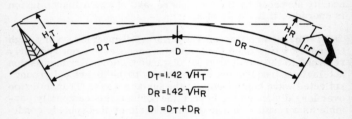

$$D_T = 1.42 \sqrt{H_T}$$
$$D_R = 1.42 \sqrt{H_R}$$
$$D = D_T + D_R$$

Figure 3. Radio horizon distance between transmitter and receiver.

tion between the transmitting distances and the height of the antennas.

5-20 Effect of Height at the Transmitting Antenna. If should be noted that whereas the distance range of the ground wave at low frequencies can be increased effectively by increasing the radiated power, the distance range at television frequencies can be increased effectively only by increasing the height of the transmitting and receiving antennas. The need for height to increase the range of transmission is the primary factor in the installation of transmitting antennas, resulting in their placement on the tallest buildings or topographical points in the community.

5-21 Range of a Metropolitan Television Station. A Metropolitan Station is limited by the Federal Communications Commission to a maximum of 50 kilowatts effective peak power with an antenna having a height of 500 feet above the average surrounding terrain.

The effective radiated power at the antenna is the product of the input power at the antenna and the antenna power gain factor. If the center of the antenna is exactly 500 feet above the average terrain, the broadcaster is permitted to operate so that this

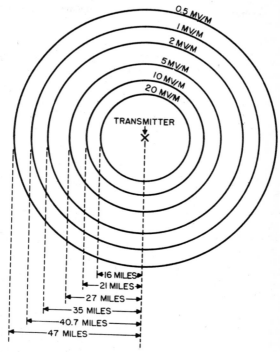

Figure 4. Ground-wave signal range of television station.

product is exactly 50 kilowatts. If the antenna height is greater than 500 feet, the product of the power input and antenna gain must be reduced in proportion to the increased height of the antenna. However, the effective radiated power is still 50 kilowatts because the propagation efficiency of the antenna is increased in proportion to its added height above average terrain. Therefore, the signal intensity for all metropolitan stations at an appreciable distance from the transmitter, is the same. Figure 4 shows the signal intensity which can be expected as the receiving distance is varied, assuming that the transmitting antenna is 30 feet high and is horizontally polarized.

5-22 Effect of Height at the Receiving Antenna. Increasing the receiving antenna elevation is often the simplest way to improve circuit performance. Raising the receiving antenna 30 feet results in a signal gain of as much as 10 to 1.

This gain represents an increased r-f signal-to-noise ratio as long as the receiver noise is the controlling factor. This might be the case where the receiver is located on the fringe of the service area and insufficient signal is available at lower

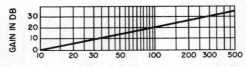

ANTENNA ELEVATION IN FEET

Figure 5. Gain in field intensity of a horizontally polarized dipole antenna when it is raised from low elevation.

elevations for adequate service. When external noise is controlling, the gain in signal intensity obtained by raising the receiving antenna may be ineffective, if in improving the r-f signal-to-noise ratio the received noise is increased along with the signal. The graph in Figure 5 shows the gain in the field intensity of a horizontally polarized dipole antenna when it is raised from a low elevation. This graph applied to both the transmitting and receiving antennas.

5-23 Multipath Reflections. Normally, television signals travel a direct line of sight path from the transmitter to the receiver. When the direct line of sight path to the receiver is blocked by such objects as hills and buildings, it is possible to receive a strong or weakened signal via a reflection.

Reflection is a characteristic of television signals which often results in more than one signal being received from the same transmitter. These signals travel via different paths of varying length and their arrival at the receiver may be staggered in time. Dependent on the attenuation encountered by these multipath signals and the relative intensity of one signal to the others, a visual pattern of interference, known as ghosts will be seen on the receiver picture tube. The reflected signal may be white or black, depending on its polarity, and it may vary in intensity from almost equal to that of the direct signal, to a point where it is just noticeable.

The ghosts of multiple images may occur so that they are not noticeable in themselves, but will instead cause a loss of definition in the picture. Obviously, in any congested area there may be multiple reflection paths that may set up multiple images. In some locations, such effects may prevent satisfactory television reception. Figures 6 through 9 illustrate various conditions which cause multipath reflections.

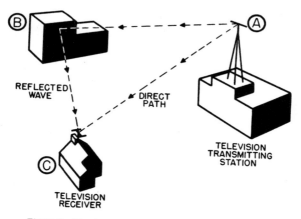

Figure 6. Direct wave and reflected wave striking antenna.

5-24 The Effect of Terrain Irregularities. Propagation characteristics of television signals over irregular terrain are in marked contrast to the uniform attenuation of the signal with distance when transmitting over level terrain. Here the variation of field intensity with distance depends largely on the profile of the terrain between the transmitting and the receiving antennas. The effects of terrain irregularities upon the television signal are illustrated in Figure 10.

Shadow losses introduced by the earth's curvature and by intervening hills are to be reckoned with. Trees or dense forests near receiving antennas cause more loss of power than at lower frequencies. Fading is often experienced, caused by reflections from airplanes and other moving objects in the path of the radio wave transmission. The limitations placed upon an adequate

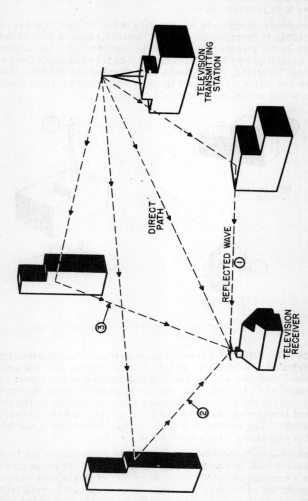

Figure 7. Several reflected waves arriving at antenna along with direct wave.

TELEVISION TRANSMITTING STATION

DIRECT PATH

REFLECTED WAVE ①

TELEVISION RECEIVER

②

③

transmission path between the transmitter and receiver are severe.

5-25 Changes in Polarization. At appreciable distances from the transmitter, the polarization of the television transmission usually varies and is essentially vertical. This is caused by the cancellation of the direct wave by the ground-reflected surface wave components at low angles of transmission (for hori-

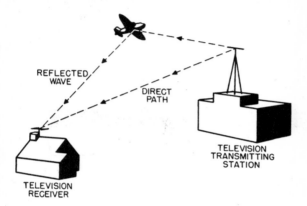

Figure 8. Reflected wave caused by moving airplane.

zontally polarized waves). See Figure 11. This is also due to the relatively greater attenuation of a horizontally polarized surface wave component as compared with that of a vertically polarized surface wave component.

5-26 Factors Affecting Television Transmission. Obviously, there are a considerable number of advantages in the use of very high frequencies for television. Some of these are:

a. Frequencies in the VHF band are usually free from atmospheric static noise except during local electric storms.

b. There are no seasonal variations in the characteristics of the transmission path. Signals are therefore solid, except when affected by changes in meteorological conditions.

c. Quarter wavelength and half wavelength antennas in the VHF band are physically small, and therefore very efficient antenna systems are possible.

d. The performance of the VHF receiving circuits may be improved substantially, except under certain conditions, by rais-

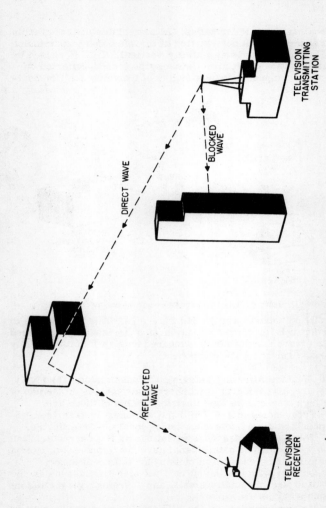

Figure 9. Reception by means of reflected signal; direct wave blocked by building.

TELEVISION TRANSMITTING STATION

BLOCKED WAVE

DIRECT WAVE

REFLECTED WAVE

TELEVISION RECEIVER

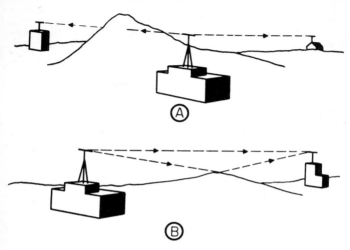

Figure 10. (A) Television signal weakened by intervening hill.
(B) Multipath reflection caused by a "bounce" signal.

ing receiving antennas to moderate elevations above the ground.

e. Directional receiving antennas for improving transmission in the desired direction are of relatively small dimensions, and directivity gains equivalent to raising the transmitting power by four times or more are not hard to attain.

5-27 Function of Transmission Lines. The term "transmission line" is applied to electrical conductors which are employed

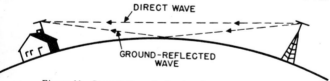

DIRECT WAVE

GROUND-REFLECTED WAVE

Figure 11. Cancellation of direct wave by ground-reflected wave.

to convey electrical energy from one point to another. The widest application of transmission lines is their use in conjunction with antenna systems.

It is almost impossible to find a modern high frequency antenna system which is not coupled or matched to the transmitter or receiver by means of a transmission line. The more complex antenna systems employ lines as a means of establishing proper phase relations between the various elements of the antenna array. Since an antenna system without an associated transmission line network is a rarity, a working knowledge of trans-

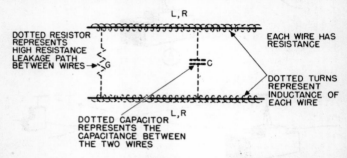

Figure 12. Distribution of resistance, capacitance, and inductance along section of two-wire transmission line.

mission line fundamentals is essential to a complete understanding of television antennas.

5-28 Properties of Transmission Lines. Transmission lines are not perfect conductors; that is, in the transfer of radio frequency energy from one point to another via a transmission line, some loss in energy occurs. This loss cannot be accounted for entirely by the resistance of the conductors.

The line has properties other than pure resistance which may cause additional losses. These properties of the line are series inductance, shunt capacitance, and resistance leakage across the line in addition to the series resistance. These properties are not unlike the common inductors, capacitors and resistors used as circuit components. In the r-f transmission line, however, these quantities are uniformly distributed throughout the length of the line and cannot be separated from each other. Figure 12 shows how resistance, capacitance, and inductance are distributed along a short section of a two wire transmission line.

In view of these properties of resistance, inductance and capacitance, it may be concluded that all transmission lines present an impedance to the flow of r-f energy.

5-29 The Non-Resonant Line. It has been pointed out that transmission lines offer an impedance to the flow of r-f. All transmission lines have a property which is called the "characteristic" or "surge" impedance of the line. If a generator with a characteristic impedance equal to that of a line is connected to an infinite length of that line, a perfect transfer of energy from the generator to the line occurs. The signal travels down the line, with its energy gradually being dissipated in the line losses, until none is left.

A resistive load equal to the characteristic impedance may be employed instead, to terminate a finite length of the line. In this case, the energy (less the line losses) is dissipated in the resistive load. A transmission line which is terminated in this manner is called a non-resonant, flat, or matched line. Such lines are excellent for feeding an antenna at some distance from the transmitter or in connecting an antenna to a receiver. They have the disadvantage that their use is normally restricted by the antenna to one narrow band of frequencies.

5-30 The Resonant Line. At frequencies above about 40 mc, sections of transmission line approach the wavelength of the energy they convey. Because of their comparatively small dimensions and their extreme flexibility, tuned or resonant transmission lines find widespread use.

A resonant transmission line assumes many of the characteristics of a resonant circuit which is composed of lumped inductance and capacitance. When sections of line are used as tuned circuits, they also produce the effect of high-impedance (parallel resonant circuits) and low-impedance (series resonant circuits) common to conventional tuned circuits. Tuned lines may also be used as transformers. The transformer is widely used as a high efficiency impedance matching circuit.

5-31 The Infinite Line. Although an actually infinite line is impossible to attain, its usefulness is due to the fact that a knowledge of its behavior is of great assistance in determining the operating conditions of an actual line. Furthermore, any length of line can be made to appear like an infinite line if it is terminated in its characteristic impedance.

5-32 Wave Motion On a Line. Figure 13 shows the r-f voltage and current waves that exist on an infinite line. The voltage and current maximums are at the same points on the line, but because of line losses they keep diminishing in amplitude as the wave travels down the line. This figure illustrates what would happen if the voltage and current could be stopped for an instant in time, as if a movie film were stopped at a single picture.

An instant later in time, all waves would have moved to the right slightly as they continue to travel down the line.

Waves exist because it takes a certain amount of time for electrons to transfer energy down a wire by means of their motion. For example, if a pebble is dropped in the center of a

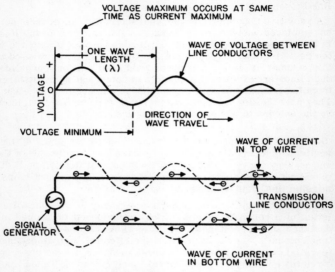

Figure 13. Voltage and current distribution along infinite line.

small pool of water, the disturbance does not reach the edge of the pool immediately. Rather, a wave of water starts out from the place where the pebble hits and proceeds toward the edge at a definite speed.

In electrical transmission lines, the time which electrical disturbances or waves take to travel to another point on the line is so small as to be negligible. This is due to the 186,000 miles per second speed of electricity.

5-33 Electrical Length vs Physical Length (Line Velocity of Propagation). The velocity of propagation of radio-frequency energy along a line varies with the type of line. Therefore, the physical or actual length of a line may differ slightly from the computed electrical length because of the capacitance effects between the conductors and between the conductors and ground. The physical quarter-wavelength for various types of line may be calculated from the formula:

$$L = \frac{246 \ V}{f}$$

where L is length in feet.
      F is frequency in megacycles.
      V is a constant dependent on the velocity of propagation for the particular line in question.

Average values for the constant V for various types of common line are as follows:

Type of Line	V
Parallel open wire	0.95
Parallel plastic ribbon line	0.85
Concentric line (Wafer spacers)	0.90-0.96
Concentric line (Solid dielectric)	0.85
Twisted pair	0.56-0.65

To obtain a half-wave or full-wave section, multiply L by 2 or 4, respectively.

5-34 Reflections On a Line. Consider an r-f transmission line in which the load impedance at the output end is infinite or an open circuit. When an r-f signal is applied to the input end, the first surge of energy traveling down the line consists of a wave of voltage and current in phase, or with their positive maximum occuring at the same time. However, when the wave of current consisting of electron motion reaches the output end, it falls to zero since there is no additional conductor in which to travel. When this current wave collapses, the magnetic field set up about the conductors also collapses. The collapsing magnetic field induces a voltage in the conductors near the output end of the line. This induced voltage acts, in a way, like a reverse signal and sets up new current and voltage waves which travel back on the line toward the input end.

The analogy illustrated in Figure 14 shows the standing waves produced on a rope by wave motion and reflection. The electrical-wave and the rope-wave actions are both forms of wave reflection.

5-35 Standing Waves. If a line is terminated with an impedance mismatch at the output or receiving end, it produces reflections. This means that as the initial energy from the input or antenna end of the line continually surges back and forth on the line, the

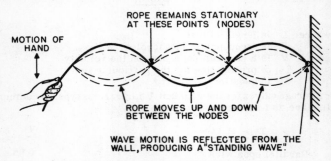

Figure 14. Standing waves produced in a rope.

reflected wave combines with the original wave and thus creates a standing wave.

When the line is unshielded, these stationary waves radiate into space, creating serious interference in other receivers nearby. In addition, the reflections increase the line losses, reducing the line efficiency; and where the line is over 50 feet long, ghost images may be seen on the television receiver screen. If the line is less than 50 feet long, the ghost effect may be negligible.

It is important to note that mismatches as high as 2 to 1 are considered acceptable, and will result in an efficiency loss of only ten percent. Under these conditions, a 150 ohm line could be used to match load impedances ranging from 75 to 300 ohms. However, it is always desirable to attempt as close a match as possible.

5-36 Determination of the Standing Wave Ratio. The voltage standing wave ratio (VSWR) is the yardstick for measuring the impedance mismatch on a line. This is simply the ratio of the minimum voltage to the maximum voltage on a line. These measurements are made with an r-f vacuum tube voltmeter at intermediate points along a length of the line at least one-half wavelength long. On a flat or matched line, the voltages measured at all points on the line would all be within ten percent of one another for a VSWR of 1.1 to 1. This is the procedure used in the field for determining the VSWR for high power transmission lines. The curve of Figure 15 shows the voltage loss

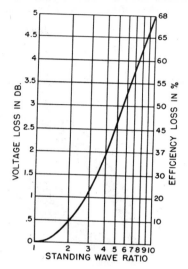

Figure 15. Curve showing the voltage loss in db and the efficiency loss in percent for various standing wave ratios.

in db and the efficiency loss in percent for various standing wave ratios.

In lines used for receiving, such a measurement would require special laboratory facilities due to the low level of the r-f signal and the modulation of the r-f signal. The determination of the VSWR for receiving lines must be practical, and therefore it is qualitative. The picture is the final measure of whether or not the line is properly matched. The effectiveness of all adjustments made to the antenna system is measured in terms of picture improvement. This is the purpose of the test pattern, which has been designed so as to lend itself to a critical qualitative analysis.

5-37 Circuit Effects of Resonant Transmission Lines. A resonant line can be defined as a line which possesses standing waves of current and voltage. The line is of finite length and is not terminated in its characteristic impedance. The resonant line is resonant at only one particular frequency.

In practical television receiving applications, the line may be considered resonant over a band of frequencies when designed to the geometric center of the frequency band desired. In such

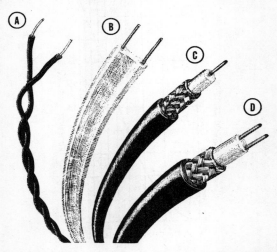

Figure 16. Four types of transmission lines. (A) Twisted pair. (B) Two-wire line. (C) Coaxial line. (D) Shielded pair.

a case it is acting as either a high-resistive or low-resistive impedance. In order to act in this manner, the line is either open-circuited or short-circuited at the output end and is cut to some multiple of a quarter-wavelength. If the length is not a multiple of a quarter-wavelength, the line acts as a capacitor or inductor.

5-38 Balanced Transmission Lines. The twisted pair and two wire parallel conductor are types of balanced transmission lines. A line is said to be balanced to ground when the capacity between each conductor and ground is uniform along its entire length. If radiation or noise pickup is to be avoided in an unshielded balanced line, the current flow in each conductor must be equal and opposite in direction.

This condition can be achieved only if the line is clear of conducting surfaces. At the higher frequencies, materials such as wood and brick will, when sufficiently damp, begin to act like conductors, adding to the difficulties encountered. In any case, these lines should not be permitted to swing free, but should be fastened securely, at regular intervals, with high quality insulators, if stable characteristics are to be obtained.

5-39 Twisted Pair. Twisted pair consists of two insulated wires twisted together to form a flexible line without the use of spacers (Figure 16A). It is the easiest line to construct. It is generally used as an untuned line in low frequency applications. It is not used at higher frequencies because of the high dielectric losses occuring in the insulation, 4 db for each one-hundred feet at 50 megacycles being typical. As in all lines, this loss increases with frequency.

Twisted pair may be used to match impedances ranging from 40 to 150 ohms. The disadvantages common to balanced transmission lines generally apply to twisted pair.

5-40 Two Wire Parallel Line. One of the most widely used types of line is the two wire parallel line. In its simplest form it consists of two parallel conductors, maintained at a fixed distance apart by means of insulating spacers placed at suitable intervals. This line is used widely because of its economy and efficiency.

A two wire parallel line, enclosed in a plastic ribbon of Polythene is a recent version of this type of line (Figure 16B). Polythene, a synthetic plastic with a yellow waxey appearance, has excellent dielectric characteristics for this type of application. In addition to its flexibility, the line has low loss, about 1.2 db per 100 feet at 50 megacycles. Common impedance values for commercially available plastic ribbon line range from 75 to 300 ohms.

5-41 The Shielded Pair. This line consists of two separate parallel conductors which are insulated from each other by a low loss dielectric, such as Polythene (Figure 16D). The conductors are contained within a tubing made of copper braid, which acts as a shield. The entire assembly is covered with a rubber or plastic composition for weather proofing.

The shielded pair has two outstanding advantages. The individual conductors are shielded against pickup from stray radiation or noise fields, and the line is balanced to ground at all points owing to the enclosing shield. It may be run close to conducting objects without fear of its becoming unbalanced. This line may be used in strong interference areas. The losses encountered in this line are not much better than for ordinary twisted pair, and its use should be restricted to strong signal locations. Typical impedance values range from 50 to 100 ohms.

5-42 Coaxial Line. Coaxial line has advantages which make it very practical for efficient operation at very high and ultrahigh frequencies. It consists of a wire inside of, and coaxial

TYPE OF LINE	SURGE IMPEDENCE		ATTENUATION IN DB. PER 100 FT. AT 50 MC.	MAXIMUM LENGTH IN FEET FOR AN EFFICIENCY OF 63%	BALANCED OR UNBALANCED	SHIELDED OR UNSHIELDED
	FROM	TO				
TWISTED PAIR	40	150	4	50	BAL.	UNS.
SHIELDED PAIR	40	100	3-1.5	66-133	BAL.	S.
TWO-WIRE PARALLEL (POLYTHENE)	75	300	1.2	167	BAL.	UNS.
COAXIAL (POLYTHENE)	10	150	.4	500	UNBAL.	S.

Figure 17. Characteristics of various types of transmission lines.

with, a concentric outer conductor (Figure 16C). The outer conductor may be flexible or solid, depending upon the inner conductor support. When the inner conductor is supported by a solid dielectric such as Polythene or Copalene, the outer conductor is normally flexible copper braid. In special cases where the line is used to connect high power transmitters to their antennas, the outer conductor is hard drawn copper and the inner conductor is supported at regular intervals by high grade insulating wafers or beads.

The signal energy is confined to the inside of this line and there is no loss of signal due to radiation. The outer shield reduces noise and stray radiation pickup. The line is unbalanced and must be properly connected to the receiver with the shield to ground in order to be effective. The line loss is dependent upon the insulating material used and may be as low as 0.4 db per hundred feet. It is available in impedances ranging from 10 to 150 ohms.

The important characteristics of the various types of transmission lines are compared in the chart of Figure 17.

5-43 Characteristic Impedance. The characteristic impedance of a transmission line is directly proportional to its L/C ratio. An increase in the separation between the conductors of a two wire line or between the inner conductor and concentric outer conductor in a coaxial line, increases the inductance and reduces the capacity. Thus the effect of increasing the spacing is to increase the characteristic impedance, since the ratio L/C is increased. Reducing the diameter of the conductors in a two wire line, or reducing the diameter of the inner conductor with respect to the diameter of the concentric conductor in a coaxial line, also increases the characteristic impedance. This change is brought about by a reduction of the interelement capacity of the line.

The characteristic impedance of both types of lines may be reduced by increasing the dielectric constant of the insulating material between the conductors. This change is due to the increased capacity of the line. Therefore, it is apparent that conductor size, spacing and dielectric material are the factors determining the characteristic impedance of the line.

5-44 Characteristic Impedance of a Two Wire Parallel Line. For a two wire parallel line the characteristic impedance is given by the following formula:

$$Z = \frac{276}{\sqrt{K}} \log \frac{b}{a}$$

where K is the dielectric constant (1 for air).
      b is the spacing between conductor centers.
      a is the radius of the conductor.

For a line using Polythene dielectric the value of $1/\sqrt{K}$ is equal to 0.675. Useful values of impedance for two wire parallel line for television use range from 50 to 300 ohms. The graph of Figure 18 shows the relationship between the characteristic impedance, spacing and conductor size for a two wire parallel line, with air spacing.

5-45 Characteristic Impedance of a Coaxial Line. For a coaxial line the characteristic impedance is given by the following formula:

$$Z = \frac{138}{\sqrt{K}} \log \frac{b}{a}$$

where K is the dielectric constant (1 for air).
      b is the inside diameter of the outer concentric
        conductor.
      a is the outside diameter of the inside conductor.

For a line using Polythene dielectric the value of $1/\sqrt{K}$ is e-
qual to 0.675. Useful values of impedance for coaxial trans-

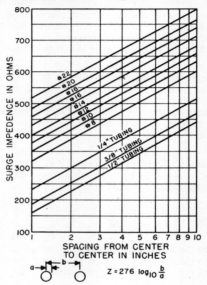

Figure 18. Characteristic impedance of two-conductor parallel
transmission lines.

mission lines for television range from 50 to 150 ohms. The
characteristic impedance of a concentric coaxial line with air
spacing is shown for different sizes of inner and outer conductors
in the curve of Figure 19.

5-46 **Impedance Matching Considerations.** In television transmitting systems, it is necessary to keep the impedance match
between the antenna and the transmission line leading to the
transmitter within plus or minus 10 percent, in spite of the fact
that the bandwidth transmitted is less than six megacycles. This
is a rather severe limitation. While the receiving antenna must

over a greater bandwidth, receiving antenna system require-
nents are much simpler, because a good impedance match be-
ween the antenna and transmission line is not important. This
s true only if there is a good impedance match between the
ransmission line and receiver input terminals. Mismatching
t the antenna is usually tolerable when the antenna impedance

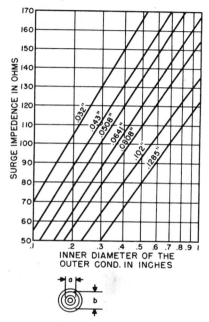

Figure 19. Characteristic impedance of coaxial transmission
lines.

is lower than that of the transmission line. A loss of energy
transfer and distortion of certain parts of the picture is produced by such a mismatch, but a considerable amount of mismatching can be tolerated before serious degradation of picture
quality occurs. The ratio of power lost in an unmatched line
to that lost in a matched line is plotted in Figure 20 as a function
of standing wave ratio. Note that the power loss does not become appreciable until standing wave ratios above 0.3 are encountered.

Reflections due to mismatching at the receiver input terminals produce "ghosts" which correspond to a delay time equivalent to the time required for the waves to travel back to the antenna and there be returned to the receiver input terminals.

5-47 Impedance Matching. To obtain maximum efficiency and the elimination of ghosts, the antenna, transmission line, and the receiver should be matched as closely as possible. The

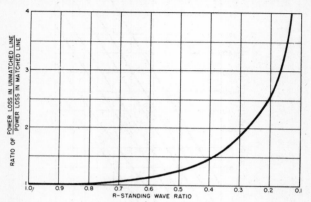

Figure 20. Ratio of power loss versus standing wave ratio.

wide variation in impedance encountered in television antennas makes it necessary to use special matching devices to avoid serious impedance discontinuities, and to keep the resulting standing wave ratio within reasonable limits.

When an antenna system must operate over a band of frequencies corresponding to several television channels, the resonant matching devices used must be designed for a compromise frequency or the geometric center of the band to be covered. The receiver input impedance, on the other hand, is fixed by the manufacturer over its operating range and is usually 75 to 300 ohms. Therefore, matching at the receiver merely involves the selection of a transmission line with a corresponding characteristic impedance. The antenna is then matched to the transmission line by a device such as a quarter-wave "Q" section or quarter-wave stub matching section. Several examples of matched and mismatched antenna systems are shown in Figure 21. Examples (A) and (B) show two systems with properly matched antennas, transmission lines, and receiver input impedances. Example (C) requires a matching resistive network of standard $\frac{1}{2}$ watt carbon resistors to match the 75 ohm line to the 300 ohm input to the receiver; it is good in high signal areas where the signal loss across the matching network can be tolerated. Examples (D) and (E) are very poor antenna systems with mismatches of 4:1, and should be avoided. Example (F) shows a 4:1 mis-

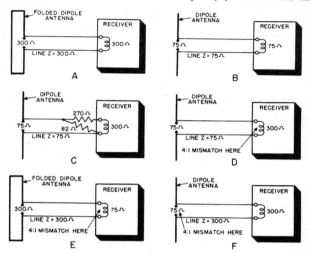

Figure 21. Examples of matched and mismatched antenna systems.

match at the antenna, but a correct match at the receiver input. This setup is tolerable where high signals prevail.

5-48 Geometric Center of Frequency Band. When an antenna system must operate over several television channels, resonant circuit elements must be designed for a compromise frequency. This frequency is usually the geometric center of the band, and is found by taking the square root of the product of the frequencies at the two extremities of the band to be covered. For coverage of channels 2 to 5 it is equal to $\sqrt{54 \times 82}$, or 66.5 megacycles. For channels 7 to 13 it is equal to $\sqrt{174 \times 216}$, or 193.8 megacycles.

In practice, the antenna system is often designed to favor the weakest station to be received, instead of cutting the antenna for the center of the band.

5-49 Quarter-Wave "Q" Matching Section. The "inverting" or impedance transformer characteristic of a quarter-wave section of line can be put to practical and efficient use when it is necessary to match a line of one impedance to an antenna of a different impedance. To do this, the section must have an impedance calculated as follows:

$$Z = \sqrt{Z_A \times Z_L}$$

where Z is impedance of matching section.
       Z_A is impedance of antenna.
       Z_L is impedance of line.

For example: A 300 ohm line can be matched to a 75 ohm dipole through a quarter-wave section of 150 ohms as shown in Figure 22. The "Q" section should be connected to the antenna

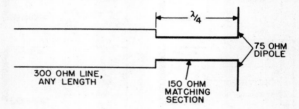

Figure 22. Q matching section.

directly and should be designed for the desired frequency, taking into account the velocity of propagation for the type of "Q" section used. The "Q" section is necessarily a compromise matching device when required to operate over several television channels.

5-50 Quarter-Wave Stub Matching Section. A popular form of matching transformer consists of a quarter-wave matching stub. If the quarter-wave stub is connected to a voltage loop of the antenna, it is necessary to short the end of the matching section. If the section is left open, it must be connected to a current loop of the antenna. The stub length is calculated from the formula:

$$L \text{ (feet)} = \frac{246}{f \text{ (mc)}}$$

The exact length of the matching section and the point of line attachment must be determined experimentally, since it depends upon the impedance of the line as well as the antenna impedance at the point of connection. The impedance of the line is not important since the quarter-wave stub can be used to match practically any impedance. In the example shown in Figure 23 an

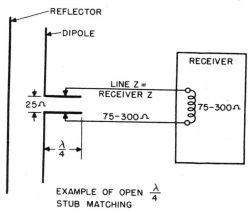

Figure 23. Quarter-wave stub matching section.

open-end quarter-wave stub is used to match a 25 ohm antenna to a line of 75 to 300 ohms. The correct match is determined by observing the operation of the television receiver with each adjustment.

ANTENNAS

5-51 Requirements of a Television Antenna. The choice of a suitable antenna system is complicated by the nature of the very high frequency waves used for television broadcasting. Such factors as broad band response, directional characteristics, the elimination of unwanted signals and reflections, and finally, the location of the antenna must all be taken into consideration if satisfactory reception is to be obtained.

A television receiving antenna should be capable of receiving several adjacent channels with equal efficiency. Antenna directivity is required to provide the strongest possible signal at the receiver, as well as to eliminate unwanted signals, wave reflections, and interference.

Antenna location involves the choice of a site where intervening objects, such as hills and buildings, do not block the radio wave path. The television antenna requirements for any location must be considered as an individual problem to be analyzed on its own merits. Constantly differing situations are encountered in the field, and it is important that the technician have a working knowledge of the characteristics of all practical antenna systems used in television.

5-52 Selection of a Television Antenna. There are many types of antennas suitable for receiving television signals, ranging from the simple and selective half-wave dipole to more complex wide-band antenna arrays. In practice, the differences in the various types is chiefly in terms of the frequency range of operation, the directivity, and gain.

A wide variety of antennas are commercially available, and it is usually possible to obtain a selective antenna having any desired degree of directivity or shape of field pattern, or to obtain a wide-band antenna system capable of intercepting all channels within either or both of the two television frequency bands. Choice of the proper type of receiving antenna is primarily influenced by the specific requirements and characteristics of each location or site.

If only one station is operating in the region, a selective antenna — such as a dipole without, or in combination with reflectors and/or directors — usually provides satisfactory reception. If two or more stations are operating on channels in the low frequency television band (44 to 88 mc), a less selective antenna — such as a folded dipole, or a wide band array, oriented in the direction which provides equally satisfactory reception of each station — is necessary. To receive two or more stations operating on channels in the high frequency band (174 to 261 mc), a proportionately smaller but similar type of antenna is installed.

The satisfactory reception of all television channels (1 - 13) with a single antenna is sometimes possible, using one of the special types of wide-band multi-channel antennas available. To favor weak signals or to minimize interference, a highly directive antenna is sometimes employed. Almost any desired shape of field pattern can be obtained with a suitable combination and arrangement of antenna elements. Such special field patterns are required in many cases in order to provide the television receiver with signals of sufficient strength for good visual reproduction.

In metropolitan areas and industrial districts, where television reception is likely to be marred by reflected waves or ghosts and other noise interference, it is sometimes necessary to in-

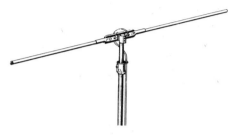

Figure 24. Dipole antenna. (courtesy Ward Products)

stall individual, highly directive, antennas for the reception of each television station. The effects of interference, due to flashing signs, diathermy machines, elevator motors, and other electrical devices, can be minimized or eliminated with a directional antenna system and a shielded transmission line.

The essential objective in the selection of a television antenna system is to provide adequate, ghost-free, interference-free reception of all the desired television stations operating in the region.

5-53 Resonant Antennas. The dimensions of a resonant antenna are dependent upon the frequency of the signal to be received. An example of a resonant or tuned antenna is the simple dipole, Figure 24, the physical dimensions of which are equal to approximately one half-wavelength. Other tuned antennas, elaborations of the dipole, are the folded dipole, V-antenna, fanned, and conical antenna.

The shape and dimensions of a tuned antenna affect its bandwidth and, to some extent, its horizontal directivity. The horizontal directivity of a resonant antenna can be increased through the use of one or more reflectors placed behind the antenna. Directors placed ahead of the antenna accomplish the same effect. Directors and reflectors are parasitic elements and have no electrical connection to the main antenna element. The vertical directivity of an antenna system can be increased by stacking antenna elements a half-wavelength apart, one above the other. A combination of stacked antenna elements with directors or reflectors combines the effects of the two systems, giving improved horizontal and vertical directivity.

5-54 Non-Resonant Antennas. The non-resonant antenna is sensitive to an extremely broad band of frequencies, provided

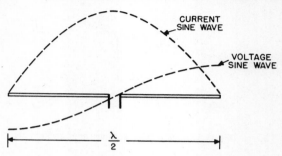

Figure 25.   Current and voltage distribution on half-wave dipole.

certain minimum dimensions are maintained. The principal disadvantage of these antennas is the space required for the erection of an antenna of suitable dimensions. The gain and bandwidth of a non-resonant antenna at any frequency of operation is proportional to its size. There is a minimum size below which it does not provide performance superior to the more compact resonant antennas. Typical types of non-resonant antennas are the long-wire, long-V and the rhombic.

5-55 Dipole Antenna. The dipole is a resonant antenna at the frequency at which its length is equivalent to a half-wavelength. When excited by an r-f signal at its resonant frequency, standing waves of voltage and current are produced along the half-wave dipole. The voltage and current distribution is sinusoidal with maximum current and minimum voltage at the center and minimum current and maximum voltage at the ends, as shown in Figure 25.

The presence of standing waves makes it possible to build up strong electrostatic and electromagnetic fields, and radiation or absorption of r-f energy takes place at the resonant wavelength of the antenna. This radiation or absorption field is maximum in any direction perpendicular to the dipole, and is minimum in either direction lengthwise to the antenna, as shown in Figure 26.

5-56 Field Patterns. The directional nature of the radiation pattern is usually indicated graphically by means of either horizontal or vertical field patterns for a fixed antenna in space. Perfect field patterns are difficult to obtain in practice, because

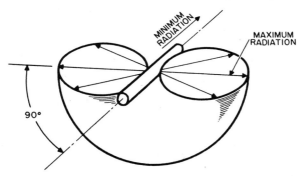

Figure 26. Radiation pattern of half-wave dipole in free space.

radio antennas are operated relatively close to the earth and the actual pattern is sometimes distorted and influenced by various ground effects. These effects become less pronounced as the frequency of operation is increased.

Field patterns apply to both transmitting and receiving antennas. In the horizontal plane, they are simple circular charts which resemble the face of a compass, with the antenna located at the center. The circumference of the circular chart is marked off in degrees from zero to 360, representing the bearing from the antenna at the center to the points around the compass. Zero degrees is usually taken at True North or some other convenient reference point.

The computed or measured field strength at each bearing is plotted radially from the center for each angular bearing from the antenna and joined together by a smooth curve. The horizontal field pattern, for receiving antennas, illustrates the relative sensitivity of the antenna at different bearings.

When the field strength of an antenna is plotted so that its amplitude in a given direction is compared to the field strength of a theoretical dipole in the direction of the dipole's maximum sensitivity, the power gain of the given antenna at any bearing may be read from the chart.

The horizontal field pattern of a horizontally polarized dipole is shaped like a figure eight, as shown in Figure 27. The

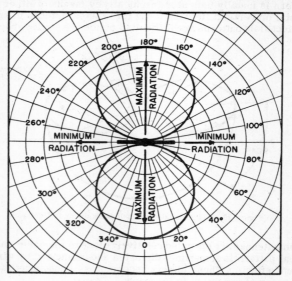

Figure 27. Horizontal field pattern of horizontally polarized half-wave dipole.

two main lobes of the antenna are not sufficiently narrow to be of great practical value; thus, the dipole antenna has only slight directivity.

A vertical field pattern is similar to the horizontal one, except that it shows the field pattern for vertical angles around the antenna. The vertical field pattern is always given for one horizontal angle of radiation, as shown in Figure 28. This is necessary, since there exists a separate vertical field pattern for each horizontal angle of radiation. For television receiving antennas, the vertical field pattern of most use is that which corresponds to the most sensitive horizontal field strength bearing of the antenna.

5-57 Directivity. The directivity of an antenna refers to the sharpness or narrowness of its field pattern in a given plane. An antenna with a sharp pattern in the horizontal plane is said to have good horizontal directivity. An antenna with a sharp pattern in the vertical plane is said to have good vertical directivity. Points on the field pattern at which radiation is zero are called nulls. The curved section between any two nulls is

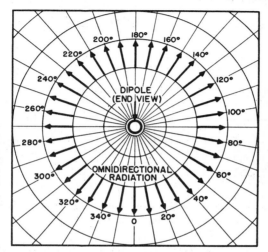

Figure 28. Vertical field pattern of horizontal dipole.

called a lobe. When the directivity of an antenna in a given plane is increased, it is usually accompanied by a reduction in effectiveness of the antenna in another plane.

5-58 Power Gain. This term is used to express the power increase of a given antenna over a standard basic antenna, usually, a half-wave dipole. When referring to a directional antenna, power gain usually means the power gain measured in the optimum direction of the antenna system.

5-59 Length of Dipole Antenna. The physical dimensions of a half-wave antenna element which equals an electrical half-wave is actually shorter than an actual half-wave of the frequency for which the antenna is cut.

In practice, a dipole antenna is usually opened at the center, forming two quarter-wave sections. These sections should be approximately 5% shorter than an actual quarter-wave of the frequency at which the antenna is to operate. The reduced length is necessary to offset end loading effects.

The physical length of the quarter-wave dipole antenna elements, considering end effect, may be calculated by the following formula:

$$L = \frac{234}{f}$$

where L is length in feet.
       f is frequency in megacycles.

The lengths of dipole antennas, which are cut for the center frequencies of each television channel, are shown in the chart

FREQUENCY (CENTER)	47	57	63	69	79	85	177	183	189	195	201	207	213
CHANNEL NUMBER	1	2	3	4	5	6	7	8	9	10	11	12	13
ELEMENT LENGTH IN FEET $L = \frac{234}{f(MC.)}$	5	4.1	3.6	3.4	3	2.8	1.32	1.28	1.24	1.2	1.16	1.13	1.1

Figure 29. Dipole dimension chart.

of Figure 29. The electrical quarter-wavelength corresponding to any frequency may be calculated by the following formula:

$$L = \frac{246}{f}$$

where L is length in feet.
       f is frequency in megacycles.

5-60 Dipole Bandwidth Considerations. When current is fed at the center, dipole and other half-wave antennas have characteristics similar to a series resonant circuit. The Q of an antenna, the ratio of its inductive reactance component to its resistive component, gives some indication of the bandwidth of the antenna.

At the resonant frequency of an antenna, its impedance is largely resistive. This condition exists over a band of frequencies whose width increases as the Q of the antenna decreases. It follows that for wide-band television applications, a low value of Q is preferable because of the increased bandwidth obtained.

Physically, the Q of a dipole antenna is a function of the ratio of its length to its diameter. An increase in the diameter of an antenna conductor reduces the inductance, increases the capacity, and thus lowers the Q of the antenna. Large diameter conductors are used for the elements of an antenna when wide band requirements must be met. An increase in bandwidth is accom-

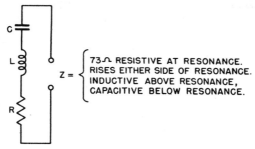

$Z = \begin{cases} \text{73-}\Omega\text{ RESISTIVE AT RESONANCE.} \\ \text{RISES EITHER SIDE OF RESONANCE.} \\ \text{INDUCTIVE ABOVE RESONANCE,} \\ \text{CAPACITIVE BELOW RESONANCE.} \end{cases}$

Figure 30. Equivalent circuit of a dipole antenna.

panied by a decrease in selectivity and a reduction in power gain at the resonant frequency. It is noteworthy that the dipole alone is used effectively for the reception of several adjacent television channels, as well as to form the basis for a wide variety of other types of antennas and arrays.

5-61 Dipole Impedance Characteristics. The equivalent circuit of the dipole antenna is a conventional series resonant circuit (Figure 30). The impedance of the dipole at its resonant frequency is 73 ohms, resistive. At frequencies above and below the resonant frequency, the dipole impedance increases, becoming more and more reactive. By keeping the inductive component of the antenna low and the capacitive component high, the impedance over a broad band of frequencies remains substantially resistive.

A dipole may be made sharply selective by increasing the inductive component and decreasing the capacitive component. In this case, the resistive component is prominent only at resonance and is insignificant in relation to the large reactive components when off resonance.

5-62 Practical Antennas. It has been shown that impedance matching between the receiving antenna and transmission line feeding the receiver is not of primary importance under certain conditions. The loss in efficiency which results, can be tolerated if the transmission line is "bridging" or has a higher characteristic impedance than the antenna. Therefore, impedance matching is not the reason for the many variations of the half-wave dipole antenna which are encountered in practice. Broad-banding is the major reason for these designs.

All resonant antennas capable of operating over a wide frequency range are characterized by a diameter, or other crosswise dimension, that is relatively large. The use of large diameter or multiple antenna elements does not affect the antenna radiation resistance greatly, but it does reduce the inductance and increase the capacitance, lowering the Q and improving the bandpass characteristics of the antenna system.

Other factors, closely interrelated, which influence television receiving antenna design, are directivity and sensitivity or power gain. Due to the quasi-optical behavior of television frequencies, there is always the possibility of receiving signals originating at the same transmitter over several different paths. These signals cannot be combined because of the time delay involved in the paths over which the signals travel to the receiving location. Directivity is essential to permit the selection of the desired signal to the exclusion of all of the others. Directivity also has the effect of increasing the sensitivity or power gain of an antenna.

A good picture is one free of distracting background noise. Added sensitivity provides increased signal strength with respect to noise. The amount of noise introduced into the receiver can be considerably reduced by limiting the horizontal signal admittance angle of the antenna to the minimum required.

To fulfill these various requirements, many types of antennas have been designed. For purposes of discussion, all antennas may be separated into three groups. These groups are: 1 the dipole and variations of it, 2 antenna arrays, and 3 long wire antennas. The balance of this section is devoted to descriptions of the antennas in these groups, starting with the dipole and variations of it.

5-63 Adjustable V Antenna. A variation of the dipole-type receiving antenna consists of a half-wave dipole whose quarter-wave elements are moveable in the vertical plane (Figure 31). This dipole is fed in the conventional manner, at its center, and pivoted in such a way that each arm can be adjusted to any desired angle above the horizon.

This antenna has its greatest application in congested city and industrial areas, where multi-path propagation is severe. Television waves are horizontally polarized at the time of transmission, and normally they retain this polarization during propagation. In urban or metropolitan districts, these waves are often reflected by large buildings and other objects before arriving at the receiving antenna. A wave which travels a reflected path to the antenna, may acquire a vertical component of polar-

Figure 31. Adjustable V antenna.

ization in addition to the original horizontal component. This combination of vertical and horizontal components effectively "raises" the angle of polarization above the horizontal plane. Therefore, when operating a receiving antenna on a reflected signal, the dipole works best when its angular position corresponds to the oblique angle of the wave polarization received.

In practice, the two arms of the dipole are adjusted until the best results are obtained visually on the television receiver picture tube.

5-64 Extended V Antenna. This wide band antenna may be used for television reception in congested city and urban locations, where polarization effects due to multi-path wave transmission are most pronounced. The extended V antenna (Figure 32) provides compensation for this polarization distortion, and has a frequency response sufficiently broad to accept television signals within either of the two frequency bands. The V-shape of the antenna may be utilized to match the antenna properly to a 300 ohm transmission line.

5-65 Crossed Dipole Antenna. In order to obtain omnidirectional characteristics, two horizontal half-wave dipoles may be arranged so that the inherent directivity of each dipole is combined to provide a circular radiation pattern in the horizontal plane. An arrangement of this type is the crossed dipole, or turnstile antenna, which is widely used for non-directional transmission and reception.

The basic antenna consists of two horizontal half-wave dipoles

Figure 32. Extended V antenna.

(Figure 33) crossed at right angles in the same plane. When the two dipoles are excited simultaneously with equal currents, differing in phase by 90 degrees, the individual field patterns are combined and the resultant field pattern is essentially circular, or omnidirectional (Figure 34). Because of the frequency sensitive phasing connection between the two sets of dipoles, this antenna is not generally suited to multiple channel television reception. It is also unsuited to many television installations because it cannot discriminate against unwanted signals, and is likely to accept multiple ghost creating signals, waves with polarity distortion, and noise interference. This type of antenna is restricted to transmitting applications, where, in its simple form or one of its many variations, it is used in stacked arrays to provide high-power omnidirectional radiation.

5-66 Folded Dipole. The folded dipole is ideal for television because of its higher input resistance and its broader bandwidth. With these advantages, the folded dipole retains the radiation characteristics of a simple half-wave dipole. The length of the

Figure 33. Crossed dipole antenna.

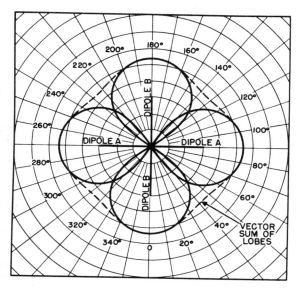

Figure 34. Horizontal field pattern of crossed dipole antenna.

folded dipole may be computed from the formula: $L = 492/f$ (mc) in feet.

Spacing between the two parallel elements is ordinarily less than 3 or 4 percent of the wavelength, and is not critical. The folded dipole is actually two parallel dipoles, carrying equal currents in the same phase. The voltage at the ends of the two dipoles is maintained equal by means of the direct short circuit connections, and the voltage distribution along both dipoles is therefore the same.

The folded dipole is shown in Figure 35. It is constructed with

Figure 35. Folded dipole antenna. (courtesy Ward Products)

elements of equal diameter. This folded dipole has an input impedance of 300 ohms. When the diameter of the fed element is decreased with respect to the other element, the input resistance increases. When the diameter of the fed element is increased with respect to the other element, the input resistance decreases. This characteristic of the folded dipole makes it possible to construct an antenna of almost any desired impedance.

Folded dipoles are often constructed of 300 ohm ribbon transmission line. This type of dielectric covered antenna should be cut approximately 85% of a half-wavelength of the frequency to be received. This is necessary because the velocity of propagation of the currents in the antenna is due to the dielectric material used. The exact length of an antenna made from 300 ohm ribbon may be found by multiplying an electrical half-wavelength of the frequency to be received by the factor 0.81. The factor takes into consideration both the antenna end effect and the reduced velocity of propagation due to the dielectric of the 300 ohm plastic ribbon transmission line.

5-67 Duo-Dipole Antenna. The unconventional arrangement of this wide-band receiving antenna (Figure 36) provides coverage of all television channels. The antenna consists of a relatively thin half-wave dipole — resonant at 70 megacycles — mounted parallel and close to a thicker half-wave dipole, resonant at 128 megacycles. The ends of the short, thick dipole are connected by means of inductive loops to the thin dipole. In addition

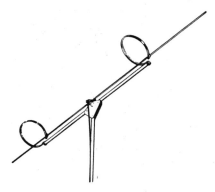

Figure 36. Duo-dipole antenna.

to feeding the short dipole, these two inductive loops also provide structural support for the long, thin dipole.

For reception in the low-frequency television band, the antenna functions as a wide-band folded dipole resonant at about 70 megacycles, since the long dipole is tuned to this frequency and the short dipole is effectively end-loaded by means of the inductive loops. For reception in the high frequency television band, both dipoles are resonant at the center of the band with all currents in phase, since the long, thin dipole is tuned to a third harmonic of the center frequency, and the short dipole is end-fed by means of the inductive loops. A matching stub permits the use of a standard 300 ohm line with minimum loss of power due to mismatched impedance. In general, the directivity of this receiving antenna remains substantially the same for all television channels. This important characteristic is evident by comparison of the field patterns at 70 megacycles (Figure 37) with the field pattern at 195 megacycles (Figure 38).

5-68 Bat-Wing Antenna. An important modification of the folded dipole, known as the duoband or bat-wing antenna (Figure 39), operates with equal effectiveness on each of the thirteen television channels. This antenna exhibits essentially the same directivity, gain, band width, and other reception characteristics on all channels. This is accomplished with a conventional folded dipole broadly tuned to the center of the low-frequency television band (44 to 88 megacycles), plus a wide band half-wave dipole resonant at 180 megacycles, connected to the terminals of the

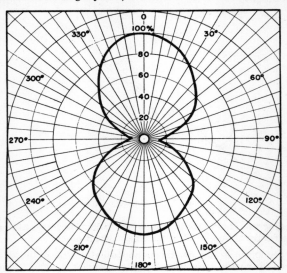

Figure 37. Horizontal field pattern of duo-dipole antenna at 70 Mc.

transmission line in parallel with the large folded dipole. The short modifying elements protrude forward at an angle of 50 degrees, accounting for the "bat-wing" appearance of the antenna.

For the reception of television channels in the low-frequency band, the antenna functions as an ordinary folded dipole, with a directional field pattern (Figure 40). For reception of television channels in the high-frequency band, however, there is a pronounced directional effect (Figure 41), produced by the resonant modifying elements at the center of the antenna.

5-69 Double-V or Fan Antennas. Another modification of the simple dipole which has a higher input impedance and broader bandwidth is the double-V antenna (Figure 42), the full-wave

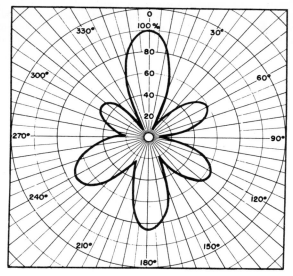

Figure 38. Horizontal field pattern of duo-dipole antenna at 195 Mc.

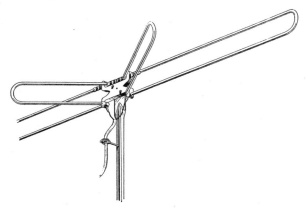

Figure 39. Bat-wing antenna.

fan antenna, or any of the several variations based on the number and arrangement of the "fanned" elements used. Maximum reception is perpendicular to the major axis of this type of antenna and, accordingly, the horizontal reception pattern is bidirectional.

The shape of the simple bi-directional pattern is considerably

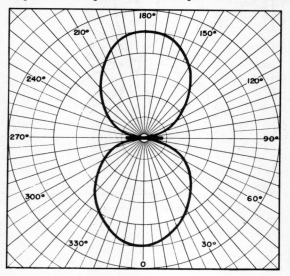

Figure 40. Field pattern of bat-wing antenna at 80 Mc.

modified at the higher television frequencies (Figure 43). In the vertical plane, the reception pattern is essentially omnidirectional, regardless of the frequency of operation.

The double-V is the simplest of these antennas. It is usually constructed of quarter-wave dipole elements. Its input impedance is in the order of 100 to 200 ohms. When a double-V antenna is used for broad-banding over all thirteen television channels, it assumes some of the aspects of the full-wave fan antenna (Figure 44). This antenna consists of three full-wave elements on each side of the center feed point. This impedance of a center-fed full-wave antenna is high, of the order of 600 to 700 ohms.

Two of these antennas, stacked a half-wavelength apart, would

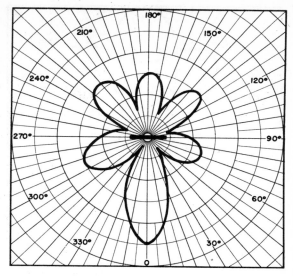

Figure 41. Field pattern of bat-wing antenna at 180 Mc.

Figure 42. Double-V antenna.

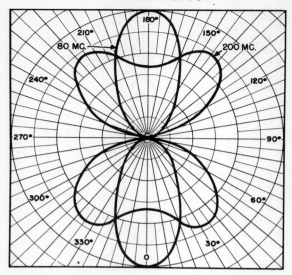

Figure 43. Horizontal field patterns of fan antenna at 80 Mc and 200 Mc.

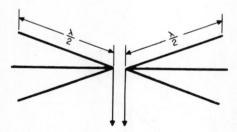

Figure 44. Full-wave fan antenna.

provide a good impedance match for a 300 ohm line.

Another fan antenna (Figure 45) is available which consists of five "fanned" elements, which present a satisfactory impedance match to a 300 ohm line from 44 to 216 megacycles. In this antenna the fans are in the horizontal plane. Its operation over the full 44 to 216 megacycle frequency range is a compromise between a half-wave resonant antenna at the lower frequencies and a full-wave resonant antenna at the higher frequencies.

5-70 Conical Antenna. One of the most effective broad-band antennas for television use is the conical antenna (Figure 46). The low Q needed to obtain broad-band characteristics is obtained in this antenna by the large cross-sectional area. The

Figure 45. Multi-channel fan antenna.

Figure 46. Conical antenna.

antenna has a high resistance and a uniform sensitivity over a wide band of frequencies. The length of each cone is critical and should be 0.365 times an electrical wavelength.

The conical antenna may be constructed of sheet metal, equidistantly spaced wires, or of copper screening suitably supported. The physical rigidity of the cone is the major problem encountered with this type of construction. Another advantage of the cone is that it can be constructed to match a selected transmission line of given impedance, by properly choosing the angle of revolution. To match a 300 ohm line, the angle of revolution of the cone should be 15 degrees.

5-71 Rotatable Antenna. Optimum reception of television signals is usually achieved when the receiving antenna is oriented in the direction of the transmitter. When conditions are such

Figure 47. Rotatable antenna. (courtesy Alliance Mfg.)

that there is a severe multipath reflection problem, or the desired television signals are originated in widely scattered directions from the receiving location, a number of individually oriented receiving antennas may be required.

In many cases a practical solution to this type of reception problem is a rotatable antenna which can be oriented for any signal, thus providing peak performance at all times. One type of rotatable antenna available is shown in Figure 47. The entire antenna assembly is motor driven and can be rotated in either direction, from a remote control box at the receiver. Results are observed directly (visually) on the picture tube as the antenna is rotated, providing an indication of accurate orientation. In multipath signal areas, the antenna may not always be pointed at the transmitter, but rather to a reflected signal which provides the best picture.

5-72 Directional Antennas. All practical antennas are directional to some extent. In general, however, the term directional antenna refers to a radiating system which has been designed deliberately to concentrate its radiation in a relatively narrow beam. For transmitting purposes, directional antenna arrays

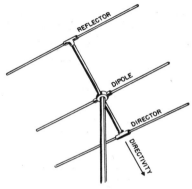

Figure 48. Three-element parasitic array; a reflector and a director with half-wave dipole.

concentrate r-f energy in the directions where the signal is desired, and minimize or prevent radiation in other directions.

When used for reception, directional antenna arrays reject or discriminate against unwanted signals arriving from directions other than that in which reception is desired. There are three general classifications into which directional antenna arrays may be grouped. These are:

(a) Parasitic arrays,
(b) Driven or phased arrays,
(c) long wire arrays.

Various combinations of the above types of arrays may be used to provide additional directivity.

5-73 Gain and Directivity. The gain of a directional antenna array is the ratio of the signal strength in the desired direction to the signal strength in the same direction obtainable with a half-wave dipole.

The directivity of an array refers to the shape of its field pattern in either the horizontal or vertical plane. A sharp or extremely narrow field pattern identifies an antenna array with good directivity.

Directivity and gain normally go hand in hand, but some systems are capable of added directivity with little or no gain. In

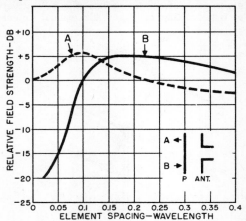

Figure 49. Maximum gain obtainable with single parasitic element. Curve A shows the gain when parasitic element, P, is director; curve B shows gain when P is reflector.

this case, the directivity is useful in reducing interference, although no increase in signal strength is obtained.

5-74 Parasitic Arrays. The simplest and most common method of obtaining a unidirectional field pattern for television receiving systems is by means of a parasitic array. A parasitic array consists of a conventional half-wave dipole, and one or more parasitic elements.

There are two types of parasitic elements: reflectors and directors. A reflector is placed behind a dipole, that is, on the side opposite that from which the signal is being received. A director is placed in front of the antenna, in the direction of the received signal. The positions of the reflector and director are shown in Figure 48.

The directivity, as well as the gain, of parasitic arrays is roughly proportional to the number of parasitic elements employed. The size of a parasitic array is proportional to the

operating wavelength. At frequencies within the television operating range, the elements which make up a parasitic array are
comparatively small. This allows for simple and rugged mechanical construction.

5-75 Two Element Arrays. The gain in field strength with a
reflector or director as compared to a dipole alone depends upon
the spacing between the antenna elements and the length of the
parasitic element. The maximum gain obtainable with a single

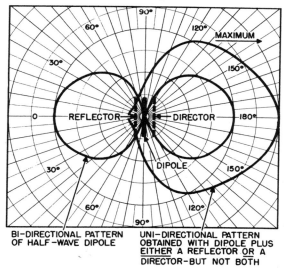

BI-DIRECTIONAL PATTERN   UNI-DIRECTIONAL PATTERN
OF HALF-WAVE DIPOLE   OBTAINED WITH DIPOLE PLUS
                              EITHER A REFLECTOR OR A
                              DIRECTOR-BUT NOT BOTH

Figure 50. Change in bi-directional field pattern of dipole when
either reflector or director is added to dipole.

parasitic element, as a function of the spacing, is shown in Figure 49. The curve shows the greatest gain to be expected when
the parasitic element is the correct length for optimum performance, either as a director or a reflector. The shift from
director to reflector, with the corresponding shift in direction,
is shown in Figure 50. In other words, the parasitic element
may be either a reflector or a director at any spacing.

5-76 Reflectors. A reflector is a metal conducting rod placed
parallel to and behind a half-wave dipole in a position opposite
the field of maximum intensity, Figure 51. It is slightly longer

than the dipole element, and is not connected to the dipole antenna or its associated transmission line. The curves in Figure 52 show the length in feet of a dipole and a reflector for frequencies from 45 to 95 mc. Since curve A (length of reflector)

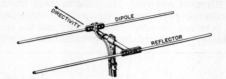

Figure 51. Dipole and reflector.

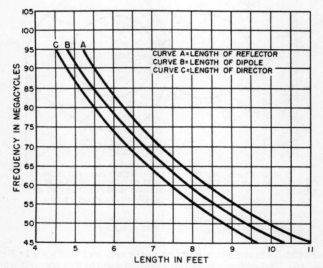

Figure 52. Curves showing length in feet of dipole, reflector, or director for frequencies between 45 and 95 Mc.

is above curve B (length of dipole), for any given frequency the reflector is always slightly longer than the antenna.

Analyzing the operation of the reflector for transmitting antennas will help the reader understand its operation when receiving.

When the dipole is energized, the resultant field induces a voltage in the reflector element. This induced voltage, in turn, produces a field at the reflector which is opposite in polarity and almost equal in magnitude to the original induction field. Thus, there are actually two separate radiation fields to be considered; that caused by the current in the dipole radiator, and that caused by the induced current in the reflector element. Very little energy travels beyond the reflector in the direction away from the dipole, because the fields are of opposite polarity and cancel

Figure 53. Dipole and director. (courtesy Oak Ridge)

one another. The r-f energy from the reflector traveling toward the dipole is in phase with the energy radiated from the dipole in that direction, and they combine, mutually strengthening the field pattern in the foward direction (Figure 50). The exact shape of the pattern depends upon the phase relation between the direct and the reflected fields. The phase of the induced current in the reflector is controlled by two factors: (a) the length or tuning of the element, and (b) the spacing between the dipole and reflector.

Almost all two-element parasitic arrays used for television consist of a dipole and reflector, rather than a dipole and director.

5-77 Directors. A director is a metal conducting rod placed parallel to and in front of a half-wave dipole in the direction of the desired field of maximum intensity (Figure 53). It is slightly shorter than the dipole element, usually about 4%. The length in feet of a director for frequencies from 45 to 95 mc is shown as curve C in Figure 52. Since curve C is below curve B, the director is always slightly shorter in length than the dipole.

The director is not connected to the dipole antenna or its associated transmission line. When the dipole radiator is energized, the resultant field induces a voltage in the director so that there is a reinforcement of fields in the forward direction, and a cancellation of fields in the opposite direction. This function of the director is very similar to that of the reflector, and essentially the same field pattern is produced (Figure 50), when either a director or reflector is used with a half-wave dipole radiator. The phase of the induced current in the director is controlled by two factors: (a) the length or tuning of the element, and (b) the spacing between the dipole and director. The function of the director is the same when used with either a transmitting or receiving antenna.

5-78 Front-To-Back Ratio. The conditions which give maximum gain forward do not give maximum signal reduction, or attenuation, to the rear. For the sake of good reception, general practice is to adjust an antenna for maximum front-to-back ratio rather than for maximum gain. Reduction of response to signals behind the antenna is brought about by adjusting the length of the parasitic element. Larger front-to-back ratios can be secured with the parasitic element operated as a director rather than as a reflector. With a director, the length must be made slightly shorter than that which gives maximum gain, with spacings of 0.1 wavelength and more. The reflector must be lengthened somewhat to achieve the same end, at spacings up to 0.25 wavelength.

The adjustment of the front-to-back ratio may be performed in practice while visually observing an interference pattern on a television receiver. If the interference pattern is originating in the opposite direction from the desired signal the results of any adjustments are readily apparent.

5-79 Impedance of Parasitic Antennas. The radiation resistance at the center of the dipole, with a reflector, varies as shown in Figure 54, with spacings of the order of 0.1 wavelength. These values are quite low, compared to the 73-ohm radiation resistance of the half-wave antenna alone. At greater spacings the radiation resistance increases. The selectivity of the antenna system becomes higher as the radiation resistance decreases. This means that optimum performance can be secured over only a narrow band of frequencies as compared with a higher-resistance antenna.

5-80 Double Parasitic Arrays. It is possible to use two parasitic elements in conjunction with a half-wave dipole to increase directivity and gain. Generally, one parasitic element is a director and the other is a reflector. The three elements are mounted in the same plane, as shown in Figure 48. The optimum spacings are the same as those for single parasitic elements; that is, director spacing of 0.1 wavelength and reflector spacing of 0.15 wavelength give maximum gain. Tuning for gain and maximum front-to-back ratio is the same as for single parasitic elements. With the director spaced 0.1 to 0.15 wavelength

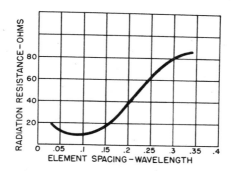

Figure 54. Variation of radiation resistance of dipole and reflector.

from the dipole, the radiation resistance is of the order of 8 to 10 ohms. Usual practice is to use a director spacing of 0.1 wavelength in combination with a reflector spacing of 0.25 wavelength, with a resultant increase in resistance.

Large size tubing of good conductivity must be used for the elements if the gain possibilities of the system are to be fully realized. This system is even more selective than the two-element antenna, so that peak performance can be secured over a very small range of frequencies.

This type of antenna is usually found in television receiving installations where a separate antenna is required for each station desired. At times, a single antenna may be used effectively for the reception of two adjacent channel television stations which are in the same direction from the receiving location.

5-81 Folded-Dipole Parasitic Arrays. The advantage of horizontal directivity and high front-to-back ratio may be obtained by using a folded dipole in an array. The folded dipole has a much higher radiation resistance than the simple half-wave dipole and, therefore, an antenna system with a wider frequency response results with its use. Such an array may consist of one or two parasitic elements (Figure 55).

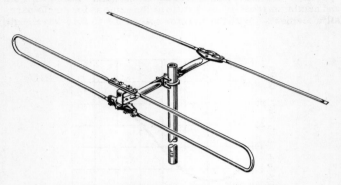

Figure 55. Folded dipole with reflector. (courtesy JFD)

5-82 Multi-Element Parasitic Arrays. When a high degree of directivity and gain are required, more than two parasitic elements may be used. Such arrays are known as multi-element parasitic arrays (Figure 56), and consist of a number of elements arranged symmetrically with respect to the line and plane of greatest directivity and gain. Any number of directors can be used with a half-wave dipole, and these elements may be combined with one or several reflectors. When four or more elements are used, the arrangement is often known as a Yagi array. With the addition of each parasitic element, the power gain of an antenna increases approximately 1.4 times. For example, if the power gain of a 4-element array is 5.0, the addition of another director would increase the gain to a value of 6.4, and so forth.

Each director and reflector must be properly tuned and spaced with respect to the dipole element, in order to provide optimum performance. A folded dipole used in the place of a simple half-wave dipole will increase the antenna radiation resistance and provide operation over a wider band of frequencies.

Since multi-element parasitic arrays are very selective they have not been widely used for television. An antenna array of this type is suitable for reception of one television channel only.

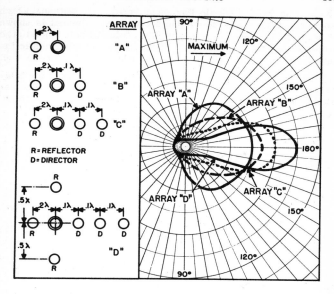

Figure 56. Field patterns of four parasitic arrays.

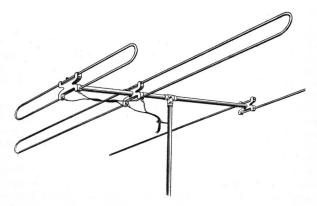

Figure 57. Duo-folded dipole parasitic array.

5-83 Duo-Folded Dipole Parasitic Array. An antenna which consists of two folded dipoles and a parasitic element is shown in Figure 57. This antenna combines a folded dipole tuned to the lower end of the television band with a folded dipole tuned to the upper end of the television band to secure broad band response.

When receiving signals at the low-frequency end of the television band, the small folded dipole acts as a director. The result is a folded dipole antenna with a director and reflector.

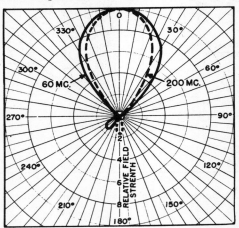

Figure 58. Field patterns of duo-folded dipole at 60 and 200 Mc.

When receiving at the high frequency end of the band, the small dipole becomes the antenna with the large dipole acting as a reflector. The resultant antenna consists of a folded dipole with two reflectors.

Field patterns for the low and high frequency ends of the television band are shown in Figure 58. These patterns show the antenna to be substantially unidirectional. High front-to-side and front-to-back ratios are maintained over the entire television band.

At 60 megacycles the power gain of this antenna is slightly better than 2, while at 200 megacycles its power gain is approximately 2.5. The antenna matches a 300 ohm transmission.

5-84 Stacked Arrays. The stacked array is used to concentrate the receiving or transmitting antenna sensitivity at low vertical angles. It has been shown how the use of parasitic elements concentrates the antenna sensitivity in one horizontal direction, and reduces the pick-up of unwanted signals and noise from the sides and back of the antenna. A stacked system reduces noise pick-up from top to bottom in the vertical plane and, therefore, further improves the sensitivity of receiving antennas in the desired direction. A stacked horizontal antenna system

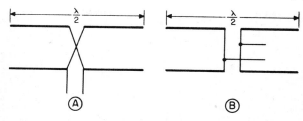

Figure 59. Stacked dipole arrays. (A) center fed; (B) transposed feeder.

for television consists essentially of two simple antenna elements and associated components, spaced a half-wavelength apart in the vertical plane.

The antenna elements are excited in phase, that is, signals arriving in the direction of orientation of the antenna system induce in-phase voltages in the antenna which add in the transmission line. Noise or other unwanted signals arriving from top or bottom induce voltages in the antenna system elements which cancel in the transmission line.

5-85 Stacked Dipole Arrays. A simple stacked array consists of two half-wave dipoles in parallel in a vertical plane. This antenna system and methods of feeding it are shown in Figure 59. The center feed method shown in B is preferred in as much as the transmission line point of attachment is centered and at the same distance from both dipole elements. Consequently, the signals from both dipoles always appear in phase at the input to the transmission line.

A transposed feeder system can be used, as shown in A. The transposed half-wave feeder system between the dipoles acts as a one-to-one in-phase impedance matching transformer, and the signal from the one dipole element appears in phase at the feed point of the other dipole element. However, the transposed feed is frequency sensitive and must be electrically equivalent to a half-wavelength at the frequency of the desired signal and, therefore, is effective over only a limited range of frequencies.

When two dipoles, or similar antennas, are stacked and fed into a common transmission line, the antenna resistance is halved. Thus, if two simple dipoles are stacked, the antenna resistance is cut to less than 40 ohms. Stacked dipoles, along with reflectors (Figure 60), are often used in a mismatched sys-

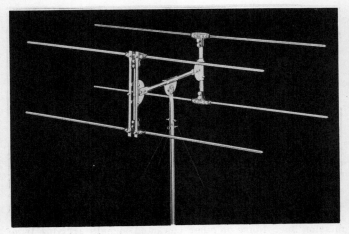

Figure 60. Stacked dipoles and reflectors. (courtesy Camco)

tem, where the lower impedance antenna system is fed across a higher impedance or "bridging" transmission line which has been selected to match the receiver input impedance.

A much better impedance match and wider band-pass antenna system can be obtained using stacked folded dipoles with reflectors. This antenna system is shown in Figure 61, and has a nominal impedance of 150 ohms over its operating range.

5-86 Other Stacked Arrays. Since only the direct line-of-sight radio wave path is useful in television, there is no practical limit to the useful vertical directivity of the stacked antenna for television reception. Limiting factors are the mechanical rigidity of the stacked system and the deterioration of the antenna system impedance to low values, which is dependent on the initial characteristics of the individual antenna elements being stacked. A four unit double-V stacked parasitic array is shown in Figure 62. A dual-band stub-tuned stacked array is shown in Figure 63. The

impedance properties of this antenna system are not as favorable as are those of other stub-tuned antennas.

5-87 Array Construction. To obtain optimum performance,
parasitic and stacked arrays should be mounted at least 7 wavelengths clear of the ground and other objects. Elements of an
array should be rigidly mounted so as to maintain their fixed

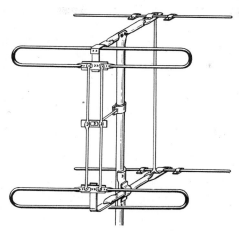

Figure 61. Stacked folded dipoles and reflectors.
(courtesy Taco)

relationship. Antenna elements are generally constructed of
metal tubing of large diameter.

Parasitic elements of large arrays may be welded directly to
a central metal rod or tube, in order to provide rigidity. A series of these central metal rods may be welded to a vertical
metal supporting rod at the proper spacing for stacked arrays.
The metal parasitic element supports do not interfere with the
operation of the antenna array, since they are perpendicular
to the direction of the horizontally polarized electric field. The
active dipole is usually insulated from the metallic support because it is center-fed. When a delta-match is used, the active
dipole may be welded to the metallic support. A folded dipole
may be welded to the metallic support at the center of its upper
sections, and still allow for center feeding of the lower section
at the normal open feed points.

5-88 Driven or Phased Arrays. These antenna systems are distinguished from the parasitic type of arrays, in that all of the elements are electrically interconnected. All phased systems are derived from three essential types: collinear, broadside, and end-fire. The elements used in phased arrays are usually

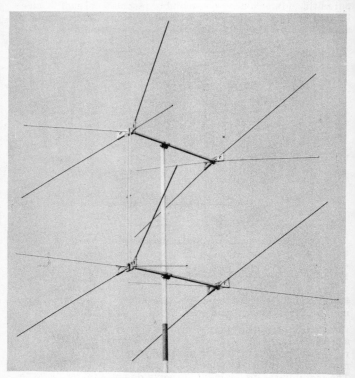

Figure 62. Four-unit double-V stacked antenna.
(courtesy Telrex)

a half-wavelength long, because elements of this length are easy to feed and phase. Some systems use elements that are five-eighths wavelength long, and some employ shortened elements. Arrays using elements other than a half-wave long are not very often used for television receiving systems.

End-fire arrays, which give a sharpened pattern in both the horizontal and vertical planes, are difficult to construct and feed. Other systems, although easier to feed, require more space. Difficulty in feeding is brought about by the fact that as antenna elements are moved closer together, radiation resistance decreases. This results in a high standing-wave ratio, with consequent losses when a tuned feed line is employed. If a matched line is used, the antenna system will have a high Q

Figure 63. Stub-tuned stacked array.

and will operate only over a narrow frequency band. In general, collinear and broadside arrays have a higher impedance, lower Q, than do end-fire arrays. As a general rule, phased array field-patterns are bi-directional, unless special measures are taken to make them unidirectional.

5-89 Collinear Arrays. In these arrays the elements are in the same line, and all currents are in phase (Figure 64). Horizontal arrays give horizontal directivity with no change in vertical directivity from that of a simple half-wave antenna. The gain and sharpness of the field pattern depends on the number of half-wave elements and their spacing, center-to-center. Spacing center-to-center is usually one half-wave, that is, the antenna elements are end to end, except for an odd number quarter-wavelength phasing section between them.

The gain of collinear arrays may be increased by increasing the center-to-center spacing of the antenna elements. The directivity and frequency characteristics of collinear arrays are such that this type of antenna has found little use in television.

5-90 Broadside Arrays. This basic type of phased array consists of two or more half-wave dipoles, arranged parallel to each other in the same plane (Figure 65). Broadside arrays can be used with either vertical or horizontal elements. If the elements are horizontal, the field pattern is sharpened in the vertical

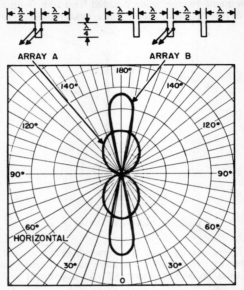

Figure 64. Two types of colinear phased arrays.

plane, giving low-angle radiation, but the horizontal-plane pattern is the same as for a single element.

The common types of broadside arrays would more properly be described as stacked collinear systems. This is true of the simple Lazy-H, Sterba, Bruce and so-called Billboard array, to name a few. These stacked-collinear broadside arrays have both horizontal (collinear) directivity and vertical (broadside) directivity. The degree of directivity and gain is dependent upon the number, spacing and geometric arrangement of the antenna elements composing the array.

5-91 Lazy-H Antenna. A simple combination of two collinear elements stacked and phased for broadside radiation, results in the so-called "Lazy-H" antenna. It is shown in Figure 66, and de-

rives its name from its resemblance to a reclining "H". The
elements are horizontal as shown for television reception. All
the half-wave antenna elements are excited in phase by means
of the transposed half-wave feeder between the stacked collinear
elements. The feed point shown has a high impedance.

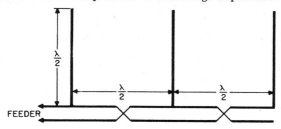

Figure 65. Broadside array.

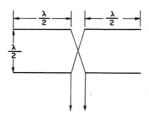

Figure 66. Lazy-H antenna.

5-92 Sterba Array. The horizontal Sterba arrays shown in
Figure 67 are another modification of the stacked-collinear
broadside array. This system is very nearly the same as the
Lazy-H, except that it is a closed circuit. Each of the four
"end" dipoles is bent at the center, and adjacent dipoles are
then joined permanently. All elements of the Sterba array are
interconnected with transposed half-wave feeders so that the
currents are in phase. Any type of tuned or matched line may
be used to feed a horizontal Sterba array. The impedance at
the feed point is high.

5-93 Billboard Array. This type of stacked-collinear broadside
array makes use of a metal screen reflector to produce a uni-
directional field pattern with sharp directivity in both the vertical and horizontal planes (Figure 68). Billboard arrays consist of at least 4, but rarely more than 64, half-wave dipoles,

mounted on a suitable metal screen frame which also functions as a reflector. All dipole elements are fed currents of equal magnitude and phase. Because of their large size, billboard arrays are restricted in use to very short wavelengths. They are useful in television for link-relay communications.

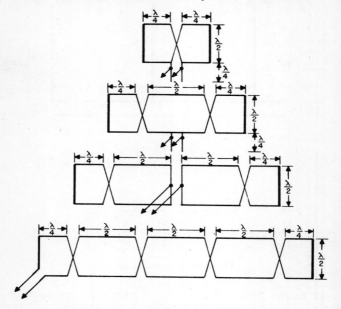

Figure 67. Four types of horizontal sterba arrays.

5-94 End-fire Arrays. This type of array consists of one or more pairs of parallel half-wave, dipoles, which are fed currents of equal magnitude but of different phase. With certain spacings and with certain phase displacements, such pairs of dipoles - known as sections - provide field patterns with pronounced directivity. Since this directivity always lies in the plane of the dipole sections, such an arrangement is known as an end-fire array. However, the antenna system is more popularly known as a flat-top array.

The actual field pattern of a flat-top array may be either unidirectional or bidirectional, depending upon the spacing or separation and the phase difference of the two dipoles constituting each section. The degree of directivity is a function of the number of dipole sections, with a maximum limit of 4 sections providing a field pattern sufficiently narrow for most practical purposes.

Flat-top arrays are classified according to their types of feed. Center-fed arrays (Figure 69) are usually preferred, because of their symmetry; a quarter-wave matching stub is used to

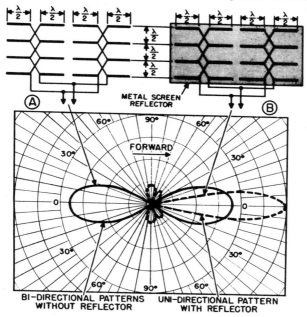

Figure 68. Field patterns of multi-element antenna array. (A) Bi-directional pattern without reflector; (B) Uni-directional pattern with metal screen reflector.

connect the feeder to the array. End-fed arrays (Figure 70) are less critical of adjustment, and often are more convenient to install.

5-95 Long-Wire Arrays. It has been shown that the maximum radiation from a half-wave antenna is broadside to the wire. However, when a wire is a wavelength or more long, the radiation tends to concentrate more and more off the ends. Such an antenna is called a long-wire antenna. It is more sensitive in its most favorable direction than a half-wave antenna in its optimum direction. The curve in Figure 71 shows the maximum radiation for long-wire antennas as a ratio to the maximum radiation for a half-wave antenna. This power gain is obtained at

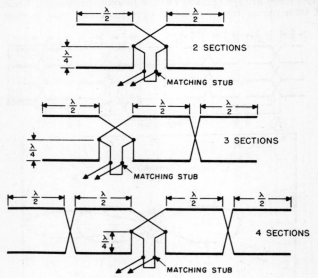

Figure 69. Center-fed flat-top arrays (top view).

the expense of radiation in other directions. Sometimes known as the harmonic antenna, the long wire radiator can be made resonant over a wide range of frequencies with good directivity. Various combinations of long wire radiators constitute an important branch of directional arrays, which includes the V antenna and its variations, and the rhombic antenna.

5-96 Long-Wire Radiators. Effectively, a long wire radiator consists of a number of half-wavelength dipoles placed end to end in such a way that at any instant current in adjoining half-wave sections flows in opposite directions. This out of phase condition is achieved by feeding the long wire radiator at one end (Figure 72). The length of a long-wire antenna is not an exact multiple of a single half-wave antenna, because end effects associated with antennas occur only at the extremities. The formula for the length of a long wire antenna is:

$$L = \frac{492 \ (N - 0.05)}{f}$$

where L is length in feet.
       N is the number of half-waves on the antenna, and
       f is resonant frequency in megacycles.

Tuned feeders, Q matching sections and quarter-wave stubs can all be used to feed the long wire antenna at one end. Be-

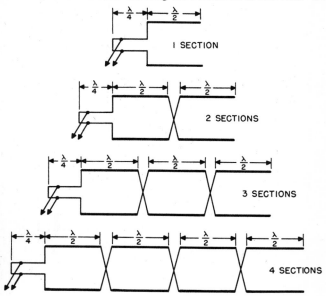

Figure 70. End-fed flat-top antenna arrays (top view).

cause of increased radiation resistance (Figure 73), the long wire antenna tunes broadly.

5-97 The V Antenna. This directional array is composed of two long wire radiators arranged horizontally in a V-Shape (Figure 74), which effectively combines the directional effects of each of the long wires with a pronounced increase in gain. If the two sides of the V are excited 180 degrees out-of-phase, by connecting the two wire feed line to the apex of the V, the lobes add up along the line of the bisector A-B and tend to cancel in other directions.

The V antenna is essentially a bidirectional system, and its gain depends on the length of the wires. The length of the legs

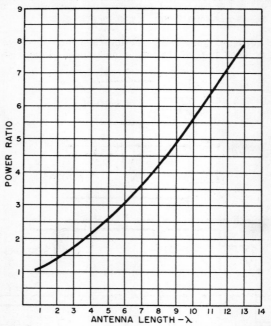

Figure 71. Power gain of long-wire antenna over half-wave antenna.

of a V beam is not critical, but it is important that both be of the same electrical length. The V antenna is simple to build and operate. It shows considerable gain over a wide frequency range, the gain increasing as the frequency increases. The longer the V, the less is the departure from the optimum enclosed angle, as the frequency is varied (Figure 75).

When the antenna is used for extended range television reception, the low-angle radiation characteristics of the antenna may be modified by tilting its plane with respect to the horizon.

It is preferable to tilt the open V end down, thus increasing the low-angle sensitivity of the antenna. V antennas may be stacked a half-wave apart and fed in phase to secure a broadside effect. Another arrangement is the formation of a W with two V antennas.

The V beam can be made unidirectional by using a reflector at least a quarter-wavelength in back of the antenna. The height

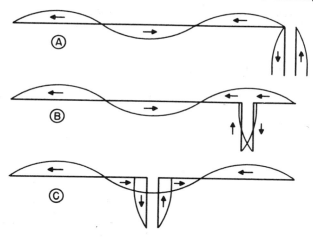

Figure 72. Long-wire antenna, showing current distribution and feed points.

of the antenna above ground should be at least a half-wavelength or better. The method of feed is conventional, any number of tuned and untuned line combinations are adaptable.

Because of its size, the V beam is used mainly in rural areas for television reception.

5-98 The Rhombic Antenna. The horizontal rhombic antenna is a form of long wire directional array which provides excellent directivity and high gain. It is an ideal solution to the problem of extended range television reception, provided there exists an adequate radio wave path to the receiving location, and sufficient space is available for its erection.

The rhombic antenna consists of four wires of equal length, arranged in the shape of a diamond and suspended a half-wavelength or more above the earth as shown in Figure 76. The rhombic is ineffective unless each leg (L) is at least two wave-

lengths long. The larger the ratio of the length of the leg (L)to
the operating frequency wavelength (λ), the greater the power
gain. If the free end is not terminated with a resistance, the
rhombic has a bidirectional field pattern. Usually the free end
is terminated with a resistance of between 600 and 800 ohm,
representing the characteristic impedance of the antenna. The

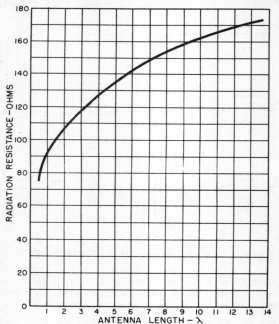

Figure 73. Radiation resistance of long-wire antenna.

terminated rhombic functions as a non-resonant transmission
line without standing waves, with its maximum sensitivity along
the axis of the antenna in the direction of the resistance. A practical rhombic antenna design problem is solved step by step in
the following discussion.

5-99 Horizontal Wave Angle. The design of a rhombic antenna
is influenced by the fact that the maximum sensitivity is not in
the plane of the antenna, but is at some angle with respect to
ground. This angle of maximum sensitivity above the ground is

called the horizontal wave length, and must be considered first.

This is done by estimating the angle from the horizon, formed by sighting the transmitting antenna in question from the proposed receiving location. Since the rhombic is herein being considered for extended range television reception, this angle will be small. It may be more convenient to assume a horizontal

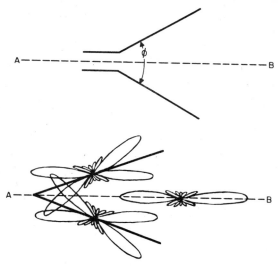

Figure 74. V antenna, and method whereby field patterns of two long-wire radiators are combined to produce highly directional V antenna field pattern.

wave angle somewhere between 10 and 30 degrees, and incline the plane of the rhombic antenna to compensate for the angle of maximum sensitivity of the resultant antenna.

5-100 Determining Dimensions. Once the desired wave angle has been selected, there are three quantities to be determined: The internal angle, the antenna height and the length of each leg. For a given wave angle there is one set of dimensions for maximum response to signals coming from the desired direction. These dimensions may be determined mathematically, but for the simplicity they are presented in Figure 77 in chart form.

5-101 A Rhombic Antenna Design. A rhombic antenna can be expected to provide good performance over a frequency range of more than 2 to 1. This means that an antenna designed for

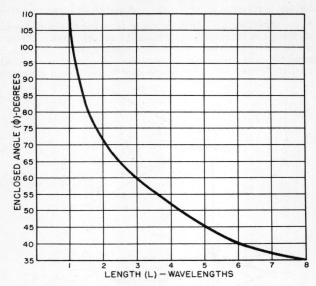

Figure 75. Curve showing change in enclosed angle of V antenna with various frequencies.

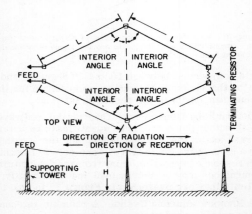

Figure 76. Rhombic antenna.

a frequency of 100 megacycles will operate properly from 50 to 200 megacycles. Rhombic antennas have an operating range equivalent to the entire thirteen television channels when properly designed.

Referring to the rhombic design chart for maximum output dimensions (Figure 77) and assuming a horizontal wave angle

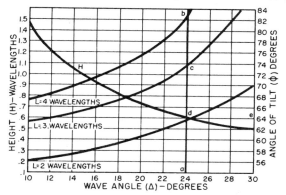

Figure 77. Design chart for rhombic antenna.

of 24 degrees, the dimensions can be found as follows:

Draw a vertical line through point a, corresponding to a horizontal wave angle of 24 degrees. Read the intersection of this line on each curve on its corresponding scale:

$$c = \text{length (L), 3 wavelengths}$$
$$d = \text{height (H), 0.618 wavelengths}$$
$$e = \text{internal angle } (\phi), \text{ 64 degrees}$$

In all cases, the linear dimensions are in terms of wavelength. These may be converted to feet by the relation

$$H = \frac{984}{f(Mc)} = (1 \text{ wavelength})$$

for height, and

$$L = \frac{492 \ (N-0.05)}{f(Mc)}$$

(where N is the number of half-waves) for the leg length.

Assuming a design center frequency of 88.7 Mc., which is close to the geometric center of the television band, H will work out to be slightly less than 7 feet, and L will work out to be 33 feet.

5-102 Television Transmitting Antennas. The super-turnstile antenna (Figure 78) is used almost by all television broadcast stations. This antenna provides an omnidirectional radiation pattern in the horizontal plane, combined with a low vertical ra-

Figure 78. Super-turnstile antenna.

diation angle over a broad band of frequencies six megacycles wide. In place of the half-wave dipoles of the basic turnstile antenna, the super-turnstile is equipped with open sections of metal framework, which act as current sheets. The open sections have the same electrical effect as solid metal sheets of the same size, but not their wind resistance. The open framework is constructed of steel tubing, and vertical members are grounded at both ends. Each bay or stack of the super-turnstile consists of four current sheets arranged in quadrature. The current sheet radiators have inherently broad frequency characteristics. Their large crosswise dimension gives them a low Q and they can be made to reflect a nearly perfect resistive impedance across their associated transmission line over the required six Mc. frequency band. This is desirable since the best picture quality is produced by equal transmission of all frequencies in the pass band.

The operation of the individual current sheet elements of the super-turnstile antenna may be compared with that of a dipole shunted by a shorted quarter-wave section of line. With increasing frequency, the dipole becomes inductive while the stub

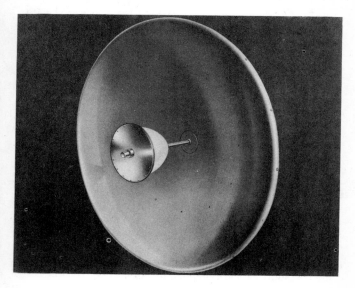

Figure 79. Parabolic reflecting antenna. (courtesy Workshop Associates)

in parallel with it becomes capacitive. Thus, the two reactances tend to cancel and the effective reactance is very low over a broad band of frequencies. The super-turnstile usually consists of three or four bays in order to provide low angle radiation in the vertical plane with a power gain in the horizontal plane. In general, field patterns are similar to those of the basic turnstile described earlier in this section.

5-103 Television Field Relay Antennas. Since the microwaves used for television field relay broadcasts have characteristics very similar to those of light waves, the parabolic reflector is an obvious directional device for use at these frequencies. A dipole placed at the focal point of a parabolic reflector, as shown in Figure 79, radiates a beam in much the same manner as a searchlight. At the frequencies used for television relays, a six-foot diameter parabola gives a power gain of 30 db or 1000 times. Therefore, a 1 watt transmitter can be made to be as ef-

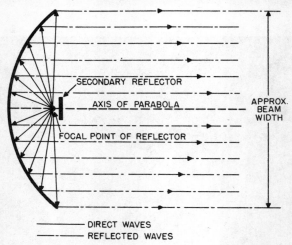

SECONDARY REFLECTOR

AXIS OF PARABOLA

APPROX. BEAM WIDTH

FOCAL POINT OF REFLECTOR

——— DIRECT WAVES
—·—·— REFLECTED WAVES

Figure 80. Reflecting action of parabolic surface.

fective as 1,000,000 watts through the use of parabolic reflectors at the transmitting and receiving locations.

This tremendous power advantage is achieved by narrowing the beam to a few degrees, Figure 80. Care in the use of these antennas must be exercised in order to line the antennas up at the receiving and transmitting locations. Jarring or vibration of such antennas during the transmission of a relay broadcast can result in a loss of the signal at the receiver.

5-104 Horn Type Antennas. Some field relay broadcast equipment is designed to operate in the super-high frequency range. In this equipment, horn type radiators are combined with parabolic reflectors in place of the conventional dipole (Figure 81). The operation of a horn radiator as an electromagnetic directing device is analogous to that of the common acoustic megaphone. However, the throat of an acoustic horn usually has di-

mensions much smaller than the sound wavelength for which it
is used, while the throat of an electromagnetic horn has dimensions which are comparable to the wavelength being used.
A horn type radiator is an adaptation of and is used with wave-
guides.

5-105 Metal Lens Antenna. This unique antenna provides sharp
beams of microwave energy by utilizing the focusing effect of a
large number of specially shaped, closely spaced metal plates

Figure 81. Electromagnetic horn: left, conical type; center,
pyramidal type; right, rectangular type.

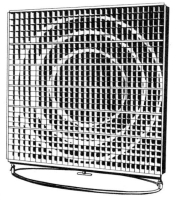

Figure 82. Metal lens antenna.

(Figure 82). When used for transmitting, this metal lens receives divergent waves from a point source — usually an electromagnetic horn — in the rear of the array. As they travel
between the parallel conducting plates, the microwaves actually
gain speed. By a suitable geometric arrangement of the plates,
outer paths are made slightly longer than paths near the center

of the array. In this way, outer waves are accelerated in such a manner that the waves are effectually focused and emerge from the array in a narrow parallel beam (Figure 83). The "stepped" construction of the metal plates provides uniform

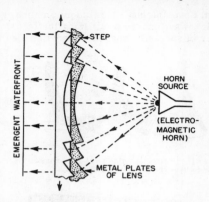

Figure 83. Focusing effect of metal plates of "stepped" construction.

transmission over a wide band of frequencies, for carrier telephone, television and other microwave services.

An identical array is used as a highly directional receiving antenna, where it funnels microwaves back into an electromagnetic horn and waveguide system for detection, amplification and disposition of the signal. Field patterns less than one tenth of a degree can be obtained with a metal lens antennas.

5-106 Master Antenna Systems. Special consideration must be given to the antenna problem which exists in large apartment houses where it is necessary to operate many television receivers in close proximity. If 100 tenants in a large multiple dwelling owned television receivers, at least 100 individual antennas and transmission lines would have to be installed to operate all the receivers. The maze of antennas and cables on the roof and running down the sides of the building under such a system would violate fire laws, building codes, and possibly even cause damage to the structure itself. Under practical conditions, satisfactory reception for all the receivers in the building would be virtually impossible. With so many antennas arrayed so closely together, interference signals from one set to another would be inevitable. There would be very few locations on the roof where an antenna could be mounted and be free from such disturbances so that the majority of tenants would have to utilize the areas of poor reception.

Master antenna systems are the only solution to this problem. The first of its kind to be approved by the Radio Manufacturer's Association is the design developed by the Intra-Video Corpora-

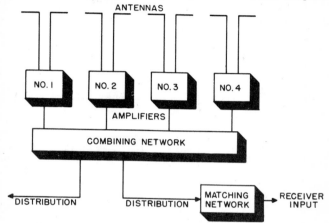

Figure 84. Block diagram of Intra-Video master antenna system.

tion of America. This system is shown in the block diagram of Figure 84. It consists of four major elements:

1. An array of antennas, each critically tuned for a different television channel.

2. Individual band pass amplifiers for each antenna.

3. A mixing and distribution network for combining the signals from all the channels and feeding them to the distribution lines at the proper impedance.

4. Matching networks to couple the receiver impedance to the distribution line as well as to provide isolation between receivers on the same line. The advantages of this system may be realized by an examination of the above features in detail.

5-107 The Antenna Array. Figure 85 shows how the antennas might be oriented in a typical installation to achieve optimum reception on each television channel. One antenna is also provided to cover the FM band so that tenants may operate their

FM receivers off the same system. Each antenna is individually cut for the station to be received. Dipoles and folded dipoles are ordinarily used, but if any multi-path reflections are troublesome, a critically directional antenna is used to single out the direct signal or a usable reflection. Each antenna is fed through a separate transmission line to the box containing the

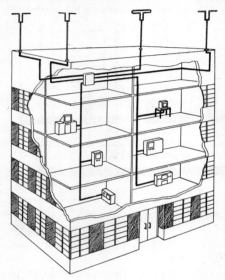

Figure 85. Typical master antenna installation.

amplifier and distribution system. This box may be mounted at a convenient point on the floor below the roof, as is shown in Figure 85, where the unit may be readily serviced.

5-108 The Band Pass Amplifiers. The amplifiers in the Intra-Video system are designed to provide uniform band pass over each six megacycle channel. Each channel amplifier consists of seven stages and the response is adjusted to obtain high selectivity. This feature is important for it improves the quality of reception of cheap receivers on the system that do not have good selectivity.

The gain of each amplifier is so adjusted that the signal output from the distribution system is the same level for each chan-

nel. This is, of course, the ideal condition for an antenna installation and is seldomly achieved in ordinary systems. It
means that the gain control of the receiver, when once set for
a station, need not be readjusted for other stations. A well regulated power supply is incorporated in the amplifier to overcome
any effects of line voltage fluctuations.

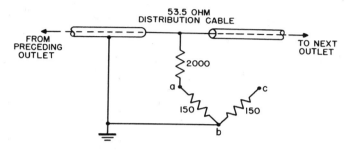

Figure 86. Matching network.

5-109 The Mixing And Distribution System. The output of each
channel amplifier is fed to a mixing system which combines the
signals of the various stations and feeds them across properly
terminated distribution lines. Two distribution lines are provided, each consisting of 52-ohm cable and going progressively
from one outlet to another in a continuous string. See Figure
85. As many as 40 to 50 outlets may be used on each distribution line. (Because of successive attenuations in the line, the
gain of the amplifiers is set to provide sufficient signal at each
outlet according to the number in the system).

5-110 The Matching Networks. The distribution system is
terminated at each outlet so that 30 db of attenuation is introduced between the distribution system and each receiver. This
brings the signal level down to a proper value to prevent overloading of the input circuits of the receiver. Also, by providing
30 db of attenuation between receiver and cable, there are effectively 60 db of attenuation between any two receivers insofar as
transmission of any radiation from one receiver to another is
concerned.

The matching network enables the matching of the 52 ohm line
to any receiver input impedance. The standard networks in the
Intra-Video system have the values shown in Figure 86. By connecting the receiver across points A and C, a balanced 300-ohm
input is provided. For unbalanced 72 ohm receivers, points A

and C are connected together and the signal taken between AC and B. Other combinations of resistances can be chosen to match receivers with other input impedances.

5-111 Simple Master Antenna System. A simple master antenna system which does not employ booster amplifiers is shown in Figure 87. The number of receivers which can be operated off a single antenna depends upon the signal strength at the antenna. Usually two to four receivers can be operated from one

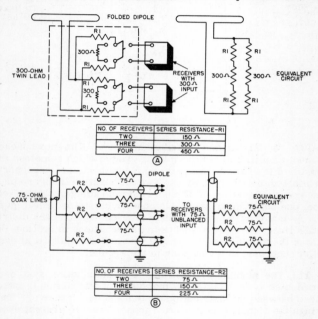

NO. OF RECEIVERS	SERIES RESISTANCE-R1
TWO	150 Ω
THREE	300 Ω
FOUR	450 Ω

(A)

NO. OF RECEIVERS	SERIES RESISTANCE-R2
TWO	75 Ω
THREE	150 Ω
FOUR	225 Ω

(B)

Figure 87. Simple master antenna system.

antenna in areas inside the prime service range of a transmitter (within 30 miles). This simple antenna system is suitable for operating several receivers in a sales room or in small, multiple dwellings.

The network shown in Figure 87A is used for operating receivers with 300 ohm balanced input. The series resistance R1 changes according to the number of receivers on the line.

Values for R1 are shown in the table. A slightly different network is used in Figure 87B for operating receivers with unbalanced, 75 ohm input. Values for the series resistance R2 are shown in the table.

When receivers are coupled across the same antenna, the signal input to each receiver is less than the signal available at the antenna. For two receivers, the signal at each is one half the available signal; for three, it is one third; for four, it is one fourth.

The resistive networks should be made of carbon resistors, mounted on suitable switches. All leads should be as short as possible. It is best to mount the switch assembly in a metal box to provide adequate shielding. If a receiver is removed from the line, a dummy load should be inserted in its place in order not to upset the balance of the system.

CREATING A TELEVISION SHOW

Programming and Production

6-1 Television requires completely new program production techniques. The medium differs from the motion pictures, the legitimate stage and radio more than is generally believed. In planning a television program the usual problems of script, cast, and direction are encountered as well as many other problems which are foreign to other forms of entertainment.

Television has its own technical problems which impose limitations on programming. Among these are the restricted number of people which can be viewed on a receiver screen at one time, the limitations of the television camera and other equipment, and the generally insufficient length of time allotted to rehearsing programs with the equipment. The lack of rehearsal time stems from the economic impracticality of engaging large crews of technicians for long periods.

In addition to technical handicaps, the television medium is peculiar in that it has an audience of "viewers" who effectively constitute a small group of people sitting comfortably in their home. Behind his closed door, many of the average man's inhibitions are released, relaxation is the mood for which he strives, and self-consciousness is usually less evident. He reacts quite differently from the way he does when in a theater among hundreds of strangers. Thus the entertainment he witnesses must be geared to his environment. When John and Jane Doe leave home, they unconsciously assume a somewhat more self-conscious attitude which tends to make them less critical

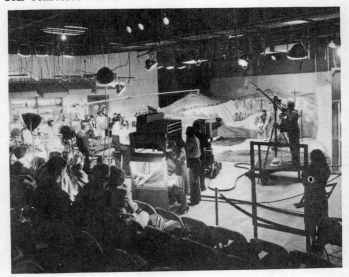

Figure 1. A typical television studio. (courtesy CBS)

of the entertainment they witness. Outside influences at large gatherings are likely to temper a man's reception of entertainment, whereas the relaxing environment of his home will sharpen his likes and dislikes and make him impatient with any entertainment which does not fit his mood. Television programs must not be intruders, but must maintain the intimate mood prevalent in the home.

To achieve this intimacy on the average ten-inch receiver screen requires the use of many close-up shots. Long shots make the characters appear so small on the screen that the action is not discernible. The small size of television screens makes it difficult to present large scale productions in which many actors are on stage at one time. Much better effects are achieved by simplifying the program so that each camera shot frames no more than three or four people in the picture. In attempting to include more than this number, it is necessary to move the camera so far back that the figures become tiny and the intimate quality of the program is lost.

Many of these problems are transitory and will be eliminated as television grows in stature and takes its rightful place in the entertainment world. These problems result from deficient equipment, lack of money for programming, and in many instances from mere lack of experience on the part of the individuals engaged in working out the fundamentals of operation of a new business. In this section, the problems of creating a television show are discussed in the light of techniques which have thus far been developed.

6-2 General Problems. Before taking up the many aspects of production, it is well to review briefly the elements necessary in the creation of a television program. A television station is composed of several distinct units, each of which functions separately. Each unit depends upon the others to achieve a well-coordinated program.

Let us begin with the studios, the equipment and personnel associated with them, and the purpose and functions of each. A typical television studio is shown in Figure 1. The ideal studio is much larger than a radio studio in order to accomodate the scenery and equipment. Large, open floor areas are needed to achieve flexibility in the movement of cameras, lighting units, and sound equipment. Scenery is usually installed around the walls, allowing the technical crew, cast, and the mobile equipment to move about in the center of the floor.

A substantial part of the lighting comes from above the set. The lighting units are secured to overhead pipes and may be adjusted according to the requirements of the particular scene. The rest of the lights are mounted on dollies. These lights follow the action of the cameras. They are moved about during the program, by technicians, in order to create special lighting effects.

Two to four cameras are used in the studio. The cameras are of the iconoscope or image orthicon type, the latter becoming the more popular because of its greater sensitivity which reduces the number of lights required to illuminate the set. The cameras are mounted on dollies and are connected to the studio control room through long power and signal cables which permit movement about the studio floor. For each camera there is a cameraman who switches lenses, adjusts optical focusing, and is responsible for positioning his camera according to instructions received from the control room. Usually the cameraman has a helper who assists him in moving the camera and keeping the cables free from entanglement.

The studio sound is picked up by microphones which are attached to booms that can be swung in any direction to follow the action on the set. A sound technician is required for each mike boom. The movement of scenery and props about the set is handled by the property man.

Heading up the technical crew on the studio floor is the stage manager who is responsible for the activities of the entire group during rehearsals and actual productions. He receives instructions from the studio control room, as do all the technicians, by means of headphones and talk-back equipment.

The operation of the equipment is directed from the studio control room which is housed in a sound-proof enclosure located at one end of the studio. A large glass window between the studio and control room permits the control room crew to watch the activities on the studio floor. The control room crew is made up of the program director, the technical director, and several audio and video technicians, who monitor the sound and pictures. Contact between the studio floor and the control room is by means of intercom phones, over which the director controls the activities of the stage crew.

The master control room is another separate unit in the station which integrates the video and audio signals coming from the studios, the remote pick-ups, and the film projection room. Station breaks and network programs are also funneled to this point. Like the studio control room crew, the master control technicians monitor the picture and sound before the program is fed to the transmitter.

The above units are the main centers of activity which contribute to the making of the program in a television station. In addition, there are dressing rooms for performers; a make-up room with a make-up artist in attendance; the crews' dressing room; property rooms and lockers; docks for storing scenery; and a paint room where the scenic artist adapts and paints the sets for each production.

The nerve center of the station is the Program Office, where production schedules are prepared and programs are thoroughly coordinated before going on the air. A library of recorded music is maintained by this office to supply background music and sound effects.

6-3 Scenery and Sets for Television. Scenery which is used in television is very similar to theatrical scenery. In fact, most of it is constructed in regular scenic studios, and then transported to the television studio for painting. The basic unit of scenery is referred to as a flat. The flat consists of a wooden frame covered with canvas or other heavy material. Flats are either lashed or bolted together, depending upon the permanency

Figure 2. A typical painted background. (courtesy DuMont)

of the set. They vary from four to twelve feet in width, and usually are no higher than ten feet, since this height has proven ample for even extreme long shots. On a theatrical stage the usual method of securing flats is by means of a stage brace which supports the flat, the brace being secured to the floor with heavy screws. On the television set, scenery changes must be made more quickly. The television flat is merely propped into position and held steady with a brace which is anchored to the floor by a heavily weighted block.

Painted canvas backdrops are used effectively in television, particularly to represent exterior scenes. These painted backdrops have an amazingly real, three-dimensional effect when viewed on the receiver screen and can be used to great advantage in conjunction with flats.

The painting of flats and drops for television requires a thorough knowledge of the medium and the camera's color sensitivity and resolution. Illusion can be resorted to far more than in a theatrical setting, for the television camera does not record the fine details which are recorded by the movie camera. A good motion picture has resolution equivalent to that of a three

Figure 3. Suitable back-drop which tends to concentrate the viewer's attention on the action in the foreground. (courtesy DuMont)

thousand line image as compared to television's 525 line image. A technique of painting which is suitable for television is illustrated in Figure 2. The unrealistic effect of the painted backdrop is caught by the film camera which took the picture of the set. When the scene is viewed on a television receiver, the lower resolution of the television system makes the background appear surprisingly realistic.

The art of painting television scenery has been developed after years of testing the sensitivity of the camera to color and detail. The true colors of a scene do not always register as equivalent shades of grey on the television screen because the camera tube does not have the same color sensitivity as the human eye.

Most image orthicon and iconoscope tubes are highly sensitive to either blue or red, depending upon their design. Other colors appear faded in relation to these colors. To avoid the distortion of color by the cameras, scenery is often painted in contrasting tones of the grey scale. To do this, the scenic artist must know the color response of the particular cameras which will shoot the scene. It has been found that scenery painted in shades of

Figure 4. The set is located against the wall, while cameras and other equipment are in the center of the studio floor. (courtesy DuMont)

grey, rather than in color, is far easier to light properly.

Painted backdrops must have very contrasty lines to register well on the screen. They must not be cluttered or detailed or they will detract from the live action in the foreground. Scenery must be planned so that it looks well both in close ups and long shots. A backdrop which exemplifies these methods and permits the viewer to concentrate his attention on the action in the foreground is shown in Figure 3.

Usually a single set is less than 20 feet wide and from 8 to 10 feet in depth. Side flats are positioned to conform to the action, and as a rule they are set at a 30° angle off the backdrop. In present television studios, scenery is set up against the four walls, with the cameras, microphones, and mobile lighting units in the center of the studio as shown in Figure 4. This arrangement allows for quick movement of the equipment from one set to another. The scenes are set up in the sequence in which they occur, so that the equipment moves in one direction only and cables are less likely to be entangled.

Figure 5 shows a floor plan of a set arranged for a complete television show. Each scene is enacted on a small portion of

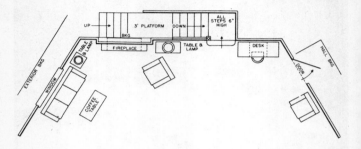

Figure 5. Floor plan for a television set.

the overall set, starting from the left and continuing to the right. Almost without exception, scenes are pre-set before the show and there is no striking or setting up of scenery during the performance. At the end of the day's programming, all sets are removed and stored in docks or rooms adjacent to the studio. The scenery, for the following morning's programs, is then set up.

The iconoscope camera requires an enormous concentration of over-all lighting. For this reason small winged flats are used to concentrate the light on the performance and scenery. With image orthicon camera less light concentration is needed, permitting sets to be spread out over a larger area and allowing for greater freedom of movement. Playing areas and backdrops can be better spot-lighted when image orthicon cameras are used because the set is not washed out by intence light as is the case with iconoscope cameras.

6-4 Projected Backgrounds. Projected backgrounds or process shots are often used in motion pictures to produce realistic, low-cost sets. To secure a background, a slide projector, located at the rear of the set, projects a scene onto a translucent screen which serves as the back wall of the set. The cost of painting scenes is thereby eliminated. Projected backgrounds cannot be used with the iconoscope camera because the intense foreground lighting washes out the projected image. Some backgrounds have been successfully projected for use with image orthicon cameras because they need less set lighting. With the trend toward the development of more sensitive pick-up tubes,

Figure 6. A miniature set. (courtesy NBC)

it is entirely possible that projected backgrounds will be used to a greater extent in the future. This will increase the variety of stage settings and lower overall production costs.

6-5 Miniature Sets. Miniature settings are used effectively on television. Here again the camera provides an effective illusion of reality even though the original scene is in miniature. Such scenes as ships in a harbor, an overall view of a city, or the burning of a building can be done in miniature rather than by recording them on film which is difficult to integrate with live action. A typical miniature set is shown in Figure 6. When this scene is picked up by the close-up camera, it fills the entire screen and appears quite realistic.

6-6 Lighting. Until the advent of the image orthicon camera, television studios required an enormous amount of light because of the low sensitivity of the iconoscope camera. Often 40 to 50 thousand watts were expended in lighting the scene and the actors sufficiently to eliminate deep shadows and to obtain proper picture contrast. With iconoscope cameras, uniform lighting was required from every angle to adequately illuminate the performers and scenery (Figure 7). The heat from the in-

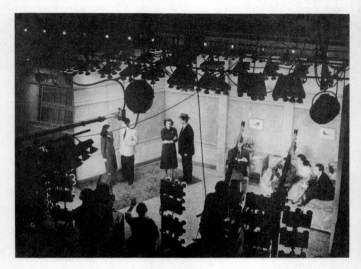

Figure 7. Large banks of lights are necessary with iconoscope cameras. (courtesy DuMont)

tense lights caused great discomfort to the performers and technicians working in the studio. Protracted periods of time before the cameras, either in rehearsal or in actual performance, were exhausting, and much of this discomfort was apparent to the viewers. Lighting from all angles eliminated the effect of depth in the picture, so that the foreground and background appeared to be in the same plane. An actor's face would often seem to be pasted to the scenery.

The lighting problem has been considerably lessened with the development of image-orthicon cameras for studio work. Requiring far less lighting on the set, these cameras are so sensitive that care must be taken to avoid over-lighting. Lighting beyond a certain point results in the saturation of the picture. On the screen the image appears "muddy", and under conditions of extreme saturation a negative of the picture is obtained. Between 2,500 and 5,000 watts of lighting are sufficient to fully illuminate a studio set when image-orthicon cameras are used.

A lighting setup for image-orthicon cameras consists of incandescent lamps clustered in broad housings to produce soft, diffused lighting. Usually, each cluster consists of approximately one thousand watts of light. These units are placed above the set and about ten feet in front of the action. The lights are directed toward the performers at an almost horizontal angle. This affords plenty of broad lighting of the faces and cancels out the shadows under the eyes and chin. Additional lights are often placed on movable floor stands at a height of approximately three feet, giving additional broad, low lighting. Backlighting is also used to light the background, to highlight, and to outline the objects in the foreground. The space between the foreground and the background is not brilliantly illuminated, thereby giving depth to the picture and separating the performers from the background. Broad, low lighting, and the highlighting of portions of the set are, of course, possible only with sensitive image-orthicon cameras.

Occassionally a 3000-watt spotlight is used effectively in conjunction with the general lighting to highlight a specific area. With the sensitive image-orthicon camera not much highlighting is necessary since the tube itself exaggerates small differences in contrast and shadow.

Incandescent, mercury, and fluorescent lights are used for illuminating television studios. A studio installation with fluorescent lights is shown in Figure 8. Each type of lighting equipment produces a different color and makes clothing, scenery, and performers' faces appear distorted to the camera. Make-up and color of clothing and sets must therefore be suited to the particular lighting installation of each studio.

6-7 Make-up. As television progressed from the early days of insensitive cameras and overpowering lighting, so did the theory of make-up change radically. Formerly, it was considered necessary to exaggerate the make-up to compensate for the color response and insensitivity of the camera. Green or blue tinted grease-paint and black lipstick was liberally smeared on the performers since these colors showed up best with the iconoscope camera. With image-orthicon cameras it has been found that simple make-up shows up best. Naturalness is the key-note for present day make-up. It is correct to think of make-up as simply an aid to lighting, not a deceiver of it. Make-up is now used only to counteract slight distortions of the actor's features, or shadows caused by the lighting.

With the preponderance of light coming from above the actor's face, the worst shadows occur under the eyes, nose, and chin.

Figure 8. A studio equipped with fluorescent lighting.
(courtesy CBS)

The male actor's beard (even though he is freshly shaven) causes some shadow. Unless the beard is covered by proper make-up, it gives the actor a slovenly, unkept look. During the epic televising of the 1948 political conventions in Philadelphia, where thousands of politicians, great and small, appeared before the television camera, and where the vote-getting possibilities of television appearances became obvious, there was a rush for the grease pots, when it was learned how unattractive a man appeared without make-up.

For men, a light base of grease-paint is sufficient to avoid beard shadow and eliminate other serious shadow pockets. The grease paint is then powdered over with a light powder; sun-tan or ruddy shaded powders are not employed. Eye shadow and lipstick are used sparingly or not at all on males since their use gives an obvious "make-up" look when picked up by image-orthicon cameras.

Television make-up for women is much like ordinary street make-up with certain qualifications. Here again a light grease base is used. If rouge is used at all, it is used very sparingly, blended in with the base. Eye shadow and eyelash make-up are applied far more subtly than for stage work. Bluish-red lipstick is required for iconoscope cameras to obtain proper rendition of the lips. A light red lipstick is adequate for image-orthicon cameras. Hair must be kept away from the face as much as possible to avoid shadows. Pan-cake make-up is not as satisfactory as a very light-weight grease-base and powder since the former produces a flat effect. The contours of the face are lost with pan-cake make-up and the texture of the skin appears on the screen to have a hard, unnatural look.

Television make-up much more closely approximates motion picture technique than that of the stage. The stage actor knows the amount and colors of the lighting, and the distance between himself and his audience. Consequently, he uses make-up to allow for these factors, and to produce whatever effect he chooses. The image-orthicon camera, however, seems to peer through any such obvious make-up and show it up for what it is. In extreme close-up shots even the pores of the skin can be seen so that the use of heavy, obvious make-up is not possible.

The time factor in quick-changes for television is important, and interesting experiments have been made in superimposing one make-up over another. For example, an actor may be called upon to age twenty years in a few seconds between scenes. With no time to effect a complete change of make-up it has been found that a light layer of make-up can be laid over the basic make-up, and then readily washed off when a quick change is necessary. However, extreme character make-up is dangerous in television for the image-orthicon cameras are quick to point up any "phoney" quality of make-up. Suitable types must be cast, wherever possible, for character roles.

Make-up for television will change constantly as camera designs improve and different lighting installations are employed. There are no set rules that can be adhered to for long. The trend toward simplification is apparent, and it is unlikely that the technique of plastering heavy make-up to meet the difficiencies of the camera will return.

6-8 The Television Camera. Some of the physical characteristics of the television camera have been touched upon during the discussion of lighting, scenery, and make-up. It is well to discuss briefly the operation of the television camera in order to understand the role it plays in helping to create the television program.

The television camera converts the varying shades of light, which constitute a picture, into varying pulses of electricity which can be transmitted through space. The image is focused by a lens onto a photo-sensitive surface in the camera pick-up tube. The electronic camera, in effect, causes a beam of elec-

Figure 9. Studio camera equipped with lens turret.

trons to sweep across the image focused on this surface. The sweeping motion of the beam cuts the picture into thin horizontal lines, which, for all practical purposes, are converted into equivalent electrical signals that are joined end to end. The picture is dissected into 525 horizontal lines, 30 times a second. The electrical signals which represent all the black and white shades on each of these lines are passed on to the transmitter.

Image-orthicon cameras are usually equipped with a group of three or four lenses mounted on a rotating turret. This arrangement permits rapid switching of lenses. The lenses are mounted on the turret as shown in Figure 9. There are generally two-inch, three and three-quarter-inch, four inch, and ten and twelve inch lenses on the turret. The two-inch lens is a wide-angle lens, used for long, overall shots of the scene. The three and three-quarter-inch and five-inch lenses are best suited for medium shots, and the ten or twelve-inch lens for extreme close-ups.

6-9 Color Response. The iconoscope camera has poor response to red. On the screen, objects of this color have a washed out appearance. Red colors must therefore be avoided in scenery, clothing, or make-up when this type of camera is used.

Figure 10. Camera and operator. (courtesy DuMont)

Dark blues, browns, and blacks are best suited for the iconoscope.

The image orthicon camera picks up most colors equally well, except for blue, to which it has a tendency to over-respond. Blue colors appear too black on the screen. For example, the bluish beard lines on men's faces show up dark and must therefore be covered with make-up.

Background scenery for the iconoscope camera is painted with great contrast to avoid its fading into a haze. With the image-orthicon camera, backgrounds must be toned down considerably. The color response of these two cameras is so completely different that one must know what type camera is in use in a studio when planning a production. The color of the scenery, as well as the costumes and make-up, is dictated by the camera.

6-10 Operation. The television camera is operated by one man as shown in Figure 10. This type of camera remains stationary during the show once it has been set into position. Only the camera head is moved from left to right or up and down. A variation of this camera is the dolly camera which is used for moving in and out of a scene while on the air. The dolly camera needs two men for operation, one for moving the camera and keeping the cables free from the dolly wheels, and the other for

Figure 11. Boom camera. (courtesy CBS)

focusing and panning. A third type of camera is the boom camera, which is also operated by two men. This is a camera which is mounted on a boom that can be raised or lowered to get angle shots from above or below eye level, as shown in Figure 11. It is important in planning camera action to know the type of cameras which are available in the studio so that they may be positioned for desired shots.

6-11 The Camera and Studio Crew. Since the operation of the cameras depends upon the activities of other personnel in the studio, it is well to describe the camera crew in relation to the entire studio crew. Heading the studio crew is the stage manager who oversees the production from the floor, gives the performers their cues, and is generally responsible for the crew's activity. A typical studio crew consists of two or more camera men (depending on the number of cameras in use), an additional man to help dolly the cameras and to keep the cables from tangling, and one or more men to position the floor lighting units (banked groups of lights mounted on dollies). There is a mike

Figure 12. Studio crew and equipment. (courtesy GE)

boom operator for each mike in use. It is his job to follow the action of the scene with the microphone. Usually there are one or two other men who see to it that equipment is moved easily and quickly. Rounding out the crew are the property men who take care of prop changes during the show. A part of the crew for a television program is shown in action in Figure 12. Note that the crew members wear headphones through which they receive orders from the studio control room.

The trained studio crew is of utmost importance if smooth running programs are to be produced. Success or failure of a production depends to a large degree on the crew's familiarity with every detail. All the careful planning and work goes for naught if a crewman errs because of unfamiliarity with the script or action sequence. It takes just one or two mistakes of this sort to cast an amateurish quality over a program and spoil its effect. Naturally, with the limitations placed upon production rehearsals, as mentioned earlier, there are many chances for technical slip-ups. But a well-trained technician can overcome these limitations and aid materially in securing a smooth performance if he is given the opportunity, during rehearsal, to learn the sequence of a show, and the camera shots required.

During the show a good cameraman needs only brief instructions from the stage manager, on the floor, and the program director, in the control room, to correlate camera shots with the script. The cameraman must prepare for the next shot coming up once he knows he is off the air, and that another camera is on. He must quickly reposition his camera, change the lens if necessary, and re-focus for his next shot within a few seconds. He must check the lighting and call for repositioning of the mobile units if necessary. The cameraman must know his job so thoroughly that he can act quickly, exercising split-second judgment. He must always coordinate his work with that of the rest of the crew, for unless all technicians on the set operate as a team, split second timing cannot be achieved.

6-12 Camera Technique. Camera action and the selection of shots is usually planned at the first script reading. This insures coverage of all important bits of action in the script and eliminates drastic changes in later rehearsal. Actors take direction more intelligently if they know from the start where the cameras will be during the performance and what kind of shots are to be taken. Action on the set must always be staged with specific camera shots in mind.

Many different techniques, to achieve a variety of shots, are possible with the television camera. In changing from one camera to another, there are several rates of speed at which one camera may be turned off and another on.

6-13 The Clip. The simplest type of camera switching is the clip. It involves the switching, almost instantaneously, from one camera to another, with no perceptible delay observable on the screen.

6-14 The Dissolve. Another popular technique, borrowed from the motion pictures is the dissolve. This is done by fading down one camera as the other is faded up so that for a brief moment both pictures are seen on the screen.

6-15 The Fadeout. A third method is the fadeout. One camera is faded down completely to black until no picture is visible, then another camera is faded up from black for a new picture. The fadeout method has a tendency to slow down the pace of a production and is usually used only in going from one set to another, or in denoting a lapse of time. The effect is much the

Figure 13. A superimposition as it appears on the television screen. (courtesy NBC)

same as a curtain being lowered briefly in a theater for similar purposes.

Unfortunately, when a picture is not being received on a teleset screen, retrace lines appear. Since the screen is not altogether blacked out, a good deal of the effectiveness of the fadeout is lost. For this reason, fadeouts are advisable on but a few occasions.

6-16 The Superimposition. As indicated above, two cameras may be on at the same time. When both cameras are on the air for a length of time, the technique is called a superimposition.

Superimposition is effective in tying into one picture the action taking place at two different points or at different time intervals.

It is ideal for time "throwbacks", portraying a dream, and other unusual effects which are limited only by the ingenuity of the program director. For a superimposition the images may be balanced in intensity, or one image may predominate over the other. A typical superimposition shot is shown in Figure 13.

6-17 De-focusing. A purposely de-focused camera is sometimes effective in creating a mood. De-focusing is often used

Figure 14. A closeup shot as it appears on the television screen. (courtesy NBC)

when changing from one scene to the next with the same camera. As a scene ends, the camera is gradually thrown out of focus until no objects are discernible. During this brief interval, the performers can change position or minor scenery changes may be made. The camera is then brought back into focus and the next scene begins.

6-18 Panning and Dollying. Panning is the vertical or horizontal movement of the camera head as compared to dollying, which consists of moving the entire camera closer to or further away from the action on the set. Panning is used to follow action, but it is wise not to resort to this technique too often as it is tiresome to the eyes. The dolly shot is effective, but is not accomplished without difficulty. It necessitates moving the camera and cables while on the air, which may cause disturbing noise and the fouling of cables. Jerky motion of the camera as it is dollied forward or backward is obvious as well as annoying on the screen. Setting up the dolly shot during the per-

Figure 15. A medium shot as it appears on the television screen. (courtesy NBC)

formance takes more time than other types of shots and can slow down a production. In preference to panning or the dolly shot, it is often simpler and more effective to clip from a camera set up for a medium-shot, to a close-up camera, or vice versa.

6-19 The Close-up. The relative area covered by the camera during a close-up shot is shown in Figure 14. The close-up is the most often used shot in television, because the small size of the television screen makes it difficult to watch a picture taken at long or even medium distance for more than a short length of time. In addition, the intimate nature of the medium itself demands full use of the close-up. Close-up shots are usually taken of every character in a scene as soon after his entrance as possible in order to establish his identity. Important lines or facial expressions are most effective when the performer is televised close-up.

6-20 The Medium-shot. If there is important action to portray which cannot be taken in entirely on a close-up, then a medium

Figure 16. A long shot as it appears on the television screen. (courtesy NBC)

shot is used. More of the performer's body or a part of the set is in view, but the camera is still not too far back to lose important details. The relative area covered by a medium shot is shown in Figure 15.

6-21 The Long-shot. The long-shot is normally used to establish a new scene and the performers in it. A typical long shot is shown in Figure 16. The camera covers the entire set and enables the viewer to relate the position of the performers to each other and the set. The camera cannot be left on a long-shot for more than a few seconds, because the small size of the performers on the screen causes the viewer to lose interest. In planning a wide-angle or long-shot, it is best to compose it with as little detail as possible, and with a large focal point of interest. Large, dark grey or black areas around the edges of the picture must be avoided on long-shots, because they cause the picture to flare at the edges.

Camera shots which cannot be labelled either close-ups, medium shots, or long-shots are often given combination names to denote intermediate distances. Thus, a camera shot between a close-up and medium-shot is referred to as a medium-close-up. A shot between a medium and a long-shot is called a medium-long-shot.

Full, front shots are uninteresting when used too often in television. Angle-shots, from one side or the other have proved more effective and give an increased three-dimensional effect.

6-22 The Microphone. The pick-up of the television sound is an important part of program production. In a television studio sound pick-up methods differ from those used in other types of sound studios, mainly in the manner of locating microphones and the type of equipment used. The audio part of television is comprised of all that has to do with sound, and here again skilled technicians are needed to insure a smooth performance. The proper placement of microphones has a great deal to do with the success of a production. Unlike the little boy who was told when company came that he should be seen and not heard, the microphone has to be placed in a position where it can hear all, and yet never be seen.

For programs where there is no action to follow, a permanently fixed mike may be pre-set in position to pick up all sound. In the interview or forum type of show, fixed mikes are sometimes placed right in the picture. For shows in which there is constant movement about the set, the mike must be mobile enough to follow the action so as to maintain a constant sound level at all times. Mobile booms of the extension type shown in Figure 17 are used for this purpose. The microphone is placed in a cradle located at the end of the extension arm. The arm can be moved in any direction and can be simultaneously retracted. By using such a boom microphone, action can be followed at all times and the microphone can be kept out of the picture.

The proper distance between the mike and the sound source depends upon the type of sound. Orchestral music, for instance, can be picked up from a distance. For the normal speaking voice, on the other hand, the mike should be suspended just high enough above the speaker's head so that it is not in the range of the camera, and about eighteen inches in front of the speaker.

Two types of microphones are employed for television sound pick-up, the non-directional and the cardioid. The classification is according to the direction in which they are most sensi-

Figure 17. Microphones mounted on booms are suspended over the heads of performers. (courtesy DuMont)

tive to sound. The non-directional microphone, as its name implies, picks up sound equally well from all directions. It is normally used on remotes to pick up audience applause or laughter, and the noise of crowds. It is rarely used in the studio, because it responds too well to the noise made by the studio crew and equipment.

The cardioid microphone is widely used because it can be made to have several different response patterns. With one response pattern the mike is sensitive toward its front and dead toward its rear. When the microphone is directed toward the performers, it does not pick up noise made by the studio crew.

A second response pattern obtainable from a cardioid microphone has a figure eight shape. The front and rear are equally sensitive, but the sides are dead to sound. This bidirectional pattern is useful for picking up sound coming from opposite directions, such as from two actors facing one another.

6-23 The Studio Control Room. The studio control room is the first terminus of all effects, both video and audio, produced in the studio. Here the camera pictures are monitored and the sound levels adjusted before being fed to master control.

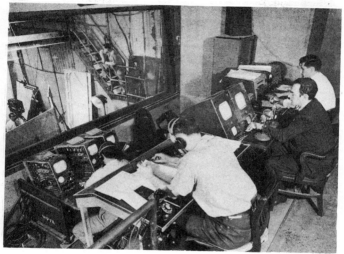

Figure 18. The studio control room. The technical director is seated before the switching console. (courtesy WPIX)

For each camera in use in the studio there is a camera monitor in the studio control room. Accompanying each monitor are controls which are used to shade and electronically change the contrast of each picture before it is transmitted to master control. The technical director uses a switching panel to shift from one camera to another, as shown in Figure 18.

An intercom system is used by the program director to instruct the studio crew and relay orders to the actors through the stage manager. Another intercom connects the program director with master control.

Most studio control rooms have several record turntables. The turntables are used to play recorded music into the studio or directly into the program circuit.

6-24 Control Room Personnel. The personnel in the studio control room is as follows:

1. The technical director who is in charge of switching cameras. In some studios he also relays directions from the program director to the crew on the studio floor.

2. The video engineers who are in charge of adjusting each picture electronically before the program director selects the picture to be sent out over the air.

3. The audio man who checks the levels of the sound from the microphones and operates the record turntables.

4. The program director and his assistant who guide and time the program from the script or outline, and who give cues to the crew, either through the technical director or directly over the intercom system.

6-25 The Master Control Room. The master control room is the nerve center of the television station, much as a switchboard is in a telephone system. It is here that programs from the various studios, remote pick-ups, and network stations are coordinated.

In the master control room a large switching panel permits the selection of program material from all of the station's facilities. Master control also has shading equipment to shade the pictures received from the various points before they are fed to the transmitter. The integration of the sound accompanying all pictures is carried out at master control. A typical layout of master control facilities is shown in Figure 19. To the left are the picture monitor and switching and shading controls. The sound console may be seen to the right rear.

The film projection room is usually close to master control. Film programs and the shading of the film pictures are the responsibility of the master control crew. If a film is to be integrated with a live show, it is readied by master control and switched into the program at the correct moment.

6-26 Master Control Personnel. The master control crew consists of the following personnel:

1. The master control supervisor who is responsible for the operation of the equipment and the activities of the master control crew. He supervises all incoming and outgoing programs and is responsible for the timing of programs so that network breaks and spot commercials are integrated at the correct time. It is his job to direct the switching back and forth from a studio, a remote, the film room, or a network station – much as the director does in the studio control room for his particular show. The master control supervisor maintains contact with

the various sources of programming over an intercom system.

2. The chief sound man who is in charge of the checking of all sound before it is fed to the transmitter, and the switching of sound from one pick-up facility to another. He also operates the turntables for recorded sound used on programs which originate directly from master control.

3. There are generally two or more video engineers in master control who are responsible for the shading of the pictures and the checking of the quality and shape of the video signals.

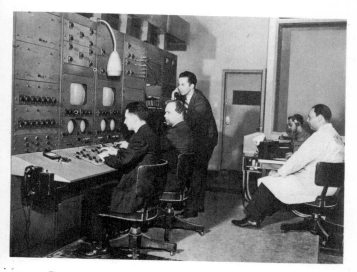

Figure 19. Master control room facilities. (courtesy DuMont)

6-27 The Projection Room. In the early days of television a large percentage of programming was devoted to films. Although stations in metropolitan areas no longer need this "crutch" to fill out their daily program schedules, film continues to play an important part in programming. With the advent of network operations through programs transcribed on film, the projection room will assume a more important role.

The projection room is equipped with specially designed film projectors which have a unique shutter arrangement to change the 24 frames per second of the motion picture film to the 30 frames per second at which television images are broadcast.

An iconoscope camera is mounted directly in front of a projector. The film is projected directly onto the iconoscope mosaic. The iconoscope is mounted on a sliding bar and can be quickly moved into position before any one of several projectors.

Four projectors are required to adequately handle different film sizes and lengths, two for 35mm film and two for 16mm film. This permits continuous projection of either size film when the picture runs for more than one reel. A slide projector is another essential piece of equipment in the projection room since many of the program titles are most easily presented on slides. A Balopticon projector is also useful for projecting pictures, cards, newspaper ads, or small objects which have not been photographed or prepared for slide projection. Equipment for quick splicing of film and for viewing of film is also essential. Two men are needed to handle the work in the projection room, one to operate the equipment and another to maintain the film library and rent and purchase film.

The integration of film into a live program produces interesting effects and affords changes of pace in the production. Film may be used to illustrate a point brought out in a live studio program. It is also effective for superimposition with either slides or live studio action. In fact, there is no end to the possible uses of film in television programs, and no question that it will continue to remain an important factor in programming.

6-28 Transcribing Programs on Films. A recent development in television has been the perfection of a camera that photographs the image on the picture tube and simultaneously records the sound. This process is known as teletranscribing (or sometimes kinescope recording), and is a tremendous step forward in creating a nation-wide network without the use of coaxial or microwave links. The teletranscription method of networking permits television stations in the smaller population centers to carry top quality metropolitan programs at a cost commensurate with their operational budget. At the same time, the national advertiser is enabled to procure nation-wide coverage of all markets with his television program.

No special precautions must be taken in producing shows which are to be teletranscribed. A program with proper lighting, makeup, scenery, and direction is just as suitable for recording on film as it is for immediate transmission.

The possibilities of this important development are manifold. Television programs, when transcribed, may be cut and edited. Necessary portions may be eliminated for different markets. Scenes may be re-shot if they are considered unsatisfactory.

PLANNING THE PROGRAM

6-29 Probably the most important rule which must be followed in planning a program is that it must be simple. A careful study of the details of the production with a view toward simplicity should be made before undertaking the mechanics of creating the program. The usual pitfall is the starting of a production which requires the use of elaborate equipment or staging and more time and money than the producer or director has available. No matter how good the idea or how well the show is produced, if the cost of production is prohibitive, a show is useless. This is true for programs produced either for commercial or sustaining markets. Knowing the current market for a specific type of program, checking over the expenses for at least a thirteen-week period, and making certain that they will not exceed the acceptable budget, are important points which the producer and director must remember.

6-30 Scripts. Developing writers who understand the television medium and who are equipped to write directly for it is one of the greatest problems facing this new industry. At present there is a dearth of material which is suitable for television production. Until there is more money with which to lure established writers away from other fields, television scripts will continue to be mediocre. The current trend of adapting material used in other media like the theater and radio, and from short stories does not fully exploit the powers of television as a spontaneous medium, different from all others. Writing for television calls for a very special technique, a different set of rules, and an entirely new approach.

To create mood and atmosphere, the motion pictures employ such devices as mob scenes, tremendous sets, and expansive scenery. To secure similar effects, radio depends upon word pictures, together with sound and musical effects. The legitimate theater, using both visual and aural techniques, does it with a more over-all effect in mind. Audience attention is easily giving the important dialogue to a good actor. The ability to carry the play lies in the quality of the dialogue and the acting ability of the leading characters throughout the performance. Television cannot use the lavish technique of motion pictures, the aural pictures of radio, or even the techniques of the theater, at least not to the same extent. While combining both visual and aural techniques, television places far more emphasis on the "bit player". The actor with a few lines is as prominently spotlighted during his few moments on the screen as is the leading character who carries the play. The elevation of the bit player in television is due to the extensive employment of close-up technique. Consequently, the casting of small parts requires a greater care than in any other form of entertainment. Likewise, the writing and direction of lesser characters and of small sub-plots demand scrupulous attention.

A television script should always be written for a minimum number of characters. The plot lines should be carefully woven to secure the credulity and natural quality necessary to maintain the intimacy of the medium. The dialogue is the very crux of a television show. A director is powerless to "direct around", or divert attention from weak dialogue. Scripts must be broken down into short scenes, with as much visual action as possible. This is due again to the limited screen area and the viewer's rapid loss of interest when presented with a static scene for more than a short period.

6-31 Choosing Actors. After the director makes his choice of a script or decides upon a format for an informal ad-lib program, the next problem is to select performers who will best carry out the production. Oftentimes a good evaluation of an actor can be obtained by talking informally with him, planting the idea of the intimacy of television, warning against over-projection and over-playing, and searching for the natural personality which can later be spotlighted in performance. Sometimes an improvised, informal chat between two actors before the camera and mike will supply the director with the clue of warmth and intimacy for which he is searching. This method of selecting actors also shows up annoying mannerisms or physical characteristics which do not register well before the perceptive eye of the camera.

6-32 Acting for Television. The spontaneity of the video medium is its most outstanding characteristic. An actor who has confidence and the ability to ad lib during unforeseen technical mishaps not only appears better before the television camera, but also helps the rest of the cast and the director. The viewing public is aware that, as in the legitimate theater, the scene is actually taking place. Therefore, a personal approach and an awareness of the camera is desirable. An illusion is created which makes the viewer feel that he is actually closer to the performer than he would be in a theater. This personal contact should be exploited to the fullest extent. The performance of the actor in television is subjected to an extremely careful examination by the viewer. Slight facial expressions are exaggerated to a further degree than in any other medium.

Most radio actors develop stock characters which they can turn on and off at will. In fact, most radio shows are cast with these stock characters in mind. They are usually given no real acting direction and are on their own from the start. Radio's emphasis on voice quality and strictly audio techniques is usually a hindrance to radio performers who turn to television. They find that they must leave behind most of the tricks and short-cuts which were learned during long running parts in day-time "soap-operas". The television camera is quick to detect the insincere or "phoney". Many radio actors, of course, have had experience in stage work. Such experience is invaluable since stage techniques most closely parallel those used in television.

The photogenic motion picture actor who is familiar with the close-up technique is generally considered ideal basic acting material for television. However, even he must learn to act for television. Motion pictures are produced under conditions completely different from those of television programs. In motion pictures, cutting and editing have eliminated the need for sustained effort on the part of the actor. He learns a portion of a scene at a time. A fluff is unimportant because retakes are possible. He receives little experience in memorizing whole scripts, or even scenes. Before the television camera the actor is on his own, out of the hands of the director. He must understand pace and tempo and be fully aware that there can be no stopping because of mistakes and that the slightest slip is immediately apparent to the viewing audience.

The legitimate theater actor also comes close to fulfilling the requirements for the ideal television actor. His experience and training are invaluable. He is more flexible and usually understands the limitations of both space and time. There are, of course, things which the actor with stage experience must unlearn. He generally shows a tendency to overproject and to play too broadly. If anything, he must learn to underplay. His voice must be projected to a sensitive microphone a few inches above his head, rather than to the back wall of a theater. Facial expressions must be subtle and gestures reduced in scope. The stage actor's manner of playing must be adjusted to a less obvious level. "Hammy" quality, or even a trace of "theatricalism" is in obvious bad taste on the viewer's screen. The stage actor must adjust to the confining, sometimes cramped playing areas of a television studio. He must learn that in order to maintain the close-up technique he has to play elbow to elbow with the other actors. Nor is he at liberty to express his feelings with great movements across the stage or with elaborate use of furniture or props. What movement he is allowed is mostly lateral to avoid going out of camera focus.

Actors become familiar with the techniques required of them by television only by watching a great number of television shows, either on a receiving set or as onlookers in the studio during rehearsals and performances. The public, in turn, as it watches more of this entertainment, will learn that the finished television show has had far less rehearsal than is generally supposed. It will gradually temper its criticism as it learns to appreciate more and more the excitement and originality, and the fresh "first-time" quality of the new medium.

6-33 Rehearsals. The lack of sufficient rehearsal time before the cameras is another obstacle which stands in the way of good television programming. As pointed out previously, it is not economically possible to pay the high costs of an adequate rehearsal schedule. To rehearse a full day's schedule of television programs, on the basis of the number of hours which the stage and motion pictures devote to shows, would require facilities and capital far beyond the limits which can be supported by commercial sponsorship. The average rehearsal time for commercial television programs, with present studio setups, is limited to a ratio of six to one; that is, approximately three hours of camera rehearsal time can be allotted to a half-hour program. For a sustaining program the ratio is a great deal less, approximately two to one, or one hour of rehearsal with cameras for a half-hour program.

The cost of talent during long rehearsal periods is heavy, but even this cost is small compared to the outlay for rehearsing with the station equipment. The average television program budget can afford only a few hours rehearsal with the station technicians. Because camera rehearsals at the station are so expensive, much "dry run" rehearsing of the cast is done at outside studios. The performers usually know their lines and actions thoroughly by the time the show is ready for camera rehearsal. This makes it possible to utilize camera rehearsal time to fullest advantage. A major part of the camera rehearsal is devoted to checking the lighting on the performers and scenery, and to determining the best camera angles.

Even though the most minute and scrupulous plans have been made, the director must be ready for unpredictable difficulties which occur during camera rehearsal. Technical breakdowns or deficiencies often require complete deletions of camera shots which had been planned for important effects. Often there is insufficient time to fully rehearse a new plan before air time. At television's present state of development it is not unheard of for a director and cast to arrive at a studio for rehearsal to find that a new type of camera has been installed and is only partially operative, or that a lighting expert has completely reorganized the lighting setup, which of necessity changes the playing areas on the studio floor and rules out certain shots which had been planned. The new lighting may call for a different type of make-up for the cast. Or there may be a new method of switching from master control to studio control. This change may require new techniques for integrating titles and film with the show.

Television rehearsals usually appear chaotic to the uninitiated. For this reason, it is considered good policy to keep prospective sponsors away from rehearsals. Actually, seeming confusion prevails at most rehearsals for all entertainment media, while in present-day television it is increased by the "growing pains" of the industry.

An unfortunate aspect of the rehearsal problem is the fact that the camera rehearsal is usually scheduled for the same day as the performance. This practice is necessary because of limited studio space and the lack of extra equipment for rehearsals. The scenery is set up in the studio for rehearsal, as close to air time as possible. As soon as the show is over, the studio space and equipment must be made ready for the rehearsing and airing of another show. This means that important changes, which are found to be necessary during the rehearsal, cannot always be made in time for the on-the-air performance. As television programming expands and relief crews and studio space are added, the practice of rehearsing programs on the day they are broadcast will undoubtedly be changed. At the present time, this practice presents a real problem to the director.

There are several things which the director can do to minimize the effects of confusion and technical difficulties during rehearsal. Some of them follow:

1. He should insist that the technical director be present at the first reading, or blocking rehearsal. At this time, the actual production can be envisioned, camera action planned, and different camera shots decided upon. If this is accomplished at

the rehearsal with the full accord of the technical director, many technical difficulties will be avoided during the airing of the show.

2. If the show is built around an original script, the writer should be on hand, or available for cuts, or rewriting.

3. Well in advance of the rehearsal, the director should obtain a layout of the stage from the scenery designer. He should also consult the lighting technician as to the areas which are best illuminated for the type of action planned.

4. Constant changes in script or in direction after the preliminary rehearsal serve only to confuse the performers. It is wise and economical to eliminate all trouble spots before the rehearsal.

5. Film insertions into a live program cannot be rehearsed if the master control personnel is busy previewing film or is occupied in some other manner at the time of the performers' rehearsal. Therefore, cues in and out of film must be rehearsed at another time and the technicians involved given complete cue sheets. A good policy is to find out first what type of coordination is technically possible, and then plan the show accordingly. All studios do not have the same facilities for integrating film with live pickup.

6-34 Details of Production. The securing of properties is a problem which must be dealt with individually by each studio. Some studios are located in department stores and have working agreements with them whereby furniture or hand props can be borrowed for productions. This is a fortunate setup, but most studios have to make arrangements for props with furniture stores and professional property companies.

Sets which cannot be assembled from stock flats must be planned and constructed about a week before a show. A sketch is submitted to the studio art director, outlining what is required. The studio art director's advice is often invaluable in deciding the scenery colors and layout which will give the best effects with the studio cameras and lighting available.

Music is used either in live or recorded form and is an important adjunct to a program. Proper care must be given to the selection. Mood or background music can do much to heighten the effect of a scene. After the musical scores are selected, they must be cleared for commercial broadcast purposes. All details of how the music is to be used are given to the station's program department, which secures the clearance.

If spot commercials are to be inserted into a program, effective cues must be given to the studio crew and to master control to insure smooth integration of the commercials with the program. Television networks have certain requirements regarding length and frequency of commercial spots.

Wardrobe problems are solved well in advance of the camera rehearsal, thereby utilizing the latter time for the more important task of planning camera shots. Costume colors must be chosen to suit the color response of the cameras. The appearance of patterns and lines in the costume materials is checked on a picture monitor before final selections are made. The materials can be brought to the studio and checked during brief moments when camera equipment is idle.

The exact times when the program goes on and leaves the air are checked with master control. This determines the exact running time for the show. A time sheet is then prepared, breaking down the program into small sections which are timed individually. With this time breakdown, a constant check can be made during the actual production to determine whether or not the show is ahead or behind time. The performers can then be paced accordingly by relaying signals to them through the floor manager. With network breaks and spot commercials scheduled to the very second, accurate timing is a must in television programming.

A well organized production staff goes far in reducing the many problems involved in preparing a television show for the air. The delegation of responsibility to competent people is as important in this work as in any business. Generally speaking, production staffs for television programming are reduced to skeleton size because of limited budgets. The size of the staff depends on the type of show to be produced. Sometimes several of the functions are performed by one person to reduce costs. For example, the director often serves as the producer and writer.

The breakdown of authority and duties of personnel is important. A typical working arrangement is shown in the organization chart of Figure 20. The responsibilities of each of the personnel are as follows:

1. Producer or Program Director: Responsible to the sponsor and the station for entire production. He directs production on the air.

2. Program Director's Assistant: Responsible to Program Director for carrying out Director's requests on entire production. He also directs the show in rehearsals.

3. Budget Manager: Responsible to Program Director. De-

termines costs of production and advises on ways to trim production costs.

4. Video Technical Director: Responsible to Program Director's Assistant and in charge of video quality.

5. Film Man: In charge of film. Is directly responsible to the Video Technical Director for cuing film into production.

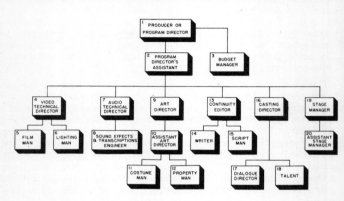

Figure 20. Organization chart of program personnel.

6. Lighting Man: Takes orders from and makes technical suggestions to the Video Director.

7. Audio Technical Director: Responsible to Program Director's Assistant and in charge of audio quality.

8. Sound Effects and Transcriptions Engineer: Responsible to Audio Director for technical problems involved in sound and music other than dialogue or microphone pickups.

9. Art Director: Responsible to Program Director's Assistant and in charge of design and execution of all art work.

10. Assistant Art Director: Responsible to Art Director. Duties are to assist in art work details and costs.

11. Costume Man: Responsible to Assistant Art Director. Secures costumes.

12. Property Man: Responsible to Assistant Art Director. Secures Properties.

13. Continuity Editor: Responsible to Program Director's Assistant. Checks scripts and times dialogue. Responsible for overall timing of production.

14. Writer: Responsible to Continuity Editor. Writes story and dialogue.

15. Script Man: Responsible to Continuity Editor. Duties are

typing and delivering of scripts to Continuity Editor.

16. Casting Director: Responsible to Program Director's Assistant for obtaining actors and their understudies.

17. Dialogue Director: Responsible to Casting Director for dialects and interpretation of roles as well as voice modulation.

18. Talent: Responsible to Casting Director.

19. Stage Manager: Responsible to Program Director's As-

Figure 21. The technical director operates the switching panel and selects the desired camera. (courtesy NBC)

sistant for handling of all properties, scenery, calls, etc. during production.

20. Assistant Stage Manager: Responsible to Stage Manager. Checks all properties before telecast.

6-35 The Program Director and His Job. The program director, or simply director, is in charge of the entire television program. His duties begin with the choosing of a script which is best suited to the format of the show. The best script is usually one that has been written especially for television rather than adapted from another form. Since such a script is not always available, the director must compromise on the quality of the script, and depend upon his own ingenuity to adapt it to the medium.

The director's next concern is the planning of camera action so as to catch each movement in the most interesting way. In blocking out the physical movement of the cast, he must constantly think in terms of camera shots. He must also take into

Figure 22. Studio crew in action. Note the camera at the right focused on the title board. (courtesy NBC)

account the position of the mike boom so that all sound is properly picked up in true prespective with the picture.

Transitions from one scene to another present certain problems, for there are no curtain falls to bridge the gap. Fadeouts, dissolves, and clips must be used to best advantage. The director must coordinate the stage action and the camera work so that there is a picture on the air at all times. A blank screen, even momentarily, is annoying to the viewer. The studio action must be coordinated with master control if film is to be integrated with the program. The director is responsible for the timing of the program on the air and cuing of studio and master control crews. A detailed cue sheet prepared by the director when first planning the show enables him to practice timing during rehearsal and to achieve precision timing on the air.

The director must not burden the actors to any great extent with camera angles, beyond making them aware of camera locations and which camera will be taking the close-up shots. There are, of course, times when an exact position on the set must be assumed by the performer in order to obtain a particular camera effect. In such cases, chalk marks are used on the floor to help both actor and cameraman.

The director must not only direct a cast of his own choosing but also the technical crew furnished by the station. Mistakes on anyone's part are his responsibility. The good director is one who trains both cast and crew to minimize mistakes.

6-36 The Technical Director. The technical director is the contact man between director and crew. He is personally responsible for what happens on the studio floor. In most studios, the technical director relays the orders of the director to the crew. This is necessary because there are many directors who are not connected with the station and who are not familiar with the equipment or operating techniques of the crew. It has been found more practical to feed all directions from the director to the crew through the technical director. The main disadvantage to this repetition of orders is that it often results in a time lag between calling for an effect and carrying it out. This shortcoming can be minimized by a good director during the running of a show by preparing each camera a few seconds in advance of switching it on the air. Relaying of orders will probably be eliminated when each studio employs full staffs of directors who can be assigned to all productions of the studio.

The technical director must be ready for any emergency that arises during a production. Usually an additional camera is kept available, should one of the regular ones break down. It is the technical director's job to get the spare camera swung into position and ready for action as quickly as possible. The technical director does the actual switching from one camera to another and coordinates the operation of master control with studio control. He and the director work in close cooperation since each contributes to the direction of the production. In Figure 21 the technical director is shown at the switching console, relaying orders over a microphone to the studio crew. The studio crew is shown in action in Figure 22.

A TYPICAL TELEVISION SHOW

6-37 In order to demonstrate how the programming techniques described up to this point are actually put to use in creating a typical television show, the planning, rehearsing, and production procedures for a live studio show.and a remote pick-up are outlined in the following paragraphs.

6-38 "Photographic Horizons" - A Live Studio Show. "Photographic Horizons" is a weekly half-hour show which concerns itself with the many aspects of photography. It is intended for the large number of people who are camera fans, either as amateurs or as potential commercial photographers. Since the television audience demands entertainment as well as instruction, a compromise must be reached between the two. Many camera addicts would like to know the temperature of developer baths or the lens opening and shutter speeds used to take the pictures which are shown during the program. The majority of the viewers prefer to overlook such technical information and learn the entertainment aspects of photography. The format is so planned that instruction is mixed with the lighter material. A pretty girl is always in the scene, and strong, arresting pictures are shown, intermixed with plenty of live action and amusing situations. A typical scene from "Photographic Horizons" is shown in Figure 23.

Heading the show is a top news photographer, whose experience, taste, and showmanship, as well as his knowledge of all aspects of photography equip him for the job. He is aided by an attractive female assistant. A loosely defined format is used, the show being split into two sections, each approximately fifteen minutes long. The first half may contain the news photographer's selection of the best news pictures which appeared in the daily papers during the previous week. These pictures are shown on an easel, with the photographer discussing their value. Often a brief comment on some aid or trick for better picture making is made at this point, and the photographer accompanies the suggestion with a sketch on a drawing board. Or perhaps the news photographers responsible for the selected pictures of the week make a brief appearance, explaining the stories behind the taking of the pictures. The first part of the program also features the activities of a large Camera Club of the Air which has several thousand members. At times a member visiting the studio is welcomed on the program.

Photography contests are discussed and winning pictures shown. A feature of the show is a contest for the best picture taken off the viewer's screen.

After discussing the above business, a guest is featured in the

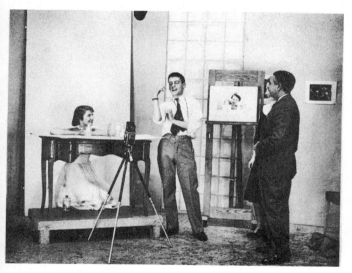

Figure 23. A scene from "Photographic Horizons". (courtesy DuMont)

final fifteen minutes of the program. The guest is usually a prominent photographer who discusses interesting aspects of his work and shows representative samples of his best pictures. The guest photographer may be from the field of fashion, news, commercial photography, crime photography, animal photography, or any phase which will provide instructive entertainment for the amateur viewer. During this portion of the show, the permanent head photographer sits down with his guest to discuss the latter's pictures which are shown on an easel. Every attempt is made to avoid the usual "radio interview" by breaking up the discussion with the showing of close-ups of interesting pictures. At some point during the second half of the program, the contest picture of the week, which is to be photographed from the viewer's screen, is posed. Sufficient time is allowed for the amateur working in his home to focus his camera and get the shot.

In order to surround the two main portions of the show with entertainment appeal, a simple device is used. A pretty assistant acts as a "frame" for the show, and opens and closes the half hour with a personalized, intimate talk with the audience. This device succeeds in making the show appear like an informal, chatty meeting of a small Camera Club, and provides a direct and intimate contact with the viewer. The opening and closing titles are worked in with the assistant's dialogue. These titles are shown on a roller. Appropriate film is sometimes superimposed or dissolved in with the titles.

With the understanding of the format of the show, "Photographic Horizons", let us examine the details of production which are carried out in order to put the program on the air.

The permanent, or host photographer, is first consulted for suggestions on guests who are top names in their fields, and who will prove interesting, relaxed, and personable performers. The suggested guests are contacted and available dates discussed. Appointments are made to go through their collections of prints in order to select pictures which will illustrate their stories well on television. An attempt is made to secure a variety of photographers from week to week. A commercial photographer, say, is followed by a magazine illustrator, who in turn is followed by a fashion photographer, and so forth.

Having arranged for the guest spot, attention is given to the many details of production. All pictures used on the show are blown up to sizes which can be picked up by the camera (usually 11" x 14" for horizontal prints, 14" x 17" for vertical prints). The pictures are mounted on stiff boards to prevent their curling under the hot studio lights. Pictures with non-glossy or mat finishes are used to avoid reflections from the lights. Black and white pictures with bold, massive objects in the foreground show best over the television system and are used whenever possible.

Appropriate music is selected and cleared for use on the air. This music provides musical backgrounds or bridging between scenes. Props are listed and collected. Guests are contacted and given the rehearsal hours, suggestions as to clothing, and recommendations for make-up. Often a model is provided for demonstration purposes in connection with the featured guest's appearance. Because of the limited time allowed for actual camera rehearsal, as much preparation as possible is done in advance by conferring with the performers in person or via telephone, and blocking out the points to be covered.

"Photographic Horizons" is mainly an ad lib program. However, a strict adherence to a time schedule is necessary to assure coverage of all activity planned. For this reason, a script is prepared in outline form. First, the narrator's material is written. This includes the announcement of the show, the names of guests to appear, mention of current contests, etc. Then a careful video and audio plot is prepared in script form and copies given to the local and master control studios so that film, sound, music, slides, and camera action are properly coordinated. This type of planning is highly important in a show where film, coming from master control, is inserted into the middle of a live show originating in the studio.

Exact timings are indicated on the script for each segment of the show. Once on the air, the director may choose to exceed the time limit at one point and borrow from the next, but to achieve a well-rounded production, he tries to stay as close as possible to the original timing. To assure that the program will get off the air on time, safety spots are inserted wherever possible. These take the form of cuing on the female assistant to speed up the action and move onto the next point. The female assistant helps to pace performers who are new to television and who often miss signals from the stage manager. The assistant is one of many devices which may be employed on this type of program as a subtle and effective means of keeping the show on schedule.

A sample script for the particular "Photographic Horizons" show described in this section is presented below to illustrate the form used to lay out the audio and video directions and dialogue, and the methods for showing the details of timing and cuing of the performers and equipment facilities. The script is divided into three sections. The first section is an outline of the show, divided into nine parts. The timing for each part is shown at the very beginning. The second section of the script is the narrator's dialogue. This is the only dialogue which is formally prepared, the rest of the show being ad-libbed. The third section of the script is the master control sheet which gives this group the cuing times for various facilities.

Section 1

PHOTOGRAPHIC HORIZONS

DIRECTOR: Bob Loewi

ASSISTANT: John Ireys

CAST:

	TIMING:	
Peggy Corday	Part 1	1:00 minutes
Okie Dokie	Part 2	1:30 minutes
Joe Costa	Part 3	2:00 minutes
Ed Carroll	Part 4	4:00 minutes
Lisa Larsen	Part 5	11:30 minutes
	Part 6	5:00 minutes
	Part 7	2:00 minutes
	Part 8	1:00 minutes
	Part 9	0:45 minutes

VIDEO	AUDIO
Part 1. Slides and film montage.	Fanfare. Music. Narration.
Part 2. Outer Office.	Peggy opening. Okie Dokie puppet.
Part 3. Inner Office.	Joe Costa and Pix.
Part 4. Inner Office.	Peggy on. Video snapshot. Rules of Contest. Ed Carroll build-up.
Part 5. Outer Office.	Carroll Explanation and 4 pix. Peggy - Introduce Lisa Larsen.
Part 6. Inner Office.	Lisa Larsen, Joe Costa, and Pix.
Part 7. Inner Office.	Peggy on for video snapshot, and Costa final word.
Part 8. Door.	Peggy close.
Part 9. Titles.	Music.

Section II

Narrator's Dialogue:

Good evening, shutterbugs. Welcome again to the informal program . . . Photographic Horizons . . . featuring another session of the camera club.

Become a member of our camera club . . . the first of its kind on television Join the ranks of members who are learning about photography by watching these programs. All you must do to receive your membership card is write us: Photographic Horizons, care of the station to which you are tuned.

As a special feature tonight we present our guest photographer . . . Lisa Larsen . . . journalist photographer, best known for her frequent picture stories in Life magazine.

Watch for the television award winning pictures in the snapshot contest. Shutterbugs. Get your camera and prepare to take a video snapshot off your television screen.
  And now, let's look to our . . . Photographic Horizons.

Section III

Master Control Sheet

VIDEO	AUDIO
1. Lica slide 5 seconds	Fanfare (Studio A)
2. Lica slide (Photographic Horizons)	Music (Studio A) Narrator (Studio A)
3. Film (16mm montage) all way in for slide change. Film 50/50 with slides. Camera Club slide. Joe Costa slide. Producer, director slide. Last slide in full, film out. Dissolve to studio.	Music (Studio A)
4. Studio A (Approx. 12 min.)	Studio A.
5. 16mm film (teletranscription) (approx. 5 min.)	1. Sound track on film. 2. Fade out sound on cue. 3. Narration from studio.

6. Studio A (approx. 15 min.)   Studio A.

7. Clip to lica slide (Photographic   Music (Studio A)
    Horizons). Dissolve film (16mm
    montage) in 50/50, then all way
    in. Change to Assistant Director
    slide. Film in 50/50, then all way
    in.
    Network slide.

END OF SHOW

6-39 Since "Photographic Horizons" is teletranscribed for
distribution to other stations in a network, anything which would
quickly date the program must be eliminated. Contests which
are limited to a certain area, or to a given time, must be edited
out of the teletranscription before it is sent to other stations.
By careful preparation of the original script and proper editing,
the program material may be confined to that which will be of
interest many months later when presented over a television
station hundred of miles away. The simplest way to cut out
material of a current nature or with a fixed time element is to
group it into one portion of the program so that it can all be
cut out together. Commercials for sponsors in a local area
are also inserted at this point and are cut out when the film
is sent to another station. The network station, in turn, may
insert other spot commercials at this point in the program.

6-40 Putting the Show on the Air. Now the program "Photographic Horizons" is ready for broadcast. Last minute checks
of the props on the studio floor are made. Voice levels are
tested on the microphones. Make-up and lighting are checked
on the studio monitors. In the studio control room the program
director reviews again with the technical director the sequence
of camera action. The pictures on the camera monitors are
examined to make certain that the video engineer has adjusted
the signal levels and shading for the best effect. A last minute
check is made with the audio man to be sure he has all the sound
effect records and musical recordings ready and in proper sequence. Master control is contacted on the intercom system and

cuing signals for film and slides reviewed. The program is then ready to go.

Let us examine, in detail, what takes place while the program is on the air. The following step by step procedure will give the reader some appreciation of the careful planning necessary to create a successful program.

1. As soon as the station break is completed, the director calls for "Fanfare" from the sound and video men. Music comes up from a transcription on the turntable. As it begins the slide "Presenting" is transmitted on the video.

2. One second before the eight-second fanfare is over, the director calls to the floor manager to "Cue Narrator."

3. As the narrator starts to speak, the director orders Master Control to "Roll Film" and "Change Slide". Upon this direction the film projectionist starts the film montage, and after approximately a five-second lapse, this film is dissolved in 50/50 with the second slide, which is the title slide of the program, "Photographic Horizons". The result is a superimposition of the film and the slide as a double exposure. At this point theme music is brought in softly by the video man in Studio Control, and remains for the rest of the narration. The film is then brought up to full contrast as the slide is faded out to permit changing to another slide. This is done to avoid the amateurish effect produced by changing slides on the air. When the next slide is ready, the film is brought back to a 50/50 superimposition with the slide. The slides are changed at a speed which coincides with the narration.

4. As the narrator concludes his script, the final slide is brought in full and the film montage faded out. Theme music is brought up full as the direction is given to Master Control to "Fade Down Slide, and Fade out Studio." Simultaneously, the studio floor manager is given the direction to "Cue Peggy." As the technical director fades the studio camera up, a close-up shot of Peggy, the mistress of ceremonies, is shown. She welcomes the television audience to another meeting of the Camera Club. Peggy stands in front of a desk, with a background which suggests a photographer's waiting room or outer office. Several pieces of photographic equipment, placed on the set serve to establish the subject matter of the program. As she begins to speak, the theme music is faded out slowly.

The two cameras with which the program is televised are focused on Peggy for her opening announcements, which include the presentation of a club member or a model who will serve later on in the show. One camera is set for a medium-long shot, while the other is adjusted for close-ups. The medium long shot camera sets the opening segment of the show and is followed by close-ups of the performers. The opening usually lasts no longer than two minutes.

5. At least 30 seconds before the end of the introduction, the long shot camera takes over, and the director orders the other camera moved to another set where the chief personality of the show, Joe Costa, is seated behind a desk. If the opening spot is running over its allotted time, the director tells the stage manager via the intercom system to "Cue Peggy to wind up." This direction is given by the stage manager with a winding circular motion of the finger, and tells the performers to finish the topic in thirty seconds. If it is necessary to cut off immediately and proceed into the next spot, a cue is given with a sliding motion of the finger across the throat. Peggy leads into the next part of the show by pointing to a door at her right, on which is painted "Joe Costa's Photo Room".

6. The director now cues in a musical selection from the studio control room turntable. The camera remaining on Peggy pans slowly to the door, creating the illusion that the camera is about to go through the door.

7. As the camera dollies toward the door and focuses in close-up on the sign "Joe Costa's Photo Room", the stage manager is ordered to "Cue Joe Costa". The technical director then dissolves from the close-up camera to the medium-long-shot camera as Costa begins to speak. The transition music is taken out slowly.

8. During Costa's opening remarks, an easel with several pictures stacked one upon the other is quickly set up in view of Costa, but out of camera range. The close-up camera which had panned to the door at the end of the previous scene is brought over and positioned for a close-up shot of the easel. As soon as this camera is properly positioned, Costa is free to begin the discussion of the news pictures which he has selected for the program.

9. As Costa speaks of the first picture in the sequence, the direction is given to clip from the medium-long-shot of Costa to a close-up of the first picture on the easel. This shot is retained for 10 to 20 seconds, depending upon the interest in the picture, and the story behind it. As Costa winds up his remarks on the first picture, the technical director is cued to clip back to the medium-long-shot camera. This allows time for a stage hand to change the picture on the easel, and for the cameraman to get it properly into focus. The procedure is repeated for as many times as there are pictures to be shown.

10. When the news pictures have been shown, Costa calls for his assistant, Peggy Corday, who alternates with him in making various announcements. These include showing the

winning pictures of current contests and the prizes which are to be awarded. Future contests and photographic trips are discussed.

11. Now the close-up camera is directed back to the easel, while the medium-long-shot camera is clipped on to show Peggy and Costa. At this point a series of pictures, usually taken by amateurs, is shown on the easel. They may be the winning pictures of the Metropolitan Camera Club Council, or the snapshot awards of a daily newspaper. Some data on how the pictures were taken is supplied, and comments, and criticisms are made by Costa.

12. The director then cues Peggy to get ready for the feature guest. The close-up camera is released at this point and moves back to another set to focus on the guest. Meanwhile, the medium-long-shot camera takes over.

13. As Peggy speaks the cue line, "And now let's go over and meet Lisa Larsen", the director tells the technical director to set his controls for dissolve, and cues in the transition music once more. The guest photographer is usually discovered in the midst of a visual demonstration, either posing his model or setting up his camera. The "dissolve" cue is given, and the picture changes to the close-up camera on the guest. Sometimes this shot is a close-up on the face of the model, or on a piece of photographic equipment, and then the camera dollies back for a long-shot. Joe Costa is then shown making his entrance and greeting the guest. Costa and the guest take their seats on a sofa placed nearby. As they begin to talk the music is faded out slowly.

14. The medium-long-shot camera is switched on and the other camera brought over to an easel which is placed so that the two people on the sofa can see it. The pictures which the guest will discuss are set up on this easel and the close-up camera focused on the first picture.

15. After preliminary discussion of Lisa Larsen's work, the conversation leads into a discussion of the pictures themselves. They are shown and commented on in the same manner that Costa's pictures were presented at the beginning of the show. The television viewer never sees the pictures being changed because the director clips from the close-up camera on the easel to the medium-long shot camera on the performers during each change. This type of clipping creates a greater feeling of movement and gets away from the static interview.

16. "Photographic Horizons" features a weekly contest in which the guest photographer poses either Peggy or a guest model. The viewers are then told to get their cameras set, and, on a signal, to snap pictures of their television screens. The

best "off-the-screen-pictures" submitted are given prizes.

At exactly $3\frac{1}{2}$ minutes before the program is to be off the air, Peggy is cued on to start the contest. She speaks of the video snapshot to be set up, and asks the guest photographer to pose the model. The model holds her pose before the close-up cam-

Figure 24. A typical prize winning "off the screen" photograph.
(courtesy DuMont)

era for eight seconds to allow sufficient time for last minute refocusing and changing of film.

Following this action, the winning "video snapshot" from the show two weeks previous is shown, and the winner's name announced. As soon as this is done, the close-up camera leaves the easel and pans to catch close-ups of the prizes, (usually various sponsors' products) shown by Peggy at the desk with Costa. Commercials which would be out of place in a teletranscription of the program are inserted at this point so that they can be edited out when the program is shown on other stations.

17. As soon as the commercials are completed, Peggy thanks the guest for appearing on the show and asks Joe Costa to close the camera club meeting with a final word of advice to the members. From this point on the timing must be accurately de-

termined down to the second in order to assure getting off the air on schedule.

18. The close-up camera which has been focused on the prizes is now released and is quickly positioned to focus on Peggy. The other camera, which is on a medium-long-shot of Peggy, Costa, and the guest, dollies in slowly, cutting out Peggy and the guest, and stops on a close-up of Costa making his final remarks. If the time is running over at this point, the director orders the stage manager to give Costa a wind-up signal. If the program is running ahead of time, Costa is given a "stretch" cue, which consists of drawing the hands away from one another. Since this program is ad libbed, it is necessary that the participants have the ability to lengthen or shorten their remarks at a moment's notice.

19. The video controls are set for dissolve; and as Costa says, "Peggy, will you close the meeting for tonight?", the director cues Peggy to begin speaking, and at the same time calls for the dissolve from one camera to another.

20. The close-up camera stays on Peggy as she sums up the meeting and tells about the guests who are to appear the following week. Here again, the stage manager will give either a "stretch" or "wind-up" cue, depending on how the time is running.

21. The other camera, which had been on Costa for his final remarks, is now released to get ready for the next program in the studio.

22. As Peggy signs off, the director cues Master Control to "Roll Film." The camera on Peggy dissolves into film. He simultaneously cues the audio man in Studio Control to bring in the music. Master Control is then directed to bring up a 50/50 superimposition of the film and the closing slide, "Photographic Horizons".

23. After a few seconds the slide is faded out and the film brought all the way through to allow for a change in slide. The second slide, a credit for the assistant director, is then brought up for another 50/50 superimposition.

24. The film is then brought all the way through a second time with the theme music full up for five seconds. Five seconds before the end of airtime, the film is dissolved into a slide identifying the network. This allows Master Control time to clip to the station break slide on the split second and bring in the next program on schedule.

This step-by-step description of the procedure followed during a typical half-hour television show illustrates the working of the personnel and equipment in a live program pick-up from the studio.

REMOTE PICK-UP PROGRAMS

6-41 On-the-spot television broadcasts are called remote pick-ups. They represent an important part of programming, and in many cases best illustrate the superiority of television to any other form of entertainment as a spontaneous medium. A remote may originate from such places as an armory, a city street, a hotel dining room, a swimming pool, a night club, etc. To cover events from these remote points, special portable cameras, monitors, sync generators, and power supplies are necessary. This equipment is conveyed to the pick-up point by a specially equipped mobile truck in which a small, local studio is set up. The mobile truck also contains facilities for relaying the program to the station.

Remote pick-ups present several technical problems which are not encountered in planning and producing a studio program. First, there is the problem of power. For a two camera, portable pick-up chain, 5000 watts of alternating current are required. This may not seem to be an overwhelming amount of power, but in many areas the only power available is direct current. Special equipment must be brought along under such circumstances to invert the D-C to A-C. Even when alternating current is available, there is the problem of obtaining enough power, for 5000 watts cannot be drawn from the ordinary outlet. Usually, power is obtained directly from the power line of a building near the pick-up point.

Once the problem of power has been solved, permits must be secured for outdoor pick-ups in order to park the truck on the street and lay the equipment cables across the sidewalk. Oftentimes this permit cannot be obtained from the police and the cameras must be set up in an elevated window or on the roof of a building.

A particular headache to the remote crew is the ever changing light on outdoor pick-ups. This change of light occurs as cloud conditions vary or the sun does down. Light changes must be quickly compensated for by the video engineers.

Despite these difficulties, on-the-spot television coverage has become a most interesting form of programming. Consider for a moment its effect on news reporting. During the 1948 political conventions in Philadelphia, the full possibilities of on-the-spot news reporting via television were fully realized. It is estimated that nearly ten million people along the eastern seaboard had a ringside view of the proceedings and watched history in the making. This remote pick-up created a new and extremely honest kind of reporting. No longer could reporters dash off brilliant paragraphs describing the enthusiastic demonstrations given a particular candidate, when the television viewers were "there" to note the lethargic attitude of the gallery. So thoroughly did the television industry cover this event that viewers in their homes often knew what was going on long before some of the delegates.

Until recently, sporting events dominated the remote television programs. As greater facility was achieved in handling remote equipment, other types of programs were covered. Today, remote pick-up brings to the television audience a wide variety of entertainment including sports, fashion shows, parades, art exhibits, historic dedications, and conventions, to mention only a few. The possibilities of remotes are almost limitless. Wherever news is in the making, the audience wants to see it. The television remote affords the viewer that opportunity.

6-42 Typical Remote. Let us consider a typical remote pick-up to understand the planning and operation of this type of program. Consider the covering of the 1948 Easter Parade on Fifth Avenue in New York.

1. First, the program idea is submitted to the Program Department so that time and announcers are allotted to the broadcast. The chief engineer and operations manager are notified of the intended broadcast to make certain that a portable camera chain will be available.

2. Having cleared the program thus far, the city department in charge of licensing such operations is contacted and a permit obtained to operate on the street. For a parade where there are marching units in definite formation, it is necessary to confer with the manager of the parade so as to forewarn the cameraman of interesting formations which should be picked up. Because of the nature of the Easter parade, this is not necessary.

3. At this point, the Remote Engineer and the Remote Manager make a survey of suitable locations for the placement of the equipment used in televising the parade. This involves a rough blocking out of camera positions, location of power lines, and the finding of convenient spots for the mobile truck. Finally, the method of relaying the program to the station master control room is determined. If a line of sight exists from the point of pick-up to the station, radio relay equipment is used. When

line of sight transmission is not possible, arrangement: are made with the telephone company to provide a telephone line to the station. All of these factors are checked before it is definitely established that the remote pick-up is possible.

4. On the day of the parade, the truck is positioned directly in front of "Saks 5th Avenue", with the truck parallel to the curb in front of the main entrance on Fifth Avenue as shown in Figure 25. Power for the equipment is tapped from an outlet on

Figure 25. Remote pickup truck and crew in action. (courtesy DuMont)

the second story of the store and fed directly to the truck.

5. The micro-wave relay transmitter is placed on top of the store and is aimed directly at the receiving antenna in the transmitter several blocks away.

6. The cameras are set up on top of the truck with the viewing monitors and switching equipment inside. The program is directed from this latter point. All equipment is in place and checked several hours before the broadcast.

7. The Program Department furnishes the announcer as well as script material, and suggests a format for personal interviews throughout the morning of the parade. A few of the in-

terviews are planned in advance to provide variety and high-
lights for the program. Noted personalities are contacted so
that they "happen" to appear in the parade at the proper time.
An announcer with a portable microphone mingles with the
crowds. He is attired in a top hat and conspicuous dress so
that he can easily be picked out in the crowd by the camera.

8. The technical director is given a complete script and plan
of operation. Reception by the station transmitter is checked,
and the Easter Parade is on.

Here then is a resume in outline form for preparing a remote
broadcast:

1. Submit plan to Program Department.
2. Notify Chief Engineer and Operations Manager.
3. Arrange contact with proper official in charge of event.
4. Arrange survey with Remote Engineer and Manager for
    a. Choice of location for equipment.
    b. Choice of camera positions and truck location.
    c. Check availability of a-c power.
    d. Check relay link (microwave relay or telephone line).
5. Secure permits and permissions.
    a. Permits.
        1. Street permit for truck and string of wires.
        2. Electrical permit for a-c power.
    b. Permissions (variable).
        1. For location of micro-wave transmitter.
6. Production work.
    a. Time of program and time of event.
    b. Announcer and script.
    c. Check production equipment.
        1. Off air monitor.
        2. Mikes.
        3. Lenses.
7. Check script and plan of program with technical director.

The foregoing description of a typical remote program illustrates some of the production problems involved and how they
differ from studio programming.

TYPES OF SHOWS

6-43 Television stations at present are offering between 28 and
40 hours of programming each week. A few have even begun
operations throughout the entire day. Once a television station

arrives at the stage where it is in full commercial operation, it is required to maintain at least two hours of programming each day of the week, with a total of not less than 28 hours for the entire week.

Selecting a properly balanced program schedule which will interest the largest number of viewers is a subject too vast to discuss in great length in this section. However, it is well to

Figure 26. Televising a football game. (courtesy DuMont)

outline some of the type of shows which are proving of interest to television viewers today.

6-44 Sports. The coverage of sporting events has been a natural for television ever since the remote pick-up was developed. Baseball games draw large television audiences, whether they are played in the afternoon or at night. Baseball is more difficult to follow with the television camera than most other sports because the action shifts quickly. Football is another television natural. With the remote pickup near the 50 yard line (Figure

26), the viewer gets the equivalent of the best seat in the stadium. The telephoto lens gives him a better close-up view of the plays than a person present at the game sees.

Indoor events such as wrestling and boxing matches are programmed regularly and are usually scheduled later in the evening after studio programs are over. Horse-racing, auto-racing,

Figure 27. An "in the studio" sports show. (courtesy DuMont)

golf tournaments, tennis matches, and bowling tournaments, all lend themselves to television broadcasting.

Sports have dominated television programming to date because they constitute a ready-made production with a well-established box-office appeal. A variation of the remote sports program which has proved popular is the instructive sports show which originates from the studio. Golf instructions are given on the program shown in Figure 27.

6-45 News. News telecasts take several forms. On the spot coverage, such as the political conventions discussed previously, is one method of presenting the news. With this kind of program, the viewer gets the entire picture, unedited by interpretive reporters. Consider how much more effective this type of reporting is than the newsreels which give only brief segments of news events several days after they take place.

When news-worthy events occur at inconvenient hours for programming, film may be shot on the spot, and televised later in the day. Another type of news broadcast which has proven successful employs the technique of showing a series of still photographs, illustrating the narration of a news commentator.

6-46 Instructive Shows. Instruction by television has proven successful because the full potentialities of the medium are exploited. When a group of teachers in a mid-western state went on strike, television sets were placed in several schools and lessons were given to the school children over the air. Lessons in cooking, artcraft, drawing, painting, and home decoration are only a few of the courses which have been successfully televised. The instructive element in the program is generally balanced with some form of entertainment to create the greatest possible audience appeal.

6-47 Dramatic Shows. Dramatic shows televised from the studio have proven popular. Unquestionably, this type of show will continue to occupy a large portion of television programming, as has been the case in radio. Dramatic shows are difficult to produce because of the high costs and the technical limitations involved. The lack of scripts suitable for television, the costs of paying large casts for rehearsal and performance, the need for much longer rehearsals than for other types of shows, and the technical problems which always accompany elaborate sets, are but a few of the factors which limit the presentation of elaborate dramatic shows. But the prestige which they bring to the station and the popularity they enjoy insure the dramatic show an important place in television's future.

6-48 Variety Shows. Variety shows on television are reminiscent of vaudeville. Here again the production need not be elaborate since the elements involved represent ready-made and pre-rehearsed acts. The intimacy of television and the suitability of most variety performers' acts to the close-up technique contribute to the success of this kind of entertainment. The mere presentation, however, of one act following another does not make a good variety show. An original format must be worked out for each program.

6-49 Comedy Shows. Comedy shows have proved successful on television. The radio comic employs jokes, dialect, routines, and sound effects to catch the imagination of the listener. On television, he can be seen, an important advantage, especially since most comedians are experienced at doing in-person shows. By setting the scene in a nightclub or on a stage, it is possible to gain considerable reality. Several programs using this technique have proved very successful.

An original and suitable technique of delivery and comic acting is still to be developed for the "tele-comic". Along with the new format must come better comedy writers for television. At present, top notch comedy writers are the highest paid in the entertainment business, and television cannot yet afford to attract them away from other fields.

Today's television comedy shows are confined in the main to a comedian and a small supporting cast and audience.

6-50 Participation Shows. The audience participation show has proved as popular on television as on radio. The chief difference between shows of this type in the two media is that television stresses the visual aspect of the quiz whereas radio must depend on dialogue. Charades acted out before cameras, or the guessing of personalities or words which are drawn in caricature on a drawing board by an artist, are but two examples of the possibilities of the visual quiz show. On some programs, prizes are given to the first viewer to phone the studio with the correct answer.

6-51 Fashion Shows. Fashion shows are ideally suited to television and have particular appeal to female audiences. Clothing manufacturers can bring their products right into the viewer's home. Fashions to fit any budget may be seen on current television shows. They have proved popular as well as commercially successful.

The presentation of fashions on television is not without limitations. Obviously, colors cannot be shown with the present black and white system. Small, intricate patterns, subtle detail of lines, and the cut of some clothes do not register well. Patterns, colors, and styles must be selected for fashion shows to suit the color response and resolution capabilities of the television equipment.

6-52 Kiddy Shows. The hours from five to seven P.M. are often devoted to children's shows. These programs feature movies, puppets, games, cartoons, and a variety of other subjects which appeal to the younger set. The televising of a puppet show for children is shown in Figure 28. Pictures appeal to children even more than radio dialogue and make the television kiddy show an extremely popular and important part of a station's programming, catering to a very large audience.

6-53 Musical Programs. The possibilities of musical programs on television have not been fully exploited. Telecasts of symphony orchestras, a few operas, and choral programs

Figure 28. Televising a puppet show. This type of program has proved very successful on television. (courtesy GE)

have been done with success. Regular televising of the musical drama shows, such as light opera or comedy is difficult because almost all action must be restaged to fit the requirements of the television camera. It remains to be seen whether television can stage such lavish productions as regular programming within reasonable economic and time limits.

6-54 Film. To date film has constituted a large part of television programming. Most of the films that are used are old and of poor quality, for few film companies are willing to permit the showing of their up to date pictures on the competing television medium. Even recent productions which have been televised are ineffective because the techniques used in regular motion pictures are not suitable for television. Unless film is expressly made to suit the small television screen, it loses its impact. Since the small television station will undoubtedly depend upon film to fill out its program schedule, just as small radio stations depend on recorded music, suitable film programs will necessarily have to be developed on a large scale. The use by network stations of films, teletranscribed from programs originating in large stations, is one solution to the problem which has thus far been found.

6-55 Commercials. Television has the advantage over radio of being able to make the commercial a vivid and interesting picture. In fact, many commercials have proven to be as popular as actual programs. Campfire scenes have been acted out to advertise camping equipment; foods are sold on television by showing their preparation and cooking in kitchens scenes; gasoline is advertized by showing a scene at a service station, stressing the quality of service the particular company offers. A common device to work the sponsor's product into the show is to display it as a prop in the set. Another subtle way to work in the commercial is to include the product's name as part of the backdrop for a skit. The viewer notices the advertising while watching the show.

6-56 Program Scheduling. The scheduling of television shows at the proper time to receive the greatest potential audience is a problem requiring considerable study. Much of the thinking on this subject has been adapted from the experience of scheduling radio programs.

Through the examination of polls as well as mail response, general information regarding the sex and age groups which make up the viewing audience at particular hours can be made. Some general rules of program scheduling are fairly obvious. It is unwise to schedule a program after 7 P.M. which appeals especially to children. Programs aimed primarily at women, such as beauty hints, cooking recipes, and fashion shows are scheduled at present in the evenings, but as television station operations expand to full daytime coverage, these programs will be scheduled for the morning and afternoons. The male audience predominates the evening hours after 7 P.M., though it has been proven that sports events will draw the male viewer at any hour of the day when he is near a receiver.

A careful study of competitive programs is another factor to consider when choosing the program hour and the format of a show. For example, it is unwise to produce a dramatic show to compete against a dramatic show which is enjoying a high rating on another station. It is far better to lure viewers away from the dramatic show with entertainment of an entirely different nature. One may count on a wide divergence of tastes among the audience and should select a program so different in appeal that it will attract its own supporters. A quiz show featuring audience participation and cash prizes might very well compete successfully against an already established dramatic series.

6-57 Conclusion. The problems of creating and producing television shows at the current stage of television development fall largely into two classifications, the economic and the technical. Despite the many handicaps which have been touched upon in this section, the future looks exceedingly bright. Television programming has grown out of the "if and when" phase and has become an actuality. As more and more sets are installed, and more viewers can be counted on by advertisers, more money will be spent on television productions. With larger budgets, most of these difficulties will be surmounted.

MODERN
TELEVISION RECEIVERS

Circuit variations
Design - Mechanical features

7-1 The fundamentals of television receiver circuit design were discussed in Section 3. Practically all of the circuits encountered in commercial receivers were covered in that section. If the reader thoroughly understands those basic circuits, he should have very little trouble in comprehending the operation of complete receivers.

In this section the mechanical and electrical design of typical television receivers is discussed. The first part of the section is devoted to descriptions of commercial r-f tuning systems. The latter portion of the section is devoted to descriptions of complete commercial receivers.

R-F tuning systems are treated separately because of their nature. A practical r-f tuner is the result of careful mechanical and electrical design. The mechanical problems involved in the design of television r-f tuners are difficult to solve. As a result, it has been necessary to resort to mechanical arrangements considerably more complex than those ordinarily encountered in electronic equipment.

Numerous ingenious solutions to r-f tuner problems have been found by the various manufacturers, as the reader will realize while reading this section. Most of the tuners described here will be found in more than one receiver model. As a rule, a manufacturer makes one tuner which he uses in all of his receiver models. Some tuners are actually used by several manufacturers since it has been the practice of a few firms to sell tuners and tuner components of their design and manufacture

Figure 1.   The RCA tuner. (courtesy RCA)

to other companies. In some instances this practice has been extended to complete receiver chassis.

The r-f tuner section of a television receiver usually consists of the local oscillator, mixer, and r-f amplifier stages. Some receivers are not equipped with an r-f stage, in which case the tuner consists of a mixer and a local oscillator. Most tuners are mounted on a separate chassis assembly which is, in turn, mounted on the main receiver chassis. This type of unitized construction makes it possible to pre-align the tuner section and then incorporate it into any one of a number of receivers.

The most difficult problem in the design of an r-f tuner is the broad frequency coverage required. At present, television stations operate on frequencies between 54 and 216 megacycles. Two solutions have been found to this problem of frequency coverage. One solution makes use of a switching system which places different condenser, coil, or condenser and coil combinations in the tuner circuits for each television station. The reader will note that some of the tuners described provide switch positions for thirteen channels. These tuners were designed before the Federal Communications Commission modified the television allocations and excluded channel one. The second solution to the frequency coverage problem has been the use of

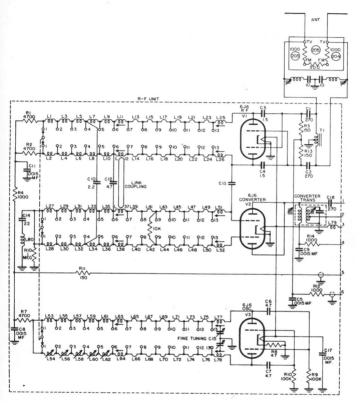

Figure 2. Schematic diagram of RCA tuner.

continuously tuned, variable inductances. This type of design eliminates some of the contact problems which arise in switch type tuners.

7-2 The RCA Tuner. The RCA Tuner is mounted on a separate subchassis as shown in Figure 1. Located on this sub-chassis are the r-f amplifier, converter, oscillator, fine tuning control, channel switch, converter transformer, r-f converter, and oscillator coils, and all their tuning adjustments. The unit provides for operation on all of the present television channels. It functions to select the desired picture and sound carriers, and amplifies and converts them to provide, at the converter plate, a picture i-f carrier frequency of 25.75 Mc and a sound i-f carrier of 21.25 Mc. As can be seen in Figure 1, this is a switching type tuner. The desired television channel is selected by means of a ganged switch which changes the inductances in the r-f amplifier, mixer, and oscillator circuits.

Figure 2 shows a schematic diagram of the tuner. T1 is a centertapped coil which short circuits undesirable low frequency signals picked up by the antenna before they can be applied to the control grids of the 6J6 r-f amplifier, V1. C1 and C2 are antenna isolating capacitors. The d-c return for the grids of V1 is through R3 and R13 which also properly terminate the 300-ohm transmission line. C3 and C4 are neutralizing capacitors necessary to counteract the grid to plate capacitance of the triode r-f amplifier in order to prevent oscillation. In the plate circuit of the r-f amplifier there is a series of inductances, L1 to L25 and L2 to L26 inclusive. These inductances act as a quarter wave section of a balanced transmission line which can be tuned over a band of frequencies by moving a shorting bar along its parallel conductors.

Coils L25 and L26 are adjusted to provide the correct length of line for channel 13 (210 - 216 Mc). L13 to L25 and L14 to L24 are fixed sections of line which are added to L25 and L26 as the shorting bar is moved progressively down the line. Each one of these inductances consists of a small non-adjustable silver strap, mounted between the contacts of a switch, as shown in Figure 3. Each strap is cut to give a six-megacycle change in frequency. When changing from channel seven (174 - 180 Mc) to channel six (82 - 88 Mc), adjustable coils L11 and L12 are inserted. To provide for the remaining five channels, L1 to L9 and L2 to L10 are progressively switched in to add the necessary additional inductance. The switch is operated in continuous rotation and has no stop.

Coils L1 to L9 and L2 to L10 are unusual in that they are wound in figure eight fashion on fingers protruding from the switch wafer. This winding form produces a relatively non-critical coil because the coupling between turns is minimized. A maximum amount of wire is used for the small inductance which is required, thus permitting greater accuracy in manufacture. These coils are visible in Figure 3 which shows the switch wafers.

The converter grid line operates in a manner similar to that of the r-f amplifier. It is arranged on the switch so that coupling is provided between it and the r-f line. C10, C12, C13, and a link, provide additional coupling which is arranged to produce a 4.5 Mc band pass on all channels.

L80 and C14 form a series resonant circuit which is used to prevent i-f feedback into the converter. The combination ef-

Figure 3. Wafer switches and coils used in RCA tuner. (courtesy RCA)

fectively grounds the grids of the converter at the i-f frequency. It also acts as a trap which rejects short-wave signals of i-f frequency which arrive at the converter grids.

A 6J6 triode is used as a converter. The grids are fed in push-pull by the incoming signal and the oscillator signal. The heterodyne products of these signals (i-f signals) appear in phase at the converter plates, which are connected in parallel. Unwanted signals of i-f frequency which arrive at the converter grids in a push-pull manner appear at the converter plates out of phase. Since the plates are tied together, these signals cancel, thus reducing the possibility of interference.

The oscillator tuning line is similar to the converter and r-f amplifier lines except that trimmer adjustments are provided for each channel and the low frequency coils are not figure eight windings. Brass screws are provided for adjusting channels seven through twelve. These screws are located close to tuning straps L66 to L76 (Figure 3). Brass cores are provided for adjusting coils L54 to L62.

C15 is a fine tuning adjustment which provides approximately 1600 kc variation of the oscillator frequency when tuned to channel one and approximately 3.8 Mc on channel 13.

The physical location of the oscillator line with respect to the converter grid line is such as to provide coupling to the con-

verter grids. This coupling is augmented by the link shown in
the schematic. The combination provides a reasonably uniform
oscillator voltage, at the converter grids, over the entire tuning
range.

The converter transformer T2 is a combination picture i-f
transformer, sound trap, and sound i-f transformer. The converter plate coil is assembled within the structure of a high Q

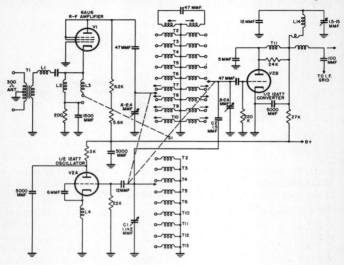

Figure 4. Schematic diagram of G.E. tuner.

resonant circuit tuned to the sound i-f frequency. This high Q
coil absorbs the sound i-f component from the primary. Thus
the sound carrier is attenuated on the primary of T2, from which
the first picture i-f amplifier is fed. The sound i-f appears on
the secondary T2. The first sound i-f amplifier is fed from a
tap on this secondary.

7-3 The G-E Tuner. Like the RCA tuner, the G-E tuner is of
the switching type. Provision is made for selecting any one of
twelve channels by means of a ganged switch which inserts different combinations of coils and capacitors into the r-f amplifier, oscillator, and converter circuits. An important difference
between the RCA and G-E tuners is in the method used to obtain

the necessary wide passband for each channel. In the RCA tuner, each channel is tuned by shorting out sections of a balanced transmission line. In the G-E tuner, individual coil and capacitor combinations are used for each of the twelve channels.

Figure 4 shows the circuit arrangement of the G-E tuner. Two tubes are used. A 6AU6 is used in the r-f amplifier stage, while a dual triode, 12AT7, is employed as an oscillator and converter.

The 6AU6 is operated as a grounded-grid, r-f amplifier. It is connected as a triode to reduce the noise generated in the stage. The input circuit contains a balanced transformer T1, whose impedance is designed to match a 300-ohm transmission line. The signal is coupled to the cathode of the amplifier. The cathode circuit is tuned to have a broad band characteristic. Only two coils, L2 and L3, are needed to broadly tune the cathode circuit over the low and high bands. The plate circuit of the r-f amplifier contains double tuned, over coupled transformers which are switched in by the channel selector.

The oscillator V2A employs a modified Colpitts circuit. Separate coils are inserted into the circuit by a switch which is ganged to the r-f switch. The oscillator voltage is capacitively coupled to the grid of the converter by a 1.5 mmf capacitor, C2, thereby eliminating the need for adjusting oscillator excitation. A triode converter is used to hold the noise generated by the tuner unit to a minimum. Because it has a low equivalent noise resistance, the triode converter aids in improving the signal to noise ratio of the receiver. Both the r-f signal and the oscillator voltage are capacitively coupled to the grid of the converter. The intermediate frequencies which result from the heterodyning of these two signals appear in the plate circuit.

The mechanical construction of the G-E tuner embodies several interesting features. For simplicity of design and to reduce cost, the tuned circuits of six of the higher channels are combined into three switch positions. This means that the band pass characteristics of the r-f amplifier and converter in these three switch positions are sufficiently wide to pass two television channels. The oscillator trimmer, C1, has sufficient range under these conditions to cover both channels.

A ground plate is used in the band switch to connect the r-f plate and converter grid coils to ground. This plate is so designed that it furnishes the coupling for the coils, making it unnecessary to adjust coupling. The coils used for the high channels have an unusual type of construction. They are self-supporting, being would with No. 20 Formex wire. The diameter and the pitch of the coils are made to conform to the threads of brass screws which are inserted into the coils. A wide range of tuning is obtained by adjusting the depth of the screw inside the coil. The adjustment is great enough to allow using the same type of coil for four different positions of the band switch, resulting in reduced manufacturing costs.

7-4 The Philco Tuner. This tuner consists of an r-f amplifier, converter, and local oscillator. The desired channel is selected by means of a switching turret which inserts the proper set of coils into the amplifier, converter, and oscillator circuits.

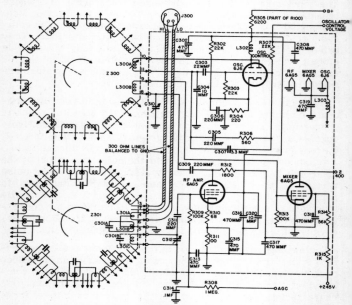

Figure 5. Schematic diagram of the Philco tuner.

The antenna coil and the r-f amplifier coil for each channel are built as an assembly. Eight separate coil assemblies are mounted on a drum type switching turret as shown in Figure 5. The converter and oscillator coils for each channel are also built as assemblies and are mounted on a second switching turret.

This tuner provides for the reception of eight different channels. The reader will recall that twelve channels have been assigned for use by television stations. Since the FCC intends to assign a maximum of seven channels in any one area, the provision for only eight channels on the Philco tuner is not a disadvantage. Twelve sets of coils are available, any eight of which may be easily installed without soldering or wiring. These coils are built as "snap-in" assemblies which fit into the switching turrets (Figure 6). The turrets are actagonal in shape

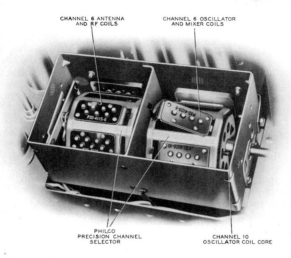

CHANNEL 6 ANTENNA
AND RF COILS

CHANNEL 6 OSCILLATOR
AND MIXER COILS

PHILCO
PRECISION CHANNEL
SELECTOR

CHANNEL 10
OSCILLATOR COIL CORE

Figure 6. Octagonal turrets used in Philco tuner showing "snap-in" coils. (courtesy Philco)

and each set of coils is mounted on a different face of the octagonal drums. The front drum carries the mixer and oscillator coils, while the rear drum holds the r-f amplifier and antenna coils. The advantage of the turret construction is that the leads connecting the coils to the r-f amplifier, oscillator, and converter states are short and of constant length for all channels. All the coils are mounted on the turret drum and each set is moved into position as required. Good contact between switch points is obtained by supporting the contact points with springs.

Provision has been made in the Philco tuner for the use of a high frequency antenna for stations operating in the frequency range between 54 and 88 Mc, and another antenna for stations operating on frequencies between 174 and 216 Mc. Separate input terminals are provided for each antenna, as shown in Figure 5. The antenna in use is determined by the position of the turret. This is accomplished by arranging the coils on the turret so that the r-f and antenna coils for the low band channels occupy contact positions 1, 2, 4, 5, and 6; while the high band coils are connected to contacts 1, 2, 3, 5, and 7.

The signal from the antenna is coupled to the first r-f stage through a small, center-tapped link, L301A. This link permits the use of a 300-ohm twin lead transmission line if the entire winding is employed. When a shielded coaxial transmission line is used in high noise areas, an impedance match can be made by connecting the shield of the cable to the chassis, and the center conductor to one of the two "LO" connections on J300 for the low band - or to one of the "HI" connections for the high band. The impedance under these conditions is one fourth of the impedance of the whole winding - a good match for 72-ohm coaxial cable.

The r-f signals, both sound and picture, are fed to grid No. 1 of the 6AG5 r-f amplifier, and are amplified in this circuit. C311 permits grounding one end of L301C without shorting out the grid bias supplied by a.g.c. action. The 6AG5 r-f amplifier is also biased through resistors R310 and R311 in series. R310 is not bypassed. This connection is made to prevent input capacity changes with variations in grid bias. If this method were not used to minimize these capacity changes caused by the "Miller Effect", they would change the response curve of the r-f amplifier as the signal strength of the received station changed.

The coupling network used between the r-f amplifier and the 6AG5 mixer consists of variable capacitor C310, coupling capacitor C309, series inductance L300B, and the input capacity to the 6AG5 mixer. In effect, the circuit is shunted by the 1800-ohm plate resistor, R312, of the 6AG5 r-f amplifier. This low value of plate resistance is necessary to secure a flat response. The screen of the r-f amplifier is bypassed to ground by parallel capacitors C316 and C320. The 10 mmf capacitor C320 is most effective at the high frequencies, while the 470 mmf condenser C316 is most effective at lower frequencies. The output of the local oscillator is coupled inductively to the mixer through L300B and L300A of transformer Z300.

An ultraudion is used as a local oscillator because it performs well at high frequencies. The tuned circuit is connected between the grid and the plate to produce the phase shift necessary for oscillation. The grid end of the tuned circuit is bypassed to ground through capacitor C304 to control the grid

excitation. Grid-current flow through grid resistor R303, during oscillation, furnishes grid bias for the tube.

Fine tuning of the oscillator is obtained by the use of an oscillator control reactance tube (half of a 6J6 which is the second
triode of the oscillator tube), controlled by the output voltage
from the f-m discriminator which is located in the Audio Section of the receiver. Drift in local oscillator frequency is corrected by the reactance tube, so that a constant i-f output is

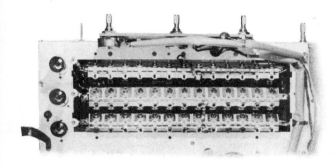

Figure 7. Layout of Hallicrafters thirteen channel, pushbutton
tuner. (courtesy Hallicrafters)

produced. R-F voltage is fed from the local oscillator to the
grid of the reactance tube through a network consisting of capacitor C305 and resistor R306 in series. Phase shift of the
voltage applied to the grid of the reactance tube is obtained by
the combination of C305 and R306. Because of the phase shift
in the voltage applied to the grid, the reactance tube draws a
current that is out of phase with the voltage appearing across
the oscillator coil. The reactance tube draws a leading current, and it therefore acts as a capacitor whose value is determined by the current flowing in the reactance tube. As the grid
bias varies the current, it also varies the frequency of the local oscillator. This grid bias is the d-c voltage fed back to
the reactance tube from the discriminator. When the sound
intermediate frequency is centered about the correct frequency, the d-c voltage at the center point of the discriminator is
zero. If the center frequency drifts above or below the correct
value, the output voltage will be a positive or negative d-c potential, respectively. This varying potential is applied to the
grid of the reactance tube. The net effect of this feedback voltage is to force the oscillator back to its correct frequency.

7-5 The Hallicrafters Tuner. The Hallicrafters tuner is an example of a pushbutton switching tuner. The pushbutton switch assembly is shown mounted on the front of the receiver chassis in Figure 7. When the desired button is depressed, appropriate capacitors are switched into the r-f amplifier and oscillator circuits.

The tuner consists of three stages, an r-f amplifier, a mixer, and a local oscillator. The input to the r-f amplifier is designed to match a 300-ohm transmission line. A balanced 300-ohm load to the transmission line is obtained through the use of a com-

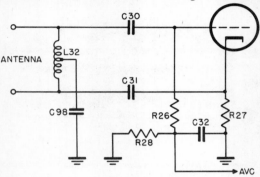

Figure 8. Antenna input circuit.

bination of grid and cathode input to the r-f amplifier. This cir-cuit arrangement is shown in Figure 8. L32 is a balancing coil. Its center tap is grounded to r-f by C98. A direct ground to the chassis cannot be used at this point because in the Hallicrafters receiver one side of the a-c power line is connected to the chassis. A direct connection at this point would constitute a shock hazard. C30 and C31 perform the same function as C98 in reducing shock hazard, and in addition function as d-c blocking capacitors. R26 and R27 are each 150 ohms, and since R27 is directly grounded and R26 is grounded to r-f through C32, they place a 300-ohm load, balanced to ground across the antenna. One end of this balanced input is fed to the grid of the r-f amplifier, the other end to the cathode. Since a signal applied to the grid of a tube has the same effect as a similar signal 180° out of phase applied to the cathode, the push-pull signals from the antenna reinforce one another in the input to the r-f amplifier.

The tuned circuits employed in this tuner are illustrated in

Figures 9A and 9B. Figure 9A shows the tuning of the plate of the r-f amplifier and the grid of the mixer. R31 (the converter grid return) and some inductors, capacitors, and resistors have been eliminated for the sake of simplicity. If the components enclosed in the dashed lines are temporarily ignored, it will be observed that the circuits on either side of C33 are the same. Cout is the output capacitance of the r-f amplifier which

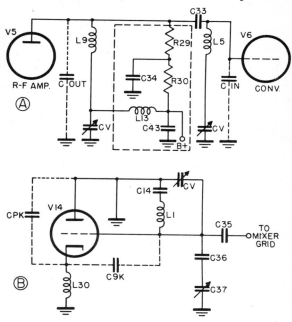

Figure 9. A. R-F amplifier circuit. B. Oscillator circuit.

is resonated with the coil L9 to provide the broadband characteristic required to pass the r-f frequencies. Cin is the input capacitance of the mixer. It also forms a broadband resonant circuit. The variable capacitors Cv are those selected by the push-button switches to tune each channel. L13 and C43 decouple the B from the plate circuit. R30 and C34 perform the same function for decoupling the screen which is connected to their junction.

A.V.C. voltage is applied to the r-f amplifier at the low end of grid resistor R29. This effectively places the A.V.C. voltage in series with the r-f grid voltage.

The oscillator, which is shown in Figure 9B, utilizes a modified Colpitts circuit. The diagram has been drawn in such a way as to emphasize the Colpitts type of circuit. The d-c grid and plate connections have been omitted for simplicity. Cpk is the plate-cathode capacitance and Cgk is the grid-cathode capacitance. The variable capacitor Cv, which is part of the tank, re-

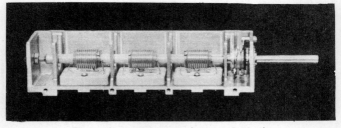

Figure 10. The Inductuner. (courtesy DuMont)

presents the tuning capacitor chosen by the push-button switch assembly for the channel in use. C36 is a fixed capacitor in series with C37, which is the fine tuning control. As is customary in television receivers, the oscillator is tuned to a frequency higher than the incoming signal. The oscillator voltage is capacitively coupled through C35 to the grid of the mixer, V6.

There are 39 tuning capacitors in the tuner. Each channel requires the substitution of three tuned circuits for the r-f amplifier, the mixer, and the oscillator. Since there are 13 channels, a total of 39 capacitors are needed. Only one set of three capacitors is in use at one time so that the alignment of each channel is independent of the others.

7-6 The Du Mont R-F Inputuner. The Du Mont Inputuner is of the continuously tuned, inductive type, and differs considerably from the switch and turret type tuners previously described. The heart of the Inputuner is a three section variable inductance. This three section variable inductance is manufactured by P.R. Mallory and Company. It is known as the Inductuner.

Figure 10 shows the internal construction of the Inductuner. It consists of three coils mounted on a ceramic shaft. At the right end of the shaft is an accumulation stop to prevent damaging the device if the shaft is turned too far in either direction. Each coil is continuously tuned for 10 turns, resulting in an inductive range of 0.02 to 1.0 microhenries. A trolley contact moves along each coil, dividing it into used and unused sections. The movable contact is shorted to the low frequency end of the coil so that the unused section is resonant at a very high frequency which lies outside of the desired tuning range.

The r-f tuned circuit consists of a closely coupled pair of these variable inductors. These inductors are capacitively and inductively coupled and have a 4.5 Mc bandwidth between double

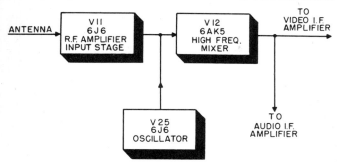

Figure 11. Block diagram of DuMont Inputuner.

peaks of the response curve, and a 6 Mc overall bandwidth. This double tuned circuit covers, continuously, a range of 44 to 216 Mc, while the third tuned circuit of the Inductuner covers the same range but is 21.9 Mc higher in frequency, and is used for the local oscillator tuning circuit. These circuits are shown in the block diagram of Figure 11 and the schematic diagram of Figure 12.

The input tube is a cathode-driven, grounded-grid, double triode 6J6 which functions as a constant impedance, 72-ohm unbalanced input to match the 72-ohm coaxial transmission line. Plate voltage is supplied through 10,000-ohm resistor R57 and decoupled by a 470 mmf capacitor C52. The r-f signal resonant circuits are damped by a pair of 12,000-ohm resistors, R58 and R59. Both the 6J6 input tube V11 and 6AK5 mixer V12 are isolated from d-c by a pair of 15 mmf capacitors, C47 and C51. V11 also acts as an r-f amplifier working into the r-f signal resonant circuits.

The 6AK5 high gain pentode V12, used as the mixer, has both the r-f signal and the oscillator signal (at 21.9 Mc higher than the r-f signal) impressed on its control grid. The output of the mixer tube consists of a wide band of frequencies which include both the video and sound intermediate frequencies which are 4.5 Mc apart.

The oscillator uses one half of a 6J6 triode V25 in a modified Colpitts circuit. It is coupled to the mixer grid by a one mmf capacitor, C55. A capacity trimmer, C53, and an inductive pad-

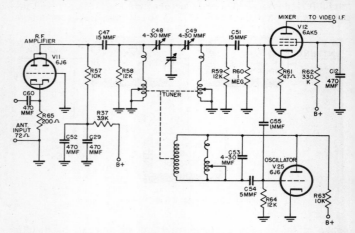

Figure 12. Schematic diagram of Inputuner.

der are used for tracking purposes. 10,000 ohm resistor, R63, isolates the oscillator from the B+ line.

The Inputuner circuits are built up on a complete assembly and are pre-adjusted and pre-calibrated, after which the entire assembly is installed in the receiver. Figure 13 shows the complete Inputuner assembly with tuning dial.

7-7 Complete Receivers. The remainder of this section is devoted to descriptions of commerical receivers which are typical of the various models now on the market. The first receiver described is the Hallicrafters Model T-54 which is a typical seven-inch, electrostatic tube receiver. There then follows a description of the Philco Model 48-1000 which contains a magnetic, 10 inch picture tube. This set is an example of the next price range of receivers. The Scott Model 13-A, employing the next size larger tube, the 12JP4, is then presented, followed by the Du Mont Model RA-101, which is operated with either a 15 inch or a 20 inch tube. Finally, the RCA Model 648 PTK is described to show the variations in circuit design which are required to produce a large screen, projected image.

In studying these circuits, the reader will become aware of the similarities as well as the differences between commercial designs. For example, the flywheel synchronization circuit for the horizontal sweep system is used by many manufacturers. The Scott, DuMont, and RCA receivers described in this sec-

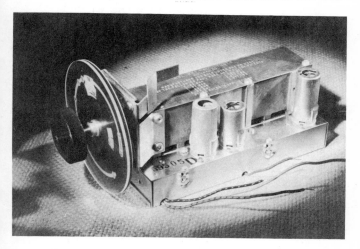

Figure 13. Complete Inputuner assembly for continuous 44-216 Mc coverage, showing manual drive dial. (courtesy DuMont)

tion employ this circuit. Similar versions of the kickback circuit for obtaining the high voltage for the picture tube will be found in the Philco, Scott, and RCA designs. On the other hand, differences will be noted in the types of tuning mechanisms, i-f amplifiers, sync circuits, and deflection circuits which are used by different manufacturers.

In order to avoid repeating detailed descriptions of circuits which are familiar to the reader at this point in the text, only those features not found in receivers already described are treated in detail.

7-8 The Hallicrafters Model T-54. The Hallicrafters Model T-54 is a table model television receiver with an electrostatic type 7JP4 picture tube. A picture approximately 5-3/8 inches wide by 4-3/8 inches high is obtained on the seven inch tube. One of the unique features of the Model T-54 is its use of the intercarrier sound system which employs a single group of i-f amplifiers for both the video and audio signals. Another distinguishing feature of this receiver is its transformerless, low voltage power supply. A selenium rectifier, operated in a voltage tripler circuit, eliminates the need for the transformer.

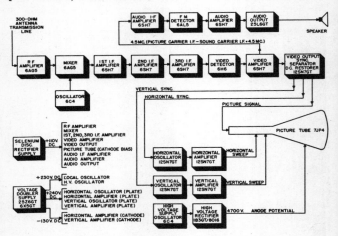

Figure 14. Block diagram of Hallicrafters Model T-54.

For ease of understanding, a block diagram is given in Figure 14. A more detailed schematic circuit is presented in Figure 15.

The Model T-54 employs the Hallicrafters 13 channel, pushbutton tuner described previously. This tuner may be seen in the view of the chassis shown in Figure 7. It will be noted that the entire receiver is built up on this single chassis.

7-9 Video Section. Included in the video section are the video i-f amplifiers, the video detector, and two video amplifiers.

Contrary to usual practice, a single channel is used in this receiver to amplify both the video and sound i-f signals. (In addition, there is a single stage of audio i-f amplification which is discussed later.) Ordinarily, separate i-f amplifiers are used for video and sound to prevent interaction between the two signals. In this receiver, this interaction is put to use. The two carriers beat together in the video detector, giving a 4.5 Mc signal. This signal may be considered as a second (sound) i-f. It is frequency modulated just as the first sound i-f, and may be demodulated by conventional techniques. This type of sound system is referred to as the intercarrier sound system.

There are three stages of i-f amplification, V7, V8, and V9, and four associated tuned circuits. A combination of broadband tuning and stagger tuning is employed to obtain an amplifier response sufficiently broad to cover the video and audio carriers. Each tuned circuit is peaked to a separate frequency as follows: L14-25Mc, L15-22.5 Mc, L16-24.5 Mc, and L17-23.3 Mc. In addition, each circuit is loaded by a resistor to broaden the response of each stage. For example, L14, the plate load of the mixer V6, is a variable inductor having a movable core. It is tuned by the output capacitance of the mixer and the input capacitance of the following stage, V7, the first i-f amplifier. In order to lower the Q of the tuned circuit in the interest of attaining a broad pass band, it is loaded by the 27,000-ohm grid resistor R33 of the following stage. L15, the plate load of the first i-f amplifier, and L16, the plate load of the second i-f amplifier, are tuned and loaded in the same manner. L24, the plate load of the third i-f amplifier is simply an untuned coil. However, the signal from this plate is fed to the cathode of the diode detector, and in this cathode there is a variable inductor, L17, which tunes the coupling circuit for broadband response. This inductor is of the same design as L14, L15, and L16. It is loaded by the input resistance of the diode. The band-pass characteristic obtained by the combination of stagger-tuning and broadband tuning is shown in Figure 16.

It will be observed from this pass band characteristic that the response curve is sufficiently narrow to exclude adjacent channel interference without the need of traps. This is possible because with a seven inch picture tube adequate definition is obtained with a relatively narrow response curve — in this case, the curve is flat for less than 2 Mc. By narrowing the response curve, the 21.75 Mc sound i-f carrier is fairly well attenuated. Therefore, one 4.5 Mc trap (C27 and L23) in the plate circuit of the video amplifier is sufficient to prevent the sound signals (which are located 4.5 Mc away from the video carrier) from getting into the picture channel. C27 and L23 form this series resonant trap. At the resonant frequency of 4.5 Mc, the impedance of this circuit is very low and the 4.5 Mc signal is shunted through this trap and therefore is not passed on to the picture tube. The 4.5 Mc sound signals, which have been by-passed by this trap from the video circuits, are fed to the grid of the 4.5 Mc sound

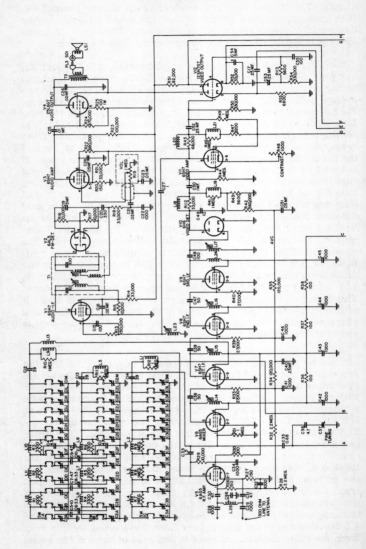

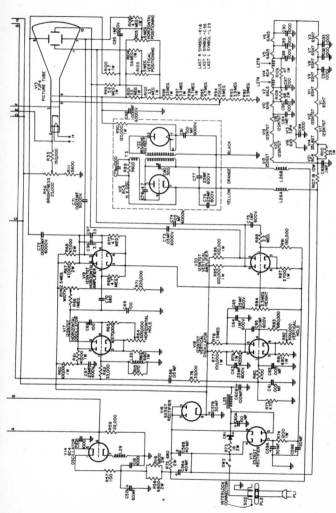

Figure 15. Schematic diagram of Hallicrafters Model T-54

i-f amplifier, V1. On the other hand, since the sound i-f carrier has been amplified along with the video i-f carrier, the combination of the two produces a sufficiently strong beat signal, which, after a single stage of audio i-f amplification, is strong enough to operate the ratio detector, V2.

A.V.C. voltages are applied to the first and second i-f amplifiers, but not to the third.

7-10 Detector. A single diode V10 is used in a conventional rectifier circuit as the video detector. The polarity of the video signal is negative at the output of the detector. The d-c output

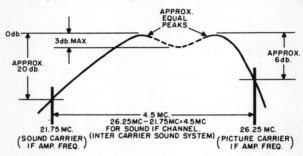

Figure 16. Response curve of intermediate frequency amplifiers which pass both the video and audio signals.

appearing across R43 is filtered by capacitor C51 and applied to the first and second video i-f amplifier as a.v.c. voltage.

7-11 Video Amplifier. The output of the detector is coupled through a high frequency compensating circuit, employing both shunt and series-peaking coils, to the grid of the first video amplifier V11. This stage employs a high transconductance pentode which gives a gain of 20 to 25. Variable resistor, R48, in the cathode circuit of this stage, serves as a contrast control. It varies the bias on the grid, thereby controlling the gain of the stage.

The output of the first video amplifier is fed through a high-frequency compensating circuit to the grid of the second video amplifier, half of V12. This amplifier is one section of a dual triode connected as a cathode follower. Its output is applied to the cathode of the picture tube and to the grid of the second section of the dual triode. (This second section functions as the d-c restorer and sync separator described later). The purpose of the cathode follower is to match the high impedance of the compensating network in the plate circuit of the first video amplifier to the low impedance of the picture tube cathode. The gain of the second video amplifier (cathode follower) is approximately 0.65 times.

A second output from the first video amplifier is obtained directly from its plate, rather than through the compensating network. This is the 4.5 Mc beat signal, which goes to the audio section. The method of coupling is illustrated in Figure 17. C27

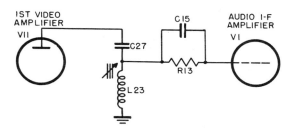

Figure 17. Coupling circuit for separating video and audio signals.

and L23 are series tuned, so that they present a near short to the 4.5 Mc beat at this point. This prevents the beat signal from continuing further to the picture tube where it would interfere with the video signal. Also, by virtue of the series tuning, a large 4.5 Mc signal appears across the individual components of the series tuned circuit. The signal appearing across the inductor provides the input to the audio i-f amplifier.

The first video amplifier has still a third function, as a noise limiter. Since the output of the detector is such that the sync pulses are negative, any high amplitude noise pulses riding on the sync signals will drive the grid of the first video amplifier very negative. This will cut the amplifier off and the noise will not pass through to the plate circuit. Elimination of these noise signals at this point helps to stabilize the sync circuits.

7-12 Sync Separator and D-C Restorer. Usually the d-c restorer is treated as part of the video amplifier, and the sync separator as part of the sweep system. However, in this receiver a single triode (the second half of V12) performs these two functions, and it is therefore logical to treat them together.

The circuit is shown in Figure 18. At the grid, the sync pulses are positive since the polarity of the output of the detector is reversed in the first video amplifier, but not in the second which is connected as a cathode follower. The cathode resistor and capacitor are very large; R52 is 33,000 ohms and C54 is 5 microfarads. This combination causes the stage to act very much like an infinite-impedance detector. The peaks of the sync pulses on the grid are just high enough to cause conduction through

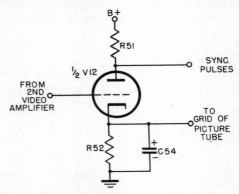

Figure 18. Sync separator and d-c restorer.

the tube; the charge developed on the cathode capacitor cannot leak off quickly through the large resistor R52, so that the tube is biased beyond cutoff except at the peak of each cycle of input. Since this bias corresponds to a value slightly below the peaks of the sync signals, it corresponds to the black level of the video signal. Therefore, if this bias voltage on the cathode is applied to the grid of the picture tube, it sets the d-c level in the video signal corresponding to black.

In addition to providing for d-c reinsertion, as described above, the same stage also separates the video signals from the sync pulses. Since the tube conducts only on the peaks of the input signal, the plate current flows in pulses, causing pulses of voltage to appear across the load resistor, R51. These are the sync pulses. However, because the tube is cut off at the video signal level, video signals do not come through. In this manner, the tube also acts as a sync separator. The sync pulses in the plate circuit are fed to the sweep multivibrators. The horizontal and vertical sweep circuits of this receiver are the same in all major respects, except, of course, there are certain differences in detail which stem from the difference in operating frequencies.

7-13 Horizontal and Vertical Sync Separation. Since both the horizontal and vertical sync pulses appear in the output of the sync separator tube, some means must be provided to distinguish between them before they are applied to the sweep oscillators. The networks which separate the two types of sync signals are shown in Figure 19. Pulses, fed through the d-c blocking ca-

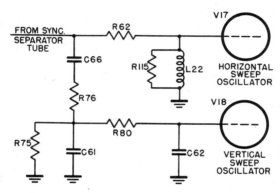

Figure 19. Networks for separating horizontal and vertical sync pulses.

pacitor, C66, to the lower integrating network, charge capacitors C61 and C62 through resistors R76 and R80. Between pulses the charge leaks off. When short duration horizontal pulses are applied to the network, the charge leaks off almost completely between pulses. The resultant voltage applied to the grid of the vertical oscillator is negligible. However, when a wide vertical pulse is applied, a voltage sufficient to trigger the vertical oscillator is built up across the capacitors. Part of the charge leaks off in the serration intervals, but they are so narrow that their effect on the operation of the network is very slight. Resistor R75 forms a voltage dividing network with R76. This voltage divider produces a vertical sync signal of the proper amplitude to trigger the vertical oscillator.

The upper network shown in the figure is a conventional differentiating circuit. The horizontal, equalizing, and serrated vertical sync pulses are differentiated into sharp negative pulses occurring at the horizontal frequency. These are fed to the horizontal sweep oscillator to maintain synchronism. Resistor R115 performs the same function of reducing sync pulse amplitude as does R75 in the lower network.

7-14 Sweep Oscillators. The sweep oscillators are multivibrators. The vertical sweep amplitude is controlled by means of potentiometer, R84, connected across the output of the sweep oscillator V18. The vertical hold control, R82, adjusts the natural frequency of the oscillator so that it is triggered correctly by sync pulses applied to the grid from the integrating network.

Since the horizontal sweep oscillator, V17, runs at a much higher frequency than the vertical oscillator, a different method of sweep amplitude control is required. If the same method of connecting the width control across the output of the oscillator were used, the distributed capacitance in the potentiometer R114 in conjunction with its resistance, would distort the sweep waveform at the horizontal frequency of 15,750 cps. In this case, then, the sweep amplitude is controlled by varying the charging voltage available at capacitor, C69, across which the sweep saw-tooth voltage is generated.

7-15 Sweep Amplifiers. The output of the vertical sweep oscillator is fed through the height control, R84, to one section of a dual triode, V20, functioning as a conventional RC coupled amplifier. The entire output of this section is applied to one of the vertical deflection plates of the picture tube. In addition, part is tapped off and applied to the second section of the tube through C75 and a voltage divider, R88 and R91. The loss in the voltage divider is just equal to the gain in the first tube, so that the signal applied to the second section is the same as that applied to the grid of the first section, but of opposite polarity. The output of the second section is therefore 180° out of phase with the output of the first section. The sawtooth voltage from the second section is applied to the other vertical deflection plate of the picture tube. Balanced, push-pull deflection is thus obtained. A similar amplifier-phase inverter combination, V19, is used to deliver the horizontal sweep signal to the picture tube.

7-16 Picture Tube. The type 7JP4 picture tube is operated with its cathode approximately 200 volts above ground. This permits the necessary direct connection to the grid from the d-c restorer, since this d-c restorer operates from the common low-voltage power supply. With the cathode operated at a relatively low voltage, the picture tube heater can be connected to the heaters of the other tubes in the receiver. D-C voltage is applied to the cathode through variable resistor R56. R56 varies the cathode bias and serves as the brightness control.

7-17 Power Supplies. There are three major power supply sections, the heater supply, the low-voltage supply, and the high-voltage supply.

Since this receiver has no power transformer to step the a-c voltage down to 6.3 volts for heater power, the heaters are connected in series in the same manner as in a-c, d-c sets. The voltage drop across the heaters adds up to the line voltage. Two diodes, V15 and V16, and a selenium rectifier, CR-1, are used in the low voltage supply. One of the tubes, V15, is a dual diode, the first section of which is used in a negative-voltage supply. The cathodes of the sweep amplifiers are returned to this supply (the bottom of R74) rather than to ground, thus increasing their effective plate to cathode voltages. The negative supply delivers 125 volts.

The second section of dual diode V15 is used with diode V16 and a selenium rectifier in a positive voltage-tripling supply. This supply is tapped at three points, giving 120, 230, and 390 volts. The 120 volts is developed across C60A which charges up through the selenium rectifier. L25 and C60B filter the rectified d-c voltage. This 120 volts is also applied to the plate of the V15 rectifier. When this tube conducts, it adds 120 volts to the 120 volt charge built up on condenser C58B. R72 and C58A filter the 240 volts across C58B. Because of the voltage drop in R72, about 230 volts d-c appear at the output of the filter across C58A.

The 240 volts across C58B is applied to the plate of V16. When this rectifier conducts, this voltage is added to the voltage built up across condenser C57B. Thus, the tripled voltage, about 390 volts, appears across C57B.

The high voltage supply is of the r-f type. It incorporates a power oscillator, V21, operating at a frequency of approximately 200 kc. The oscillator is of the tuned-plate, tickler feedback type. The output voltage of rectifier V22 can be varied by changing the operating frequency of the oscillator by means of tuning capacitor C80. Plate power for the oscillator is supplied from the 230 volt tap on the low voltage power supply.

A supply of this kind has several advantages over one designed to operate directly from the a-c power line. The transformer T3 has an air core, making it light and compact. Also, the required filter capacitors, C81 and C82, are comparatively small, saving space and weight, and at the same time are less dangerous. The danger is less because the small capacitors store less energy than larger capacitors operating at the same voltage. A shock from them is less likely to be lethal. Further, the regulation of such a supply is poorer than that of a 60-cycle supply, so that if accidental contact is made with it, the voltage will drop considerably because of the added load.

The high-voltage power supply is mounted on a sub-chassis, which is completely shielded. This reduces radiation and danger of accidental contact with the high-voltage circuit. Coup-

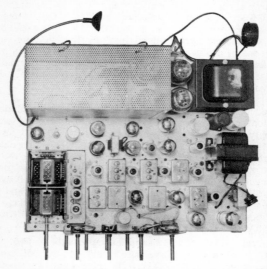

Figure 20. Chassis layout of Philco Model 48-1000.
(courtesy Philco)

ling of the r-f voltage to the other circuits is further reduced by r-f chokes L26A and L26B in the low voltage leads.

7-18 Audio Section. The audio section is quite conventional. As shown in Figures 15 and 19, the 4.5 Mc intercarrier beat signal is fed from the plate of the first video amplifier to the grid of the audio i-f amplifier V1. Grid bias is developed by grid rectification of the signal, in conjunction with C15 and R13.

The audio i-f amplifier feeds a ratio detector V2, having a bandwidth of approximately 200 kc between peaks. The output

of the ratio detector is fed through volume control R19 to the
first a-f amplifier V3. The case of the volume control is grounded through capacitor C23 to minimize noise pickup. This control cannot be grounded directly because of shock hazard. The
output of the first a-f amplifier, V3, is resistance coupled to the
power amplifier, V4, a beam-power tube. The speaker is an
oval, p-m dynamic.

7-19 Philco Model 48-1000. The Philco Model 48-1000 is a
ten inch, direct view, table model, television receiver. This
model features a turret type of r-f tuner which can select any
combination of eight of the thirteen possible television chan-

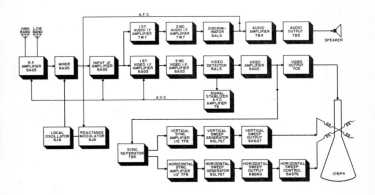

Figure 21. Block diagram of Philco Model 48-1000.

nels. Provision is also made in the design of this tuner to use
two antennas, one each for the low and high bands. Good stability is obtained through the use of an automatic frequency control circuit which prevents the oscillator from drifting off frequency. An a.v.c. circuit automatically controls the video and
audio signal levels to maintain constant amplitude when the signal is fading.

The circuits are built up on one chassis, with the tuning unit
enclosed in a separate sub-assembly (Figure 20). The cathode-

ray tube and speaker are mounted in the cabinet and are connected via cables to the chassis.

A block diagram of the model 48-1000 is shown in Figure 21.
This receiver uses the Philco turret tuner described earlier
in this section.

7-20 Video Section. The output from the tuner is fed to broad-
band input i-f transformer, Z400, as shown in Figure 22. This
transformer is a capacity-coupled type, with no inductive coupling between the primary and secondary windings. The amount
of coupling is determined by the coupling capacitor C400B in
series with C400A — the more capacity used, the greater is the
coupling. The use of decoupling networks consisting of R403
and C404 in the primary and R404 and C405 in the secondary,
prevents interaction between stages. These networks, used
throughout the receiver, may be recognized by the fact that they
consist of a low-value resistor, feeding d-c voltage to plate,
screen, and grid circuits, bypassed to ground at the point receiving voltage.

The input i-f transformer is of the over-coupled, broad-band
type. The primary and secondary windings are tuned to the
highest frequency of the band pass. The capacity of C400B is
then increased, until an overcoupled double hump appears and
spreads out to cover the desired band width. Both the primary
and secondary windings are shunted by 10,000 ohm resistors,
R400A and R400B, to broaden the band pass and to provide more
nearly uniform frequency response. The output from Z400 is
fed to the 6AG5 input i-f amplifier.

The signal from the input i-f amplifier is fed to i-f transformer Z401. The design of this transformer is different from the
one already described. A wave trap is inserted between the
primary and secondary windings. By offering a high impedance
to the sound i-f frequency, this sound i-f trap (C401C, and L401B)
eliminates coupling between the primary and secondary, and prevents the accompanying sound from getting through. The trap
is tuned to 22.1 Mc, the sound i-f carrier frequency. The sound
i-f signal is taken from a point preceding the sound trap, at the
bottom end of the primary of the transformer, and is coupled to
the input circuit of the sound section of the receiver.

The first video i-f amplifier, a 6AG5, is biased by a combination of the a.g.c. voltage fed to its grid and the voltage developed across unbypassed, 68 ohm cathode resistor R408. The
r-f voltage appearing at the screen of the video i-f amplifier
is bypassed to ground by the combination of two capacitors,
0.004 mf capacitor C408 and 10 mmf capacitor C427.

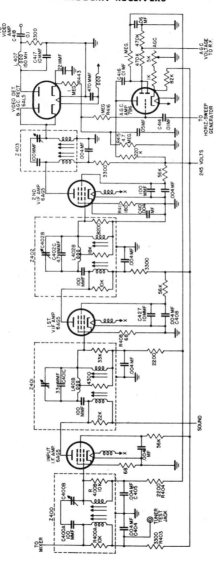

Figure 22. Video i-f amplifiers, second detector, and a.g.c. circuit.

The output of the first picture i-f amplifier is coupled to the primary of transformer Z402. This transformer, which is similar to the input i-f transformer Z401, consists of slug-tuned primary and secondary windings, with fixed capacity coupling and a parallel tuned trap circuit (C402B, C402C, and L402B). The trap circuit in this transformer is tuned to 28.1 Mc. This trap is the adjacent channel sound trap.

A.G.C. voltage is not applied to the second video i-f amplifier. A 180 ohm resistor, R411, bypassed for r-f by C410, is the only bias on the tube. The i-f transformer Z403 is similar to Z400.

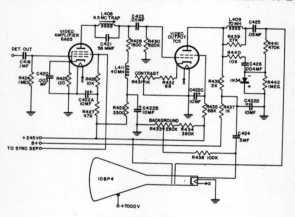

Figure 23. Video amplifier.

The output from the plate of the second i-f stage is fed to the last i-f transformer Z403. No shunt resistors are necessary to broaden the response curve of this transformer because it is loaded by the 6AL5 diode detector. A 150 mh choke L407 and condenser C417 are used to filter the output of the second detector. Then the output is fed to the grid of the 6AG5 video amplifier. A 0.1 mf coupling condenser C418 feeds the signal to the first video amplifier.

7-21 A.G.C. Circuit. A.G.C. voltage is secured from the cathode of one of the diodes of the 6AL5 which acts as the second detector (Figure 22). This diode functions as an a.g.c. rectifier. The rectified voltage developed across the network consisting of R443 and R415, at the cathode of the a.g.c. rectifier, is fed to the grid of the a.g.c. amplifier stage through resistor R416.

A signal from the horizontal sweep generator is also fed to the grid of the a.g.c. amplifier through condenser C414. The signal at the plate of the amplifier is fed to the diode section of the 7B6 through condenser C416. Rectification takes place, and the voltage developed is filtered and fed to the grids of the tubes under a.g.c. control. The strength of the signal from the a.g.c. rectifier controls the amplification of the a.g.c. amplifier.

7-22 Video Amplifier. The 6AG5 video amplifier, shown in Figure 23, is designed to have as flat a response as possible. The combination of 1,800 ohm resistor R428 and 40 mh inductance L411 provides the plate load of the amplifier. This type of plate load provides uniform output over a wide frequency range by maintaining a constant load impedance. The choke L411 increases the amplification at high frequencies, thus extending the frequency response of the amplifier to more than 4 Mc. A 10 mf condenser is used to by-pass the low frequencies. The output of the video amplifier is fed through 0.05 mf capacitor C423 to the control grid of the 7C5 video output stage.

Output voltage is also developed across load resistor R426 in the screen of the video amplifier. This voltage is fed to the sync separator. The output from the plate is fed through a 4.5 Mc trap, consisting of L408 and C421, to the grid of the 7C5 video-output stage. The sound carrier, beating with the picture carrier of the received signal, produces a beat frequency of 4.5 Mc. If this beat frequency is not eliminated, it will produce a fine interference pattern in the picture. The purpose of the 4.5 Mc trap is to prevent this beat pattern from appearing on the picture tube screen.

The plate load of the 7C5 consists of a network of resistors, inductors, and capacitors which are required to provide uniform frequency response. This plate load consists of 2,000 ohm resistor R436. A 70 mh peaking coil, L409, shunted by 27,000 ohm resistor R439, is used to compensate for the input capacity of the cathode ray tube and the stray capacities of the wiring.

7-23 Picture Tube. The d-c grid bias on the picture tube determines the average brightness of the picture. This average changes with the picture content, being one value for a picture composed mostly of blacks. The use of a d-c restorer establishes a voltage level which is independent of picture content, but which depends upon the sync pulses. This restorer consists of a crystal didode (1N34), shunted across a portion of the grid resistor of the cathode ray tube. The crystal conducts on the negative peaks of the video signal, developing on the cathode-ray tube a positive grid bias equal to the peak value of the negative sync pulses.

The desired brightness of the picture is controlled by control R433 which adjusts the cathode bias on the picture tube. The contrast of the picture is determined by the amount of video amplification and is controlled by contrast control R431.

7-24 Sweep Section. Positive sync pulses, both vertical and horizontal, are taken from the screen of the first video amplifier, and are fed to the grid of the 7B5 sync separator, shown in Figure 24. The sync separator tube has its cathode grounded, and the sync pulses charge condenser C500 through the tube.

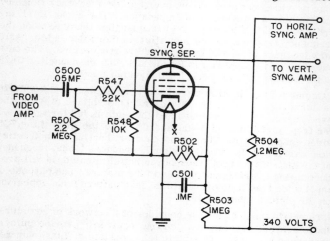

Figure 24. Sync separator.

The charge cannot leak off immediately, because of the long time constant of C500 and C501. Thus, the charge biases the tube at approximately cutoff. The charge on the condenser is almost equal to the peak amplitude of the positive sync pulses. The picture portion of the signal has no effect on the plate current of the sync separator, as only the tips of the positive sync pulses can cause the tube to conduct. A 22,000 ohm resistor, R547, in the grid lead of the sync separator is used to prevent sharp noise pulses, such as ignition noise, from driving the grid highly positive and causing a blocking voltage to be developed.

Such a voltage would result in loss of sync for a portion of the picture. This resistor limits the amount of grid current that can flow for any one pulse. R504 and R548 form a voltage divider across the power supply, which places 2.6 volts on the plate of the tube. The voltage divider consisting of R503 and R502 places 3.2 volts on the screen grid. The very low plate voltage permits the sync pulses to drive the tube to saturation, clipping the sync pulses to uniform amplitude.

The negative output at the plate of the sync separator consists of vertical sync pulses and horizontal sync pulses. The pulses

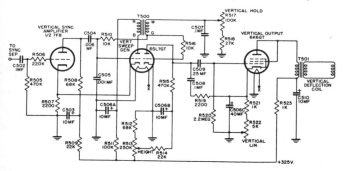

Figure 25. Vertical-deflection circuits.

are fed to the inputs of the vertical sync amplifier. Both the vertical sync and horizontal sync pulses are applied as negative pulses to the grid of the vertical sync amplifier (half of a 7F8) but only the vertical pulses are effective. The vertical deflection circuits are shown in Figure 25. Being of very short duration compared to the vertical pulses, the horizontal pulses are not able to cause conduction in the vertical sync amplifier tube. The negative vertical pulses cause a positive output pulse to be developed at the plate of the vertical sync amplifier. This signal is fed to C504 and C505, connected in series as an integrating circuit. At the output of the integrating circuit, a vertical sync pulse is obtained which is of sufficient amplitude to trigger the vertical sweep oscillator.

These pulses are applied to the grid of the vertical sweep generator. This oscillator is half of a 6SL7, operated in a conventional blocking oscillator circuit. The other half of the 6SL7 functions as a discharge tube to produce the vertical sawtooth voltage. The cathode of the discharge tube is at ground potential, and its grid is tied to the grid of the vertical blocking oscillator through R510. The discharge tube remains at cutoff until it is triggered. When the vertical oscillator fires, a sharp positive pulse is applied to the grid of the discharge tube. This pulse causes heavy plate current to flow and discharges the 0.1 mf charging condenser C508. R519 in series with C508 is a "peaking resistor" and adds the necessary negative pulse to the sawtooth voltage to create the waveform required by magnetic deflection circuits. The amount of sweep voltage is determined by the adjustment of the 250,000 ohm height control R513, which varies the d-c voltage at the plate of the discharge tube.

The sweep signal is coupled to the grid of the 6K6 vertical output stage through 0.25 mf capacitor C509. A 1,000 ohm cathode resistor R521 and a variable 5,000 ohm vertical linearity control, R522, are used to adjust the bias on the vertical output stage. This bias adjustment is used to maintain linearity of the output sawtooth voltage. The 6K6 is triode connected, and its output is fed to the vertical deflection transformer, the low impedance secondary of which is connected to the vertical deflection coil in the yoke. The vertical deflection coil is shunted by two 1,000 ohm resistors to damp out oscillations in the coils.

Vertical as well as horizontal positioning of the picture on the screen of the tube is accomplished by means of a movable magnetized ring which is built into the deflection yoke assembly. The magnetized ring is moved in a horizontal plane to center the picture vertically, and in a vertical plane to center the picture horizontally.

The output of the sync separator is also applied to the grid of the horizontal sync amplifier shown in Figure 26. Since the cathode is grounded, this stage operates without grid bias, and the negative sync pulses on its grid cause a voltage rise across R527 and produce positive sync pulses at the plate. These sync pulses are coupled through the 0.001 mf capacitor C513 to the bottom end of the grid winding of the blocking oscillator transformer. The grid of the horizontal discharge tube is connected to the grid of the horizontal oscillator, and its grid is driven positive during the firing of the horizontal oscillator tube. This discharges the charging capacitor C516.

The horizontal sawtooth voltage is coupled to the grid of the 6BG6 horizontal output stage through 0.01 mf capacitor C517 and 100 ohm resistor R536. The resistor is used to prevent oscillation in the horizontal output stage. Cathode bias for the 6BG6 is developed across cathode resistor, R537 bypassed by

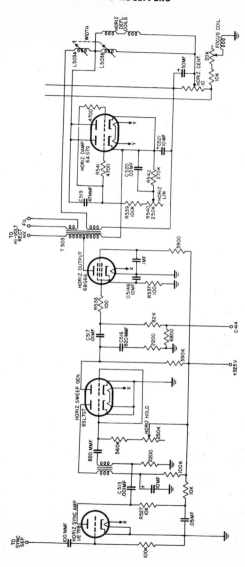

Figure 26. Horizontal-deflection circuits.

capacitor C514B. The sweep output is fed to a tap on the primary of the horizontal output transformer. One winding of this transformer is connected to the horizontal deflection yoke and the horizontal damping tube. The positive portion of the oscillations generated in the deflection coil during the rapid decay of the sawtooth signal is rectified by a 6AS7G horizontal damping tube and charges the condensers C519, C520, and C521. This voltage is applied to the horizontal output tube through trans-

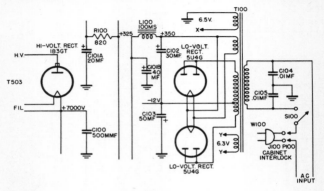

Figure 27. Power supplies.

former T503. The polarity of this charge is such that the voltage appearing at the plate of the horizontal output tube is equal to the B+ supply voltage, plus the charge across the condensers. This higher voltage results in greater sawtooth current through T503 and a greater deflection without an increase in the voltage of the power supply. The action of resistors R539, R540, R541, and R542, shunting the 6AS7G damping tube, together with C519, C520, C521, and L503 provides damping across the deflection yoke.

7-25 Power Supplies. The low voltage power supply is a heavy duty type, designed to supply the relatively heavy currents required by a receiver with magnetic deflection circuits. See Figure 27. The primary circuit of the transformer is provided with an interlock to open the primary circuit when the cabinet back is opened. The primary is bypassed to ground by 0.01 m capacitors C104 and C105. These capacitors help to eliminate noise pickup from the a-c line. Four secondary windings are provided. One supplies 6.5 volts for the filaments of all tubes,

except the 5V4G, the high voltage rectifier and damper tube.
A 5 volt winding is provided for the two parallel connected rectifiers. A separate 6.3 volt winding supplies current for the
6AS7G damper tube filament. A high voltage winding supplies
approximately 300 ma at 360 volts. The center tap of the high
voltage winding is connected to ground through the 10BP4 ion
trap coil, the focus coil, and focus control. This method of connection results in the development of about -12 volts.

The high voltage for the second anode of the picture tube
is obtained by means of a high voltage winding on the horizontal
output transformer T503. This high voltage winding steps up

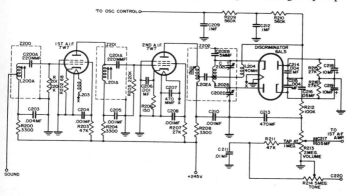

Figure 28. Sound i-f amplifier and discriminator.

the horizontal sweep voltage to approximately 7,000 volts. The
reader will recognize this type of power supply as the kickback
circuit. The high voltage is rectified by a 1B3GT rectifier tube
and filtered with a 500 mmf ceramic capacitor C100. Adequate
filtering is obtained with this small capacitor since the ripple
frequency is 15,750 cps. The capacitance between the high voltage anode of the picture tube is added to the filter capacitance
and further filters the high voltage supply.

The 1.25 volts for the filament of the 1B3GT heater is obtained
by a single turn of wire on the horizontal sweep output transformer.

7-26 Sound Section. After the video i-f signal and the sound
i-f signal are separated, the sound i-f signal is fed to the input
tap on Z200 in Figure 28. Z200 is an autotransformer, which

steps up the voltage and applies it to the grid of the 7W7, first sound i-f amplifier. A 220 mmf coupling capacitor C200A couples the voltage to the grid, and 220,000 ohm resistor R201 provides the d-c grid to ground path. The output from the plate is fed to second sound i-f transformer Z201. This transformer which is similar to Z200, is capacity coupled to the grid of the second i-f amplifier stage. The output from the second sound i-f amplifier is fed to discriminator transformer Z202, operated in a ratio detector circuit.

The 6AL5 twin diode in the ratio detector is so connected that the output voltage to the audio amplifiers from the center tap of the two 0.004 mf condensers C214 and C215 is the algebraic sum of the voltage across each condenser. The peak output voltage of the two diodes is applied to two 10 mf capacitors connected in series (C218 and C219), with their center tap connected to ground. When a signal is received, the output of the two diodes charges the two 10 mf condensers to a voltage where amplitude depends upon the strength of the received signal. The center tap of the discriminator transformer secondary is connected through a 40 mh choke L204 to the midpoint of 0.004 mf capacitors C214 and C215. This center tap is connected to the midpoint to create a d-c charging path for the 0.004 mf condensers.

With the signal at resonance, the voltage developed by one diode section is equal to that developed by the other diode section. Under these conditions, the voltage to the audio amplifiers, at the center tap of the 0.004 mf condensers, is zero. If the carrier frequency shifts higher, the voltage produced by one diode section is greater than that produced by the other diode section. The total voltage across the two 0.004 mf condensers C214 and C215 will equal the d-c potential of the two 10 mf storage condensers. However, the output to the audio amplifiers will be the algebraic sum of the voltage across each of two condensers C214 and C215. This means that the maxium audio output from the discriminator is dependent upon the d-c voltage at the two 10 mf storage condensers C218 and C219. Sudden noise peaks will be lost in the charging of C218 and C219 because of their high capacity. Hence, no limiter stage is needed.

If a stronger station is tuned in, a greater charge is produced on the two series storage capacitors. This greater charge results in a greater audio variation. The mid-point of capacitors C214 and C215 will also assume a d-c potential to ground, varying as the received signal varies, higher or lower than the resonant frequency of the discriminator transformer. This d-c potential is filtered to remove the sound component. The filter consists of R210, C212, R209, and C209. It is then fed back, as control grid bias, to the grid of the reactance modulator which automatically controls the frequency of the local oscillator. A de-emphasis circuit consisting of R212 and C213 is connected from the discriminator output to the 2 meg. volume control R213.

The audio amplifier section of the receiver, as shown in Figure 29, is a conventional audio amplifier. The output of this

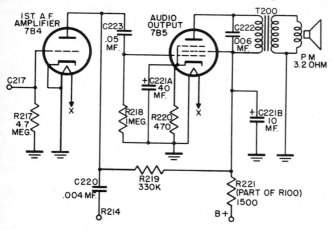

Figure 29. Audio amplifier.

amplifier is fed to a 7B5 output stage, where it is amplified and fed to a p-m speaker.

7-27 Scott Radio Laboratories, Inc. Model 13-A. The Scott Model 13-A is a console television receiver with a magnetic type 12 inch picture tube. A 12 inch direct view picture tube produces a picture 10 inches wide by 7.5 inches high. This receiver uses the Du Mont Inputuner which provides continuous tuning from 44 to 216 Mc. The tuning range includes coverage of the low frequency television band (44-88 Mc); the fm band (88-108 Mc); the amateur, aviation and government frequencies (108-174 Mc); and the high frequency television band (174-216 Mc). Thus, in addition to providing for reception of all television channels, the Scott receiver will receive frequency modulation stations. The tuner is described earlier in the section.

The Scott video receiver was designed to operate in conjunction with a Scott radio, the radio supplying the audio power amplifier and speaker while the Scott video receiver provides all the remaining circuits necessary for the reception of both television and f-m programs. A 30 foot length of audio cable is provided to connect the video receiver to the Scott radio in order to utilize the high quality Scott audio system in the radio to reproduce the sound of the television and f-m programs.

The video receiver consists of two chassis, the main receiver chassis and the power supply chassis. The low voltage power

Figure 30. Main chassis of Scott Model 13-A.

at 300 volts d-c and 400 volts d-c, as well as the high voltage 10 kv for the picture tube are located on the power supply chassis.

The main chassis contains the r-f input circuit, the video i-amplifier, video detector and amplifier, the f-m sound i-f amplifiers and detector, the vertical sweep circuits, horizontal sweep circuits and audio amplifiers.

A single multiconductor cable which is permanently attached to the power supply and plugs into the male connector on the main chassis connects the two chassis. The only other external connections outside the chassis are the high voltage cable from the power supply to the high voltage connector on the picture

Figure 31. Power supply chassis.

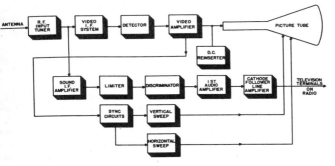

Figure 32. Block diagram of main chassis.

tube, and the a-c power cord to the power supply. Figures 30 and 31 show the arrangement of components on the two chassis.

A block diagram of the main chassis is shown in Figure 32. The component circuits on the main chassis are:

1. R-F tuner.
2. Video i-f amplifier and detector.
3. Video amplifier and d-c restorer.
4. Sound f-m i-f amplifier, limiter, and discriminator.

5. Audio amplifier and cathode follower.
6. Vertical sweep circuits.
7. Horizontal sweep circuits.

7-28 Video Circuits. The video i-f amplifier consists of three over-coupled, wideband circuits employing three 6AU6 high gain pentodes as shown in Figure 33. The gain of this system is varied by means of the contrast control R6 which changes the negative bias voltage on the first two video i-f amplifier signal grids (V1 and V2). The band of frequencies applied to the video channel is determined by the mixer plate transformer which consists of L1, L2, and L4. Inductance tuning of L1 and L4 is accomplished by means of a movable core which is adjustable from the top of the chassis. The bandwidth of the stage is determined by L2 while the resonant frequencies which are the limits of the band are dependent on L1 and L4. Plate voltage is isolated from the first video i-f signal grid by C4. The broad band characteristic of the amplifier stage is enhanced by damping resistors R1 and R4. R2 and C1 are mixer plate supply decoupling components.

The combination C2-L3 is series resonant to the sound i-f frequency of 21.9 Mc, thus permitting the sound i-f to be tapped off across L3 and applied to the first sound i-f amplifier. This series resonant circuit also prevents sound signals from entering the video channel.

The first video i-f tube V1 has both screen and plate voltage removed by the selector switch S1 when the switch is in the f-m position.

The second video i-f stage V2 has the same characteristics as the first, except that the associated channel sound trap consisting of C11, C10, and L8 is located in the grid circuit of this stage. This trap operates in the same manner and at the same frequency as the first i-f sound trap, C2-L3.

The third video i-f stage V3 has no traps and operates exactly as the first and second stages. Variable control grid bias which is applied to the first and second video i-f stages is not applied to the third video i-f stage. A 1N34 crystal rectifier CR1 is used to detect the video i-f carrier and its associated sidebands. R23 is the video detector load resistor. Capacitors C21 and C22 are video bypass capacitors which shunt to ground all frequencies from 30 cps to 4 Mc.

The video amplifier uses a high gain pentode V4, compensated to pass a band of frequencies from 30 cps through 4 Mc. Control grid bias is secured from a voltage divider which is connected across a negative 40 volt supply. This negative voltage

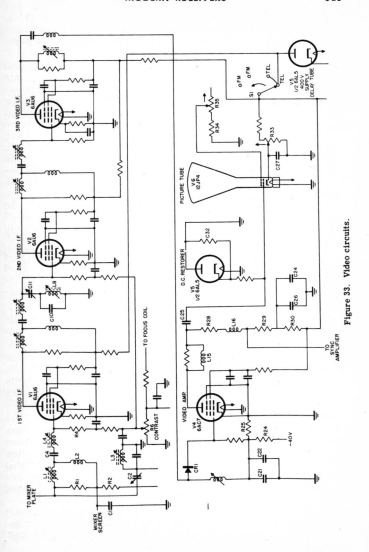

Figure 33. Video circuits.

is developed across the positioning controls and focus coil which are in series with the ground return of the low voltage transformer. The divider consists of R24 and R25 and provides the proper bias for the video amplifier.

Inductors L15 and L16 are shunt and series components for high frequency compensation. R28 is the load resistor for the tube. Part of the output of the amplifier appears across R29, a portion of the total load resistor. The sync circuits are fed from this point. Plate decoupling and low frequency compensation are provided by R30 and C26 in parallel with C24.

One half of dual diode V5 is used to reinsert the average d-c level of the picture which is lost in the capacity coupled video amplifier stage. On negative peaks of the sync signal, capacitor C25 charges to a d-c voltage determined by the average brightness of the picture. Resistor R32 is chosen so that the d-c voltage does not change before the next sync pulse occurs. This d-c voltage is applied to the picture tube grid. The 10kv for the second anode of the picture tube is supplied from the power supply chassis. A voltage divider composed of R34 and R35 permits variation of this voltage. R35 is called the drive control and is adjusted so that the control grid cuts off the beam when the minus 50 volts is present on the control grid. This insures that the signal from the video stages will be able to drive the picture to full blackness. The brightness control R33 varies the cathode potential and thus the tube illumination. Capacitor C27 shunts the cathode to ground for all signal voltages.

7-29 Vertical Synchronizing and Sweep Circuits. The video signal and the horizontal and vertical sync pulses are taken from a portion of the video amplifier load R29 and fed through capacitor C62 to the signal grid of the sync amplifier V15, shown in Figure 34. The composite signal is amplified across load resistor R80 and coupled through C63 to the second half of V15 which acts as a sync separator.

Bias voltage for the sync amplifier is secured from a voltage divider consisting of R79 and R78 in series. The sync separator is self biased. Across its load resistor R83 there appear only the vertical and horizontal sync signals, because resistors R81 and R84 reduce the plate voltage of the sync separator so that the tube cuts off the video signals which appear below the sync level. The sync signals appearing at the plate of V15 are applied to the grid of V16 through C64. In the plate circuit across the primary of T2, only the differential of the vertical sync signals appear. The integrating effect of R87, C66, R88, C67, and R89 eliminates the horizontal sync signals.

The vertical sync pulses, applied to the vertical blocking oscillator transformer primary T2, tend to sync the natural frequency of this oscillator to the sync pulses. The operating frequency of the vertical oscillator V16 is determined by R90, R91, C68, and by the vertical sync pulses applied to its control grid. The vertical hold control, R91, varies the natural oscillator frequency until it locks into the sync pulses.

V16, in addition to acting as a blocking oscillator, also serves as a sawtooth generator. The charging resistors R92, R93 and capacitor C69 determine the size and shape of the sawtooth waveform at the signal grids of V17. Peaking resistor R94 adds a negative peaking pulse to the sawtooth wave at the grid of V17. The size control R93 varies the amplitude of the waveform on the grid of V17 and thus the vertical height of the picture. Coupling to the grid of V17 is through C70 and R95. Resistors R96 and R97, bypassed by C71A, determine the operating point of V17 and thus affect the linearity. This linearity is changed by R97.

The vertical deflection transformer T3 couples the vertical scanning coil to the dual 6SN7 output amplifier, V17. Positioning of the picture vertically is obtained through the use of control R98 which varies the d-c potential across the deflection coil.

7-30 Horizontal Sweep Circuits. The horizontal and vertical sync pulses from the plate of V15, the sync separator tube, are applied to sync clipper tube V18 through capacitor C80 and resistor R140, as shown in Figure 35. The sync clipper tube is self-biased and operates at low plate voltage to provide further clipping of the sync signal and to eliminate video signals which pass through the sync separator. Resistor R141 acts as the plate load resistor, while R102 drops the plate voltage to a low level to provide the proper grid bias for clipping. Capacitor C72 isolates the plate load from R102. The inverted, amplified, and clipped sync pulses are then coupled to a flywheel synchronization circuit. The sync pulses are fed to the center tap of the secondary of phase discriminator transformer Z6 through capacitor C82. An electron coupled oscillator tube, V23, operating at the horizontal frequency (15,750 cps), also is coupled inductively to the secondary of this discriminator transformer.

The primary of this transformer is tuned by a movable core, and the oscillator frequency is varied in this manner. Grid bias for the oscillator is provided by capacitor C86 and resistor R130. R133 is the plate load resistor.

The d-c output voltage developed by the phase discriminator

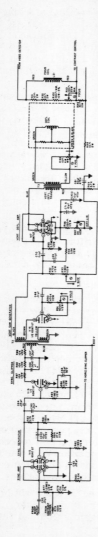

Figure 34. Vertical-deflection circuits.

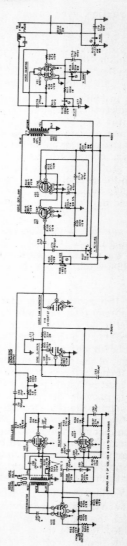

Figure 35. Horizontal-deflection circuits.

tube V22 is dependent upon the phase difference between the incoming sync pulses and the oscillator signal. This differential d-c voltage is developed across load resistors R126 and R124. If the oscillator and external sync signals are on frequency and in phase, the net voltage across R126 and R124 is zero. If the oscillator should tend to change frequency or phase with respect to the incoming sync pulses, the differential voltage across R126 and R124 becomes negative or positive depending on the phase shift direction of the oscillator signal. This varying d-c signal is applied to the grid of reactance tube V24, which is in parallel with the primary of the discriminator. The changing reactance of this tube affects the oscillator frequency in such a manner as to bring the frequency or phase of the oscillator back in synchronism with the incoming sync signals. The capacitor C89 tunes the primary of Z6 while C88 couples the reactance tube across the primary.

In order to prevent the oscillator frequency from being disturbed by random noises which come in with the sync signals, a filter is placed across the output load of the discriminator to eliminate these noise signals. This filter consists of R128 and C85, whose time constant is fairly long, so that rapid random noise pulses do not pass through to the reactance tube.

The oscillator plate voltage is differentiated by resistor R138 and capacitor C91 to form sharp negative and positive pulses. The pulses are applied to the grid of the horizontal sawtooth generator V18 through capacitor C92 and resistor R139. The sawtooth voltage at 15,750 cps is generated across capacitor which is charged through resistors R105 and R106 from the 400 volt supply. The horizontal size is varied by control R106. R107 varies the negative pulse that is fed back from the secondary of scanning transformer T5. This peaking voltage is combined with the sawtooth on the grids of deflection amplifiers V19 and V20 to provide a peaked sawtooth signal which will produce a linear sawtooth current in the deflection coil.

Two type 807 power tubes are operated in parallel as the deflection amplifier, and are coupled to the deflection coil through output transformer T5. Across the secondary of this transformer is connected a horizontal damping tube, V21, which has two triodes operated in parallel. This tube damps out the natural periodic oscillations of the transformer secondary at the beginning of the trace period. The voltage on the plate of V21 is a negative pulse. This pulse is differentiated by C76, R115 and R116, and applied through R118 and R120 to the grids of V21. The shape of this grid voltage is determined by the position of the horizontal linearity control R116. This control affects the amount of current drawn by V21 and, therefore, the degree of damping. The net effect is to control the linearity of the saw-tooth current in the deflection coil. The horizontal damping control R119 connects both cathodes of V21 to ground. The adjustment of this control affects both linearity and horizontal size by varying the static bias on the cathode of V21. This bias determines the fraction of each cycle during which the damping triode draws current.

In series with the horizontal deflection coil is resistor R122. A sawtooth voltage is developed across this resistor by the sawtooth current of the horizontal deflection coil. This saw-

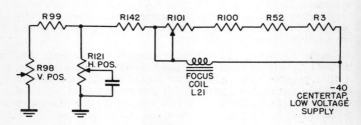

Figure 36. Focus coil circuit.

tooth voltage is used to trigger the oscillator in the high voltage supply which is described later.

The direct current flowing through the horizontal scanning coil affects the positioning of the electron beam in the horizontal direction. The direct current can be varied by the setting of the horizontal positioning control R121.

7-31 Focus Coil. The focusing coil L21 is in series with the low voltage supply, as shown in Figure 36. The path of the returning current to the power transformer center tap to ground is through the vertical and horizontal positioning controls in parallel, separated by isolating resistor R99; then to a negative voltage takeoff resistor, R142, where the negative voltage bias for the contrast control and sync circuits is obtained; then to the parallel combination of R101 (the focus control) in series with R100. By changing the resistance of the focus control R101, it is possible to vary the current through the focus coil which is in parallel with it.

7-32 Sound Channel. The sound i-f amplifiers utilize two 6BA6 remote cutoff pentodes, as shown in Figure 37. The sound sig-

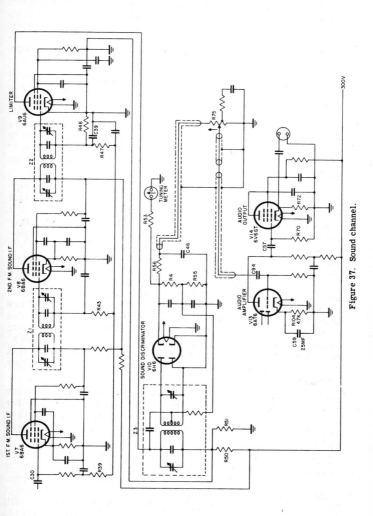

Figure 37. Sound channel.

nal at 21.9 Mc, after being separated from the composite video and audio i-f frequencies, is applied through coupling capacitor C30 to the grid of V7. The sound i-f transformers are double tuned with variable shunt capacitors. A.V.C. voltage secured from the grid of the limiter stage is applied to both i-f stages through isolating resistors R39 and R43.

A 6AU6 pentode tube is used as both a grid and plate limiter, causing limiting on both the positive and negative peaks of the signal voltage. The grid bias and the plate and screen voltages on this tube result in a very short operating curve. The combination of R48 and C39 provides negative grid bias dependent on incoming signal level. Their values are chosen to provide fast limiting on noise impulses. The 300 volt supply voltage is reduced by a voltage divider composed of R50 and R51, to provide a low plate and screen voltage for the limiting tube.

A 6H6 diode tube V10 is used as a conventional balanced discriminator. Both the primary and secondary of Z3 are tuned 20 21.9 Mc, and are capacitively and inductively coupled to one another. The audio output voltage is dependent upon the frequency deviation from the center frequency of 21.9 Mc. A tuning meter is connected to one cathode of the discriminator and indicates the d-c voltage appearing across the discriminator load resistors. This d-c voltage is indicative of proper or improper tuning of the signal. As the receiver tunes across the sound carrier, the meter deviates plus and minus from zero reading. When the receiver is properly tuned, the d-c voltage across the discriminator is zero, and the meter shows no plus or minus deviation. The discriminator transformer is linear to plus and minus 75 kc from 21.9 Mc, and is usable to 100 kc on either side of zero center. Resistor R53 limits the current through the tuning meter, while R54 and R55 are discriminator load resistors.

A de-emphasis network, consisting of R56 and C46, produces an attenuation of the higher audio frequencies to compensate for pre-emphasis at the transmitter. The audio voltage is then passed to volume control R75, and thence to the first audio amplifier.

The triode section of the 6AT6 voltage amplifier, V13, is used to amplify the audio voltage. The signal is fed to the grid of V13 through C94. Bias for the tube is provided by a 4700-ohm cathode resistor bypassed with a 25 mf capacitor, to prevent low frequency discrimination. Capacitor C57 and resistor R70 couple this amplified audio voltage to the control grid of V14, which is a 6V6 operated as a cathode follower. This tube is connected as a triode with its screen grid attached to its plate to reduce the plate impedance of the tube. Output is taken from a-cross cathode resistor R72. The impedance at the cathode is low enough in value to permit attaching a connecting audio cable to the audio system in the Scott a-m radio.

7-33 The Power Supply Chassis. A block diagram of the circuits located on the power supply chassis is shown in Figure 38, while the complete schematic circuit is shown in Figure 39. The power supply consists of three sections, a 300-volt d-c supply, a 400-volt d-c supply, and a 10 kv high voltage d-c supply. The 400-volt supply is used for the sweep amplifiers and

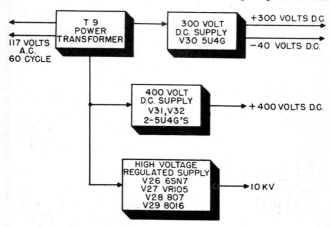

Figure 38. Block diagram of power supply chassis.

for the high voltage supply circuits. The 10 kv is used as the accelerating potential on the second anode of the picture tube. The 300-volt supply serves the remainder of the receiver.

The power supply is so designed that if the 300-volt supply should fail, the 400-volt supply immediately becomes inoperative. The 10 kv supply is also shut off in as much as it receives its power from the 400-volt supply. This receiver is equipped with a unique high voltage supply cutoff circuit, consisting of delay diode V5, located on the main chassis, relay K1 (Figure 40) on the power supply chassis, and the service selector switch on the main chassis. This circuit serves three main functions.

It turns off the 10 kv source of high voltage for the picture

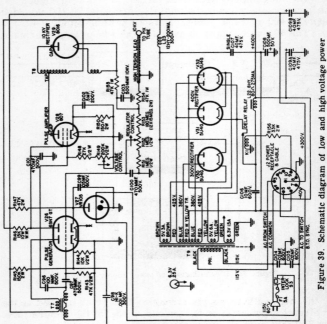

Figure 39. Schematic diagram of low and high voltage power supplies.

tube, shuts off the sweep circuits, and disconnects the first video i-f amplifier voltages when the selector switch is in the f-m position.

When the service selector switch is in the video position, a 300-volt d-c voltage is applied to the diode delay tube V5. The diode therefore draws current, energizing the 400-volt delay relay K1, and applying 400 volts d.c. to the high voltage and

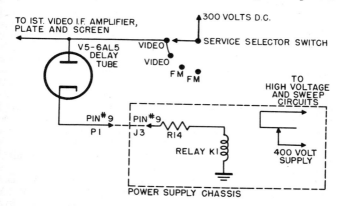

Figure 40. Automatic, high-voltage cutoff circuit.

sweep circuits. If the service selector switch is in the f-m position, the diode is not supplied with 300 volts and consequently the 400-volt delay relay is not energized. This leaves the high voltage and sweep circuits without voltage and permits listening to f-m without the scanning raster appearing on the picture tube.

The second purpose of the delay tube is to protect the fluorescent screen of the picture tube. In the above discussion, it was noted that relay K1 must be energized in order for the sweep circuits and the high voltage circuits to operate. When the set is turned on, there is a period before the delay tube warms up. Therefore, no high voltage will be generated until the end of this warm up period. This delay gives the sweep circuit tubes a chance to warm up before the high voltage is applied to the picture tube. Scanning current therefore flows through the deflection yoke before the high voltage comes on. If this were not the case, the high voltage applied to the picture tube without deflection currents in the yoke would cause a bright spot on the screen. If a spot occurred for any length of time, it would damage the screen material.

A third function of the delay tube is to allow the tubes to warm up properly before voltage is applied to the filter capacitors. This protects the capacitors against excessive voltage, which would exist during the warm up period when the tubes are not drawing B+ current from the supply.

7-34 300-Volt Supply. The 115-volt, 60-cycle, a-c current passes through a 5 amp fuse, F1, 4 and 2 pins of plug J2, an interlock switch, S3, then through the connecting cable between chassis, to the on-off switch on the main receiver chassis, back to the power supply chassis, through the primary of the power transformer, and back to the a-c line. The interlock switch is so located on the power supply chassis that when the back panel of the receiver is removed, the switch is opened and the set automatically shut off. Thus no harm can come to an inexperienced person who opens the receiver and attempts to tamper with the circuits. When servicing a receiver with an interlock switch, the technician must temporarily short the switch terminals.

The single 5U4G rectifier tube, V30, has a separate filament winding, while its plates are connected to the 380-volt taps of the transformer secondary, as shown in Figure 39. A single section pi filter is utilized with capacitor C107 acting as the input filter. This capacitor is not grounded at the negative terminal, but connects to the negative electrode of capacitor C108 which shunts all a-c signals and sweep voltages across the negative bias supply to ground. Filter inductor L23 and capacitor C109B provide additional filtering. The 300-volt d-c voltage is then fed to pin 1 of J2 on the power supply chassis.

7-35 400-Volt Supply. A second filament winding supplies two 5U4G rectifier tubes with filament power while their plates are connected to the 425-volt taps on the power transformer secondary. The first filter capacitor, C106, is isolated from the rectifier tubes by delay relay K1, which allows the sweep and high voltage tube filaments time to warm before voltage is applied to capacitor C106. This capacitor is returned directly to the negative side of the supply. Filter inductor L22 terminates in filter capacitor C109A, the negative side of which is grounded. The 400-volt d-c voltage is then connected to pin 5 of J2 on the power supply chassis.

7-36 High Voltage Supply. A block diagram of the high voltage supply is shown in Figure 41. The high voltage supply is of the high frequency pulse type. One half of V26, a 6SN7 tube, is used as a pulse generator to create the sharp high voltage pulses which are applied to the grid of V28, on 807 pulse amplifier tube. The blocking oscillator, V26, is normally biased to cutoff so that no current flows and no pulses are generated. The tube is triggered into operation by a sawtooth voltage which is applied to its cathode through R145 (Figure 39). This sawtooth voltage, which occurs at 15,750 cps, is developed across resistor R122 (Figure 35) in series with the horizontal deflection coil.

When this sawtooth voltage is fed to the cathode of V26, the blocking oscillator conducts and produces pulses of short duration. These pulses appear on the grid of V28. Resistor R150

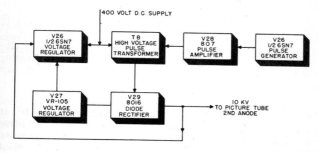

Figure 41. Block diagram of 10KV high voltage supply.

and capacitor C102 provide bias for this pulse amplifier tube. The plate of V28 is coupled to an autotransformer T8 with a high voltage step-up winding. The pulses are increased to approximately 10 Kv by this autotransformer. The high voltage pulses occur at 15,750 cps and are rectified by V29, an 8016 diode. Filament power for V29 is obtained from the high voltage autotransformer by coupling a few turns to its primary. The high voltage is filtered by a two section filter. R155 and C103 comprise the first section, while R154 and the capacity of the high voltage coaxial cable, which carries the high voltage to the picture tube, act as the second filter section.

To minimize the effects of line voltage variations on the output of the high voltage supply, a regulator circuit, consisting of V27 and one half of V26, is used. A portion of the high voltage is tapped across the high voltage bleeder, consisting of R153 in series with R152 and R151. This voltage is fed to the grid of a regulator tube, the second half of V26. The amount of current which this tube draws determines the screen voltage of the pulse amplifier V28, and hence affects the amplitude of the high voltage pulses. A VR-105 tube, V27, is used in the cathode of the regulator tube to hold this voltage constant. All current variations through the tube are then due only to the grid voltage variations.

The regulator circuit operates in the following manner to maintain constant high voltage d.c. Assuming that the high voltage output decreases (caused by an increase in line voltage), the portion fed back to the grid of the regulator tube, V26, also decreases, thereby decreasing the current through R146 and the voltage drop across R146. The screen voltage of the pulse amplifier tube immediately increases and the high voltage output increases to maintain the original operating voltage.

Another feature of this high voltage circuit is the automatic cutting off of the high voltage if the horizontal sweep should fail. If no horizontal sweep voltage is generated, no sawtooth voltage is fed to the cathode of the first half of V26. The pulse generator is then biased to cutoff and no pulses or high voltage are produced.

7-37 Du Mont Model RA-101.

The Du Mont Model RA-101 is an example of a complete console receiver containing facilities for television, f-m and a-m reception, and an automatic record changer. The Model RA-101 circuits appear in both the Du Mont 15-inch tube models and the 20-inch tube models.

This receiver consists of several chassis and sub-assemblies, as follows.

1. The r-f/i-f chassis, containing both sound and video i-f circuits, video amplifier, and r-f tuning system.

2. The sweep chassis, containing sweep circuits, a power supply for low voltage, and the high-voltage supply for the picture tube. A sync stabilizer sub-chassis, containing an automatic frequency control circuit for the horizontal sync system.

3. The a-m tuner chassis, containing the tuning unit for a-m reception.

4. The audio amplifier chassis, containing the audio amplifier and its own power supply. All sound facilities of the receiver use this amplifier.

5. The tuning meter assembly, containing the tuning meter for the television and f-m sound plus the cable connecting it to the r-f/i-f chassis.

6. The tone selector assembly, consisting essentially of a push-button switch and the tone control components.

7. Picture tube assembly, consisting of the cathode-ray tube,

focusing coil, and deflection yoke.

8. The service selector switch assembly, consisting of a push-button switch system, which selects either one of the facilities.

9. The record changer.

A block diagram of the receiver showing the relationship of the various circuits is given in Figure 42.

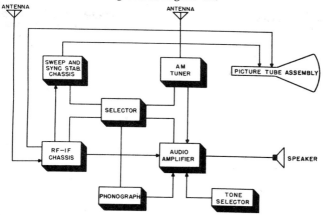

Figure 42. Block diagram of DuMont Model RA-101

7-38 R-F/I-F Chassis. A block diagram of the circuits located on the r-f/i-f chassis is shown in Figure 43. This receiver employs the Du Mont Inputuner described at the beginning of this section. This tuner is the same one which is used in the Scott receiver previously described. There is one difference between the two. The tuner dial in the Scott receiver is manually rotated, whereas a motor drive is provided on the Model RA-101. A sliderule dial (Figure 44) is used on this model rather than rotating discs employed on the Scott receiver. The pointer travels from the low frequency (channel 1), lower right hand side of the dial, to the lower left hand side. When it reaches the left side of the dial it makes a U turn and continues traveling from left to right along the upper scale of the dial till it reaches channel 13. A slipping clutch is built into the motor drive so that when the pointer reaches the end of its travel at either the low frequency or high frequency ends, it cannot be damaged.

Tuning is accomplished by closing a switch on the motor. The

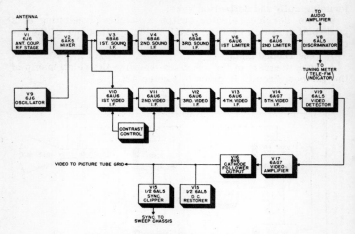

Figure 43. Block diagram of r-f, i-f chassis.

Figure 44. R-F, I-F chassis showing slide-rule dial.
(courtesy DuMont)

operator holds the switch closed until the pointer travels to the desired station. A vernier tuning knob is geared to the motor drive for precise manual adjustment to the station frequency after the motor has moved the pointer to the station.

The tuned circuit in the plate of the mixer tube (Figure 45) is tuned to have a band pass of 21.5 to 26.4 Mc. The sound i-f frequency is picked off prior to the tuned circuit and the video i-f

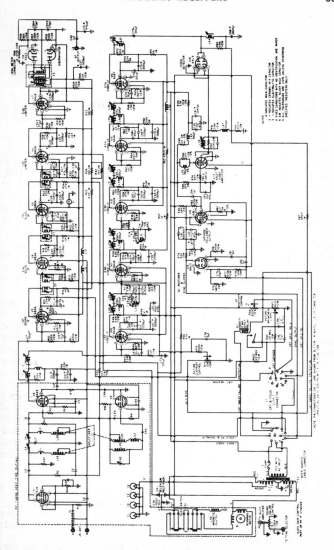

Figure 45. Schematic diagram of r-f, 1-f chassis.

frequency passes through to the grid of V10, the first video i-f amplifier. Five broad-band coupled video i-f amplifier stages are provided. These five stages consist of V10, V11, V12, V13, and V14. All stages employ 6AU6s, except V14 which uses a 6AG7. The over-coupled transformers between stages are each tuned to provide a band pass of 4 Mc. Two sound traps are employed, one in the grid of the second video i-f stage V11, and one in the grid of the third stage V12. These sound traps prevent the sound i-f signals from passing through the video i-f amplifier.

The output of the fifth video i-f stage, V14, feeds V19, the video detector. V19 is a dual diode connected as a push-pull detector. The detected output is applied to the grid of the first video amplifier, V17, a 6AG7. V17 in turn feeds V16, a 6V6, connected as a cathode follower output stage. The output of V16 is coupled directly to the grid of the picture tube. One section of V15, a dual diode 6AL5, is connected across the output of V16, to act as a d-c restoration circuit. The other half of V15 is a diode sync clipper. It too is connected across the output of the cathode follower and is biased so that conduction takes place only when the sync signals occur. The video portion is thus effectively clipped. The sync signal is taken from the plate of the sync clipper, and is fed to the sweep chassis in composite form.

The sound i-f amplifier is a three-stage amplifier consisting of V3, V4, and V5, type 6BA6 tubes. The interstage transformers are over-coupled and have uniform response over a 200 kc pass band. After passing through the sound i-f amplifiers, the sound signal is fed to two limiter stages, V6 and V7, which are connected in cascade. These tubes remove amplitude modulation from the f-m signal. The output of the second limiter is coupled to the discriminator by means of transformer Z5. The discriminator, V8, is a conventional balanced type, and is tuned for zero output voltage at the sound carrier i-f frequency of 21.9 Mc. A tuning meter (similar to the type used with the Scott receiver) is connected to one of the cathodes of the discriminator and registers zero when the f-m or television station being received is properly tuned. The output of the discriminator is the audio signal which is fed to the audio amplifier chassis for further amplification.

There are a number of other components located on the r-f/i-f chassis. These items are enumerated below.

1. The Contrast Control, R73, varies the video i-f amplifier gain by changing the negative bias voltage applied to the grids of the first two video i-f amplifiers.

2. The Picture Brightness Control, R97, is located on this

chassis. It sets the positive d-c voltage applied to the cathode of the picture tube and so determines the intensity level of the picture.

3. The Sound Volume Control, R17, is also located on this chassis to consolidate all controls on a single chassis. R17, which is a gain control in one of the audio circuits located on

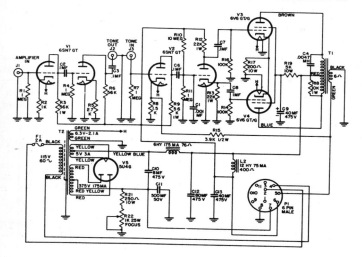

Figure 46. Audio amplifier schematic.

the audio chassis, is connected by shielded cable from the r-f/i-f chassis to the audio stage.

4. The motor drive switch and the hand vernier tuning mechanism are also included on this chassis for further consolidation of controls on the front panel of the receiver.

7-39 The A-M Tuner Chassis.

The a-m tuner chassis, which is employed in the Model RA-101, consists of a conventional a-m receiver except for the audio output stage. A single r-f stage, a converter, i-f amplifier, and detector are provided. A 6SA7 serves the function of both oscillator and mixer to convert the r-f signal to an intermediate frequency of 456 kc. Another 6SK7 serves as the i-f amplifier, which feeds a dual triode 6SN7. The first section of the 6SN7 is connected as a diode and acts as a detector. The other half is operated as a triode cathode follower which couples the audio signal to the audio amplifier chassis.

7-40 **The Audio Amplifier Chassis.** The audio amplifier (Figure 46) consists of four tubes, two type 6SN7s, and two type 6V6s. All stages in the amplifier are resistance coupled. V1 is a dual triode, both sections of which are connected as voltage amplifiers in cascade. The volume control is connected in the input circuit of the first stage and is located on the r-f/i-f chassis. The tone control is connected in the plate circuit of

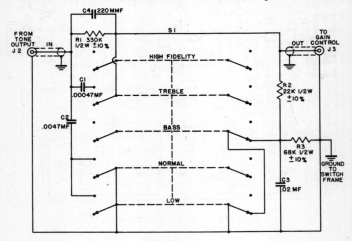

Figure 47. Tone selector schematic.

the second half of V1. Any one of five tones may be selected by means of a tone selector switch (Figure 47), connected across J2 and J3 in the plate circuit. The tone selector is a separate assembly with five different RC circuits which vary the response of the amplifier. This separate assembly is located on the front panel of the receiver with the rest of the operating controls.

The output of the tone circuit is fed to the first half of V2, another voltage amplifier. This stage in turn feeds the second half of V2, which is a phase inverter. Since the voltages on the cathode and plate of an amplifier are 180° out of phase, signals may be taken from these points to drive a push-pull circuit. The plate resistor, R12, and the cathode resistor, R13, are so chosen that the voltage output from the cathode and plate are of the same amplitude. These voltages, which are 180° out of phase, are applied to push-pull 6V6s, V3 and V4. The push-pull output stage is coupled to the speaker through transformer T1.

7-41 The Sweep Chassis. The sweep chassis contains the power supply which furnishes B+ and bias voltages to the sweep circuits and to the circuits on the r-f/i-f chassis. A block diagram of the circuits located on the sweep chassis is shown in Figure 48. The low voltage power supply contains two 5U4G

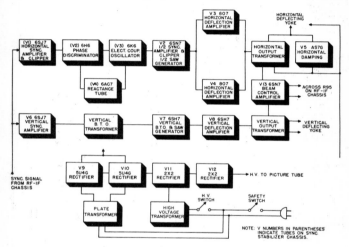

Figure 48. Block diagram of sweep chassis.

rectifiers, V9 and V10 as shown in Figure 49A. A time delay relay, K1, in this supply prevents B+ from being available for about 30 seconds after the set is turned on. This time delay permits the filament to warm up so that the tubes immediately conduct when the B+ is applied. Otherwise, the load on the power supply would be low when the set is first turned on and the B+ voltage would rise above the safe operating voltage of the filter condensers. The filter section consists of L1, L2, C19, and C33. The voltage between L1 and L2 is higher than the output of the filter. This higher voltage is used for vertical and horizontal sweep amplifier stages while the lower voltage of 300 volts is used for the rest of the receiver.

The sweep chassis also contains the high voltage power supply.

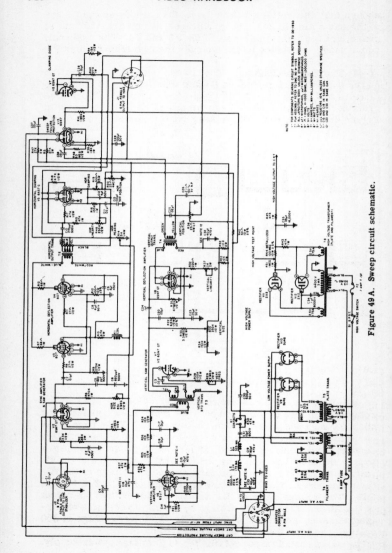

Figure 49A. Sweep circuit schematic.

This power supply is of the 60-cycle type and uses two type 2X2 rectifiers, V11 and V12. The rectifier tubes are connected in a voltage doubler circuit to provide 12 kv d-c output. On the negative half of the a-c cycle, V11 conducts and condenser C34 charges to 6 kv. This charge is applied to the plate of V12. On the positive cycle, V12 conducts and charges C35. The voltage on C34 is added to the charge on C35, producing 12 kv across this condenser.

The clipped sync signal from the r-f/i-f chassis is fed to V6, a 6SJ7. This tube amplifies the vertical sync signal. An inte-

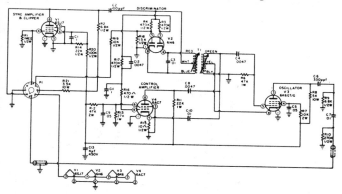

Figure 49B. Sync stabilizer schematic.

grating circuit (R25, R26, R24, C16, and C17) in the plate circuit of V6 separates the vertical sync pulses from the horizontal sync pulses. The vertical sync signal is applied to the blocking oscillator, one half of V7, through a sync winding on the oscillator transformer. The sync pulse is coupled by the transformer to the grid of V7 and locks the oscillator into synchronism. The oscillator and sawtooth generator functions are combined in this stage. The charging circuit is located in the plate circuit. C20 is the charging condenser, which is charged through R33 and R30. The vertical sawtooth voltage developed across C20 is fed to deflection amplifier, V8, a dual triode with both halves operating in parallel. The vertical deflection amplifier drives the primary of T4, the vertical output transformer. The secondary of T4 is coupled to the vertical deflection coil. Vertical positioning is obtained by means of a potentiometer, R36, which injects a negative d-c voltage into the deflection coil.

The horizontal sweep circuit is very similar to the type in the Scott Model 13-A, already described. Flywheel synchronization is employed to stabilize the sync system. The clipped sync signals coming from the r-f/i-f chassis are first amplified by V1, a 6SJ7 sync amplifier (Figure 49B). These signals are then fed to the sync discriminator transformer. The flywheel sync circuit is identical in design to that found in the Scott receiver. V3 is the Hartley oscillator, V2 the discriminator, and V4 the reactance tube. A stabilized triggering pulse is obtained from the circuit in the plate of V3. This triggering pulse is applied to the second half of V2, the horizontal sawtooth generator. The

Figure 50. Sweep chassis. (courtesy DuMont)

remainder of this circuit is again similar to the Scott horizontal sweep circuit. The sawtooth voltage is developed across C5 and applied to two 807 deflection amplifier tubes, operated in parallel. The output of the 807s is coupled to the deflection coil through T2. V5 is a 6AS7G, operated as a triode damper.

The layout of the sweep chassis is shown in Figure 50. Note the holes punched in this chassis to help dissipate the heat generated in the power supply and sweep components.

7-42 The Picture Tube Assembly. The picture tube for the 20-inch versions of the model RA-101 is the type 20BP4. Since the 20-inch tube is about 29 inches long, it is mounted vertically in a cradle. The picture tube, its focusing coil, and its deflection yoke are all mounted in the cradle. This cradel is raised into a horizontal position for viewing by a mechanical driving mechanism. To bring the tube into the horizontal position, the lid on the cabinet is raised. This automatically throws a switch which starts the lift mechanism.

The picture tube used in the 15-inch versions of the model RA-101 is the type 15AP4. It is mounted in a fixed horizontal position in the cabinet and is not provided with a tilt mechanism.

7-43 RCA Victor Model 648 PTK. The RCA model 648PTK is a forty-eight tube projection television, a-m/f-m radio, console receiver. The television receiver employs four chassis with a total of thirty-five tubes, plus a five-inch projection tube. These chassis are:

1. An r-f/i-f chassis which includes the r-f tuner, the video and sound sections, and the vertical sweep circuits.

2. A chassis on which is mounted the horizontal sweep system and the 27 kv high voltage supply, which is a part of the horizontal sweep circuit.

3. A low voltage power supply chassis which furnishes power to the entire receiver.

4. An audio amplifier which is switched into the sound circuits of either the television, f-m or a-m sections of the receiver.

The four chassis are located in a large console as shown in Figure 51. The heavy black lines indicate the interconnecting cables. In the lower right hand corner is the optical barrel which houses the projection tube and optical components of the Schmidt reflective system, which is employed in this receiver. A 15-inch by 20-inch picture is obtained on the screen.

The reader will note in the following description of the 648PTK that the r-f and video circuits are similar to those found in direct view receivers which produce smaller pictures. Only in the horizontal deflection circuits and the high voltage power supply are there radical departures from direct view receiver designs. The latter circuits differ only because the projection tube must operate at higher voltages and therefore requires greater deflection power.

A block diagram of the Model 648PTK is shown in Figure 52. This receiver employs the RCA¯ 13-channel switch type tuner described earlier in this section.

7-44 Video Channel. The picture i-f amplifier is of the stagger tuned type. To obtain the necessary wide band characteris-

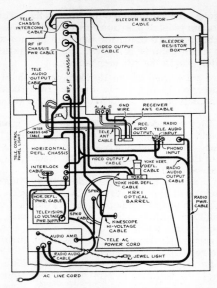

Figure 51. Arrangement of chassis in RCA console Model PTK. (courtesy RCA)

tic with adequate gain, four stages of i-f amplification are employed, as shown in Figure 53. The converter plate and each successive i-f transformer utilize one tuned circuit each, and each is tuned to a different frequency. The effective Q of each coil is fixed by the shunt plate load or grid resistor so that the total response of all the stages produces the desired overall pass band. Figure 54 shows the relative gains and selectivities of each coil and the shape of the curve formed by the combination of stages.

In order to obtain this band pass characteristic, the picture i-f transformers are tuned as follows:

Converter transformer . . . . . 21.8 Mc (T2 primary)
First picture i-f transformer. . 25.3 Mc (T4 primary)
Second picture i-f transformer . 22.3 Mc (T105 primary)
Third picture i-f coil . . . . . . 25.2 Mc (L104)
Fourth picture i-f coil . . . . . 23.4 Mc (L106)

In such a stagger tuned system, variations of individual i-f amplifier tube gain do not affect the shape of the overall i-f response curve if the Qs and center frequencies of the stages remain unchanged. This means that the i-f amplifier tubes are non-critical in replacement because variations in Gm do not affect the response curve.

Four traps are used to shape the i-f response curve and attenuate the sound signals, and the adjacent channel picture carrier. The first trap (T2 secondary) is tuned to the accompany-

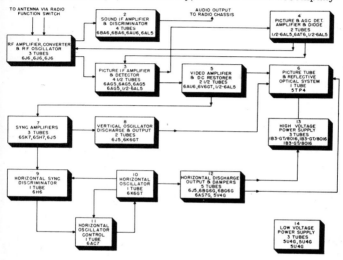

Figure 52. Block diagram of Model 648 PTK.

ing sound i-f frequency. The second trap (T104 secondary) is tuned to the adjacent channel sound frequency. The third trap (T105 secondary) is tuned to the adjacent channel picture carrier frequency. The fourth trap (T106 secondary) is in the cathode circuit of the fourth picture i-f amplifier V111, and is tuned to the accompanying sound i-f carrier. The primary of T106, in series with C137, forms a series resonant circuit at the frequency to which L106 is tuned (23.4 Mc). This provides a low impedance in the cathode circuit at this frequency and the gain of the tube is high. However, at the resonant frequency of the secondary (21.25 Mc), a high impedance is reflected into the cathode circuit, reducing the gain of the tube. At 21.25 Mc, therefore, the response curve takes a decided dip.

The 6AL5 detector, V105B, is a conventional half-wave rectifier connected to produce a video signal of negative polarity.

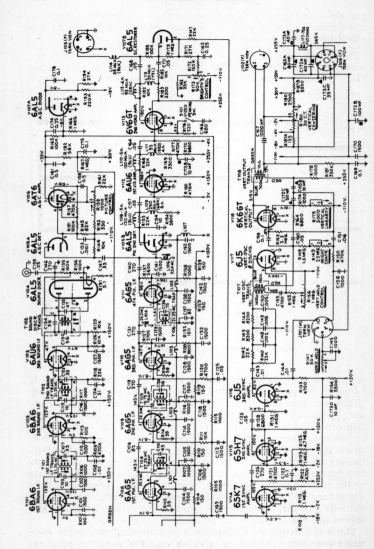

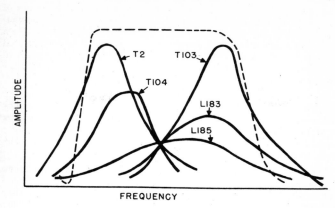

Figure 54. Relative gain and selectivity of each coil in staggered i-f amplifier. Resulting overall response curve is shown dotted in background.

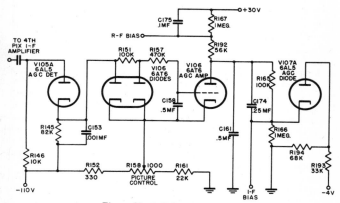

Figure 55. A.G.C. circuit.

7-45 A.G.C. Circuit. An automatic gain control circuit is employed in connection with the picture i-f system to hold the output from the i-fs substantially constant over a wide range of signal inputs.

In the a.g.c. system of the picture i-f amplifier (shown in Figure 55) a portion of the output from the fourth i-f amplifier is fed into V105A, the a.g.c. detector. Since the time constant of the diode load resistor and filter (R145 and C153) is somewhat greater than one horizontal line, the detector is essentially a peak reading voltmeter at sync frequency. The d-c voltage that appears on the cathode of V105A is therefore proportional to the peak strength of the received signal and is substantially independent of the picture content.

Such a system will also tend to read the peak of noise pulses. To prevent this, R151 and the diodes of V106 are used as a two-stage clipper or noise limiting network. For further protection against noise, the d-c output is fed through an integrating network (R157 and C158) which tends to minimize the effect of random noise.

The d-c output from the integrator is less than that required to control the gain, and since it increases in the positive direction with increase in signal strength, it is necessary to amplify and invert it. To accomplish this, the output from the integrator is d-c coupled to the grid of V106, the a.g.c. amplifier. V106 is operated with approximately minus 110 volts on its cathode, and with its plate at or slightly below ground potential. The voltage available at the plate is suitable for use as a control bias.

With a weak signal input, the bias on V106 (obtained across R152 and R158) is sufficient to cause the plate current of V106 to be nearly cut off. The plate of V108 is at approximately ground potential, no bias is applied to the r-f and i-f grids, and the receiver operates at maximum gain. When a strong signal is applied to the receiver, the d-c output from the a.g.c. detector opposes the fixed bias on V106 and causes more plate current to flow. As a consequence, the plate goes negative with respect to ground and this negative voltage is applied to the r-f and i-f grids, reducing their gain and maintaining constant output from the i-f system.

Since the grid control characteristic of pentode i-f amplifiers is different from that of the triode r-f amplifier in the tuner, different bias voltages are required and must be taken from different points in the system. The r-f bias is taken from the junction of R165 and R166.

In order to obtain the maximum signal-to-noise ratio from the receiver, it is desirable to allow the r-f amplifier to run at full gain on any signal which will not cause overloading of the first i-f stage. The circuit arrangement of Figure 55 including the a.g.c. diode, V107A, permits maximum use of r-f gain on weak signals and prevents overloading of the i-f amplifier on strong signals. With an input signal of 1000 microvolts (and the picture control set for normal contrast) the plate of V106 is at approximately -2 volts. Since the a.g.c. diode plate is placed at a -2.5 volt tap on the dividers R193 and R194, the diode does not conduct and the -2 volts on the V106 plate is applied to the i-f grids. With a signal of 10,000 microvolts, the a.g.c. amplifier plate is at approximately -5 volts. Under this condition, the a.g.c. diode conducts and due to the drop in R165, prevents the i-f bias from rising appreciably above -3 volts.

A manual gain control, R158, is also provided since it is necessary to vary the picture contrast because of variations in room lighting, transmitting technique, and to suit personal preference in picture balance. The control varies the i-f gain by varying the initial bias on the a.g.c. amplifier, which in turn varies the r-f and i-f bias.

The detected video signal is fed to two stages (V112 and V113) of video amplification (Figure 53). A noise saturation circuit is incorporated into the video amplifier. The first stage V112 is designed so that with a normal negative signal input level at its grid, the tube will be working over most of its operating range. Any large noise signal above the sync level will drive the grid to cutoff and the noise will be limited. In effect, the signal-to-noise ratio is improved and better synchronization results.

Since the video amplifier is an a-c amplifier, the d-c component of the video signal that represents the average illumination of the original signal will not be passed. The 6AL5 d-c restorer V107B reestablishes the d-c level and provides a bias on the picture tube grid that varies with the scene.

7-46 Optical System. The picture tube employed in this receiver is a 5TP4, five-inch projection tube, used with a Schmidt reflective system. The tube operates at approximately 27 kv and employs magnetic deflection and electrostatic focusing. The tube and deflection yoke are mounted in an optical barrel. This barrel also supports a spherical mirror at the bottom, and a corrector lens at the top. The image formed on the picture tube is projected onto a 45° mirror and then onto a translucent screen. The screen is composed of two lucite sheets, with a partial diffusing layer between them. The back sheet has tiny lenses molded into its rear surface. The front sheet has vertical ribs molded into its outer surface. This combination of lenses and ribs transmits five times more light than a ground glass.

7-47 Sweep Circuits. The signal from the d-c restorer is fed to a sync amplifier, V114 (Figure 53), which is a 6SK7 with a remote cutoff characteristic. The video signal at the grid of V114 is negative, so that any noise signals above sync which remain after the limiting action of the first video grid are further compressed when they drive the grid beyond the cutoff point. The output of this stage, which is positive in polarity, is fed to the grid of V115, another sync amplifier. The operating voltages applied to the grid and plate of this amplifier are such that the negative portion of the applied signal is cut off. Thus, the video and blanking pulses are removed and only the sync pulses appear at the plate.

The sync pulses are further amplified by V116. Since they are negative in polarity on the grid, they appear positive at the plate. This is the required polarity for triggering the sweep oscillators. The signal at the grid of V116 is sufficient to drive the tube beyond cutoff and the signal is again clipped. This final clipping removes all amplitude variations between sync pulses due to noise, hum, etc.

The vertical sync pulses are separated from the horizontal sync pulses by the intergrating network consisting of R142, R143, R144, C148, C149 and C150.

A single 6J5 triode, V117, with its associated components, forms a blocking oscillator and discharge circuit. The vertical sync pulse from the integrating network is applied to the grid of V117 and locks the oscillator to the vertical frequency. On the plate of V117, a sawtooth voltage appears due to the slow charging and rapid discharging of C160. A sharp negative pulse also occurs during the discharge period because of the peaking resistor R164 in series with C160. C160 charges through R148 and R149. Adjustment of the height control R149 varies the amplitude of the sawtooth voltage on the plate of V117 by controlling the rate at which C160 can charge. The voltage present on the plate of V117 is of the shape required to produce a sawtooth current in the vertical deflection coil. It is now necessary to amplify it in a tube capable of supplying a sufficient amount of power.

A 6K6 is connected as a triode for the output stage, V118. The vertical output transformer T108 matches the resistance of the vertical deflection coils to the plate impedance of the 6K6. R175 is provided as a vertical sweep linearity control. Since the grid-voltage, plate-current curve of V118 is not a straight line over its entire range, the effect of adjustments of R175 is to produce slight variations in the shape of the sawtooth by shifting the operating point of the tube to different points along the curve. Since the slope of the curve varies at these different points and thus varies the effective gain of the tube, it is apparent that adjustments of linearity affect the picture height, and that such adjustments must be accompanied by readjustments of the height control R149.

The horizontal sweep circuit in the RCA 648PTK is very similar to the flywheel synchronization type described in the Scott Model 13-A receiver. The horizontal sweep circuits are shown in Figure 56. The horizontal oscillator is an extremely stable Hartley oscillator operating at the scanning frequency of 15,750 cps. The primary of T301 (terminals A, B, and C) is the oscillator coil. The coil is closely coupled to the secondary winding (terminals D, E, and F) and thus feeds a sine wave voltage to V301. The sync discriminator V301 is a 6H6 dual diode which produces the d-c output voltage proportional to the phase displacement between the incoming sync pulses and the sine wave horizontal oscillator voltage.

V303 is the reactance tube which controls the oscillator frequency. A change in the d-c output of the sync discriminator produces a change in Gm of V303 which in turn changes the frequency of the oscillator. If the phase of the oscillator shifts with respect to the synchronizing pulse, the corresponding change in output from the sync discriminator causes the oscillator to be brought back into correct phase.

C304 and C306 form a voltage divider to attenuate rapid changes in output from the sync discriminator, such as are produced by the vertical sync pulses or a burst of noise.

The oscillation in V302 takes place between the screen-grid and cathode. Since the peak-to-peak voltage on its grid is as high as 100 volts, overloading takes place and a square wave voltage is produced in the plate circuit. This wave is differentiated by C312 and R314. The pulse so obtained is applied to the grid of the discharge tube V304. The discharge tube is normally cut off during the period that the condenser C318 is charging. Then the pulse from V302 overcomes the cutoff bias and drives the tube into heavy momentary conduction. During this period, C318 charges rapidly. Then, when V304 again becomes non-conducting, the plate voltage rises slowly, and approximately linearly, as C318 charges through R316 and C315.

The output of the discharge circuit is applied to two power amplifier tubes, V305 and V306, connected in parallel. Two such tubes are required to provide sufficient horizontal scanning current in the deflection coil because of the high operating voltage of the 5TP4 projection tube. With 27 kv on the tube, it is more difficult to deflect the electron beam. The horizontal deflection current needed is slightly greater than the capabilities

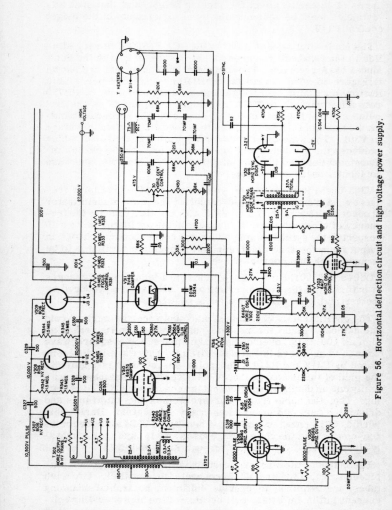

Figure 56. Horizontal deflection circuit and high voltage power supply.

of a single 6BG6 tube. When two horizontal output tubes are employed as in the 648PTK, proper damping cannot be obtained by a single damper tube due to the heavy damping current. V311, a 5V4G, provides damping action over the entire trace. V310, a dual triode, is employed to provide the extra damping action during the first portion of the trace when large oscillations occur. When the voltage on the plate of damper tube V310 swings positive during the start of the trace, the differentiating network (C331, R350, and R351) changes this rising voltage to a pulse and feeds it to the grid. This positive pulse lowers the plate resistance of the triodes and permits heavy damping current to flow. Then, due to the short time constant of the grid network, the positive pulse decays and the bias due to the grid rectification of the pulses cuts the triode damper off, leaving the 5V4G to provide the damping for the remainder of the trace.

The 6BG6 plate voltage is supplied through the 5V4G which is conducting over the major portion of the trace. Capacitor C324A is charged during this period and this charge is sufficient to supply the 6BG6 plates when the 5V4G is not conducting. Ordinarily the output amplifier stage is run at 475 volts from the low voltage supply. The charge from capacitor C324A, however, is added to the d-c power supply voltage. Thus, the output amplifiers are operated at a higher voltage than is obtainable from the receiver power supply and produces an increase in the circuit efficiency by salvaging energy that would otherwise have been wasted.

The output tubes are coupled to the deflection coil through T302. L302 is provided to vary the output and hence the picture width by shunting a portion of the T302 secondary winding. The horizontal size is also affected by R340 which varies the amount of negative pulse added to the sawtooth voltage that is applied to the grid of the output tubes. The negative pulse is added to the sawtooth by feeding back a portion of the pulse from the secondary of the output transformer. The size of this pulse, which is controlled by R340, affects the point at which the output tubes conduct. This in turn determines the amount of deflection current fed to the yoke, and hence the horizontal size. Clockwise rotation of the control increases the picture width, crowds the right side of the picture, and stretches the left side.

The horizontal linearity control R351 changes the time constant of the differentiation network in the 6AS7G (V310) grid circuit and determines the portion of the trace over which this tube conducts, thus controlling linearity on the left side of the picture. Counterclockwise rotation of the control causes the left side of the picture to stretch. R340 and R351 are adjusted together to set the horizontal size and linearity.

7-48 Low Voltage Power Supply. The low voltage power supply chassis contains two separate power supplies. One supply provides the filament and plate voltages for the r-f/i-f chassis, and the other supply provides for voltages for the horizontal de-

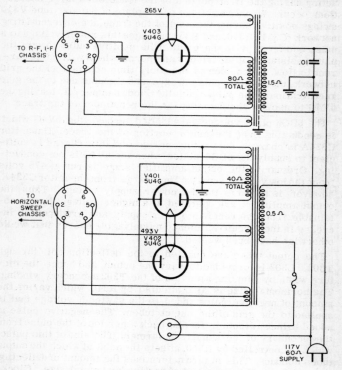

Figure 57. Low voltage power supply.

flection circuits. This latter supply employs an interlock cable to the horizontal deflection chassis and a fuse in the power transformer primary to protect the supply in case of short circuits in the horizontal deflection chassis. The supplies employ conventional full wave rectifier circuits. A single 5U4G, V403 (Figure 57), is adequate to furnish the current for the r-f/i-f chassis. L117, C173A, C166A, and C172A (Figure 53) provide filtering of the B+ supply. The center of the transformer secondary is grounded through a bleeder consisting of R188A, R187A, R180. Negative voltage is obtained across this bleeder for the positioning circuits and bias voltages on the r-f/i-f chassis.

7-49 High Voltage Power Supply. The high voltage power supply which feeds the intensifier of the projection tube is of the kickback type. It is located on the horizontal deflection chassis, and its circuit is shown in Figure 56. When the 6BG6 plate currents are cut off during the flyback time of the horizontal sawtooth voltage, a positive pulse appears on the T302 primary due to the collapsing field in the deflection coil. This pulse of voltage is stepped up by the autotransformer action of T302 and is applied to the plate of the high voltage rectifiers. Three type 8016 tubes are employed in a voltage trippler circuit which produces approximately 27 kv d-c for operation of the projection tube. The pulses are first rectified by V307 and charge capacitor C326 to near peak voltage. Since the cathode of V307 is connected to the plate of V308 by resistors R342 and R343, capacitor C327 will charge to the same voltage as C326. The charge on C327 is thus added to the incoming pulse, and V308 rectifies the sum of these voltages, thus charging C328 to double the pulse voltage. The cathode of V308 is connected to the plate of V309 through R344 and R345, charging C329 to the same voltage as C328. The charge on C329 is added to the incoming pulse. V309 rectifies the incoming pulse and the d-c charge on C329 to charge C330 to three times the pulse voltage. The initial pulse voltage is about 9 kv, so that approximately 27 kv are obtained at the output of the voltage trippler.

Since the frequency of the supply voltage is high (15,750 cps), relatively little filter capacity is necessary. C330, a 500-mmf capacitor, and the capacitance of the lead to the projection tube are all that are required. A bleeder consisting of R329 through R333 is connected across the first rectifier stage to provide the 4 - 5 kv for the focus electrode of the electrostatically focused 5TP4.

7-50 Audio Circuits. A portion of the energy absorbed by the trap T2 is fed to the first sound i-f amplifier V101, shown in Figure 53. Three stages of amplification V101, V102, and V103 are used to provide adequate sensitivity. A conventional discriminator, V104, is used to demodulate the signal. The discriminator band width is approximately 350 kc between peaks. This wide frequency response allows for some drift of the oscillator in the r-f tuner, for normally only a 50 kc pass band is

needed for the television sound. The output from the discriminator is fed into the radio audio system and is controlled by
the radio volume and tone control.

The a-m/f-m receiver in the 648PTK is comprised of an eight
tube a-m/f-m tuner unit and a four tube audio amplifier and
power supply. The tuner unit employs an r-f amplifier on all
bands. One 455 kc i-f stage and a conventional diode detector
are employed on a-m. On the f-m band, three 10.7 Mc i-f stages
and a ratio detector are employed. These circuits are entirely
independent of the video sections of the receiver.

INSTALLING

TELEVISION RECEIVERS

8-1 In the past it has been the practice of the vendor of radios to sell a receiver to his customer and more or less forget that it existed. Not so with television. A television receiver requires careful installation, or else, results which will satisfy the customer cannot be obtained. Because of this, many television receivers are being sold on the condition that they can be installed in the customer's home so as to operate properly. It is apparent that installation is an important job, vital to the success of the industry.

The directional characteristics of the ultra-high-frequency radio waves used for television broadcasting introduce a multiplicity of problems in their reception. At these frequencies, television signals must travel along a "line of sight" from the transmitter to the receiver. They do not follow the curvature of the earth, as is the case with lower radio frequencies, and are limited for high quality reception to the distance from the transmitter to the horizon - about 50 miles.

Television signals act like light waves, being readily reflected by buildings, hills, airplanes, bridges, and other massive objects. These obstacles are particularly troublesome in large cities. In these areas, it is not unlikely that the receiving antenna will pick up the signal coming directly from the transmitter as well as several signals reflected from various buildings and surfaces that are located at appreciably different distances. These reflections arrive at the antenna at different times and with varying intensity, depending upon the attenuation they encounter in their transmission path. The reflected signal image may be white or black, according to its polarity, and often is as intense as the direct signal. Sometimes extremely weak reflections that are barely noticeable will cause the picture to appear blurred.

Another consideration in the reception of ultra-high frequencies is the need for tuning the antenna to the resonant frequency of a specific transmitting station. With the present frequency allocations, however, it is possible to have as many as seven stations operating in one area. These stations may operate in both the low and high frequency bands, making it difficult to receive all stations with simple dipole antennas. Often the stations are located in different directions with respect to the receiving antenna. It becomes a difficult problem then to tune an antenna to one station, at the same time orienting it so as to avoid reflected signals, and then expect this same antenna to be suitable for receiving the other stations.

These and many other problems make the installation of the television receiver and its antenna system a complex job, requiring the skill of a trained technician. In a majority of cases, satisfactory results can be obtained by following a few straightforward procedures. When these procedures fail, a considerable amount of skill and judgment must be exercised to overcome the difficulties encountered.

8-2 Antenna Location. Of considerable importance in installation work is the problem of locating the receiving antenna. With private homes, the technician is usually permitted to use the most convenient point on the roof for the antenna, but this advantage may be offset by the fact that the private dwelling is low and not in "line of sight" with the transmitter. Although apartment houses are higher than private homes, they present even greater problems. Their height sometimes permits the reception of a direct signal, but where separate antennas are permitted by the landlord for each tenant's receiver, there is usually trouble encountered with radiation from one antenna to the next. In many cases, antennas are not permitted on the apartment house roof. This situation forces the customer to do without a receiver, unless the technician can install a suitable indoor antenna inside the apartment. Another solution that ap-

pears even more promising is the installation by the landlord
of a multiple antenna system capable of feeding each apartment.

8-3 Choice of Antenna. Complex as the antenna problem may
be in view of the many factors that influence good reception at
ultra-high frequencies, the greatest difficulties still remain to
be encountered as television activity expands. A study of the

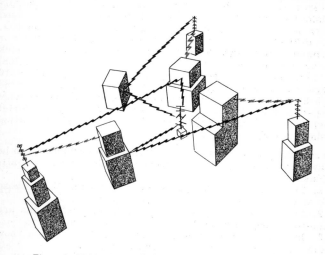

Figure 1. Multipath reflections which commonly occur in large,
metropolitan centers.

growth of television in the New York City area brings out several important facts that hold true for large cities in the rest
of the country. Seven stations are assigned to this area, all of
which are situated relatively close together in the borough of
Manhattan and nearby New Jersey. A single antenna, located in
the suburbs of the city and properly oriented for one station,
ordinarily provides satisfactory reception for the other stations,
because at distances of ten or more miles the signals arrive
from about the same direction.

Such is not the case closer to and inside the city. The more
common condition is that no direct path exists from any station
to the antenna because of the many intervening high buildings.
A typical example is shown in Figure 1. Several very directional

antennas must be employed to pick up the best multi-path reflections as well as direct signals. It is not uncommon to find as many as two or three antennas for one installation in the New York City area.

In large cities a second factor is important, which often makes it necessary to use more than one antenna. If multi-path reflections exist for certain stations, the antenna must be made as directive as possible for particular stations. Should the television stations in the area be operating on the low and high band channels and not be located in the path of the directive antenna, it is difficult for a single antenna to operate satisfactorily. For example, a dipole which is cut to a compromise length to pick up the stations operating in the low band (54 to 88 megacycles) is too far off tune to receive the high band stations (174 to 216 megacycles). Another antenna is generally needed to cover the high band. The effects of multi-path reflections and the wide ranges over which television stations operate make it difficult to obtain good reception on all stations in crowded areas, using a single antenna.

From these considerations, the following conclusions can be drawn and recommendations made regarding antenna installations:

1. In very few installations will one antenna suffice if there are stations operating on the low and high bands.

2. In metropolitan areas where multi-path reflections are numerous, several directive antennas may be necessary.

3. In making a new installation, the technician should know the number of stations that have been allocated to the area, their operating frequencies, and possible locations. If at all possible, the customer should be sold the antenna which bests suits the needs of the area. If more than one antenna is likely to be needed when new stations go on the air at a later date, the customer should be duly advised. He may then wish to invest in a better installation to cover all eventualities.

4. A list of all stations assigned by the Federal Communications Commission is presented in the Data Section to enable the technician to determine exactly which stations will be operating in each area of the country.

The many factors contributing to good reception of television signals result in a wide variety of installations. The trial and error method of installation is therefore inevitable. However, certain procedures have been set down in this section for simple, routine installations. By noting the complex and unusual problems that are likely to be encountered, technicians will develop methods which will result in fewer trials. With an understanding of the solutions of typical installation problems, the technician should be able to obtain good reception, even under extremely adverse conditions.

8-4 The Installation and Service Contract. The purchase of a television receiver is usually contingent upon the technician's ability to install an antenna system which will provide satisfactory reception. The majority of complaints of reception difficulties can be traced to signal losses and distortions in the antenna system. It is apparent, then, that the sale of even the highest quality receivers depends upon the performance of the antenna and the manner in which it is installed.

It is common practice, when making television receiver installations, to give the customer a guaranty that his installation and receiver will perform satisfactorily for a period of one year. For this guaranty a charge is paid by the purchaser to cover a standard installation. At the time of sale, the customer is asked to sign a contract covering the terms of installation and servicing. Each point in the agreement should be carefully explained so that, if it is necessary to make charges for a non-standard installation, no ill feeling is likely to arise which might cause the loss of the sale. Because it is important that a contract be carefully worded so as to be legal and binding, a typical Installation and Service Contract is presented in the Data Section. Service organizations may wish to use this contract as a pattern for their own contracts.

8-5 The Pre-Installation Survey. The experience of the technician with conditions in his particular area will determine the manner in which he conducts his installation procedures. If experience proves that good reception is obtainable in a certain area, he may prefer to make installations without making an advance survey of each location. On the other hand, where there is doubt as to the possibility of obtaining good reception, it is often desirable to make a preliminary survey of the location. Such a survey eliminates a great deal of expense, trouble, and lost time, if conditions at the installation prove to be non-standard.

Contour maps of surrounding terrain are helpful in familiarizing oneself with receiving conditions in an area. These maps often forewarn the installation crew of obvious obstructions, which can be dealt with by the use of high masts or towers. Signal maps are also of considerable aid in anticipating the quality of signal that can be expected at the receiver location. This information permits the installation crew to come prepared with one or more suitable antennas. Contour and signal strength maps can generally be obtained from the television stations in the area. The signal strength map shows the signal level which can be expected in the areas surrounding the transmitter. It is necessary to study the signal strength map for each transmitter in order to predict whether or not the receiver will be able to pick up all the stations in the area.

Pre-installation surveys can be made by one man. His purpose is to gather sufficient information to enable the installation crew to come fully prepared for the conditions which exist at the receiver location. Outlined below are several procedures which should be carried out during the preliminary survey, or at the time the installation is made.

8-6 Contacting of Superintendent. In apartment house dwellings, it is advisable to first contact the superintendent and establish his good will. He should be informed of the type of antenna that is contemplated, its location, where the antenna lead-in is to be run, how it is to be brought into the building, and the time and day when the permanent installation will be made, so that he can arrange to provide access to the roof and other parts of the building. The superintendent can usually advise as to the best means of conveying the receiver to the apartment if the set is large and heavy. The technician should impress the superintendent with his willingness to cooperate and avoid undue disturbances to the other tenants. He should also impress him by making a neat installation. Such courtesies will be appreciated and reciprocated, particularly if other installations have to be made in the same building at a later date.

8-7 Determining Height of Building. A glance at the building will tell the technician how many stories there are from the customer's floor to the roof. An equivalent estimate of this distance in feet should be noted for reference later when computing the length of antenna lead-in required for the installation.

8-8 Type of Power. The type of power available is important since most present receivers are designed for use with 110-volt, 60-cycle alternating current. In some areas, only direct current is available. If the customer is willing to meet the added expense involved, a rotary converter, properly rated for the receiver, can be installed. In areas where 25-cycle or 50-cycle power is used, a frequency converter must also be provided. Finally, installations may be encountered where 220 volts, alternating current is the only power available. In this case a suitably rated step-down transformer is required.

8-9 Location of other Sets and Antennas. Often the best antenna location is already occupied, or there are several antennas on the roof. When the latter condition exists, trouble from cross radiation between receivers is likely. A careful examination of all possible antenna locations should be made in an effort to find one which will give the greatest possible assurance of freedom from interference effects.

Even after an installation has been made and satisfactory reception is obtained, there is no assurance that another antenna,

Figure 2. Cross-radiation is often caused by locating receivers back to back.

installed nearby at a later date, will not cause disturbances that previously did not exist. When the technician encounters a roof on which several antennas are likely to be installed at a later time, he should forewarn the customer of the possibility of future trouble. Cross radiation usually necessitates a relocation of the antenna and additional expense for the customer.

Radiation troubles arise not only because of antenna location, but also because of close proximity of receivers. Two receivers, located in different rooms of an apartment building, but situated back to back on opposite sides of the same wall, may suffer in performance because their oscillators beat with each other. This situation is illustrated in Figure 2. During the pre-installation survey, or at the time a receiver is installed, the technician should attempt to learn the locations of all television and f-m receivers in the building. The existence of other receivers may mean that the customer must locate his receiver in a part of the room other than that which he prefers, in order to avoid oscillator interference.

8-10 Interference. Inquiry should be made as to the existence of diathermy machines or amateur radio apparatus in the nearby vicinity. Little can be done about diathermy interference, except to get the owner of the apparatus to shield it. The customer should be informed of the characteristic effect of diathermy on the television picture, so that he will not complain to the service organization that the receiver is operating improperly. Amateur radio operators sometimes unintentionally and unknowingly interfere with television reception. Such interference is usually due, in part, to the present state of television receiver design. If informed of the fact that he is causing interference, the amateur will almost invariably be willing to cooperate in eliminating the source of the interference. Amateur interference is a temporary problem; new techniques are rapidly being evolved which will make it a rare occurrence. Until such time, a spirit of cooperation among all parties involved usually results in mutual satisfaction. Interference to television reception by other services, such as short wave broadcasting, has been encountered on numerous occasions.

The technician should always note the location of such things as elevator housings, motors, etc., and when possible avoid mounting an antenna or running a transmission line near them.

8-11 Locating the Television Receiver. Generally, the customer's choice decides the location of the television receiver. The location of the receiver is important if it is to be fully enjoyed. For this reason, the factors affecting the operation of the set should be made known to its user. Since programs are transmitted during the daylight hours as well as in the evenings, the receiver should be located in a room that can readily be darkened with curtains or shades. The amount of light which can be tolerated in the room depends upon the receiver design. Projection screens appear best in almost total darkness, because the contrast of the image suffers considerably if direct light falls upon the screen. Pictures on direct view tubes appear satisfactory in daylight if no intense light is reflected from the tube face. The most satisfactory arrangement is to have the set so located with respect to the observers that light from windows or lamps is at right angles to the line of vision.

As much light as can be permitted is desirable because it minimizes eye strain, which can result from long periods of watching the screen. For this reason, the room should not be left in total darkness, even at night. A 60-watt bulb, covered with a shade and located as far as possible from the receiver, will provide sufficient ambient light in the average room and at the same time will not affect the screen.

The receiver should be located in the room so that as many people as possible may view the screen without movement of furniture. In locating the receiver, the accessibility of adjustments and provision for ventilation should be kept in mind.

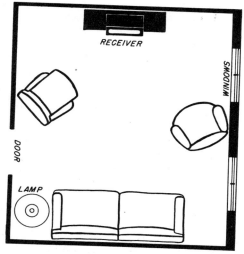

Figure 3. Room arrangement for comfortable viewing.

Closets and wall recesses are poor places for a receiver. Although it is desirable to have the receiver as close as possible to an a-c power outlet, this factor is not too important if interference signals can be avoided and better viewing locations found by moving it away from the outlet. The power cord from the receiver may easily be lengthened or an extra base plug may be installed by an electrician. Figure 3 shows a typical room arrangement that permits good screen visibility.

8-12 Lead-in Required in House. Once the location of the set has been determined inside the dwelling, the technician can estimate the number of feet of lead-in that will be required from the receiver to the point at which the lead-in comes into the building. Antenna leads are generally not permitted on the front of apartment buildings. If the receiver is in a room facing the front of the building, it is necessary to run the lead through the apartment to a side of the building where the transmission line can be run up to the roof. This usually requires drilling through walls between rooms. The exact path of the lead-in inside the building should be determined and the required number of feet estimated. An additional length of cable (about 20 feet) should be added to the estimated length to permit moving the receiver to another part of the room at a later date.

8-13 Surveying the Roof. In addition to the positions of other antennas on the roof, several other factors will influence the choice of antenna location. An attempt should be made to find a location which provides direct signal paths to all stations. If all transmitters cannot be sighted directly, attempt to pick out surrounding buildings or objects that are likely to provide good reflecting surfaces. From the surrounding terrain and pattern of buildings, it should be determined whether or not a combination of direct and reflecting signals can be expected to provide satisfactory reception from all stations. Previous study, at the shop, of contour and field strength maps will prove helpful to the technician in solving signal path problems. From this information and the roof analysis, the technician conducting the pre-installation survey can advise both the customer and the shop whether one or more antennas will be necessary to obtain satisfactory reception from all stations.

Before finally setting the tentative location of the antenna, make certain that the position is as far away as possible from conducting surfaces on the roof and elevator housings which contain drive motors. The number of feet of lead-in required to reach the side of the building should be noted and about 20 additional feet allowed for movement of the antenna, if the necessity arises, when making the installation. The total number of feet of lead-in from the antenna to the receiver can be determined from this figure and previously noted estimates, which include:

1. Length of lead inside the building.
2. Length of lead to roof.
3. Length of lead from roof edge to antenna.

The lead should be provided in one piece to avoid splicing and possible mismatch in the line.

8-14 Counselling the Customer. The preliminary survey before the actual installation provides the installation crew with all necessary information regarding conditions at the location. The technician can thus advise the customer of deviations from the clauses in the Installation and Service Contract, when required, and settle points of difference. He can point out conditions which may hamper perfect reception of all stations and which cannot be overcome. By thus counselling the customer in advance of the permanent installation, and by getting his approval on compromise performance, the technician may avoid later dissatisfaction and a request for removal of the receiver and installation. On occasions he may have to advise that the set cannot be expected to operate well in the particular area, and permit the customer to cancel his order for the receiver.

8-15 The Portable Television Receiver or Field Strength Meter. The possibility of obtaining good reception in certain areas, particularly those lying on the fringes of station coverage, is at times extremely doubtful. Under such conditions, it is good practice to make a temporary or experimental installation to determine the quality of the signal. For this purpose a portable television receiver is recommended. Some installation organizations utilize elaborately equipped trucks carrying a receiver and antenna mast that is capable of being raised to installation heights. The mast is raised to the expected height and the quality of reception checked on the receiver. In this way, the customer can be advised as to the quality of reception that can be expected from a permanent installation. Smaller service organizations will need the following equipment to check signal strength.

1. A portable receiver, mounted in a cabinet equipped with carrying handle. No special noise limiting circuits should be incorporated which would minimize the effects of noisy devices in the area and cause them to go unnoticed. Some television receivers have "automatic frequency control" synchronization circuits which are more immune to noise than conventional "triggered" sync circuits. The portable test receiver should be equipped with triggered sync, which shows more readily the effects of noise on the stability of synchronization. Several portable receivers suitable for this purpose are being marketed. If the receiver used has a.f.c. sync, it should be suitably modified.

2. A portable antenna kit which can be easily assembled into several simple, directive arrays.

3. Lengths of coaxial cable and/or parallel lead-in equipped with connectors.

4. Lengths of a-c power cords, equipped with plugs.

5. A portable two-way telephone system.

The portable receiver should be placed in the location where the customer's receiver is to be, and a temporary transmission line dropped to it from the roof. One observer should watch the receiver while another moves the antenna about the roof to locate the position which provides an optimum signal from each station. The correct dipole should be used for each station. The observer on the roof should record the position and direction in which each dipole is faced for best reception. After the antenna location and position is determined for each station, an attempt should be made to find a point on the roof at which the antenna can be faced for all stations. If such a compromise po-

Figure 4. Field strength meter. (courtesy Transvision)

sition cannot be found, the antenna should be oriented for receiving the majority of stations. It should then be determined whether or not a second antenna will provide good reception of the rest of the stations. If not, additional antennas will be required. From this data, the roof observer can determine how many and what type of antennas will be required to receive all stations.

It is sometimes simpler to use a field strength meter instead of a portable receiver to check the signal strength at the customer's location. Although a field strength meter does not actually show the quality of picture that can be expected, it does indicate the signal level. If this signal level is above the minimum recommended for the receiver, then good reception can probably be obtained with a permanent installation. A field strength meter is illustrated in Figure 4. This unit is provided with a switching dial for all television channels. The antenna is connected to the meter with a length of transmission line. The signal level for each station may be obtained by orienting the antenna and switching the meter to the desired channel. By noticing the direction of the dipole for each station, the observer can predict whether or not a broad-band antenna, faced in a compromise direction will suffice for all stations.

8-16 Pre-Installation Checking of the Receiver. Before the television receiver is taken to the installation, it should be given a thorough performance check in the shop. The following characteristics of the picture should be observed and controls adjusted.

1. Band switch - Tune in each station in the area.
2. Contrast Control - Sufficient gain should be available for good picture contrast.
3. Brightness control - Proper brightness should be obtained with normal picture contrast.
4. Focus control.
5. Sound volume control.
6. Horizontal hold control.
7. Vertical hold control.
8. Horizontal centering control.
9. Vertical centering control.
10. Horizontal linearity control.
11. Vertical linearity control.
12. Horizontal size control.
13. Vertical size control.

These controls are mounted on the front and back of the receiver. All controls should be working properly and a good quality picture should be obtained before the receiver is made ready for shipment. This shop check will often avoid the necessity of returning a defective receiver to the shop.

INSTALLATION EQUIPMENT

8-17 Most service and installation crews carry a kit of equipment that has been built up through experience in making many installation and service calls. Such apparatus is outlined below. To this, of course, is added any equipment called for in the findings of the pre-installation survey.

8-18 Truck or Trailer. All installation equipment and the television receiver may be carried in a truck, or a trailer attached to a car. Some service organizations have elaborately equipped trucks which can handle service work right at the installation. A service bench is set up inside the truck, and power for the receiver and test equipment is obtained from an inverter which operates off the battery. To handle large console receivers, the truck should be equipped with a hoist or pulley system to lift the receiver on and off the truck floor.

8-19 Ladder. An extension ladder, equipped with roof hooks, is needed for installing antennas on most private dwellings. The ladder should be capable of being extended to about 50 feet.

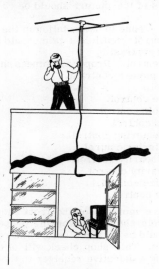

Figure 5. Sound-powered phones connected through transmission line help in locating antenna.

Wood, lightweight aluminum, or magnesium ladders may be used. Caution must be exercised when using metal ladders, for they are conductors of electricity. When setting up a metal ladder, no part of it should be permitted to touch an electric power line. The ladder can be conveniently carried if the truck is equipped with a roof carrier or brackets for side mounting.

8-20 Interphone System. Two men are needed to conveniently install the antenna. One observes the picture on the receiver screen, while the other rotates and orients the antenna. To maintain contact between the two men, some type of interphone system is needed. The most convenient phone communication is obtained with sound-powered phones. This type is advantageous because batteries or other power are not required. Each technician simply hooks his phones across the antenna transmission line. The operator on the roof connects his phones across the antenna terminals, while the observer at the receiver hooks his phones across the lead-in coming into the receiver.

Figure 6. Sound-powered handset. (courtesy Wheeler Insulated Wire)

See Figure 5. The audio signals produced in the line by voice modulation do not interfere with the television signal when the transmission line is used with sound-powered phones. This Figure 6 shows a handset of the sound-powered type which may be used for communicating over distances up to several miles. Many technicians prefer a headset to the hand type phone. Headphones and chest microphones leave both hands free for work on the antenna or receiver.

When phones are used which require power from a battery, a separate telephone line must be strung between the observers on the roof and at the receiver. A shematic diagram for hooking up this type of phone system is shown in Figure 7.

8-21 **Small Tools and Equipment.** In addition to the equipment just described, the following additional tools and equipment are necessary:

1. Drills - A quarter-inch electric-drill (high speed) and hand brace is required for boring holes into walls and window sills, through which the transmission line is run. A half-inch slow speed drill is desirable for drilling into masonry. If such

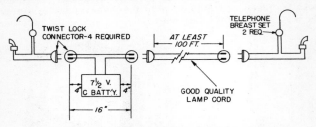

Figure 7. Battery-operated phone system.

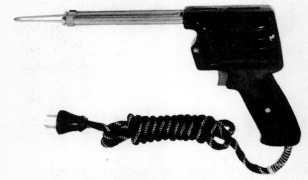

Figure 8.. Soldering gun (courtesy Weller Mfg.)

a drill is not available, star drills may be used.

2. 18-inch Bit - This length bit is required to bore through the usual thickness of walls. Its diameter should be slightly larger than that of the transmission line.

3. Soldering Iron - The most desirable type is that which heats up quickly when triggered. See Figure 8. Such an iron saves considerable time, both when heating and when the job has been completed. If an ordinary iron is used, some means of carrying it in the tool kit, while hot, should be provided.

4. Alcohol Torch - When soldering on a roof or other open places where no power is available, an alcohol torch is required.

5. Rosin Core Solder.

6. Hammer and Masonry Drilling Tool - It is often necessary to drill into a brick chimney or the wall of a building to mount the antenna or the standoff insulators which hold the transmission line. A hammer and several masonry drills are useful adjuncts to the kit for this purpose. A rawl tool for starting

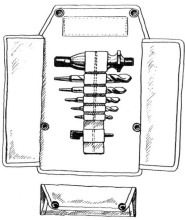

Figure 9. Masonry drill kit.

holes in concrete or brick is useful. Masonry drilling bits are shown in Figure 9.

7. Expansion Shields and Toggle Bolts - These are recommended wherever objects are fastened to brick.

8. Staples - For tacking the transmission line along molding in the interior of the building.

9. Insulators - To support the transmission line that is run down the side of a building, insulators are spaced about every twelve feet. They hold the line and prevent "whipping". Several types of insulators are shown in Figure 10.

10. Transmission Line - For receivers with 72-ohm input impedance, coaxial cable is normally used. Type RG/59U is recommended. Parallel-line is required for receivers with balanced, 300-ohm inputs. If a large amount of installation work is to be done, spools of the various types of transmission lines, supported on yoke trunnions, may be carried in the truck.

11. Multitest Meter - A combination voltmeter, ammeter, and ohmmeter should be carried on the truck. This meter is useful for checking the continuity of the transmission line, measuring line voltages, and for troubleshooting a defective receiver.

12. Small Tools - The following small tools should be carried in the tool box for routine installations and service calls:

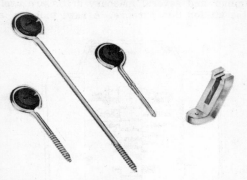

Figure 10. Stand-off insulators. (courtesy Amphenol)

Pliers (long nose, side cutting, diagonal, and slip-joint)	Screw drivers (small medium, large, and off-set)
Hack-saw	Claw hammer
6-inch adjustable end wrench	Center punch
Half-inch cold chisel	Files (round, half round, bastard)
Socket wrenches (5/16-inch and one quarter-inch)	Electrician's knife
Half-inch wood chisel	Emery cloth (assorted)
Friction and rubber tape	Flashlight

13. Antenna Kit - This should consist of an antenna, reflectors which may be needed, and the antenna mast. If an extension mast is called for, this should be included.

14. Mounting Brackets - Several types of mounting brackets for supporting the antenna should be carried in the truck. If a high mast is used which cannot be fully supported by a mounting bracket alone, guy wires should be included in the kit.

INSTALLING THE RECEIVER AND ANTENNA

8-22 Transporting the Receiver. When the receiver has been checked and all accessory apparatus for the installation assembled, the installation crew is ready to transport the equipment to the place where it is to be installed. Table models and small consoles can be handled by two men and conveyed on a dolly to and from the truck and into the building. A very large receiver imposes all the problems of moving a good-sized piano. The installation crew may wish to move such a set, or else call in professional movers for the job. In buildings without elevators, it may be necessary to erect a hoist on the roof to lift a receiver of large size. If elevators are available, three men can usually handle a large console receiver on a dolly.

The receiver should be brought to the building and placed in its approximate location, but not against the wall. Sufficient room should be left for adjustment of controls on the back of the receiver, after the antenna is permanently installed.

With the television receiver tentatively located in the room, the installation crew should proceed to the job of erecting the antenna and laying the transmission line. In this discussion consideration will be given first to the installation procedure for locations where simple antennas (single and double dipoles, and their variations) may be used successfully. Later in this section, complex installations, which require deviation from regular procedures, will be discussed.

8-23 Assembling the Antenna Kit - Instructions for assembling the antenna are provided by the manufacturer. Assembling the antenna can absorb a great deal of valuable time if the antenna is not properly designed. For this reason, an organization which installs television receivers continuously should choose antennas which have been designed so that they may be assembled in a reasonable period of time.

If the elements of the antenna can be adjusted for the frequency range of the operating stations, they should be set for one quarter the wavelength of the mid-frequency in the range. It may be necessary later to readjust the elements to favor a weak station.

If it is expected that parasitic elements will be required to obtain good reception, these rods should be attached to the antenna. After the antenna array is assembled on the supporting mast, the transmission line should be attached to it.

8-24 Attaching the Transmission Line - There are several methods for finishing up the end of the transmission line and attaching it to the antenna terminals. Three methods are sug-

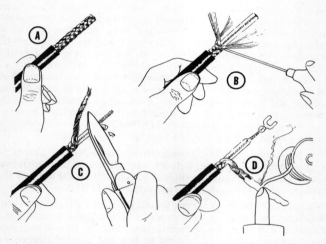

Figure 11. Step-by-step method of preparing coaxial cable by unbraiding and tinning braid. A, cut back rubber insulation. B, score braid. C, twist scored braid and cut back insulation to expose center conductor. D, tin braid and add lug.

gested for coaxial cable, which is more difficult to prepare than parallel-line.

The simplest method for preparing coaxial cable is to cut back the rubber insulation around the braid as far as necessary. With a scriber or an icepick, the braid is then unweaved back to the insulation. The plastic insulation separating the center conductor and the braid is then cut back about one inch to expose the center conductor. The opened braid is tinned and forms the ground lead, as shown in Figure 11. Both the center conductor and ground lead can then be connected to the antenna binding posts with soldering lugs.

Another method of finishing off coaxial cable is shown in Figure 12. The rubber covering is cut back and the entire end of the cable quickly dipped into a lead pot. By scoring the tinned braid at the desired point with a knife, it may then be peeled off without the undesirable fraying which normally occurs. Connection may be made to the braid by wrapping two or three turns of a length of tinned solid wire around the braid and quickly soldering it to avoid melting the plastic dielectric.

Some technicians object to applying solder to the coaxial cable because it becomes brittle and snaps easily when whipped about

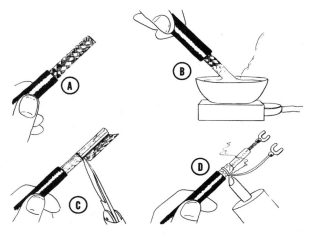

Figure 12. Finishing end of coaxial cable by tinning end of cable and scoring tinned braid. A, cut back rubber insulation. B, dip braid into solder. C, score braid and peel off. D, attach lead and lug to braid.

by the wind. A method of finishing off the end of the transmission line which eliminates the need for soldering is shown diagrammatically in Figure 13. Of the three methods, this one provides the strongest and most durable connection to the antenna.

The outer covering is first removed from about six inches of the cable. With a pointed tool, such as an icepick or a scriber, the braid is pushed apart three quarters of an inch from the place where the outer covering has been cut. After the hole in the braid has been made, the inner conductor and its insulation are pulled through the hole. The braid is then pulled until it stretches to maximum length. The insulation is removed from about one inch of the inner conductor and the cable is ready to be connected to the antenna or the receiver.

A parallel line is relatively simple to attach to the antenna. The polyethylene insulation is split in the middle and the ends are stripped with a knife. The open ends may be wrapped around the terminal studs and bolted, or they may be soldered to lugs which can be slipped over the studs, as shown in Figure 14.

8-25 Stringing the Transmission Line. Once the transmission line is connected to the antenna, it is desirable to run the line to the receiver. This will enable contact between the roof tech-

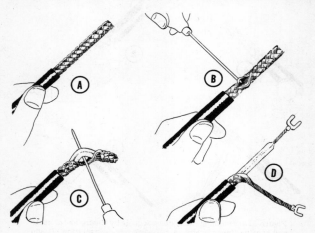

Figure 13. Finishing end of coaxial cable by making hole in braid. A, cut back rubber insulation. B, make hole in braid. C, pull center conductor through hole. D, strip insulation off center conductor and make hole at end of braid.

nician and the observer at the receiver if sound-powered phones are used. A sufficient length of cable should remain on the roof to permit probing for the best antenna location.

Some means of fastening the line to the antenna mast should be used. This is necessary because the point where the line is attached to the antenna will not stand much strain without breaking. Several devices are available for this purpose. The type shown in Figure 15 is one of the best.

Insulated porcelain eyelets, or similar supports, should be used to hold the line away from metal or brick buildings. If the house is made of wood, the line may be attached directly to it with insulated staples. The insulated supports should be spaced about every 12 feet along the line. The eyelets are installed first and the transmission line is dropped from the roof and threaded through successive eyelets.

Figure 14. Method for connecting twin-lead to antenna. (courtesy Taco)

Figure 15. Mast eyelet for holding twin lead. (courtesy JFD)

When the side of the building is constructed of brick or stone, the problem of screwing the eyelets into the wall is somewhat difficult to solve. Elsewhere in this section, several methods of drilling holes in masonry are described. After drilling, the holes are plugged with wood or expansion bolts, into which the insulated eyelets are screwed.

The installation crew should carry an assortment of insulators, clamps, expansion bolts, and screws of various sizes to meet the requirements of all installations.

When locating the insulating supports, care should be exercised that they are not too close to metal surfaces such as drain gutters, pipes, or metal roofs.

When all eyelets have been mounted, the transmission line is dropped through them to the point where it is to enter the building.

Ribbon-type transmission line may be run into the building under a window sill. It should be neatly tacked to the window frame so as to conform to the shape of the molding. To run

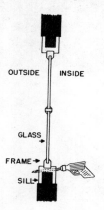

OUTSIDE   INSIDE

GLASS →

FRAME →

SILL →

Figure 16. Drilling window sill at an angle to make hole for lead-in

coaxial line into a building, a hole must be bored through the side wall. One means of making an entrance is to drill a one-quarter inch hole through a window sill. A high speed electric drill and 18-inch bit may be used to make this hole. The hole should be drilled from inside the house to the outside with the drill tip at a downward angle, as shown in Figure 16. Drilling the hole at an angle prevents water from running into the building. If a cable is used which fills the hole, no caulking is necessary. If the transmission line does not completely fill the hole, the hole should be closed with caulking compound after the line is fed through it. The cable is run through the interior of the building along the path that it will eventually be permanently tacked. Enough slack should be allowed when connecting it to the receiver to enable the set to be moved for cleaning or for changes in layout of the room.

8-26 Orienting the Antenna. With the antenna and receiver connected by transmission line, two-way communication may be established over the phone system and the task of orienting the antenna for optimum reception begun. The technician on the roof probes different areas and rotates the antenna, while the observer at the receiver watches the test pattern of one of the stations and indicates to the roof observer which of the antenna positions affords the best reception. The receiver is then tuned to another station and the procedure repeated. This routine is tried for each station until the best compromise orientation of the antenna is obtained.

If the signals from each station are about equal in strength, a compromise on the length of the antenna elements can be made by cutting them for a frequency midway between the upper and lower channels. If one of the stations is weaker, the dipole length should be adjusted to favor that station.

8-27 Multipath Signals. If there is trouble from multipath signals, the antenna must be oriented to minimize the ghost effects in the picture. If no position of the simple dipole will give results, then a double dipole should be tried. Finally, reflectors should be added if necessary.

Very often it is of aid, when orienting the antenna so as to minimize ghost reflections, to be able to locate the object which is causing the reflection. The air-path distance to the reflecting surface can be estimated by analyzing the ghost picture which appears on the receiver screen. Knowing this distance, it is possible to pick out the reflecting surface.

Since a reflected signal travels a greater distance than the direct signal, it arrives later than the direct signal and, therefore, causes a ghost. The approximate additional air-path distance traveled by the reflected signal may be computed from the following considerations:

1. The beam in the picture tube moves from the left to the right side of the screen in approximately 53 microseconds.

2. Since radio waves travel approximately 1000 feet in one microsecond in air, the length of one horizontal line represents approximately 53,000 feet, or about 10 miles of signal travel.

3. The approximate additional air-path distance traveled by the reflected signal is therefore

$$\frac{d}{W} \times 10 \text{ miles},$$

where W is the width in inches of the picture on the receiver screen (excluding blanking), and d is the distance in inches measured between the direct image and the ghost image. For example, if the picture is 10 inches wide, and the ghost is displaced one inch, the additional air-path distance traveled by the reflected signal is

$$\frac{1.0}{10.0} \times 10 = 1 \text{ mile (approx.)}$$

Ghosts which appear in the picture may also be caused by reflections on the transmission line and cannot be eliminated by orienting the antenna. To determine whether a ghost is due to a multipath reflection or an incorrectly terminated transmission line, first compute the air-path distance of the ghost as described above. Then compute the equivalent air-path reflection length of the transmission line. This value is

$$\frac{2L}{k} \text{ feet,}$$

where L is the total length of the transmission line in feet, and k is the velocity of propagation of the line (approximately 0.83 for twin-lead). As an example, if L is 100 feet and k is 0.83, the equivalent air-path distance of a reflection caused by an improperly matched transmission line would be

$$\frac{2 \times 100}{0.83} = 240 \text{ feet.}$$

If the ghost were due to line reflection, it would be displaced on the screen by a distance equivalent to 240 feet, or less than one twentieth of a mile. Compare this value with the computed additional air-path distance of the ghost to determine whether the ghost is due to line reflection or to an external reflection. An external reflection can be avoided by properly orienting the antenna. A line reflection can be eliminated by using an impedance matching transformer, described later in this section.

8-28 Mounting the Antenna. After the most suitable site has been located for the antenna, the antenna may be permanently mounted. The manner in which the antenna is mounted depends upon the shape of the object to which it is fastened, and the material of which the object is made. Described below are typical methods for supporting antennas. A number of good supporting brackets are available commercially, which simplify the problem. In some cases, the technician may have to construct a mounting to suit the needs of a particular installation.

8-29 Mounting on a Chimney. A chimney is a good support for an antenna. The antenna mast may be fastened to the chimney by several methods. Figure 17 shows an antenna pole fastened to a chimney with two pipe clamps. Two holes are drilled into the brick for each clamp. Expansion bolts are then inserted into the holes. Machine screws, which fit into the threaded inserts of the expansion bolts, hold the clamps and pole.

Another means of fastening the antenna pole to the chimney is shown in Figure 18. An adjustable bracket, which fits most chimneys, is used to hold the mast. The steel bands are placed over the chimney and are held in place by tightening the studs.

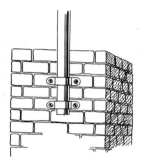

Figure 17. Antenna pole fastened to chimney with two pipe clamps.

Figure 18. Chimney mounting bracket. (courtesy South River Metal Products)

The antenna pole is slipped through the holes provided and the studs tightened. A good chimney bracket eliminates drilling into the brick, takes little time to mount, is sturdy and durable, and therefore preferred.

8-30 Mounting on a Wall. If the antenna is mounted on a wall, the same type of clamps used for mounting on a chimney may be used. Wood screws may be used to hold the clamps if the wall is made of wood. For mounting the clamps on a wall made

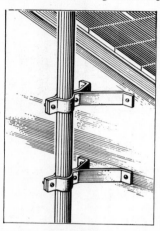

Figure 19. Wall mounting bracket. (courtesy Taco)

of masonry, expansion bolts and machine screws should be employed. Several brackets designed specifically for wall mounting are commercially available.

The brackets shown in Figure 19 hold the antenna mast away from the wall permitting it to pass such projections as roof eaves

8-31 Mounting on a Vent Pipe. Almost every roof has one or more vent pipes coming through it. Brackets are available which make it possible to mount an antenna on such a pipe, as shown in Figure 20. Before deciding on a vent pipe mounting, make sure that the vent pipe is secure and will provide a reliable support. As a rule, vent pipes are suitable mountings for light antennas with little wind resistance, such as a dipole or folded dipole. If the antenna is heavy, it is better to choose another more suitable way to support it.

8-32 Mounting on the Roof. As a general rule, an antenna should not be bolted directly to a roof. Drilling holes into the roof covering usually ruins its weatherproofing properties. Most roof coverings are guaranteed by the roofing companies

Figure 20. Bracket for mounting on vent pipe.

which lay them. Any damage to this covering caused by the installation of an antenna may be grounds for a legal suit against the service organization. It is therefore wise to avoid mounting an antenna directly to a roof, if possible. If it is absolutely necessary to rest the antenna on the covering of a flat roof, then the type of mounting shown in Figure 21 should be used. The antenna pole is set on a block of wood. A hole, the diameter of the pole, is counter-bored in the center to prevent slippage of the pole. Guy wires, attached to the antenna pole, are fastened to the surrounding roof parapet or other objects. Instead of counter-boring a hole, a pipe staple or a mast base, such as shown in Figure 22, may be fastened to the board to hold the antenna pole.

8-33. Window Sill Mounting. In rural areas, or where urban apartments are located in high buildings, it is often possible to obtain good reception by simply mounting the antenna outside a window. The mounting shown in Figure 23 is suitable for this purpose.

8-34 Universal Mounting Bracket. A variety of mounting

brackets are available on the market. Many of these brackets can be used for several types of mountings and are often referred to as "universal" mounting brackets. Some of the brackets currently being marketed are of ingenious design and will save the installation crew many hours of labor. If universal

Figure 21. Mounting antenna on a roof.

brackets are used, a careful choice should be made, since a few of the brackets available are rather flimsy and difficult to use.

Figure 24 illustrates two types of brackets and the manner in which they can be used. Both brackets can be used for wall or chimney mounting. The bracket on the bottom is particularly suitable for chimney or corner mounting.

A third type of mounting bracket, which can be used in several ways is shown in Figure 25. It is particularly suitable for mounting on a sloping roof. This type of mounting requires that screws be tapped into the shingles. If this is to be done, the permission of the owner should first be obtained. The screws should be covered with caulking compound to prevent water seepage. Usually, one can avoid mounting the antenna pole on a shingled roof by fastening it to the chimney or by mounting the bracket on the gable of the roof.

8-35 Antenna Towers. In weak signal areas it is sometimes impossible to obtain a usable signal unless a tower of considerable height is used. Increasing the height of the antenna makes

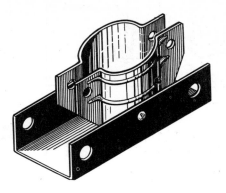

Figure 22. Mast base. (courtesy Taco)

Figure 23. Window sill mounting bracket. (courtesy JFD)

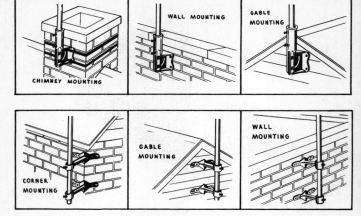

Figure 24. Two types of mounting brackets and the manner in which they are used. (courtesy General Cement).

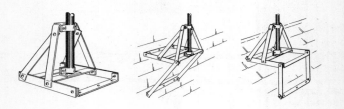

Figure 25. Bracket which can be used in several ways but is particularly suited for sloping roof. (courtesy Workshop Associates)

it possible to receive direct signals which are otherwise blocked by intervening buildings or landmarks. A tower for mounting a television antenna is shown in Figure 26. The tower shown weighs only 65 pounds. Its light weight, structural strength, and ease of assembly make it particularly adaptable to television use.

The following precautions in setting up towers should be noted.

1. If the tower is to be mounted on a roof, check with the builder to make certain that the tower's weight can be supported.

Figure 26. Lightweight tower for mounting television antenna. (courtesy Easy-Up Tower Co.)

Take into account the fact that during the winter, ice forms on the tower and increases its weight.

2. Towers which extend above a certain height must be marked with a light on top. Check with the Civil Aeronautical Authorities in the area for the height at which towers must be marked.

3. Metal towers, which are mounted on the roof, should be grounded so that they do not constitute lightning hazards.

8-36 Guying Antenna Masts. Antenna masts up to about 40 feet in height may be constructed by the technician by coupling sections of pipe together. One of the previously described mounting brackets can be used for supporting the bottom of the mast, while guy wires hold it erect. The method for attaching guy wires is shown in Figure 27. At least three guy wires, spaced 120° apart, are required for adequate support of a ten-foot mast. Between ten and twenty feet, six guy wires are recommended; and masts above twenty feet require as many as nine guy wires. The point on the pole where the guys should be attached, and the

distance they should extend from the base, are determined by
the height of the antenna pole. These dimensions are shown in
Figure 27.

No. 6 and No. 8 stranded steel wire is generally used for guy
wires, although some manufacturers of antenna kits may rec-
ommend other sizes for a particular structure. The guy wires
should be broken by insulators at intervals which are shorter
or longer than the length of the antenna. This prevents the guy

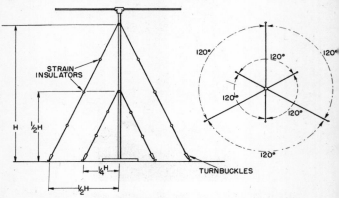

Figure 27. Guy-wire spacing.

wires from resonating at the frequencies for which the antenna
is tuned. Turnbuckles (Figure 27) may be inserted in each guy
wire leg to take up slack in the wire.

When the antenna is located at a point where it is impossible
to space the guy wires 120° apart, an outrigger should be used.
An installation using an outrigger to mount the antenna near the
edge of a roof is shown in Figure 28.

8-37 Securing the Transmission Line. After the antenna is
mounted, the transmission line should be permanently tied down.
To prevent the line from swaying in the wind, tape or clamp it
to the antenna pole and then run it along the roof to the side of
the building, taking care to keep the line away from metal objects. Insulating devices suitable for this purpose are described
elsewhere. All slack in the line should be removed up to the
point where the cable enters the building.

Inside the building, the transmission line may be concealed
behind molding or run along the tops of the base-boards a

shown in Figure 29. Tacks or staples should be used to hold it in place. Care should be exercised that the tacks or staples do not pierce the cable and cause a short. Normally, the line should be kept off the floor to prevent damage to it. When the floor is covered with a broadloom rug which extends up to the base-board, the cable can be forced between the edge of the rug and molding, and be completely hidden. No damage can result to the cable when it is fastened in this position.

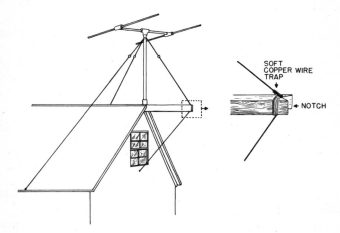

Figure 28. Outrigger used to obtain proper guy spacing.

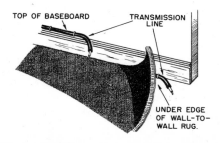

Figure 29. Two methods of running transmission line inside of building.

An ideal way to run the line when a receiver is installed on the ground floor of a private dwelling is across the beams of the celler ceiling and up through the floor, directly behind the television receiver. In an installation of this type, the transmission line is run from the roof, down the side of the building, and through a window sill in the cellar. It is then brought across the ceiling beams and up to the receiver through a small hole in the floor. When running the line in this manner, do not pull it around pipes, radiators, or other metal objects.

The cable is finally run up to the receiver through the floor. Allow several feet of line to be coiled up behind or inside of the

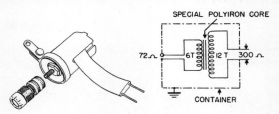

Figure 30. Circuit and appearance of line matching transformer.

receiver, so that the set can be moved away for servicing and housecleaning.

After the transmission line has been installed, a final check for a short in the line should be made. Connect an ohmmeter across the receiver input terminals. An open circuit reading should be obtained if the line is not shorted.

8-38 Matching Transmission Line to Receiver. Television receivers are being manufactured with antenna input impedances of 72 and 300 ohms. As a rule, a transmission line whose impedance matches that of the receiver should be used.

If it is necessary to use a transmission which does not match the impedance of the receiver, a matching transformer should be provided. Otherwise, the performance of the installation may be seriously impaired.

The circuit and appearance of a suitable matching transformer are shown in Figure 30. This transformer consists of a six-turn primary and a 12-turn secondary. A special core material is used. The transformer will match a 72-ohm line to a 300-ohm line to a 72-ohm receiver.

8-39 Grounding the Receiver and Antenna Mast. A television receiver should be connected to a good ground to protect the user in case of breakdown of the high voltage transformer. To reduce noise pickup, the antenna mast should also be grounded. If coaxial cable is used, the outer braid should be grounded in order to take full advantage of the shielding properties of this type of transmission line. These objects may be fastened to a pipe driven into the ground, to water pipes, or any other well grounded metal conductor.

8-40 Lightning Arrestors. The building codes of some municipalities require that a lightning arrestor be fitted to antennas and other metal objects on a building. The service organization

Figure 31. Lightning arrestor. (courtesy RCA)

should check the building codes of each area in which it installs antennas to determine whether a lightning arrestor is required by law.

In areas where lightning arrestors are not mandatory, the technician should use his discretion as to whether lightning is likely to strike the building. If the antenna is surrounded by higher metal objects on other buildings, there is little likelihood of lightning striking it. If any doubt exists as to the susceptibility of the building to lightning, it is best to install a lightning arrestor.

A typical lightning arrestor is shown in Figure 31. The transmission line is placed in a slot and a cap placed over it to hold it in position. The arrestor should be mounted at a point close to where the line enters the building. If a grounded pipe is close by, the arrestor may be secured to it. Otherwise a lead should be run from the arrestor to a metal stake in the ground, to a water pipe, or other object which is known to be well grounded. Unless the ground connection is good, the lightning arrestor will be ineffective.

8-41 Drilling Holes in Masonry. The quickest means of drilling holes in brick is to use an electric drill with a masonry bit. A one-half inch slow speed drill is best suited for this job. About 100 feet of power-cord should be available to connect the

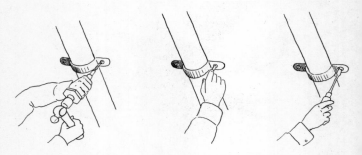

Figure 32. Drilling and mounting to masonry.

drill to an outlet in the building. When making holes in a brick structure, the holes should be drilled into the brick itself, and not into the cement between bricks. Holes in the cement cause leaks in the wall. If the drilling is done carefully, the hole may be made entirely with the electric drill and masonry bit. However, since there is the likelihood of overheating the expensive bit while starting the hole, it is recommended that the hole be started with a rawl tool.

If electric power is not available, a percussion drill may be used. This is slower than using an electric drill, but is the only method possible when electric power or an electric drill is not available. The drill is rotated while being hit with light blows by the hammer. With a little experience in controlling the drill and hammer the technician can make holes comparable to those produced with an electric drill. Figure 32 shows holes being made with a percussion drill.

After the hole has been made, an expansion shield is inserted into it as shown in Figure 32. The type shown is intended for use with nails. Other types are available for use with machine screws.

An expansion shield is not necessary when little strain is to be encountered, as with transmission line eyelets. For such purposes a wooden peg may be driven into the hole and the eyelet screwed into the peg.

8-42 A Typical Installation. At this point it is well to review briefly the important features of a typical antenna installation. Figure 33 shows all the features of a completed installation.

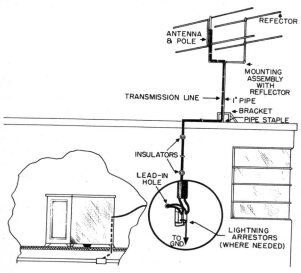

Figure 33. A typical installation.

The antenna and reflector are mounted on a pole near the edge of a roof. The pole rests on a pipe staple and is secured to an all-purpose mounting bracket which is fastened to the roof. If the screws which hold the bracket pierce the roof insulation, tar or other sealing compound is used to cover the screws.

The transmission line is passed through insulators mounted on the antenna pole to keep it from whipping in the wind. The line is run along the roof and down the side of the building. In-

sulators are used to fasten the line to the roof and brick wall.
The lead is brought into the building through a hole in the wall
and attached to the antenna input terminals of the receiver. A
lightning arrestor is attached to the transmission line near the
point where it is brought through the wall. The receiver is
grounded by running a lead to a steam or water pipe in the
apartment.

The foregoing discussion of antenna installations has dealt with
those cases where little difficulty is encountered in obtaining
good reception.

SPECIAL PROBLEMS

8-43 No set procedure can be given for difficult installations.
At best, only examples of typical problems can be presented as
a guide to the technician.

Only experience will enable the installing technician to tackle
any type of antenna problem without difficulty. Trial and error
techniques must be followed to some extent under non-standard
conditions. The technician will often use methods which do not
follow normal procedure but which, in the final analysis, bring
results.

8-44 Typical Difficulties. Very often the technician is called
upon to install receivers at locations where normal practice
will not give satisfactory results. Some of the problems encountered are illustrated in Figure 34.

B illustrates a location, in the primary service area of a station that suffers from undesired reflections and an interfering
signal on the same channel. These difficulties can be eliminated
by utilizing an antenna with suitable directive characteristics.

D illustrates another location in the primary service area of
a station. The location is such that the direct signal path is
blocked by an obstruction, in this case, a tall building. Two reflected signals reach the location and therefore a high-gain directive antenna can be used to pick up the strongest reflected
signal and at the same time eliminate the other reflection.

E and F illustrate locations on the fringe of the station's service area. While it is not always possible to obtain satisfactory

reception at distances of over fifty miles from the station, good results can often be secured by using high gain arrays mounted on towers.

Weak signals, excessive noise, interference from other services, and combinations of these troubles also result in installation problems which require special procedures. The following

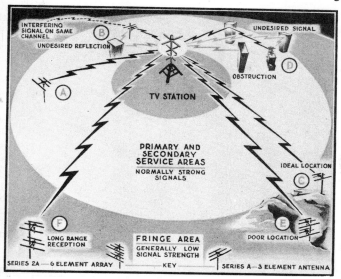

Figure 34. Typical reception problems. (courtesy Workshop Associates)

paragraphs describe the general procedures to follow when these problems are encountered.

8-45 Weak Signals. When the signal strength at the receiver is of insufficient amplitude, only a faint picture with considerable noise and poor synchronization can be obtained. If the signal level is below the minimum for which the receiver is designed, several things can be done to increase its strength at the input to the receiver.

Increasing the height of the antenna generally increases the signal pickup. The increased height means that a longer transmission line, with greater loss, must be used. As a rule, the loss will not be great enough to offset the increased pickup secured, unless the use of a taller mast makes it necessary to locate the antenna in a new location, further from the receiver.

At installations where the signal strength is low, every effort should be made to locate the antenna as close as possible to the receiver in order to minimize the length of transmission line required. If a long line must be used, choose one which has low loss. While they are normally considered to be prohibitively expensive, air-spaced coaxial and parallel lines are available which have extremely low losses.

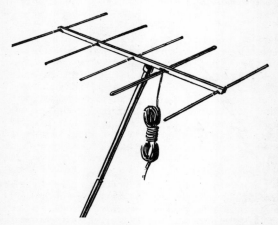

Figure 35. High-gain, five-element array, suitable for reception of single high band television station. (courtesy Roger Television)

If the signal level is low, a considerable improvement can be brought about by using a high gain array. Many types are available, from the dipole and reflector type to complex stacked antennas and reflectors. The ultimate in antenna arrays is a series of three element parasitic beams, one for each station to be received. Each beam is especially directed and tuned for a specific station.

For channels seven through thirteen, five element parasitic beams are available which give excellent results. The appearance of such an antenna is shown in Figure 35. Five element beams are not satisfactory for use on the low-band channels because they respond to a comparatively narrow band of frequencies. Antenna bandwidth is expressed as a percentage of the resonant frequency of the antenna. An antenna design which gives a bandwidth equal to five percent of its center frequency will have a bandwidth of approximately 2.5 megacycles on channel two. If cut for channel thirteen, it would have a bandwidth of approximately 11 megacycles, more than sufficient to cover a six megacycle television signal.

Other types of high-gain antennas are described in Section 5.

The performance of a television receiver can often be considerably improved with respect to weak signals by the addition of a pre-amplifier or "booster". This is particularly true when the receiver has an r-f amplifier of compromise design or no r-f amplifier at all.

If the r-f amplifier in the receiver has not been designed for optimum results, a booster amplifier of good design will improve the signal-to-noise ratio of the receiving equipment. This is true because, as a practical matter, the first stage of a receiver determines its absolute sensitivity. The noise generated in the first stage establishes the signal-to-noise ratio on weak signals and thus the overall performance of the receiver. If the noise, due to thermal agitation and shot effect, is equal in magnitude to the received signal, a satisfactory picture will not be obtained. It is evident that the noise generating characteristics of an r-f amplifier are just as important, and in many cases more important, than the gain it contributes.

When a booster amplifier is added to a receiver, the first stage of the booster becomes the first stage of the receiver and the minimum signal amplitude which will produce a satisfactory picture is determined by the booster. It is apparent, then, that if the noise characteristics of the booster surpass those of the first stage in the receiver, an improvement will be brought about.

Many of the booster amplifiers presently being marketed have not been designed so as to give the best results obtainable, and it is therefore important that a careful choice be made. The noise generating characteristics of the tubes used is one of the factors which determines the effectiveness of a booster amplifier. The noise generated by the tube is expressed in terms of the resistance of an actual resistor which would create noise of equal amplitude.

Since triodes have lower equivalent noise resistances than pentodes, they are superior in this respect. As an example, a 6J4 triode has a noise resistance of 210 ohms, while a 6AK5 pentode has a noise resistance of 1800 ohms. Connected as a triode, the 6AK5 has an equivalent noise resistance of 385 ohms, and is superior in this respect to the same tube, pentode connected.

The circuit used also determines the noise characteristics of an amplifier, as well as its other characteristics, such as stability. A triode used in a grounded-grid circuit is approximately equivalent to a well designed pentode amplifier. A circuit capable of probably the best performance obtainable at this time is one referred to as the "Cascode". A simplified diagram of such a circuit is shown in Figure 36. This circuit uses two

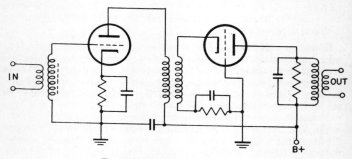

Figure 36. Cascode r-f amplifier.

triodes, a grounded-cathode stage, followed by a grounded-grid stage. While this circuit has a gain equivalent to that of a single pentode, it is superior because it generates less noise.

While the improvement in signal-to-noise ratio secured by the use of a booster is important, several other advantages are also realized. Among them are increased gain, improved image rejection, and reduction of local oscillator radiation.

When selecting a booster, it is important that its input and output impedances match those of the transmission line and receiver input.

Many boosters have response characteristics which are not sufficiently broad to cover the complete television signal. As a result they attenuate portions of the signal, causing loss of video response. The response characteristic of a booster should therefore be determined before it is selected.

The following is a summary of the points to remember in attempting to secure satisfactory results under weak signal conditions.

1. Use a high gain antenna or antennas.
2. Mount the antenna as high as possible.

3. Mount the antenna as near to the receiver as is practicable, in order to keep the transmission line short.

4. Use low-loss transmission line.

5. Use a pre-amplifier of good design and construction.

The technician should be careful not to mistake a noisy location for one where the signal level is low. Booster amplifiers are only effective if the prevalent noise level at the installation is comparatively low. If a great deal of man-made noise is encountered, somewhat different procedures, to be discussed later, should be followed. If the signal is weak and in addition man-made noise is high, both procedures should be followed.

8-46 Man-made Noise. Ignition systems of automobiles, electric motors, trolley lines, and other electrical apparatus cause man-made static which enters the receiver via the antenna or the transmission line and cause the picture to tear. Other random noises, either in the atmosphere or in the set, evidence themselves as light and dark spots in the picture. From a distance, the effect resembles snow.

The effects of noise can be minimized or eliminated in two ways. One is to increase the signal at the receiver and simultaneously reduce the noise being picked up by the antenna system. The second method is to eliminate or reduce the noise at its source.

The methods outlined in the paragraph on weak signals, with the exception of the part referring to booster amplifiers, will increase the signal at the receiver and are therefore helpful. In addition to raising the height of the antenna, an effort should be made to find a location for it which results in lower noise pickup. High gain arrays are effective because they increase the signal at the receiver in addition to reducing noise pickup. They pick up less noise because of their directivity. If an antenna is not sensitive to energy reaching it from the direction of the noise source, it will not pick up the noise. Thus, an improvement in the overall signal-to-noise ratio of the installation results.

The use of a shielded transmission line will help reduce noise effects. In noisy locations, coaxial line is preferable to parallel line because its pickup is lower. If parallel line is used, it should be twisted several times for each foot of length, since this procedure reduces pickup. Several new shielded-pair lines are available, which are superior to both coaxial and parallel-pair lines with respect to noise pickup. These cables have comparatively high losses and are only suitable when a short transmission line is required.

If the source of the noise is known, the transmission line should be relocated so that it is as far away as possible from the noise source. This should be attempted even if it necessitates the use of a longer line. Other points which should be checked are the impedance match at the receiver input and at the antenna. If a shielded line is used, make certain that the shield is connected to a good ground.

As previously mentioned, noise can also be eliminated at its source. Commercial filters are available for this purpose. In many instances, 0.05 mf condensers, connected across the power line at the point where it enters the electrical equipment causing the noise, will prove effective. While this method of handling the problem is the most effective, it is only applicable in a few instances, as with oil burners and other appliances in private dwellings. In urban areas, the source of the noise is usually not easy to determine, and when it is, the cost of filters is prohibitive. It is therefore best, in most cases, to follow the procedure outlined for improving the antenna system.

Summarizing the procedure to be followed for reducing noise pickup:
1. Use a directional, high-gain antenna.
2. Attempt to find antenna location which gives minimum noise pickup.
3. Mount antenna as high as possible.
4. Twist parallel-line or use coaxial or shielded-pair line with good ground.
5. Locate transmission line as far as possible from noise source.
6. Make certain transmission line, antenna, and receiver, are correctly matched.
7. Locate and place filters at noise sources.

8-47 Too Strong a Signal. In a few instances, a receiver is situated in an area where the signal strength is so high that the input circuits are overloaded. This condition is characterized by a loss of synchronization, sound modulation in the picture, and an over-contrasty or distorted image.

To prevent the effects of too strong a signal, the television receiver is equipped with a contrast control, and often with automatic gain control. However, the contrast control is almost always located in the video i-f circuit, or the video amplifier stage. An extremely strong signal will overload the first r-f stage before the contrast or gain control can be of help. Obviously then, until means are provided in television receivers to reduce signal strength before the first stage is reached, this must be done by the installing technician. Preferably, the task should be accomplished without the need to remove or rewire the chassis. This can be done by using an external attenuator in the antenna transmission line. Several commercial attenuators are available. Figure 37 shows an excellent one called the Tel-Adjust.

Basically, the attenuator is a low-loss switch and a series of attenuator pads made up of half-watt carbon resistors. Provision is made to mount different fixed pad arrangements in the

Figure 37. The Tel-Adjust and the Tele-Pad, used to reduce too strong a signal. (courtesy Roger Television)

box for different types of transmission lines. By means of the switch, a choice of several attenuation values is available, and each station's signal may be attenuated by the required degree even though the signal level from each station varies greatly.

Several types of fixed pad arrangements can be used in the transmission line. For balanced lines, however, such as 300-ohm twin-lead, a balanced attenuation network is preferred, such as the "O" and "H" types shown in Figure 38. On the other hand, when coaxial cable is used, an unbalanced pad is sufficient, and cheaper to install. Examples are the "I" and "Pi" types shown in Figure 38.

In order to install these attenuator pads, two things must be known: (a) how much attenuation is needed, (b) the resistance values which will produce exactly the needed attenuation without upsetting the impedance match between the receiver input and the transmission line. The signal strength is measured with a field strength meter and the needed attenuation calculated. A simpler method is to insert a variable pad box into the transmission line and vary the attenuation until the trouble is eliminated. If the variable attenuator is calibrated, the correct amount of attenuation can be read directly. Such a variable attenuator is shown in Figure 37 and is known as the Tele-Pad. This variable pad box has a constant impedance equal to that of

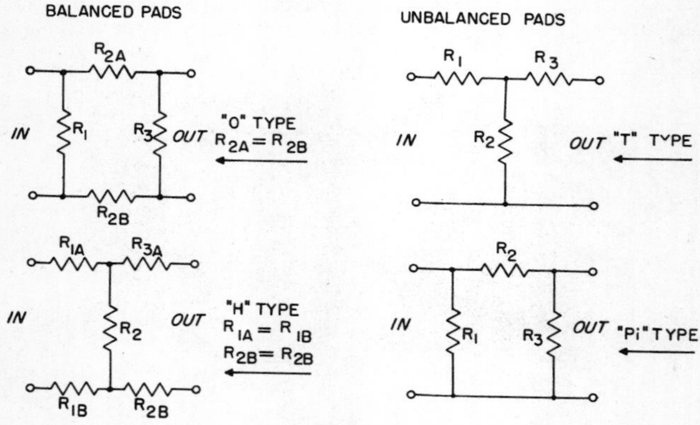

Figure 38. Attenuator network and component values.

the transmission line and an accurately calibrated dial which reads to 30 db attenuation in steps of 3 db.

In using the Tele-Adjust and Tele-Pad, the first step is to determine the amount of attenuation needed on each overloading station. This is done with the Tele-Pad. When the required amount of attenuation is known, the values of the resistors in the attenuation network may be calculated. To avoid calculations, a table of such values is shown in Figure 38, which lists different attenuation factors and corresponding values of R1, R2, and R3 for 300-ohm and 72-ohm lines. These resistors should be of the half-watt carbon type.

8-48 Diathermy Interference. Although most modern diathermy machines are equipped with r-f filters so that radiation into the power line is reduced, many machines installed in doctors' offices and hospitals interfere with television reception. When the frequency of the diathermy apparatus is close to the i-f frequency of a nearby television receiver, an interference pattern is produced in the television picture. Little can be done at the installation to remove this type of interference. If the diathermy machine can be located, the owner should be asked to cooperate by shielding the machine, by seeing to it that the machine is operating on its correct frequency, and by grounding it properly. An ordinary battery-operated, portable radio is an effective probing device for locating diathermy machines which cause disturbances in the television receiver. A buzzing sound is heard over the entire broadcast band if a diathermy machine is in the vicinity of the portable receiver. As the receiver is

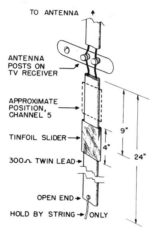

TO ANTENNA

ANTENNA POSTS ON TV RECEIVER

APPROXIMATE POSITION, CHANNEL 5

TINFOIL SLIDER

300Ω TWIN LEAD

9"

4"

24"

OPEN END

HOLD BY STRING ONLY

Figure 39. Simple wave trap.

brought closer to the diathermy machine, the buzzing sound grows louder. Diathermy machines which are situated as many as several thousand feet away may be located in this manner.

8-49 Beat Frequency Interference. Strong a-m and f-m broadcast stations near the receiver can heterodyne with the television sound or picture carrier, resulting in a beat frequency which appears on the screen as a series of fine vertical or slanting lines which drift through the picture. If the unwanted carrier is fixed in frequency, it may be filtered out by a trap which is inserted in series or shunt with the antenna transmission line.

A simple way to make a wave trap is to connect a piece of

coaxial cable or parallel lead across the antenna input terminals of the receiver. Starting with a piece about two feet long, cut the cable off in one inch pieces, until the beat frequency is eliminated. In this way, the trap is cut to a length which is resonant at the frequency of the unwanted carrier and by-passes it from the receiver input.

Another simple wave trap is shown in Figure 39. It is basically a quarter-wave open-end stub of 300-ohm line. The line should be about two feet long. Instead of tuning out the interfering frequency by clipping the line, a tin foil slider is slipped over it. The slider is moved up and down the stub to tune out the disturbing frequency. The advantage of the slider is that it

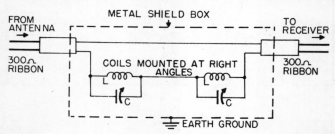

Figure 40. Circuit for wave trap.

may be reset if the disturbing frequency shifts. The receiver owner should be familiarized with the slider adjustment if this type of trap is used, since he may have to reset it as the interfering frequency changes. Since the tuning of the trap is affected by hand capacity, a string is added to the stub. The string is held by the user when tuning adjustments are made. The slider should be pushed with an insulated rod such as a wooden pencil with an eraser.

If the simple traps just described are not effective, a trap such as that shown in Figure 40 may be tried. This trap consists of two resonant circuits connected in series with one leg of the line. The tuned circuits are mounted in a shielded box. These traps should be adjusted to the frequency of the interfering signal. If two interfering signals are present, one trap can be tuned to the frequency of each signal. The two coils should be mounted at right angles to each other to minimize cross-coupling.

Several commercial wavetraps are available, which are also very effective.

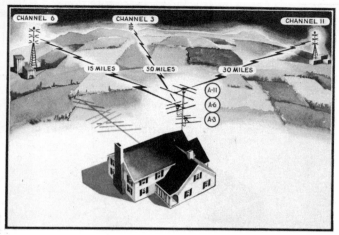

Figure 41. A typical multiple antenna installation. (courtesy Workshop Associates)

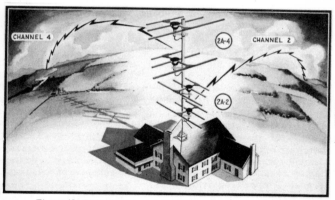

Figure 42. Multiple antenna installation using two six-element beams. (courtesy Workshop Associates)

8-50 Multiple Antenna Installations. As previously mentioned, the difficulties encountered in poor locations can often be overcome through the use of more than one antenna. Typical multi-antenna installations are shown in Figures 41 and 42. In Figure 41 three separate antennas are used. The location is such that one antenna cannot satisfactorily cover more than one station. Three element parasitic beams are used. Each beam is tuned to a different station and directed so as to obtain maximum pick-up from the station to which it is tuned.

Figure 42 illustrates a second multi-antenna installation. Here two six-element parasitic arrays are used. Each array is specially tuned and directed to secure maximum pickup from a single station.

Similar problems are encountered in large cities where large buildings either block direct signal paths or cause reflections. It is generally possible to obtain satisfactory results by utilizing

Figure 43. Coaxial switch. (Workshop Associates)

separate antennas for each channel or for channels which present particularly difficult problems.

If more than one antenna is used, some means must be provided to permit switching from one antenna to another. A switch suitable for use with coaxial cable is shown in Figure 43. This switch permits the use of as many as four different antennas on a single receiver. It can also be used to advantage in dealers' display rooms were it is desired to connect several antennas to several different receivers.

Figure 44 illustrates the details of the installations of Figures 41 and 42. These installations use the four-position coaxial switch of Figure 43. The three antennas of the installation on the left are connected by coaxial cable to the switch. The output of the switch is connected to an impedance matching transformer which matches the 72-ohm transmission line to the 300-ohm input of the receiver. The second installation consists of two six-element parasitic arrays. These arrays are connected

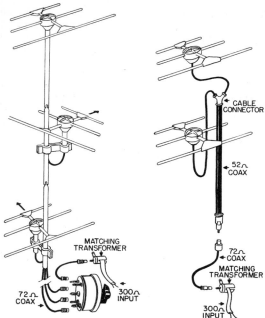

Figure 44. Typical application of coaxial switch.

by coaxial cable to a junction; from the junction the signal passes through a length of 52-ohm coaxial cable, and then through an impedance transformer consisting of a quarter-wave section of 72-ohm coaxial cable. If the receiver has a 300-ohm input impedance, a transformer can be added to secure an exact match.

A third multi-antenna installation is shown in Figure 45. Here two antennas are used, one for the high-band channels and the second for the low-band channels. In order to avoid running two transmission lines, the antennas are paralleled and a single line is used. The transmission line is connected to the lower antenna. The top antenna is connected to the lower antenna by a piece of parallel line cut to one quarter of the wavelength of the frequency for which the lower antenna is cut. The same type of line is used for paralleling the antennas as is used for the main transmission line in order to avoid an impedance mismatch.

In cases where the above array is to be used for increasing the signal on the high channels, and no reflections are present, each antenna should be oriented toward the desired stations. The lines should be connected in phase at the point where they are joined if the orientation of the antennas is not more than 45 degrees apart. Proper phasing is obtained by connecting the left-hand element of one antenna to the left-hand element of the other. The right-hand elements are similarly connected.

If reflections are encountered, mount both antennas on the mast, but connect the transmission line to only one antenna at a time. By rotating the mast, determine the best orientation for

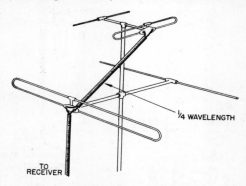

¼ WAVELENGTH

TO
RECEIVER

Figure 45. Antennas connected in parallel.

each antenna separately, using a station whose frequency falls within the response of the antenna. When the antennas are properly oriented, tighten them on the mast so that they will both point in the proper direction when the mast is in place. Then parallel the antennas, as above, with a quarter-wave section of line. If any increase in reflections is noticed, try reversing the connections of the main transmission line to the lower antenna. If this does not improve the picture, try reversing the line which parallels the two antennas; that is, connect the left-hand conductor from one antenna to the right-hand terminal of the other antenna, and the right-hand conductor from the first antenna to the left-hand terminal of the second antenna. If none of these connections of the lines clears up the reflections, it is necessary to use separate transmission lines from each antenna to the receiver.

8-51 Indoor Antennas. The need for indoor antennas usually arises because landlords forbid the erection of individual antennas on their roofs. The objection of apartment house owners to a disfiguring and hazardous maze of antennas is well under-standable. As objectionable also is the signal interaction be-tween a number of antennas operating in close proximity, as a result of which reception in the individual receivers may be impaired. The practical solution to this problem lies in the in-stallation by the landlord of a master antenna system which feeds signals to each apartment. Such systems were described in Section 5. However, it will be many years before all apart-ment houses are equipped with master antenna installations. Until then the tenant, desirous of having a television receiver in an apartment house where outdoor antennas are not permitted, may be able to secure satisfactory performance with an indoor antenna.

Though indoor installations are difficult, they are sometimes perferable to roof systems. For example, if it is possible to receive good signals in a third floor apartment that is located in a ten-story building, there is little point in erecting the an-tenna on the roof and investing in the long transmission line. There is also less likelihood of interference from other anten-nas when indoor installations are used.

It should not be assumed from this that indoor installations are better in all cases. Actually, very few instances occur in which an indoor installation is preferable. However, no rule can be made and the technician must use his own judgment.

An inspection should first be made of the direction in which all the windows of the apartment face to ascertain whether there are possibilities of ''line of sight'' reception. If such is the case, an antenna may be mounted on the window sill. Installing the transmission line then becomes a routine matter.

If no direct signal can be obtained, locating the best antenna site becomes a matter of trial. A dipole with sufficient cable between it and the receiver to allow one technician to probe in all the rooms of the house for the best signal should then be tried. The probing should begin near the receiver, the antenna being set in different positions and rotated while the screen of the receiver is watched. If no position of the antenna gives a good picture, the technician with the probe should proceed to the other rooms. If a terrace adjoins the apartment, it should also be tried. When the best position of the antenna has been found for all stations, the observer should look for closeby objects to conceal the antenna. Inside closets, under cornices, and behind moldings are a few locations which have proved successful for indoor antennas. When the dipole cannot readily be concealed, it can be mounted on a wooden rod, and the entire assembly painted a color to match the room. Many people, anxious to

have a receiver, have accepted a neat antenna installation mounted in the corner of a room. In other installations, the antenna
has been suspended from the ceiling. Figure 46 shows an indoor
antenna which can be placed on a table, the receiver cabinet,
etc. It can be rotated for the best reception of each station and
folded when not in use.

8-52 Multiple Indoor Antennas. It is very probable that many
indoor installations will require more than one antenna in view
of the fact that direct or strong reflected signals are not likely
to exist for all stations. If probing all rooms does not indicate

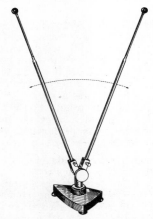

Figure 46. An indoor antenna (courtesy Delson Mfg.)

a site that provides reception of all signals on one antenna, then
a second antenna should be tried. These antennas may finally
be situated in different parts of the apartment, or may be mounted on window sills facing in different directions, depending upon
the location of the various stations with respect to the receiver.
Under the most difficult conditions, a separate antenna may have
to be installed for each station.

If more than one antenna is required, a switching arrangement
must be provided to enable the owner to select the proper antenna for each station. For installations with two antennas, a
double-pole, double-throw knife switch is recommended, wired
as shown in Figure 47. Rotary or toggle switches are to be
avoided as there is excessive leakage across the contacts at

the high television frequencies. The switch can be mounted in a location convenient to the customer, as for example on the side of the cabinet, or concealed behind a curtain near the set.

When three or more antennas are required, a terminal board with connectors can be used. The owner then moves the lead running to the receiver to the proper set of terminals. A coaxial switch, as described under multiple outdoor antenna sys-

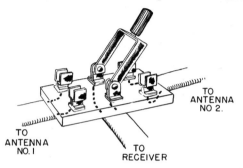

Figure 47. Double-pole, double-throw knife switch for connecting two antennas to receiver.

tems is the ideal solution to the multiple transmission line problem when coaxial cable is used.

Many apartment houses in which only indoor antennas are permitted are located so close to the transmitter of one or more stations in metropolitan areas that very often no antenna at all is needed, or at most a piece of coaxial cable approximately one-quarter wavelength long will suffice. A unique installation in New York, located very close to station WCBS-TV, illustrates these conditions. It was found that WCBS-TV came in very well without an antenna. WABD was also strong, but ghosts were in the picture. These could be suppressed by attaching a piece of cable, 39 inches in length, to the receiver antenna terminals and by rotating the cable in an arc until a good signal without reflections was selected. An antenna was needed only for WNBT, and a favorable point in the room was found for it. A terminal board, mounted very close to the receiver, enabled the owner to select either WCBS-TV (no antenna), WABD (a 39-inch piece of cable, mounted on a wooden rod and attached to the receiver at the correct angle), and WNBT (dipole antenna). With this antenna system, the receiver cannot be moved without disturbing the entire field pattern. It should be remembered that, with indoor installations, receivers cannot so readily be moved about. The length and direction of the antenna and transmission line are more critical than for outdoor installations.

8-53 The Power Line. Most television receivers thus far introduced to the public have been designed for operation on 110-volt, 60-cycle power lines. (A few low-priced, small screen a-c/d-c receivers have made their appearance, but thus far they constitute a small proportion of sets sold.) Three non-standard conditions of the power line may exist, any one of which prevents the direct connection of the receiver to the power outlet: (1) direct current, (2) 25 or 50-cycle line, and (3) incorrect a-c voltage. Any of these conditions requires accessory equipment before the receiver can be made to operate.

8-54 D-C Line. Rotary converters which change D-C to A-C have proved suitable for operation with television receivers. Investment in a high quality converter is advised so that 60-cycle voltage of good waveform is obtained. Otherwise, strong low-frequency harmonics may exist which will not be adequately filtered out by the receiver power supply filter. Brush design of the converter is important, because excessive brush noise causes interference with reception. Since the converter is generally located in a closet or in some other poorly ventilated place, it is well to use a converter whose power rating is well above the actual requirements.

Once the converter has been installed, it requires no further attention. A switch mounted on the side or rear of the receiver cabinet will make it convenient to turn on and off. It is not recommended that the technician rewire the receiver's power switch so as to turn on the converter at the same time, because it necessitates another rewiring job, should the customer move into an area with a-c power.

8-55 Voltage Transformer. If an a-c power line voltage other than 110 volts exists, a power transformer of sufficient rating to handle the requirements of the receiver and having the correct step-up or step-down ratio will solve the problem. In large console models, there may be room to mount the transformer inside. With small sets, the transformer may be concealed in a closet or behind a piece of furniture. The receiver is plugged into the transformer, which in turn is connected to the power line. No on-off switch is required.

8-56 Voltage Regulators. If a receiver is located in an area where there are continuous line voltage fluctuations, which cause annoying changes in picture size and intensity, a voltage regulator may be used. A voltage regulator is similar to a transformer. Its primary is connected to the power line and its secondary to the power plug of the receiver.

8-57 Frequency Converters. If a receiver is to be used with a 50-cycle or 25-cycle power line, a frequency converter is required. Frequency converters are similar to rotary converters. The input is connected to the power line and 60-cycle power is available at its output. If such a converter were not used, the power frequency would not be properly filtered by the receiver power supply and difficulty would be experienced in synchronizing the picture.

8-58 Operating the Receiver. The final link in the chain of events between selling the television receiver and its adjustment and installation in the customer's home is the instruction of the owner in the correct operating procedures for tuning the set. Though operation has been simplified by the reduction in the number of controls on modern television receivers, it is well to give the customer a brief explanation of the function of each control and its effect upon the receiver's performance. At this time, it is also advisable to acquaint the customer with such interference effects as diathermy, auto ignition, etc., which will cause occasional picture disturbances despite the best possible installation.

Since many technicians will often find themselves in the role of salesman, selling techniques are necessary adjuncts to their knowledge. As with any new piece of equipment, the customer will look to the technician for advice and guidance. The technician's knowledge and integrity in selling television receivers is particularly needed now when it is important to help create satisfied receiver owners. A brief illustration is selling will emphasize this point. Suppose the customer lives in an area which is considerably disturbed by ignition noises. This may be a location on a street with heavy automobile traffic, trolley lines, or neon signs. The average customer, unaware of these effects, may choose a low priced receiver which has conventional synchronization. An alert salesman, thoroughly familiar with the advantages of flywheel synchronization, would do the customer a great service by swinging him over to a higher priced model equipped with this circuit, which is more immune to ignition signals. Similarly, all other features which determine the prices of receivers should be discussed with the customer. For at one time or another he will see another television receiver, and unless his provides a picture of equal contrast, brightness, stability, and sharpness, he will immediately question the integrity of the store which made the sale. By understanding that better performance can only be achieved by a higher priced set, the customer will make his choice and be satisfied with it.

Learn how to interpret test patterns and convey as much information as possible to the customer. Make him aware of those conditions which are the fault of the receiver and those which cannot be avoided even with the best of installations. This type of customer education will pay dividends.

SERVICING TELEVISION RECEIVERS

Troubleshooting - Repair

Interpreting test patterns - Alignment

9-1 The troubleshooting and repair of television receivers is a task requiring considerable skill. It should not be attempted without careful preparation. With a basic knowledge of television circuit design, and by application of systematic methods of service and use of proper test equipment, no real difficulties should be encountered.

The servicing of television receivers can be broken down into three separate operations: 1. Troubleshooting, 2. Checking and Adjusting, and 3. Alignment. Troubleshooting is the determination of what is wrong with the receiver. Before repairing, adjusting, or aligning a receiver, the trouble must be isolated to a particular stage, and if possible to a particular component. Because of the complexity of a television receiver, troubleshooting procedures must be carried out in a systematic, organized fashion; otherwise, considerable time will be wasted in probing aimlessly from one circuit to another. Experience in servicing television receivers for the past few years has indicated that the majority of faults can be located quicker without test equipment and without the need for readjusting or aligning the circuit, if logical troubleshooting methods are used.

After a repair has been made, it is usually necessary to make one or more adjustments. For example, if the linearity control in the vertical sweep circuit is replaced, it must be adjusted to give a picture of proper vertical linearity.

The alignment of television receivers generally refers to the tuning of the amplifiers in the r-f, video and sound circuits. These circuits operate at high frequencies and their alignment is critically affected by component or wiring changes. Realignment is often required when a tube is replaced or because one of the fixed components has changed in value.

9-2 Test Equipment. Several pieces of test equipment have been developed for television servicing in order to simplify the task of troubleshooting, adjusting, and aligning. The operation and function of each of these instruments are described in detail in the Test Equipment section. It is well, at this point, to briefly outline the test equipment which applies to the three categories of television servicing.

For troubleshooting the receiver, a cathode-ray oscillograph is the most useful and versatile piece of test equipment. Discontinuities in circuits can be checked and the shapes of the various waveforms can be observed on the oscillograph. By recognizing certain characteristic oscillograms, the technician can readily determine the cause of a fault in a circuit.

A vacuum tube voltmeter is another useful instrument for troubleshooting. All operating voltages in the receiver may be checked with it to determine whether the power supplies are functioning properly and whether a faulty component is responsible for the wrong potential at a certain point in the circuit. Shorted or open components and faulty wiring are best located with a multimeter. Other useful instruments for troubleshooting are a voltage calibrator for the oscillograph, a kilovoltmeter for checking the high voltage power supply, a tube checker, and a resistance-capacitance bridge for testing critical components.

Most adjustments to the receiver can be made while observing a test pattern that is transmitted by a television station. When such a pattern is not available, it is possible to make most adjustments with a signal generator, oscillograph, square wave generator, and a vacuum tube voltmeter.

Three pieces of test equipment are basic requirements for alignment. They are a sweep frequency generator, an oscillograph, and a marker generator.

In addition to the instruments listed above, there are several accessory devices which are now available for television servicing. Although not essential, they often greatly simplify the problems of servicing. Into this category fall such instruments as grid dippers, Q-meters, and cross-hatch generators.

TROUBLESHOOTING

9-3 In order to approach the subject of troubleshooting with logical and well coordinated procedures, the television receiver is broken down into six sections, each of which has character-istic faults. By first localizing the trouble to one of these sec-tions, the technician will save considerable time and effort.

Figure 1 shows a block diagram of the television receiver di-vided into these six sections: 1. The R-F Section, 2. The Sound Channel, 3. The Video Channel, 4. The Sweep Circuits, 5. The

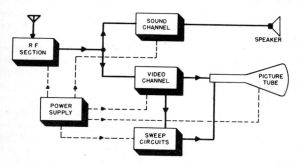

Figure 1. Block diagram of six basic sections of television re-ceiver.

Picture Tube, and 6. The power supplies. The heavy lines and arrows on the block diagram indicate the paths of the television signals as they travel through the receiver. This diagram em-phasizes the fact that a television receiver is actually made up of several sections, each of which can be considered to operate almost independently of the other. If the fault can be isolated to one of these sections, there is generally no need to work on the other sections. The following discussion will help clarify the reasoning upon which this method of fault isolation is based.

1. The signal enters the R-F Section and branches out into the Sound Channel and the Video Channel. If poor sound and

picture exist, it is probable that the fault lies in the R-F Section, because after this point the signals are separated.

2. When the signal branches off to the Sound Channel, it passes through several audio stages which make up an independent f-m receiver, except for being connected to the common power supply. If trouble exists only in the sound, the Sound Channel is the logical section of the receiver to troubleshoot first.

3. The output of the R-F Section is also fed to the Video Channel. Here again a separate amplifier system is used to amplify the video signals. If the sound and all other sections of the receiver appear to be operating correctly, the trouble probably exists in the Video Channel.

4. The amplified video signal is fed to the Picture Tube and the Sweep Circuits. Certain troubles in the Picture Tube circuits can be recognized readily by watching the picture. For example, a misaligned yoke or focus coil causes characteristic distortions of the picture.

5. Since the video signal is fed to the Sweep circuits to synchronize the sawtooth deflecting signals, the Sweep Circuits will be partially interdependent with the Video Channel. If the picture is synchronizing well and scanning trouble exists, the fault is usually accredited to the Sweep Circuits.

6. The Power Supply affects all the other sections of the receiver. If the receiver is completely dead, the trouble usually can be traced to the Power Supply. Other Power Supply faults will show up in a characteristic manner in other sections of the receiver, as will be described later.

While it is not always possible to treat each section of the receiver as a unit operating independently of the others, the majority of faults can be isolated in this manner. When more than one section appears to be contributing to the trouble, the technician must attack each suspected section in logical order.

Several typical examples of the methods of fault location just described follow:

1. Assume that sound, but no picture can be received from all stations.

2. The intensity control should be turned up to see if there is a raster. If the raster is present, there is nothing wrong with either the vertical or horizontal sweep circuits, or with the power supply. Since the sound channel is working properly, the trouble must be in the picture channel.

3. The next step is to tap the grid of the video amplifier. If white bands appear on the screen of the picture tube, the video amplifier is functioning properly. Therefore, the trouble must be in the picture i-f section. (The r-f channel must be operating properly because sound is being received.)

4. Having isolated the fault to the picture i-f channel, the tubes in this section should be checked. If the trouble is not the tubes, the next approach is to feed a modulated signal into the grid of each i-f stage and note the output on an oscillograph. The faulty stage in the section can be located in this manner.

5. Once the trouble has been tracked down and corrected, the receiver should be tried immediately.

If it is assumed that in the previous example no raster was observed when the intensity was turned up, but that instead a spot appeared on the picture tube, the trouble would then not be in the picture channel. In all probability the trouble is not in the sweep generators because neither vertical nor horizontal sweep is present. It is probably in the power supply which furnishes plate and screen voltages to both of the sweep generators. The rectifier tube and other components in the power supply should be checked. If a component has not failed, a check should be made for an open circuit.

As another example, assume that when the intensity control is turned up only a horizontal line is observed. The place to look for the trouble, in this case, would be in the vertical sweep generator; or conversely, if a vertical line is observed, in the horizontal sweep generator.

These examples will serve to illustrate how a visual analysis of the receiver assists in the isolation of faults. By recognizing the characteristic troubles of the various sections, the technician will develop similar fault isolation techniques of his own.

9-4 Other Troubleshooting Techniques. Much of the technician's work in troubleshooting television receivers can be simplified if he fully understands the significance of the test patterns transmitted by stations. A thorough familiarity with these patterns will enable the technician to recognize the majority of receiver faults in a matter of minutes. A complete analysis of test patterns is presented later in this section.

Another approach to troubleshooting is the signal tracing of the receiver circuits with a cathode-ray oscillograph. This method is particularly useful in checking the sweep section when visual analysis indicates this section is at fault.

The checking of tubes and voltages is the best approach to tracking down trouble after it has been isolated to a stage in the receiver. The manufacturer's literature often contains the approximate voltages which should be present at various points in a receiver when it is operating properly. By comparing measured voltages with those given by the manufacturer, the tech-

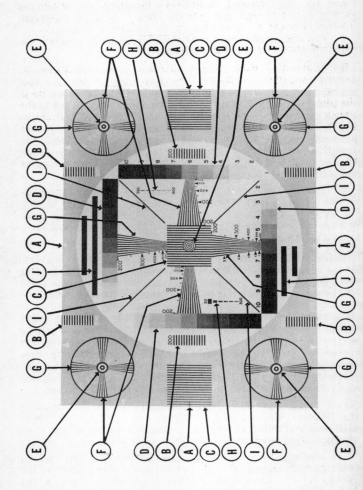

nician can locate faulty components. Resistance and continuity checks will also usually turn up faulty components in a circuit.

After the trouble has been isolated and corrected, one or more of the adjustment and alignment procedures described later in this section may have to be carried out in order to put the receiver back into perfect working order.

9-5 Troubleshooting with Test Patterns. For several minutes before each broadcasting period, and at intervals as long as several hours during the day, each television station transmits a test pattern which displays the station's call letters. The test pattern contains geometric designs which are very useful in troubleshooting and adjusting receivers and installations. In the succeeding paragraphs, the significance of the features of the various test pattern designs which are in common use are discussed. Following this discussion there is a group of typical test patterns, as they appear on the television screen. They illustrate a major portion of the faults which the technician is likely to encounter in troubleshooting and servicing television receivers and installations. Each test pattern is accompanied by a description of the faults which cause it to appear.

9-6 The R.M.A. Test Pattern. In order to assist in standardizing the performance of television transmitters and receivers, the Radio Manufacturers Association has designed a test pattern which it recommends for use in testing television equipment. This pattern is shown in Figure 2. It is considerably more complex than the test patterns which are transmitted by television stations, but an understanding of its design will enable the technician to make use of any type of station test pattern. For pur-

◄──────

Figure 2. The R.M.A. Standard Test Chart. The call-out letters identify the geometric designs which are used to check the following:

(A) Vertical and Horizontal Size and Aspect Ratio.

(F) Vertical Resolution.

(B) Vertical Linearity.

(G) Horizontal Resolution.

(C) Horizontal Linearity.

(H) "Ringing" or Damped Oscillations.

(D) Contrast and Brightness.

(I) Interlacing.

(E) Spot Size and Focus.

(J) Low Frequency Phase Shift.

poses of explanation, "call-out" letters have been marked on the R.M.A. pattern to identify its important features. A key to these letters is given below the pattern and a more detailed description of the various geometric designs follows.

9-7 Vertical and Horizontal Size, and Aspect Ratio. The test pattern which is transmitted by the station has an aspect ratio of 3 to 4. To make certain that the scanning circuits are correctly adjusted in the receiver so as to reproduce the pattern in the same aspect ratio, four crosses (A) are marked on the R.M.A. test pattern. These crosses, two black and two white, are located at the center of each edge of the chart. The height and width of the received pattern should be adjusted so that the white crosses touch the top and bottom of the mask opening and the black crosses touch the left and right sides. The correct picture size and aspect ratio are then obtained on the receiver screen.

9-8 Vertical Linearity. The vertical linearity is adjusted with reference to the six groups of horizontal lines marked (B). The linearity should be adjusted for equal spacing between the lines. Note that the vertical linearity lines do not extend continuously from top to bottom, but appear in three groups at the top, center, and bottom. The lines could have extended the full height of the pattern. This was not done in order to minimize confusion. It is necessary only to adjust the vertical linearity for equal distribution of the lines in each group. The scanning lines between each group will then be linearly displaced, unless the vertical sawtooth voltage has an irregular shape - an unlikely condition.

9-9 Horizontal Linearity. The vertical lines in the three groups marked (C) are used to check the horizontal linearity. If the horizontal linearity controls in the receiver are correctly adjusted, the lines in each group will be equally spaced.

9-10 Contrast and Brightness. The four groups of squares marked (D) are used to measure the ability of the receiver to reproduce a picture of good contrast and illumination. They also help to correctly set the contrast and brightness controls. The squares are numbered from 1 to 10 and extend from pure white through several shades of gray to the tenth square, which is black. An ideal receiver will enable the viewer to distinguish each of the ten squares in the gray scale. The quality of the receiver is measured in terms of how far up on the gray scale the squares can be distinguished. When making this measurement, the contrast and brightness controls should be adjusted for maximum contrast between adjacent squares, as well as for even illumination of the grey background of the pattern.

9-11 Spot Size and Focus. The small, white dots (E) at the centers of the five bulls-eyes on the R.M.A. pattern are provided to make possible the checking of the spot size and shape of the electron beam in the picture tube, and to help focus the image. The focus control on the receiver should be adjusted to obtain the roundest and sharpest white dots possible. If the receiver is equipped with an astigmatism control, the control should be adjusted with the focus control to obtain a round, sharply focused spot.

9-12 Vertical Resolution. Vertical resolution is expressed as the maximum number of evenly spaced horizontal lines which can be resolved on the test pattern. The horizontal wedges marked (F) are designed for the measurement of vertical resolution. The wedges are calibrated with numbers from 200 to 600. If the horizontal wedges are distinct all the way across the point marked 600, the picture is said to have 600-line resolution. Lower resolution is indicated by a blurring of the narrow part of the wedge. For example, if the lines are distinct only half way across the horizontal wedges, the picture has 300-line vertical resolution. The significance of this figure, which expresses the degree of vertical resolution, is explained by the manner in which the wedges are calibrated.

Although there are 525 scanning lines in the television picture, only about 93% (490) of these lines are visible in the picture. The other seven percent are blanked out during the vertical blanking period. If the electron beam in the picture tube can be focused to a spot small enough to trace out 490 lines without overlapping, the maximum vertical resolution will be 490 lines. In other words, the present 525-line television system is only capable of 490-line vertical resolution. In actual practice, the vertical resolution is even less. It should be noted that the R.M.A. test chart indicates 600-line resolution which is more than the present television system can reproduce.

The vertical resolution, as measured on the test pattern, is determined mainly by the size of the spot on the picture tube screen. It is not affected by the low or high frequency response of the receiver. The construction of the electron gun in the picture tube and of the focusing system are the principal factors which affect spot size.

9-13 Horizontal Resolution. Horizontal resolution is dependent upon the spot size of the electron beam and the high frequency response or bandwidth of the receiver. The bandwidth determines the number of video signal frequency components which are passed by the amplifiers, and in turn determines the number of distinct, vertical black and white lines which can be reproduced on the screen.

Horizontal resolution can be expressed in two ways, in terms of the number of vertical lines which can be resolved, or in terms of the frequency response of the receiver amplifiers.

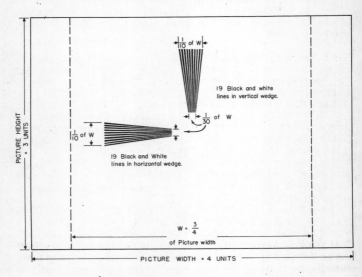

Figure 3. Method used to compute calibration numbers on resolution wedges.

The vertical wedges marked (G) on the R.M.A. test pattern are designed to measure horizontal resolution. The upper wedge is calibrated in terms of number of lines, while the lower wedge is calibrated in number of lines and frequency response. The numbers to the left of the bottom wedge represent frequencies from 3 to 7 megacycles; the numbers to the right of the wedge indicate the equivalent number of lines, ranging from 200 to 600. Like the vertical wedges, the horizontal wedges are designed to exceed the resolution capabilities of the present 525-line television system.

To understand the significance of the numbers on the vertical wedges and the method by which they are calibrated, it is necessary to explain the geometric configuration of the wedges in relation to the overall size of the test chart.

1. In order to have a common basis for comparison of the horizontal and vertical resolution, horizontal resolution is based on the number of distinct black and white vertical lines which can be resolved by the electron beam scanning across three-quarters of the usable width of the picture. This distance (3/4 of picture width) is equal to the picture height and gives a square area in which an identical number of lines can be fitted vertically or horizontally. This square is shown in Figure 3 in relation to the overall picture size. For convenience, three quarters of the picture width, which is the length of a side of the square, is labelled "W". Also shown are the vertical and horizontal wedges of the R.M.A. test chart.

2. The vertical wedge has 19 alternate black and white lines. The top of the wedge is slightly more than 1/10 of W. Considering only the top of this wedge, 10 x 19, or 190 lines, so spaced, could be fitted across the length W. The lower part of the wedge is only 1/30 of W. 30 x 19, or 570 lines, so spaced, could be fitted into a space equal to W. Actually, the above calculations are only approximate because the ratio of the width of the wedge to the length W is not exact. The same points on the R.M.A. test chart in Figure 2 which are determined precisely, are marked 200 lines and 600 lines, respectively. The other numbers on the wedges are calculated in a similar manner.

3. To use the vertical wedges to measure horizontal resolution, simply note how far down toward the narrow portion of the wedges the lines can be distinguished. The resolution may then be read directly from the numbers on the wedges.

The horizontal resolution may also be expressed in terms of frequency to indicate the bandwidth of the amplifiers in the receiver. The numbers on the wedges which provide a line calibration may be converted into an equivalent frequency by dividing the number of lines by 80. This conversion factor is arrived at in the following manner:

1. It takes the electron beam 1/15,750 seconds, or 63.5 microseconds to scan one horizontal line. Of this time, 10.2 microseconds are consumed by the horizontal blanking period, during which the spot retraces its path and begins the next line. The spot actually appears on the screen for 63.5 minus 10.2, or 53.3 microseconds.

2. To compare the horizontal resolution with the vertical resolution, only 3/4 of the length of a horizontal line is considered. The spot requires 3/4 of 53.3, or 40 microseconds to scan three quarters of the line.

3. Consider now a signal of one megacycle frequency which

produces one complete cycle in one microsecond. When this signal is fed to a picture tube, the positive half of each cycle produces a white dot, and the negative half a black dot.

4. In one microsecond, or one cycle, two dots are produced on the screen by a one-megacycle signal. In 40 microseconds, a one-megacycle signal produces 80 dots, alternately black and white; a 2-megacycle signal, 160 dots; 3 megacycles, 240 dots; 4 megacycles, 320 dots.

5. As the electron beam scans successive lines, the dots appear as vertical lines. The word lines may therefore be substituted for the word dots in step 4. Thus a relationship is established between video frequency and the number of vertical lines which are produced in three quarters of the scanning width. A one-megacycle signal is equivalent to 80 lines. To convert the number of lines to frequency, divide by 80. Conversely, to convert the horizontal resolution of a receiver, as expressed in frequency, to the equivalent number of lines, multiply the frequency (in megacycles) by 80. For example, if the vertical wedge can be read down to 300 lines, the equivalent bandwidth of the receiver amplifier is 300/80, or 3.75 megacycles. Or if the amplifiers have a bandwidth of 3 megacycles, it should be possible to resolve down to the point on the vertical wedge which corresponds to 3 x 80, or 240 lines.

9-14 Precautions in Checking Resolution. When the wedges in a test pattern are used to measure the vertical and horizontal resolution of a television receiver, several precautions should be observed in order to obtain accurate results.

The contrast, brightness, and focus controls should be adjusted to give a uniformly illuminated picture with sharply focused lines. As pointed out previously, the spot size of the electron beam affects the resolution. Do not over-drive the contrast control, for an over-contrasty picture makes the resolution appear better than it actually is.

Do not measure the resolution with a very weak signal or when the picture is marred by "snow" or other noise interference. Under these conditions, the resolution appears poorer than the true capabilities of the receiver.

Always try to measure the resolution on more than one station test pattern as a check on the quality of signal transmitted by the station. Some stations may be transmitting pictures of low definition, in which case the poor resolution may exist at the transmitter and not at the receiver.

9-15 "Ringing" or Damped Oscillation. The lines marked (H) on the R.M.A. test chart are provided to show "ringing" or damped oscillations which occur in the receiver amplifiers at certain frequencies. These lines are marked 50 to 300 on one range and 350 to 600 on the second range. The significance of these markings and different weights of lines is as follows:

It takes 50 alternate black and white lines, equal in thickness to the line marked "50" to fill three quarters of the width of the picture. It takes 600 alternate black and white lines, equal in thickness to the line marked "600", to stretch across three quarters of the full width of the picture.

If an amplifier in the receiver breaks into spurious oscillation when excited by a particular frequency, the single line in the groups marked (H) which is equivalent to the frequency of os- cillation, will be distorted. For example, a video amplifier may break into oscillation at 2 megacycles when a video signal con- taining this frequency is fed into it. When the electron beam scans across the line in group (H) which corresponds to 2 meg- acycles, the video amplifier will oscillate momentarily. The oscillation will take place when line 160 (160/80=2 Mc) is scan- ned. As a result of this oscillation, several echoes or ghosts will be visible on the pattern, trailing off in diminishing inten- sity after line 160, and perhaps those lines above and below it.

9-16 Interlacing. The four diagonal lines marked (I) are in- cluded at the center of the pattern to check the quality of inter- lacing. Jagged diagonal lines indicate that the scanning lines are not interlacing and that the lines in successive fields are not displaced from one another by exactly half a horizontal line.

9-17 Low Frequency Phase Shift. The heavy black bars mark- ed (J) at the top and bottom of the R.M.A. pattern are used as a check for low frequency phase shift. Since the black bars are relatively long with respect to the total scanning width, the video signal does not make many changes in amplitude while the elec- tron beam scans across these bars. Therefore, the video signal contains very low frequency components which must be passed by the video amplifiers. The longer and heavier the bars, the lower is the video frequency and the more severe is the test of the ability of the amplifiers to reproduce low frequencies with- out amplitude or phase distortion. If such distortion is present, the right ends of the black bars trail off, rather than cut off sharply. This trailing off appears as a grey smear. All thick, black, horizontal lines in the test pattern exhibit this smearing on their right edges if low frequency phase distortion is present in the amplifiers. For example, the 10 black squares in the grey scales will be similarly distorted by poor low frequency response.

9-18 The "Indian Head" Test Pattern. Some manufacturers and stations use the "Indian Head" test pattern, which is generated by a monoscope camera, to check the performance of receiving and transmitting equipment. This pattern is shown in **Figure 4.** It is simpler than the R.M.A. chart, but it is adequate—

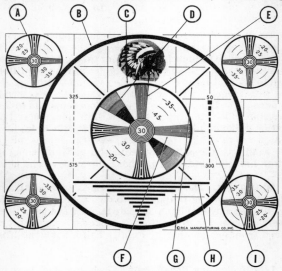

Figure 4. The "Indian head" test pattern.

ly suited for routine test work. The functions of the various geometric designs are as follows:

1. The circles marked (A) should touch the four corners of the mask for a picture of correct size and aspect ratio.

2. The circles marked (A), (B) and (C) are used to check vertical and horizontal linearity. All the circles are round when the sweep signals are linear.

3. All sections of the grey scale marked (D) should be sharp and distinct. These scales check contrast and brightness.

4. Focus is checked using the small circles in the center of the pattern as well as the circles (A) at the four corners of the pattern.

5. The vertical resolution is checked using the horizontal wedges marked (E).

6. The horizontal resolution is checked using the vertical wedges marked (F).

Note that on the Indian Head pattern the last zero is omitted on the calibration numbers near the resolution wedges. Thus "20" actually means 200 lines.

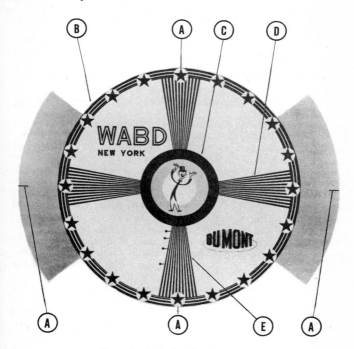

Figure 5. Typical station test pattern.

7. The interlacing is checked using the diagonal lines marked (G).

8. Low frequency phase shift is checked using the heavy horizontal lines marked (H).

9. "Ringing" or damped oscillations are checked by the groups of lines marked (I).

9-19 Typical Station Test Pattern. Test patterns are used by almost all television stations to display their call letters. These patterns are much simpler than the Indian Head pattern just described. A typical station test pattern is shown in Figure 5. The following performance checks can be made using such a station test pattern:

1. The points marked (A) should touch the edges of the mask for a picture of correct size and aspect ratio.

2. The circles marked (B) and (C) are used to check vertical and horizontal linearity. Non-linear Scanning in either direction is readily apparent by distortion of the circles.

3. The gray scale is made up of the circles in the bulls-eye marked (C). The relative clarity of these circles is a check on the setting of the contrast and brightness controls.

4. Focus can be checked by observing the sharpness of the stars on circle (B) and the sharpness of the wedges.

5. Vertical resolution may be checked by using the horizontal wedges marked (D).

6. Horizontal resolution may be checked by using the vertical wedges marked (E). Note that the wedges are not numbered, but that the lower vertical wedge is marked by dots. Since most stations do not show the calibrating resolution numbers on the test pattern, the technician must calibrate the wedges himself, or he may contact the station for the information. The equivalent number of lines at any point on either the vertical or horizontal wedges may be calculated by multiplying the number of black and white lines in the wedge by the ratio of picture height to the width of the wedge at the desired point on the wedge. To convert to frequency, divide the number of lines by 80. These measurements are subject to the errors introduced by non-linearity of scanning when the width of the wedge is scaled off the received test pattern.

7. Interlacing may be checked by using the sharpness of the alternate black and white lines in the horizontal wedges. If the interlacing is poor, the black lines will appear blurred and jagged.

8. Low frequency phase shift may be checked by observing heavy black objects, such as the stars and the black circle in the bulls-eye.

9-20 Test Pattern Analysis. Having studied the significance of the various geometric designs in television test patterns, the technician should be able to use these patterns to check the performance of receivers. On the following pages there are presented a series of test patterns illustrating the effects of various faults which are commonly encountered in television receivers and installations. Below each pattern are trouble-shooting clues for locating and correcting the faults.

Until he is completely familiar with them, the technician will find it advantageous to keep this series of patterns handy when servicing a receiver. By comparing the faulty pattern on the receiver screen with one or more of the patterns which follow, he may quickly diagnose the trouble. Most of the effects illustrated are also discernible on the screen when a program is being broadcast; and when the technician has learned to recognize the effects when they appear in a test pattern, he will usually be able to recognize them when they appear during a program.

It would be difficult to overemphasize the important part which an ability to diagnose test patterns can play in rapid television troubleshooting.

CONTRAST AND BRIGHTNESS CONTROLS MISADJUSTED

Figure 6. Contrast control set too high.

The test patterns which illustrate the misadjustment of the contrast and brightness controls are grouped together, for these two controls are adjusted simultaneously to obtain a properly illuminated picture. Various conditions of adjustment of the contrast and brightness controls are shown in Figures 6, 7, and 8.

Figure 6 illustrates the appearance of a test pattern when the contrast control is set too high. The various shades of grey in the bulls-eye appear as a solid black area. The details of the picture are blurred and there is a lack of half-tone quality. When the brightness control is set too high, as shown in Figure 7, the picture appears white, fuzzy, and washed out. Figure 8 illustrates a condition where the contrast control is set too low and the brightness control too high so that the vertical retrace lines can be seen.

To properly set the contrast and brightness controls, turn the contrast control fully counter-clockwise (no picture on the screen). Advance the brightness control until illumination barely appears on the screen. Then advance the contrast control until the best picture is obtained.

If a properly illuminated picture is not obtained by setting these controls, check the d-c voltages across them.

Figure 7. Brightness control set too high.

Figure 8. Contrast too low, brightness too high.

IMAGE OUT OF FOCUS

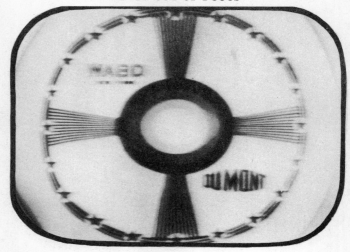

Figure 9.

The appearance of the test pattern when the electron beam is improperly focused is illustrated in Figure 9. The lines in the pattern as well as the scanning lines are not sharply defined.

In most cases this condition may be corrected by simply adjusting the focus control of the receiver. The focus control should be readjusted whenever the brightness control or contrast control is reset.

Often the picture goes out of focus when a receiver has been operating for a long period of time. This happens because the temperature of the focus coil increases, thereby changing the resistance of the coil and the current flowing through it. Or, over a long period of operation, the line voltage may vary and change the focus current. The viewer must readjust the focus control periodically and should be informed of this necessity when an installation is made.

If no setting of the focus control gives uniform focus over the full area of the screen, the focus coil should be rotated slightly and moved back and forth along the neck of the tube, while simultaneously adjusting the focus control. Picture tube and focus coil combinations which uniformly focus the scanning lines over the entire face of the tube are rarely encountered. The best compromise focus should therefore be sought.

FOCUS COIL OR ION TRAP MISALIGNED

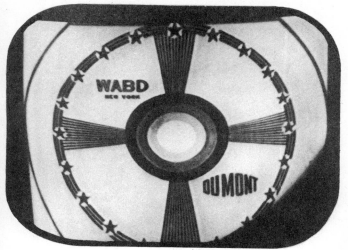

Figure 10.

The shadowed corner and improper positioning of the pattern in Figure 10 indicate that the electron beam is off center and is striking the neck of the tube during part of the scanning cycle. This trouble is due to misalignment of the ion-trap magnet or of the focus coil on the neck of the tube. Since the positions of both coils affect the centering of the beam, it is necessary to adjust both of them in proper sequence in order to determine which coil is causing the trouble.

The ion-trap magnet should be adjusted first. Rotate it slightly, while simultaneously moving it back and forth along the neck of the tube, until the brightest pattern is obtained on the screen with minimum cutoff of the picture. The focus coil should then be tilted back and forth and left and right until the pattern is properly centered and the shadow eliminated.

If it is impossible to locate positions of the ion-trap magnet and focus coil which clear up the trouble, check the yoke to make certain that it is up against the funnel portion of the picture tube. If it is not, the beam is probably striking the neck, even though the ion-trap magnet and focus coil are correctly aligned. If the yoke is properly located and not causing the trouble, then the d-c positioning voltages on the yoke may have moved the beam off center while the ion-trap magnet and focus coil were being adjusted.

PINCUSHIONING OR BARRELING OF THE PATTERN

Figure 11.

Pincushioning (or barreling) of the test pattern, as the name implies, appears as bowing or curving of the edges of the picture. Figure 11. This type of distortion is confined mainly to magnetically deflected and focused picture tubes, but may sometimes appear in electrostatically deflected tubes when the deflection plates are not operated at the same potential as the second anode.

In magnetic tubes, pincushioning is caused by improper positioning or faulty construction of the yoke, focus coil, or ion trap. The effects of the magnetic fields surrounding these components are interdependent, and pincushioning can result because of the cumulative action of all of them. The most likely cause of pincushioning is the focus coil. It may be either tilted or not properly centered on the neck of the tube. At times, stray magnetic fields from the focus coil interact with the yoke and cause this condition. The focus coil should be moved back and forth along the neck of the tube to find a position which produces the minimum distortion.

Poorly shaped vertical or horizontal deflection coils in the yoke can produce pincushioning. If it is found that the focus coil is not causing the trouble, a new yoke should be tried. It is also possible that the yoke is not designed for the face curvature of the tube with which it is being used.

PICTURE ROTATED

Figure 12.

The test pattern in Figure 12 is "out of square" with respect to the edges of the mask opening. In the case of receivers employing magnetically deflected tubes, rotation of the picture in this manner is caused by the improper positioning of the deflection yoke. This fault can be corrected by loosening the bolts which hold the yoke in place and rotating the yoke until the edges of the picture line up with the mask. The bolts may then be tightened to secure the yoke in its proper position.

The improper orientation of the picture with respect to the mask may also be caused by a damaged yoke in which the vertical and horizontal coils have been moved out of line and are no longer mutually perpendicular. A damaged yoke is indicated when it is found that rotating the yoke around the neck of the tube does not line up the picture with the edges of the mask.

In receivers equipped with electrostatic deflection, the condition shown in this test pattern is caused by an improperly oriented picture tube. The tube itself has rotated with respect to the mask opening. The trouble may be corrected by rotating the tube until the picture is "in square" with the mask. If rotating the tube does not overcome the trouble, the vertical and horizontal deflection plates are probably out of line. Another tube must be substituted to check this possibility.

UNSTABLE HORIZONTAL SYNCHRONIZATION

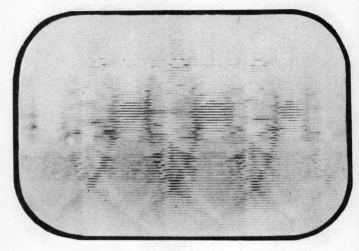

Figure 13.

Figures 13, 14 and 15 illustrate three degrees of unstable horizontal synchronization of a receiver with conventional triggered sync. The main characteristic of these patterns, which distinguishes them from those appearing on a receiver equipped with automatic frequency control of the sync circuit is the tearing of the picture into strips. If a receiver is equipped with a.f.c., the picture as a whole rolls out of synchronism.

In Figure 13 the horizontal hold control is far off frequency. As it is adjusted to approach synchronism, the pattern of Figure 14 is obtained. In Figure 15 the picture is correctly synchronized, but there is a slight tearing at the top and bottom which may be due to a microphonic or noisy tube in the sync circuits or a loose connection in the r-f, i-f, or horizontal sync circuits.

Unstable horizontal synchronization can exist regardless of the setting of the horizontal hold control. It may be due to too weak a signal, too strong a signal, a defective sync separator or amplifier tube, or a circuit defect such as loss of supply voltages, an open circuit, etc. Under these conditions it is best to signal trace the sync circuits to isolate the fault. Pull out the horizontal sweep oscillator tube and signal trace the sync signals with an oscillograph, starting at the grid of the sweep oscillator and working back toward the input of the sync separator.

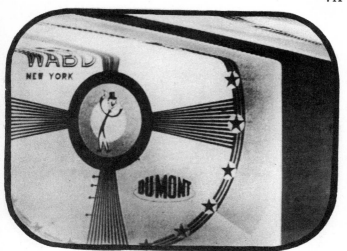

Figure 14.

Figure 15.

HORIZONTAL SYNC OFF FREQUENCY

Figure 16.

Figure 16 shows the test pattern as it appears when the horizontal oscillator is off frequency in a receiver with automatic frequency control of the horizontal sweep circuit. The picture as a whole rolls rather than tears out, as is characteristic of a triggered sync circuit.

The unstable sync condition illustrated above may be caused by an incorrectly set horizontal hold control. If no setting of the horizontal hold control pulls the picture into synchronism, the oscillator in the a.f.c. sync circuit is probably out of tune. The oscillator frequency should be so adjusted that the picture locks in when the hold control is set at either end of its range. This condition may be checked by tuning the receiver to a station while the hold control is in its center position. If the picture is synchronized, turn the control to either end and switch to another channel. Upon switching back to the original channel, the picture should immediately lock-in when the hold control is at either end of its range. If the picture does not readily synchronize over the entire range of the hold control, the oscillator frequency should be readjusted until this condition is achieved. Since adjustment of the oscillator also affects the phasing control in an a.f.c. sync circuit and visa versa, it is best to consult the manufacturer's service manual for the sequence in which these adjustments should be made.

HORIZONTAL SYNC DISCRIMINATOR PHASE MISADJUSTED

Figure 17.

Figure 17 shows the effect, on the received test pattern, of an incorrectly adjusted phasing control in the discriminator circuit of an automatic frequency control sync system. The picture is synchronized to a constant frequency, but the horizontal saw-tooth sweep voltages occur at the wrong time in the scanning cycle. As a result, the horizontal retrace, which occurs during the blanking period (the vertical black bar near the right side of the image), appears on the screen.

In most cases proper phasing of the picture can be obtained by simply readjusting the phasing control on the discriminator transformer. This balances the voltages at the plates of the discriminator diodes so that their output is zero at the time when the start of the sweep should occur. Adjustment of the phasing control may also affect the horizontal oscillator frequency. The latter must then be readjusted according to the procedure described on the preceding pages. Most manufacturers' manuals outline the proper sequence for adjusting these controls with a minimum of difficulty.

The unbalanced sync and oscillator voltages in the discriminator circuit which lead to the trouble shown in this pattern may also be caused by a defective diode or other component.

VERTICAL HOLD CONTROL MISADJUSTED

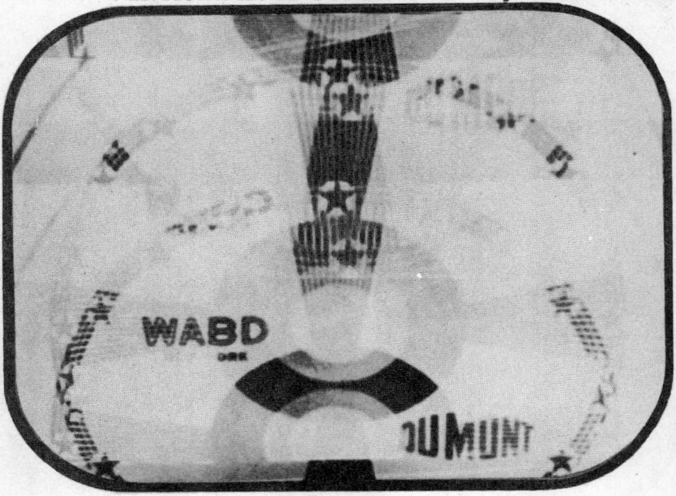

Figure 18.

The appearance of the test pattern when the vertical scanning is out of synchronism is shown in Figure 18. The picture rolls or jumps from top to bottom. In most cases, this trouble is caused by the incorrect adjustment of the vertical hold control which sets the frequency of the vertical scanning oscillator. The vertical hold control should be turned until the picture locks in vertically. This control is on the front panel of some receivers and must periodically be set by the viewer. In other receivers it is located on the rear of the chassis and is adjusted by the technician, after which it needs no further attention.

If the vertical synchronization is unstable, check the signal level coming into the receiver to make certain that it is above the minimum strength recommended by the manufacturer.

If the signal at the input of the receiver is adequate, and if resetting the vertical hold control does not synchronize the picture, then the trouble is probably in the vertical sync circuits. It is best to signal trace the vertical scanning system to locate the fault. Starting at the grid of the sweep oscillator, check for a clean, positive vertical sync pulse (the oscillator tube should be pulled out when making this check). Then proceed to each section of the integrating network and check for vertical sync signal continuity. Continue to the plate of the sync separator where clean sync signals should exist.

POOR INTERLACING

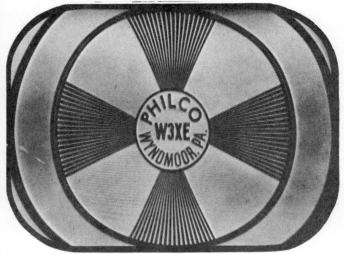

Figure 19.

Figure 19 shows the appearance of the test pattern under conditions of poor interlacing. The scanning lines are easily visible because the odd and even lines overlap, rather than fall between each other. In some cases, the scanning lines may drift in and out of interlace as is evidenced by the ripples in the horizontal wedges.

Poor interlacing at the receiver may be caused by improper adjustment of the vertical hold control, by erratic vertical sync pulses which do not repeat at constant frequency and phase, or by spurious signals which modulate the vertical sync pulses.

A defective component in the vertical integrating network is likely to distort the vertical sync pulses and therefore affect the stability of synchronization. The operation of the integrating network may be checked by removing the sweep oscillator tube and connecting a cathode-ray oscillograph between the grid pin on the empty socket and ground. The vertical sync pulses at the output of the integrating circuit can be observed at this point. The pulses should be sharp and free of jitter. If not, trace back through each section of the network with the oscillograph to locate the faulty component. Cross-coupling with the horizontal deflection circuits due to improper lead positioning, defective B+ by-pass condensers, or a leaky sync separator tube may cause poor vertical interlacing.

INCORRECT HORIZONTAL SIZE

Figure 20.

The width of the picture is determined by the amplitude of the sawtooth voltage applied to the horizontal deflection coils or deflection plates. The test pattern in Figure 20 illustrates the effect which results when the sawtooth amplitude is not properly adjusted. The amplitude of the sawtooth voltage is controlled, in most receivers, by varying a potentiometer in the charging circuit of the sawtooth generator. The range of adjustment is usually sufficient to permit setting the picture to the correct width. In some receivers other controls, such as the horizontal linearity, horizontal drive, and horizontal damping controls, also affect the width of the picture. These controls should be adjusted simultaneously with the horizontal width control to obtain correct picture size and optimum linearity.

A faulty horizontal sweep amplifier tube or a defective component in the sawtooth charging circuit will also affect the picture width. Signal tracing with an oscillograph is the recommended troubleshooting procedure when no setting of the horizontal size control results in proper adjustment. Check the amplitude and waveshape of the sweep voltages against those given in the manufacturer's instruction book at the following points in the circuit: across the horizontal deflection coil, the grid of the sweep amplifier tube, and the output of the sawtooth generator.

INCORRECT VERTICAL SIZE

Figure 21.

The most common cause of the condition shown in Figure 21 is improper adjustment of the vertical size control. The pattern shown illustrates a condition caused by excessive vertical sweep amplitude. If the amplitude of the vertical sweep is low, the pattern will be compressed, leaving a dark space above and below it. The vertical size control is generally located on the rear of the receiver chassis and should not be disturbed by the viewer. It must be set by the technician when the receiver is installed. The vertical size control is a potentiometer located in the vertical sawtooth generator or vertical sweep amplifier circuit. By varying this control, the sawtooth voltage fed to the deflection yoke or deflection plates is changed, thereby changing the height of the picture. The vertical size control should be set so that the picture just fills the mask opening.

If no setting of the size control produces a picture of sufficient height, the amplitude of the vertical sawtooth voltage is low. With an oscillograph, check the peak-to-peak sawtooth voltage at the output of the sawtooth generator across the yoke and compare with the manufacturer's recommendations. A weak sweep amplifier tube, defective yoke or defective sweep output transformer are common causes of insufficient sawtooth voltage. Check the a-c line voltage and the plate supply voltage.

HORIZONTAL CENTERING MISADJUSTED

Figure 22.

If the horizontal centering control is not correctly adjusted, the test pattern will appear as shown in Figure 22. Two methods of centering the picture are employed in television receivers. The simplest method, used in low-cost receivers, is to center the picture horizontally by adjusting the mechanical position of the focus coil. When centering the electron beam by positioning the focus coil, adjustments of the ion-trap magnet must be made simultaneously to prevent cutting off of the picture at its corners. It may also be necessary to compromise on the quality of focus in order to achieve a centered picture. Receivers in which horizontal centering is achieved by positioning the focus coil usually have adjustable mounting bolts to vary the orientation of the coil.

Electrical centering of the picture is used in some receivers. A potentiometer, the horizontal centering control, varies the d-c voltage applied to the deflecting yoke or deflection plates. By varying this control in a properly operating receiver, the picture may be centered horizontally. The centering control is generally located on the rear of the receiver chassis and is set by the technician, after which it should require no adjustment by the user. If the picture cannot be centered with the horizontal centering control, check the d-c voltage across the control to see if it corresponds to the manufacturer's rating.

VERTICAL CENTERING MISADJUSTED

Figure 23.

When the vertical centering control is not correctly adjusted, the pattern is not properly centered, as shown in Figure 23. Vertical centering is accomplished in two ways, by the mechanical positioning of the focus coil, or by injecting a d-c voltage into the deflection yoke or deflection plates.

In receivers employing mechanical positioning of the focus coil to center the electron beam, adjustable mounting bolts are provided to move the coil into the correct position. The focus coil and ion-trap magnet should be adjusted simultaneously in order to avoid cutting off the corners of the picture, to properly center the picture, and to secure the best possible focus.

When vertical centering is obtained by electrical means, a variable d-c voltage is applied to the deflection plates or deflection yoke. The amplitude of this voltage is controlled by a potentiometer referred to as the vertical centering control. If proper centering cannot be obtained by varying the vertical centering control, check the line voltage and d-c voltage across the positioning potentiometer. If these voltages do not meet the manufacturer's specifications, check the power supply and all components in the centering circuits.

HORIZONTAL LINEARITY MISADJUSTED

Figure 24.

The method used to adjust the linearity of the horizontal deflection signal differs widely in the various television receiver designs. Many receivers use more than one control. It is therefore best to consult the manufacturer's service manual to determine the effect each control has upon the linear distribution of the picture elements. Distortion of the horizontal linearity is easily recognizable by an egg-shaped test pattern, as shown in Figure 24, or by cramping of one side of the picture.

In the simplest type of deflection circuit, as used with electrostatic deflection, a potentiometer in the cathode circuit of the sweep amplifier serves as the linearity control. Adjustment of this control changes the operating bias of the tube and corrects for distortion of the sawtooth voltage. In magnetic deflection systems, linearity controls are located in the cathode of the sweep amplifier tube as well as in the damping circuit. Usually, the linearity control must be adjusted in combination with the horizontal width control in order to obtain an image of proper width and linearity. If no combination of settings of these controls produces linear scanning, check the values of the components in the horizontal sweep circuits. A defective component in the horizontal deflection circuits, such as the charging capacitor, charging resistor, etc., can cause a non-linear sweep.

HORIZONTAL LINEARITY MISADJUSTED (cramped on right)

Figure 25.

It is sometimes found that no matter how the horizontal linearity control is adjusted, the right side of the picture is cramped as shown in Figure 25. This condition is sometimes caused,
in magnetic deflection circuits, by an improperly adjusted horizontal drive control. The control is located in the output of the
sawtooth generator circuit and controls the voltage applied to
the deflection amplifier tube and the point on the scanning trace
at which it conducts. By virtue of its position in the circuit, the
drive control affects the width and horizontal linearity of the
picture. It is normally set for the widest possible picture without cramping the right side. The width control and linearity
control are then adjusted to obtain the correct scanning width
and good line distribution across the middle and left side of the
image. However, if the drive control is set too far, the right
side is crowded, and no amount of adjustment of the linearity
or width controls can compensate for the distortion.

In some horizontal deflection circuits, a feedback system is
used to feed a negative pulse from the output transformer to the
grid of the sweep amplifier, in order to determine its point of
conduction. In such circuits, the drive control is a potentiometer, connected across part of the secondary of the output
transformer, to control the amplitude of the feedback pulse.

DEFECTIVE DAMPING OF THE HORIZONTAL SWEEP

Figure 26.

Receivers employing magnetically deflected picture tubes use a damping tube or damping network to suppress shock oscillations which occur during the retrace period of the saw-tooth voltage. The damping components are subjected to high peak voltages during the retrace period and may break down if their ratings are exceeded. When failure occurs in the damping circuit, the left side of the pattern is distorted as shown in Figure 26. The picture folds over at the left, or white, vertical bars appear near the left edge. Note that only the horizontal scanning can be affected by such a failure.

No amount of adjustment of the horizontal linearity controls can eliminate the foldover caused by a damping circuit failure. If a diode or triode is used as a damping tube, it should be replaced by a new tube as the first step in tracking down the trouble. Some manufacturers provide waveform diagrams in their service manuals which illustrate the voltage waveshapes which should be obtained at various points in the damping circuit of a normally operating receiver. These points should be checked with an oscillograph. Signal tracing in this manner often turns up a defective component, other than the damping tube.

In some receivers, a variable potentiometer in the cathode of the damping circuit may be in need of adjustment.

VERTICAL LINEARITY MISADJUSTED

Figure 27.

Misadjustment of the vertical linearity control distorts the vertical scanning as shown in Figure 27. The vertical linearity control is generally a potentiometer located in the cathode circuit of the sweep amplifier tube. By varying this potentiometer, the tube is made to operate on either the straight or curved portion of its characteristic curve and corrects for distortions in the sawtooth voltage. When adjusting the linearity control, it may be necessary to re-set the vertical size control because the linearity control also affects the amplification of the tube.

Other conditions which cannot be corrected by setting the linearity control may cause distortion of the vertical linearity. A defective sweep amplifier tube or defective component in the output stage are common faults. A partially shorted winding in the vertical output transformer or deflection coil also affects the linearity. A defective component in the sawtooth generator circuit or low plate supply voltage to the sweep circuits is another possible cause of vertical sweep distortion.

An examination of the waveshape of the voltages at the grid of the sweep amplifier tube and across the deflection coil will help to isolate the trouble to either the sawtooth generator circuit or the sweep amplifier stage.

FOLD OVER AT TOP OF PICTURE

Figure 28.

A type of vertical distortion which may occur in magnetic deflection systems is shown in the test pattern of Figure 28. The top lines of the picture are crowded and, in extreme cases, overlapping or foldover of the lines occurs. This distortion is caused by the vertical discharge circuit and no adjustment of the vertical linearity or size control can eliminate it. It will be recalled that in order to produce a linear sawtooth current in the vertical deflection coil, it is necessary to add a pulse to the sawtooth voltage which is applied to the coil. This pulse is produced in the discharge circuit by inserting a resistor, referred to as a peaking resistor, in series with the charging condenser. The value of the resistor is chosen to suit the design of the deflection coil, the coupling transformer, and the sweep amplifier tube. If the peaking resistor or charging condenser is defective, the amplitude and shape of the pulse added to the sawtooth voltage are affected, causing crowding of the lines or foldover at the top of the picture.

To correct the peaking voltage, replace the peaking resistor with a potentiometer whose total resistance is greater than that specified for the peaking resistor. Vary the potentiometer resistance until the crowding or overlapping of lines disappears. Then measure the portion of the potentiometer resistance which is used and solder a fixed resistor or equal value in its place.

NO HORIZONTAL SWEEP

Figure 29.

Failure of the horizontal sweep circuit cuts off the horizontal deflection of the scanning beam, leaving only a vertical line on the screen as shown in Figure 29. In order to avoid burning a line in the screen while troubleshooting for the fault, turn down the brightness control so that the line is barely visible.

Since the vertical sweep is still working, it is probable that the plate voltage which is fed to the sweep circuits is all right. The fault is most likely caused by a defective component or open lead in the horizontal sweep circuit. A systematic waveform check with an oscillograph should readily isolate the trouble. Signal trace the horizontal sweep circuit, starting at the horizontal deflection coil and work back in the circuit toward the sawtooth generator. The check points across which the oscillograph may be connected safely are as follows: the horizontal deflection coil, the cathode and grid of the sweep amplifier tube, the plate of the sawtooth generator tube, and the grid of the sweep oscillator tube. At each check point, compare the waveform obtained with that illustrated in the manufacturer's service manual. The waveform should check both in amplitude and shape. Signal tracing in this manner will indicate whether or not the sweep oscillator is functioning and the sawtooth voltages are being generated.

NO VERTICAL SWEEP

Figure 30.

A horizontal line on the screen as shown in Figure 30 indicates that vertical scanning is not present. Before attempting to troubleshoot the vertical sweep circuit, turn down the brightness control so that the screen will not be damaged.

Since the horizontal sweep is working (as are probably the sound and video circuits), the power supplies are functioning properly. The fault is generally due to a defective component or open lead in the vertical sweep circuit. The most common failures in this circuit are open vertical deflection coils or sweep transformer windings, and defective sweep amplifier and vertical discharge tubes. The trouble may readily be isolated by signal tracing the discharge circuit and the sweep amplifier stage with an oscillograph. With the oscillograph connected across the following points in succession, check for signal continuity as well as proper amplitude and waveshape: the vertical deflection coil, the grid and cathode of the sweep amplifier tube, and the plate of the vertical discharge tube. Finally, check the waveform at the grid of the vertical sweep oscillator tube to make certain that this stage is oscillating and feeding discharge pulses to the sawtooth generator. There is no need to check further into the sync circuits for they do not affect the generation of the vertical sawtooth sweep voltage.

NO VIDEO SIGNAL, RASTER ONLY

Figure 31.

When a raster appears on the screen as shown in Figure 31, the following line of reasoning may be used to isolate the trouble. Since a raster is obtained, there is no trouble in the sweep circuits, sweep power supplies, and probably not in the sync circuits. If the audio is coming through, the r-f circuits must be operating properly. On the other hand, if both the audio and video are dead, then the trouble most likely lies in the r-f section or the power supplies.

Assuming that the audio and video sections are not working, check the supply voltages with a voltmeter. If the voltages are correct, proceed to the r-f section. Tap the grid of the mixer tube. A click should be heard in the speaker and dark bands should appear on the screen if the audio and video i-f circuits are working. The same results should be obtained when the input to the antenna coupling stage is tapped if the r-f section is functioning. Also check the oscillator stage by simply looping the oscillograph input lead around the oscillator tube or coil. A high frequency oscillation should be observed on the scope if the oscillator is operating. If it is assumed that the audio is coming through, the trouble probably lies in the video section. It can be isolated by tapping the grid or plate of each tube. Dark bands should be observed on the screen when the tubes are tapped if there is signal continuity.

POWER SUPPLY HUM OR RIPPLE IN PICTURE

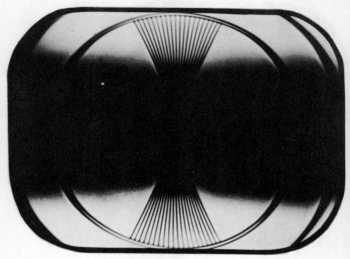

Figure 32.

Hum or ripples show up in the test pattern as dark, horizontal bands of constant intensity or wavy edges of the picture. The cause is usually a defective component or an open lead in the power supply filter section, or in the by-pass circuits of any stage in the receiver. The hum bars are due to excessive 60-cycle or 120-cycle ripple. Troubleshooting should start at the output of the plate and bias supplies. Check these points with an oscillograph for any noticeable ripple. If hum does not exist at this point, the trouble is probably a defective by-pass condenser in the video or sweep circuits. The fault may readily be confined to a particular section of the receiver by recognizing on the screen the hum pattern which shows up in a characteristic manner when a stage is troubled by excessive ripple. The patterns are illustrated in Figures 32, 33 and 34.

Figure 32 shows a test pattern in which 60-cycle hum, coming through the video amplifier or video i-f stages, produces uneven illumination.

Excessive 60-cycle ripple in the horizontal sweep circuits is shown in Figure 33.

The effect of 120-cycle ripple appears as twice the number of dark and light bands that are produced by 60-cycle ripple as shown in Figure 34.

Figure 33.

Figure 34.

LOSS OF HIGH VIDEO FREQUENCIES

Figure 35.

The loss of the high video frequencies shows up in the test pattern as a lack of sharpness of the fine details, particularly apparent in the vertical wedges. Figure 35 shows a test pattern as reproduced by a receiver which suffers from a considerable loss of high video frequencies. Note that the fine lines in the vertical wedges wash out before they reach the bulls-eye.

In order to reproduce fine details in the test pattern, the amplifiers in the r-f and video sections of the receiver must have uniform response up to 3.5 to 4 megacycles. An improperly aligned amplifier stage will narrow the overall bandwidth and attenuate the high frequencies. If this condition exists as indicated by the lack of detail in the vertical wedges, it is best to first check the alignment of the video i-f amplifiers with an oscillograph, sweep generator, and signal generator. An overall check of all the video i-f stages will suffice, unless this check indicates that the trouble exists in one of the stages. A stage-by-stage check should then be made to locate the misaligned coupling transformer.

If the video i-f stages are correctly aligned, the r-f tuner should be checked on each channel. Finally, the frequency response of the video amplifier should be measured with a signal generator and sweep generator (or square wave generator) in conjunction with an oscillograph.

LOSS OF LOW VIDEO FREQUENCIES

Figure 36.

Poor low frequency response in the amplifiers of the r-f and video sections is generally accompanied by phase distortion at these frequencies. This condition is indicated by a smearing of large objects and letters, and a blurring of the horizontal wedges in the test pattern, as shown in Figure 36.

If the sound is loud and undistorted, it is reasonable to assume that the r-f section is correctly aligned and that the low frequency distortion is occurring in the video i-f amplifiers or the video amplifier. Improper alignment of the video i-f amplifiers generally permits sound signals to enter the video circuits. These signals appear as horizontal bars, drifting up and down on the screen. If these bars are not present and only the smearing effect is observed, it may be assumed that the i-f amplifiers are correctly aligned and that the trouble is in the video amplifier.

To definitely establish whether or not the low frequency distortion is taking place in the video amplifier, feed a 60-cycle square wave into the grid of the amplifier and observe its output on an oscillograph which has good low frequency response. If the top of the square waves slopes downward, low frequency distortion is present in the video amplifier. The poor response is mostly likely caused by a shorted load resistor or an open by-pass condenser in the plate or screen supply circuits.

SOUND IN THE PICTURE

Figure 37.

Figure 37 shows a test pattern which is marred by sound signals riding through the video channel to the grid of the picture tube. The sound signals are those accompanying the video information. When they get into the picture, they appear as horizontal black bands which closely resemble a power-supply ripple in the video amplifier stage. Sound ripple shows up as many bands, changing in intensity and moving up and down the screen in synchronism with the amplitude and frequency of the audio. The black bands produced by excessive a-c ripple do not vary in intensity, and are one or two in number, depending on whether the ripple is 60 cycles or 120 cycles.

The most common cause of sound modulation of the video signals is improper adjustment of the r-f tuner. To tune a receiver correctly, the fine-tuning control should be set for maximum sound. If the sound bars cannot be eliminated by resetting the fine-tuning control, or can only be removed by a tuning adjustment that causes the sound to be distorted, the receiver is probably out of alignment. Misalignment can exist in the r-f tuner or the sound traps of the video i-f amplifier. First check the alignment of the video i-f amplifier and sound traps with a sweep generator, signal generator, and oscillograph. Check the alignment of the r-f tuner in the same way.

TOO WEAK A SIGNAL

Figure 38.

The signal strength at the receiver may be so low that only a faint picture can be obtained, accompanied by considerable noise and poor synchronization. See Figure 38. This condition may be deceiving and prompt the technician to attempt to realign the video circuits for greater gain, a procedure which would be to no avail. A field strength meter or calibrated receiver connected to the antenna system will readily indicate the signal level. If this level is below the minimum signal for which the receiver is designed (as indicated in the manufacturer's manual), a few things can be done to increase the signal. Increasing the height of the antenna may help, provided the increased length of transmission line does not introduce additional losses which offset the gain in signal strength. A reflector may be added to the antenna if one does not already exist, or one of the high gain antennas described in Section 5 may be tried. Or, finally, an r-f amplifier stage may prove effective. R-F amplifiers or "boosters" are available commercially and are easily inserted in the transmission line.

In some areas the signal strength may be sufficient on all stations except one or two. Erecting separate antennas which are cut and directed for the weak stations may prove a convenient solution.

TOO STRONG A SIGNAL

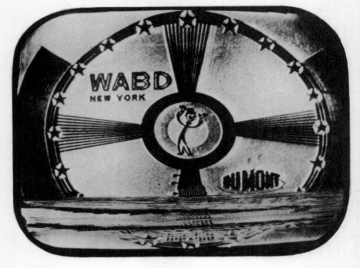

Figure 39.

Often the signal level at the receiver input is so high that it overloads the input circuits. This condition is indicated by a loss of synchronization, an over-contrasty image, and sometimes by sound modulation in the picture. The overload condition may be remedied by reducing the signal input, using an H-pad attenuator inserted between the receiver input terminals and the antenna transmission line so that the signal is below the overload value for the particular receiver. The signal input should be measured with a field strength meter and resistor values selected to make up the required H-pad. Half-watt carbon resistors should be used. If a field strength meter is not available, various H-pads may be made up and tried. The pad with the minimum attenuation that removes the overload conditions should then be wired into the transmission line.

Another effective means of reducing the signal is to hook a piece of solder, several inches long, directly across the antenna terminals of the receiver. Although this solder may appear to be a short circuit, it actually is long enough at the television frequencies to have sufficient impedance so as not to by-pass the signal completely. In some areas the signal strength is so strong from all stations that it is possible to prevent overloading by eliminating the outdoor antenna.

GHOSTS OR MULTIPLE-PATH SIGNAL

Figure 40.

A ghost or multi-path signal appears on the screen as an off-set duplicate of the pattern as shown in Figure 40. The amount of offset is proportional to the difference in the path distance of the direct signal and that of the reflected signal.

If the reflected signal is almost equal in amplitude to the direct signal, it will affect the sync stability of the receiver, since the sweep circuits can synchronize on either the direct or reflected signal.

The reflection can usually be eliminated if a directive antenna, oriented so as to accept the main signal and discriminate against the reflected signals, is used. Under some conditions, where there is no direct path between receiver and transmitter, it is possible to orient the antenna so as to receive a reflected signal. The antenna must then be positioned to accept the best reflected signal and discriminate against all others.

If the reflected signal is received from the same direction as the direct signal, a directive antenna cannot reduce the reflection. The only solution to this problem is to attenuate the composite signal until the reflection disappears. The direct signal will probably still be strong enough to be usable.

If it is impossible to eliminate ghosts on more than one station with a single antenna, separate antennas may be used.

TRANSIENTS IN THE PICTURE

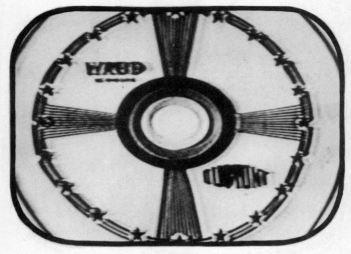

Figure 41.

Transients are caused by improper matching in the antenna system or by improper tuning of the video circuits. As shown in Figure 41, transients closely resemble ghosts in the picture. In order to establish whether or not the effect is a transient or a ghost, the antenna should be rotated. If the interference disappears or changes, then it is caused by a reflected or ghost signal. If it remains the same, then the effect is due to poor transient response in the antenna system or the video circuits. Poor transient response is the inability of a tuned circuit to pass sudden amplitude changes without distortion. Instead, there is a tendency toward oscillation when these components occur, resulting in a double image.

To check the antenna system for mismatch, determine the input impedance of the receiver and compare it with that of the transmission line and antenna. If the transmission line or antenna does not match the receiver impedance, suitable matching stubs should be inserted. If it is established that there is no mismatch in the antenna system, then the alignment of the r-f amplifier, picture i-f amplifier and video amplifier stages should be checked. A sweep generator and oscillograph may be used for the alignment of the r-f and video i-f amplifiers. No overshoot of the response curve appears when the amplifier has good transient response.

IGNITION INTERFERENCE

Figure 42.

The ignition systems of automobiles produce static which enters the receiver via the antenna system and causes light and dark spots and horizontal streaks in the picture, as shown in Figure 42. When severe ignition noise is present, picture tearing occurs.

When ignition noise is encountered, an attempt should be made to increase the signal pickup while attenuating the noise. Often this can be accomplished by using a high-gain directive antenna. Anything else done to increase signal strength will improve the signal-to-noise ratio and improve the picture. Shortening the antenna transmission line, using a low-loss transmission line, and elevating the antenna are effective. Coaxial or shielded parallel cable is usually more effective than twin-lead in reducing noise pickup. If twin-lead is used, it should be twisted, since this reduces noise pickup. The outer shield of coaxial or shielded pair lines should be connected to a good ground.

Moving the antenna out of the direct noise field, even at the expense of signal strength, is often beneficial. If the signal strength is extremely low, a long wire "V", rhombic, or similar type high-gain antenna will help if one can be erected.

DIATHERMY INTERFERENCE

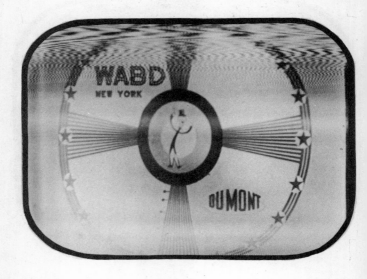

Figure 43.

Although most modern diathermy machines are equipped with
r-f filters so that radiation and feedback into the power supply
system are reduced, there are still many old and defective
machines in existence which cause considerable interference
with television reception. The high frequency diathermy signals
beat with the television carrier and cause the rippled pattern
shown in Figure 43. Some diathermy machines operate on fixed
frequencies which are close to the i-f frequency of television
receivers. Often the frequency of the diathermy apparatus drifts
and moves into the i-f frequency band of the receiver, causing
an interference pattern which slowly drifts up and down on the
viewing screen. Little can be done to the antenna installation
to remove this interference, although a directive antenna may
sometimes help. A more practical solution is to locate the
machine and ask the owner to maintain the apparatus at its correct operating frequency or shield it. If the technician is absolutely sure that the diathermy machine is operating outside of
the assigned frequency band for diathermy machines and the
owner is unwilling to cooperate, a report should be made to the
Federal Communications Commission.

BEAT FREQUENCY INTERFERENCE

Figure 44.

Often strong a-m and f-m signals beat with the sound or picture carriers of a television station. If the resulting heterodyne frequency falls within the channel to which the receiver is tuned, an interference pattern is produced which appears in the picture as a series of fine vertical or slanting lines, as shown in Figure 44. The interference pattern drifts slowly through the picture as the television carrier or the interfering carrier changes frequency slightly.

The unwanted carrier may be filtered out by inserting a wavetrap in series or shunt with the antenna lead-in. Suitable values for such traps can be found in Section 8. Another method which is often effective in trapping out the interfering frequency is to connect a piece of coaxial cable or parallel lead-in across the antenna input terminals of the receiver. Starting with a piece about two feet long, the cable is clipped off, a little at a time, until the beat frequency is eliminated. Of course, the use of a wavetrap or piece of transmission line to eliminate the interfering carrier is predicated on the condition that the unwanted signal is fixed in frequency. If it is not and varies over a wide range, little can be done to eliminate it.

9-21 Troubleshooting for other Faults. Many common troubles which occur in the receiver cannot be detected by observing the picture on the screen. In order to locate the cause of such troubles, the technician should first isolate the fault to a particular section of the receiver, as described earlier. To locate the faulty stage and component, two procedures are possible. One is to be thoroughly familiar with the functions of each stage in the section and thus be able to spot characteristic troubles. The other is to signal trace the circuit, looking for the waveforms which are characteristic of a properly and improperly operating receiver. Both of these methods are described, wherever applicable, in discussing other troubles which are common to the six basic sections of a television receiver.

9-22 Troubleshooting the R-F Section. This section includes the antenna, r-f input circuit, r-f amplifier (if present), the local oscillator, and the first detector. Troubleshooting the r-f section must start at the installation itself. Unlike the servicing of a radio receiver which can be brought to the shop and repaired, the location of the television receiver and its antenna and transmission line all affect its performance. Before removing a receiver from the installation, the technician should carefully examine the complete installation to make certain that the trouble does not exist outside the receiver. The troubleshooting procedure for the r-f section can be divided into two steps: 1. preliminary checks at the receiver installation, and 2. troubleshooting the set at the shop. A third step might also be considered, that of re-installing the receiver after repairs have been made. This again involves the routine of step 1.

The following troubles can be attributed to the antenna installation and receiver input.

    a. Local interference.
    b. Too strong a signal.
    c. Too weak a signal.
    d. Diathermy.
    e. Beat frequencies.
    f. Transients in the transmission line.
    g. Multi-path signals.

These faults were treated in Section 8 and in the previous group of test patterns, where methods were outlined for their cure.

9-23 Switch Contact Troubles. In r-f tuners employing a switch arrangement, the transmission line is coupled to the receiver through coupling transformers, each tuned for a different channel. Ganged to the coupling coil switch are the oscillator circuit coils. At the high television frequencies, the contact resistance and inductance of the switch terminals are critical. Slight variations in contact resistance are enough to detune the oscillator or change the characteristics of the band pass circuits. Gradual wear of the contacts changes the contact resistance and the inductive path. This trouble occurs especially with knife-type switches which do not close in the same position at all times and cause severe oscillator drift.

Most receivers using switches have a small variable trimmer in the oscillator circuit to correct for this drift. The trimmer may or may not have sufficient range to compensate for circuit changes, depending upon the design of the oscillator and the seriousness of the change.

9-24 Oscillator Faults. Severe oscillator drift results in the loss of sound, although the picture is still present. The picture obtained under these conditions will not be good, but some of it will come through, since the picture channel is 4 Mc wide — greater, as a rule, than the oscillator drift. The sound channel for television, on the other hand, is only 50 kc wide and the change in oscillator frequency is often sufficient to move the sound intermediate frequency out of the pass band. If parts of the oscillator circuit, such as the switch or tube sockets have to be replaced, the oscillator frequencies on all channels are usually affected and all the oscillator coils have to be reset.

When neither picture or sound are present it is possible that the oscillator is at fault. If the power supplies are functioning properly, check to see that the oscillator is working by holding the input lead of the oscillograph near the oscillator and noting whether the high frequency is picked up. If no oscillations are generated, the oscillator tube and wiring should be checked. If the oscillator is functioning, the trouble is probably in the r-f amplifier (if one is used), or in the tuned r-f circuits. Test the r-f tube and associated circuit wiring. If any changes are required, the circuits should be realigned.

9-25 The Video Section. If a poor picture is present on the receiver screen at the installation, and the installation does not suffer from antenna or r-f section trouble, it is likely that the trouble lies in the video channel. In this case, the receiver should be brought to the shop for troubleshooting and alignment.

If no picture is being received but the sound is coming through, it is a good indication that the r-f section is functioning properly and the trouble lies somewhere after the first detector. Obvious faults in this case are open leads, burned-out components, or defective tubes. An efficient method of troubleshooting the video channel rapidly is that of signal substitution. This consists of substituting a signal from a signal generator, for the normally received signal, and noting the output on an oscillograph or vacuum tube voltmeter. The procedure should start from the grid of the picture tube and work back toward the input of the i-f amplifiers. For example, a 2 Mc signal can be injected into the video amplifier grid and the output observed at the grid of the picture tube. If output is obtained, the video amplifier is operating. Now, putting the oscillograph with its probe detector across the grid of the video amplifier and injecting a modulated i-f carrier signal into successive i-f stages (starting from the output of the last stage), these circuits can be checked. If during the above procedure an injection point is reached which does not produce output, the fault is in the circuits between this point and the last injection point used. The components of the circuits thus indicated should be checked and the faulty ones replaced. The overall response of the video channel should then be checked.

Microphonic resistors, condensers, or tubes in which the elements are not rigidly fixed, cause patterns of splotches in the picture. Any vibration of the receiver sets the elements in motion, generating transient currents. Noisy components can usually be located by tapping each suspected component with a light object such as the eraser end of a pencil. Sometimes, substitution of tubes is necessary to isolate a faulty one.

9-26 Sound Channel Faults. The usual faults in the sound channel fall into two main categories. 1. No sound at all, and 2. Distortion of sound.

Lack of sound is due to one of two troubles. The first is obvious and is due to an open lead or defective component in the sound channel. A stage-by-stage signal substitution check should isolate such a fault quickly. The second cause of loss of sound reception lies outside of the sound channel and in the r-f section. The oscillator may have drifted so far off frequency that the sound i-f carrier and its associated side-bands fall outside of the pass band of the sound i-f amplifiers. If tapping the grid of the first audio i-f amplifier produces an audible click in the speaker, it is likely that the sound channel is operating properly, and that the fault lies in the r-f section.

The location of the cause of sound distortion is most quickly accomplished by an alignment check, starting from the audio amplifier and working through the discriminator, limiter, and i-f amplifiers. Alignment methods are described later in this section. If in the course of aligning a particular stage it is impossible to obtain the required band-pass characteristic or stage gain, then a check should be made of the tubes, operating voltages, and possible off-value components.

9-27 Vertical Sweep Circuit Faults. If part of the vertical sweep system fails, vertical scanning ceases and a bright horizontal line appears on the picture tube. If the receiver is left on too long after the failure occurs, the line may be burned permanently into the tube screen because of the concentration of the electron beam on a small area of the tube. When attempting to locate the fault, the set can be left on, but the brightness control should be turned down so that the beam is barely visible.

An oscillograph will most rapidly facilitate the isolation of a fault in the vertical sweep circuit. Set the oscillograph for 60-cycle sweep so that the waveforms in the vertical sweep system can be observed. Starting at the grid of the oscillator, check for the characteristic blocking oscillator pulse at that point. If this stage is oscillating, proceed to the plate of the discharge tube where a sawtooth voltage should be observed. Continue tracing the signal path to the grid of the sweep amplifier tube where the sawtooth voltage is injected. If the signal is coming through to the grid, the next point at which the sawtooth voltage should be checked is across the yoke which is connected to the secondary circuit of the sweep output transformer. Do not place the oscillograph across the high side of the output transformer primary, because an induced voltage as high as 1000 volts is generated in some circuits, which would break down the input circuit of the oscillograph.

If the vertical sweep is not synchronized properly, the picture will jitter or roll in the vertical direction. Usually readjustment of the vertical hold control will re-lock the oscillator, if it has drifted out of synchronization. In some cases, a component may have failed in the integration circuit or in the sync separator circuits so that the sync pulse is distorted or is not coming through, permitting the sweep oscillator to run free.

To check for the presence of a good synchronizing pulse at the oscillator grid, connect the oscillograph between the grid pin of the oscillator tube socket and ground. Pull out the oscillator tube to stop oscillation and make it easier to observe the sync pulse. If no sync pulse appears at this point, go back to the input of the integrating circuit where the composite, clipped sync should be present. Continue the signal tracing, if need be, to the input of the sync clipping circuits, and finally to the output of the second detector. If the sync level appears compressed at the second detector, or a poor video signal is obtained at this point, the fault lies in the video i-f or r-f circuits.

In the simplified schematic of Figure 45 the points at which the vertical sync signal should be checked are indicated. Figure 46 shows the waveforms of the signals as they appear at these points in the circuit. A in Figure 46 is the composite video signal at the input to the sync separator. B shows the composite vertical and horizontal sync signals at the input of the integrator circuit. C is the waveform at the output of the integrator circuit. The horizontal sync signal has been removed and only the vertical pulses remain. This waveform should appear on the grid pin of the blocking oscillator tube socket when the tube has been removed. D is the waveform on the grid of the vertical sweep generator. The vertical sync pulses are not visible because they overlap the sharp blocking oscillator pulses.

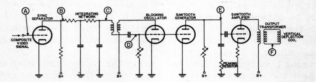

Figure 45. Simplified schematic showing points in vertical sweep circuits where waveform checks are made.

This signal is used to trigger the sawtooth generator. E is the output of the sawtooth generator. The small peaks in the lower part of the waveform are the peaking pulses produced by the peaking resistor. This signal is applied to the grid of the sawtooth amplifier. F shows the waveform of the signal as it appears across the secondary of the vertical output transformer and deflection coil.

Several vertical sweep troubles occur over which the technician has little control. For example, momentary loss of vertical synchronization due to line voltage surges or ignition interference from a passing automobile is quite common. Severe r-f interference also causes unstable synchronization. Unless the interference can be trapped out of the r-f stages or reduced by relocating the antenna, there is nothing the technician can do about it.

9-28 Horizontal Sweep Circuit Faults. As with the vertical sweep system, most of the troubles in the horizontal scanning circuits can be readily located by signal tracing and examination of waveforms in each stage. If the horizontal deflection has failed, a bright vertical bar will appear on the screen of the picture tube. To locate a fault in the horizontal sweep circuits, set the oscillograph sweep for about 15 kc and examine the waveforms at the following points in the circuit:

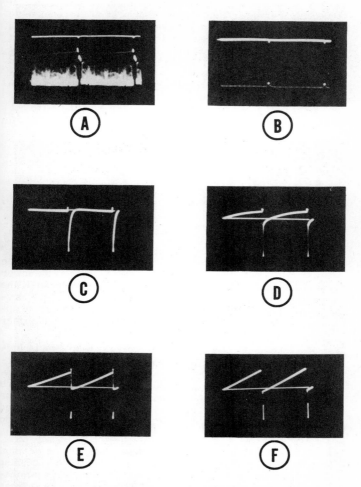

Figure 46. Waveforms at points in vertical sweep circuit indicated in Figure 45.
A. Input to sync separator, B. Input to integrating network
C. Output of integrating network, D. Grids of blocking oscillator and sawtooth generator. E. Plate of sawtooth generator
F. Secondary of vertical output transformer.

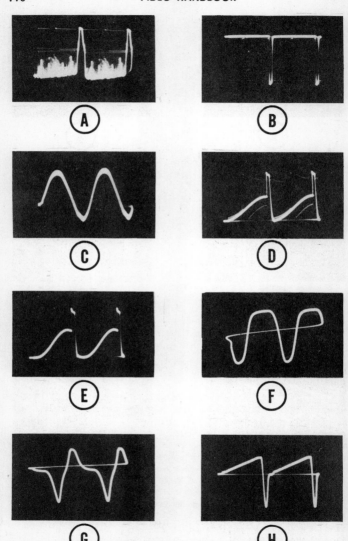

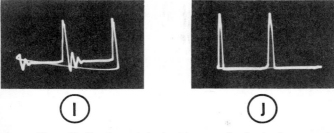

Figure 47. Waveforms in horizontal sweep circuit using fly-wheel synchronization. Points at which waveforms appear are indicated in Figure 48.

A. Input to sync separator, B. Output of sync separator, C. Primary of sync discriminator transformer, D. Center tap of sync discriminator transformer secondary, E. Plates of sync discriminator diodes, F. Plate of horizontal oscillator, G. Grid of discharge tube, H. Plate of discharge tube, I. Plate of horizontal deflection amplifier, J. Secondary of horizontal output transformer.

1. Across the horizontal deflection coil in the yoke, where a sawtooth voltage should be observed.

2. At the grid of the sweep amplifier. Note that the plate circuit of the amplifier tube and the primary of the output transformer are not check points. In the horizontal circuit, induced voltages at these points are sometimes as high as 5 kv, far above the allowable input to the oscillograph.

3. Check for sawtooth voltage on the plate of the discharge tube.

4. The final check point is the grid of the oscillator tube where oscillations should be detected.

A step-by-step procedure for signal tracing a horizontal sweep circuit containing automatic frequency control synchronization is given in the oscillograms of Figure 47. These circuits are somewhat more complicated but a careful examination of the waveforms at important points makes it quite simple to locate a fault. A in Figure 47 shows the waveform of the composite video signal at the input to the sync separator. B is the waveform at the output of the sync separator. Only horizontal pulses remain. C is the sine wave oscillator voltage which should appear on the primary of the sync discriminator transformer. D is the signal at the center tap of the sync transformer secondary. It consists of the sine wave oscillator voltage and the horizontal sync pulses. E shows the signal which should be present on the plates of the sync discriminator diodes. F is the signal at the plate of the horizontal oscillator. It is a sine wave with a flattened top brought about by overloading the oscillator. G is the waveform which should be secured at the output of the differentiating circuit. These pulses are applied to the horizontal discharge tube. H is the waveform at the plate of the discharge tube. It consists of a sawtooth voltage and a peaking pulse. This signal is applied to the horizontal deflection amplifier. I is the signal on the plate of the horizontal deflection amplifier. This signal has a peak-to-peak amplitude in excess of 5000 volts, and while it can be checked through the use of a suitable capacitive voltage divider, it is usually ignored in normal signal tracing procedure. If the oscillograph is connected directly to this point in the circuit, it will be damaged. J is the

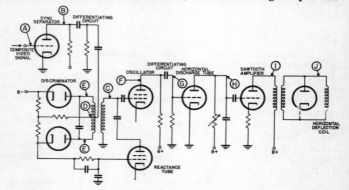

Figure 48. Simplified schematic of horizontal sweep circuit employing fly-wheel synchronization. Waveforms of Figure 47 appear at points indicated.

signal on the horizontal deflection coil and horizontal output transformer secondary. This point may be checked without fear of damaging the oscillograph.

In Figure 48 the check points described are indicated by letters which correspond to the waveforms of Figure 47.

9-29 Picture Tube Faults. Servicing the picture tube calls for extreme caution. These tubes are evacuated and are thus under great pressure. A sharp blow against the glass may cause the tube to shatter. It is wise to wear goggles when handling the picture tube.

Very high voltages are used to operate the picture tube so that the set should be turned off and the high voltage condenser in the power supply given time to discharge before disconnecting the high voltage lead from the intensifier electrode.

Aging of the tube through use causes the cathode emission to become weak and the screen material to decay from continual bombardment by the electron beam. The result is a picture with reduced brightness and a brownish tinge. Most manufacturers guarantee their picture tubes for one thousand hours of operation, or one year, whichever occurs first.

When deflecting circuits fail, the electron beam concentrates at one point and burns away the screen material, leaving small black spots in the center of the tube. Some receivers are provided with protective circuits which shut off the high voltage if the sweeps fail, thus cutting off the beam and preventing screen burning.

Not all television tubes are designed with ion-trap guns which prevent burning of the screen by positively charged ions. An ion burn shows up in the center of the tube screen as a brown spot about the size of a half dollar.

Picture tubes sometimes develop leaks and, as a result, they gradually fill with air. No usable picture will be obtained under this condition and the ''getter'' will appear milky white.

When the screen of the picture tube remains blank and the receiver is operating normally in all other respects, an open picture tube filament may be the fault. A glance at the electron gun will determine whether or not the filament is lit and in good condition.

If a receiver uses electrostatic deflection, the deflection electrodes can be knocked out of line as a result of a severe jarring of the tube. This results in a distorted picture. Severe jarring can also throw the entire gun assembly out of line and prevent proper focusing of the beam.

9-30 Power Supply Faults. Most receivers have interlock switches which break the a-c line circuit when the chassis is removed from the cabinet. A jumper must be placed across the interlock switch in order to operate the receiver outside the cabinet.

If trouble is suspected in the high voltage supply, first make continuity and resistance checks with an ohmmeter while the set is off. Most faults can be located in this manner. Should it be desirable to actually measure the high voltage, connect the meter across the supply while the set is off. Then turn it on and take the reading. Be sure to turn the set off again and allow ample time for the condensers to discharge before removing the meter lead from the high voltage terminal.

If the picture tube filament is lit, but no beam current is flowing to the screen to give at least a spot, there is probably an open in the high voltage circuit. Check the rectifier tube and the filter condensers and resistors. The effects of defective filter components are described elsewhere in this section.

If there is a poor contact at the intensifier terminal, caused by a loose connector or dirt between the high voltage connector and the terminal, there will be intermittent breakdown at this point, resulting in picture "bop". The trouble is easily cured by cleaning the terminal and making a secure connection.

Low output voltage from r-f high voltage supplies may be caused by drift of the r-f oscillator from its correct operating frequency. By tuning the tank circuit of the oscillator and noting the output voltage on a kilovoltmeter, or by observing the brightness of the picture tube while the oscillator frequency is varied, the maximum voltage can be obtained.

Low voltage may be caused also by a defective oscillator or rectifier tube. The filament of the type 8016 rectifier tube, which is used in most r-f supplies, is very susceptible to damage. Even a momentary overload of the heater due to a sudden line voltage surge will cause damage. Although the color of the filament may appear normal to the eye after the overload, the tube will not perform satisfactorily, and insufficient output voltage will be obtained. Substitution of a new tube is the simplest and quickest means of checking for a defective rectifier.

The mechanical construction and layout of r-f power supplies are critical, for at the high voltages at which they operate, corona discharge points are difficult to avoid. Corona results in power loss. When present in the r-f coil windings, the corona gradually destroys the fine strands of litz wire. Corona on the r-f coil is generally due to the weakening of the vacuum varnish with which the coil is impregnated. Corona discharge appears as a bluish glow. It becomes greater in humid weather, so that a coil which appears to operate normally in a dry atmosphere may break down when more moisture is in the air. Applying a good grade of varnish to the points of corona discharge will usually clear up the trouble.

Corona at points of high potential, particularly at poor solder joints and irregularly surfaced conductors is common. The solder should be flowed on all high voltage joints. In general, it should be remembered that a smooth, round surface is less susceptible to corona than a sharp, pointed one. Severe corona will produce noise in the television picture.

If the filament loop on the high voltage, r-f coil should move out of place, the filament voltage will drop. If the loop must be moved, care should be taken to place it in the same position it originally occupied. Otherwise, the coupling to the r-f transformer may be increased and the rectifier filament overloaded. Similarly, a loose coupling will not permit the filament to be heated sufficiently, resulting in low output voltage and poor high-voltage regulation.

The mechanical troubles described for the r-f supply also apply to the pulse-type supply. The autotransformer is pi-wound with litz wire and is subject to corona damage as is the r-f transformer. The same precautions hold for the filament winding of the rectifier tube in the pulse-supply as were discussed for the r-f supply.

Since the high voltage that is generated in a kickback supply is dependent upon the horizontal sweep circuit, a failure in this circuit will result in loss of high-voltage output. If no high voltage is obtained at the picture tube, signal trace the horizontal sweep circuit, starting at the output transformer and working toward the sawtooth generator. If this circuit is operating correctly, the trouble exists in the high voltage rectifier circuit. The rectifier tube or a component in the R-C filter is usually the cause.

The foregoing paragraphs have dealt with procedures for troubleshooting television receivers. After the fault is located, it should be repaired and necessary checks and adjustments made to put the receiver back in working order. These checks and adjustments are described on the following pages.

CHECKING AND ADJUSTING THE RECEIVER

9-31 To assist the technician in adjusting a receiver, television stations send out a test pattern several hours a day. The use of the test pattern alone for checking and adjusting the receiver is a hit or miss affair, and in many cases may require undue time and effort if no other technique is understood. A more important reason for not depending entirely upon test patterns for adjustment is that such signals are on the air only a few hours each day. Obviously a shop with several sets to repair and adjust must have other methods available. For this reason, adjustment procedures will be described which depend mainly upon instruments. Minor adjustments can then be made when an "on the air" test pattern is available.

Usually a fault in a receiver is located by the technician during the troubleshooting procedure. When the fault has been located, adjustment is usually necessary to compensate for the slight changes which occur when the repair is made. In addition, it is good practice to make a general check and adjust a receiver before returning it to the customer.

9-32 Checking and Adjusting the Picture Tube. It is important that the picture tube be carefully adjusted so that maximum resolution and definition in the picture will be obtained. It is useless to employ a picture channel with a bandwidth of 4 megacycles unless the size of the luminescent spot produced on the picture tube is small enough to permit the reproduction of the detail possible in a 4 Mc signal. Such resolution can be obtained only if the gun structure is properly aligned and the electron beam is in focus. Receivers employing picture tubes ten inches or less in diameter are generally designed with bandwidths between 2 and 3 Mc, because the size of the spot produced in these tubes will not permit greater picture detail. In any event, to realize the full benefits of the band width of a receiver, the spot size must be made as small as the design of the tube permits.

9-33 Adjustment of Electrostatically Focused Tubes. To focus an electrostatic picture tube, it is only necessary to vary the focus control potentiometer. This potentiometer is connected in series with the bleeder of the high voltage supply and controls the voltage on the first anode. The focus adjustment should always be made with a picture on the tube. Since the focus depends upon the amount of beam current, some manufacturers locate the focus control on the front panel of the receiver so that the operator can vary the focus when changing the picture brightness. Other manufacturers place this control on the high voltage chassis, where it is inaccessible to the user. In this case, the technician must adjust the focus for an average brightness condition.

Another control is often used with electrostatically focused and deflected picture tubes. This control is the astigmatism control, which is used to balance the d-c potential on the deflecting plates, and to correct for differences in potential between the plate and second anode. Large differences in potential between these electrodes cause the spot to be astigmatic (oval-shaped). An astigmatic spot causes defocusing of the beam as it scans certain parts of the screen. The astigmatism control, if present, is usually located on the rear of the chassis.

It should be varied simultaneously with the focus control to a-
chieve optimum picture sharpness. There is no need for an
astigmatism control if an electrostatically focused and magnetically deflected tube is used.

9-34 Focusing the Magnetic Tube. The focusing of a magnetic tube is dependent upon the position of the focus coil with respect to the electron gun, and the amount of current flowing
through the coil. The positioning of the focus coil can best be
carried out using a test pattern. The effects upon the test pat-

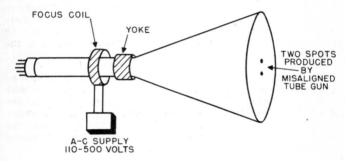

Figure 49. Method used to align focus coil using 60-cycle supply.

tern are observed while the coil is moved about on the neck of
the tube. When a test pattern is not available and careful positioning is required, as is necessary with large tubes, the
following procedure may be employed:

Pull out the vertical and horizontal oscillator tubes in the deflection circuits so that, when the set is turned on, only a spot
will appear on the face of the picture tube. Note: Be sure the
power is off when pulling out the tubes, and be careful to have
the brightness control down to avoid burning a spot on the screen
when the power is turned on again.) Disconnect the focus coil
leads from their d-c supply source and connect the coil across
an a-c supply. If the focus coil is of low impedance, the line
voltage of about 115 volts will be sufficient. If the receiver has
a high impedance focus coil, three to five hundred volts will be
required, which may be obtained from a transformer. The connections for this adjustment are shown in Figure 49. With the
a-c on the focus coil and the receiver turned on, two spots will
appear on the face of the tube if the focus coil is misaligned with
respect to the electron gun. The two spots are produced by the

positive and negative peaks of the a-c current in the focus coil. The focus coil should be moved around the neck of the tube until the two spots are superimposed. It is only when this condition is achieved that there will be no astigmatism of the electron beam. The focus coil is then properly aligned to avoid trapezoidal distortion and pincushioning.

Receivers with magnetically focused tubes generally have a mounting for the focus coil which enables it to be moved in three planes. After the spots have been lined up, re-connect the coil to its d-c supply, and replace the sweep oscillator tubes. The focus control which changes the amount of current flowing in the coil may now be varied to obtain the sharpest picture. This control is generally located on the front panel of the receiver and is adjusted by the operator for the desired setting of the brightness control.

9-35 Orienting the Picture. With the focus coil properly aligned, the raster may be oriented so that it is "in square" with the mask aperture. In receivers with magnetic tubes, the deflection yoke is rotated to correctly orient the picture. In order to better observe the orientation, the horizontal width and vertical height should be decreased by adjusting the respective controls until the edges of the raster can be seen.

In receivers using electrostatic deflection tubes, the tube itself must be rotated until the raster is oriented correctly with respect to the mask aperture. The same technique of reducing the width and height with magnetic tubes should be used. Note that in a correctly oriented raster the vertical retrace lines, which are normally blanked out when the picture signal is applied, slope upward from left to right, which indicates that scanning is in the proper direction. Sometimes the connections from the sweep amplifiers to the deflecting plates or the yoke are reversed, and the retrace lines do not slope in this direction. This results in a picture that is backward or upside down.

Adjusting Ion Traps. Magnetic tubes which have ion traps require a different procedure for adjusting the electron beam. The ion trap magnet should be adjusted before attempting to line up the focus coil and deflection yoke, for unless the magnet is correctly positioned, the electron beam will strike the second anode in the electron gun and no illumination will appear on the tube.

The ion trap magnet is initially positioned so that the rear magnet poles are over two small flags attached to the electron gun. This pre-positioning insures some illumination of the screen. Starting from this position, adjust the magnet by moving it forward or backward, at the same time rotating it slightly around the neck of the tube to secure the brightest raster on the screen. Tighten the magnet adjustment clamp sufficiently to hold it in this position, but leave it free enough to permit further adjustment. Reduce the brightness control setting until the raster is slightly above average brilliance. Adjust the focus control until the line structure of the raster is clearly visible. Readjust the ion-trap magnet for maximum raster brilliance. The final touches on this adjustment should be made with the brightness control at the maximum position with which good line focus can be maintained.

Since an improperly positioned focus coil can cut off the electron beam, the focus coil should be positioned as carefully as possible before adjusting the ion-trap magnet. After the magnet is set, final positioning of the focus coil can be accomplished by using the methods previously described.

9-36 Adjusting the Sweep Circuits. An instrument test procedure to check and adjust the sweep generators and amplifiers in the vertical and horizontal scanning systems is presented here. The technician should not depend upon a test pattern alone to adjust linearity. In addition to the fact that a test pattern is not always available, linearity of the test patterns transmitted by stations varies considerably from day to day. Thus, if the sweep linearity of the receiver circuits is adjusted on one day to give a linear test pattern on a particular station, on another day or on another station the linearity may be very poor. Until the FCC requires that all stations adhere to a rigid standard for linearity, the instrument method is the only positive procedure for checking and adjusting the scanning system. Once these adjustments are made, no further changes should have to be made when a picture appears on the tube.

It is possible to check the amplitude and linearity of scanning in both vertical and horizontal directions with the aid of a variable frequency oscillator. The oscillator should be capable of supplying at least 20 volts of signal and have a frequency variable from about 60 cps to about 700 kc. Very few shops have such an oscillator available. They will, however, usually have an audio oscillator and an r-f oscillator which will provide the necessary coverage. The output of the oscillator is connected between the grid and cathode of the picture tube and also to the grid of the sweep oscillator, as shown in Figure 50. Note the use of an isolating capacitor in the output lead of the signal generator. If sufficient voltage is not available to operate the picture tube directly, the oscillator output may be fed into the video amplifier.

To adjust the vertical circuits, the external oscillator should
be set at 60 cps. The vertical hold control should then be adjusted until the circuit locks into synchronism with the applied
sine wave. The electron beam in the picture tube is modulated
by the 60-cycle oscillator signal and consequently, the scanning
motion and variation in brightness occur synchronously, result-

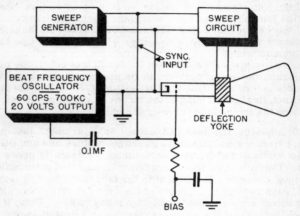

Figure 50. Method used to check linearity of scanning circuits.

ing in two stationary horizontal bars, one bright, the other dark.
The scanning circuits are operating at standard line frequency
and most of the characteristics of the vertical scanning system
can be checked.

The scanning amplitude is indicated by the total height of the
synchronized scanning pattern. If the amplitude is insufficient,
the height control may be adjusted. When using this method to
adjust the height control of a magnetic receiver, it is important
that the oscillator be set at a frequency of 60 cps, because in
magnetic scanning the sweep amplitude is dependent upon the
sweep frequency. The sweep linearity varies with frequency in
both magnetic and electrostatic scanning.

The oscillator method enables the technician to pre-set the
vertical hold control so that the sawtooth oscillator is operating
at the correct frequency. It may be necessary to vary the vertical sync control very slightly when a television signal is tuned
in, in order to obtain proper interlace of the vertical sweep.
The oscillator method does not offer a means of simulating the
equalizing pulses necessary for interlaced scanning. However,

Figure 51. Linearity bars for checking vertical scanning. A. Linear scanning, B. Non-linear scanning.

as long as the sync control is set close to 60 cps, the amplitude and linearity will not be affected by the small sync control variation which may be necessary to interlace the "over-the-air" pattern.

After the vertical scanning amplitude has been adjusted, the linearity of scanning may be checked by increasing the frequency of the oscillator successively to 120, 240, 480, 960, 1920, 2400, and 3600 cps (or any other multiple of 60). Since these frequencies are multiples of the 60 cps scanning frequency, the scanning circuit will synchronize on every second cycle at 120 cps, every fourth cycle at 240 cps, and so on.

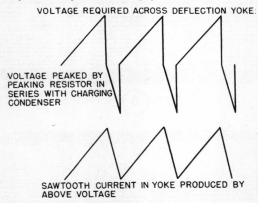

Figure 52. Voltage and current waveforms required for magnetic deflection.

At a frequency of 2400 cps, the scanning circuit synchronizes every fortieth cycle. Since this signal is also applied to the grid of the picture tube, 40 horizontal bars will appear on the screen. If the vertical scanning is linear, these bars will be equally spaced as shown in Figure 51A. If the scanning is not linear, the bars will be spread out or compressed over part of the screen as shown in Figure 51B. By adjusting the vertical linearity control, it is usually possible to obtain equal separation between adjacent bars.

With the vertical size and linearity correctly adjusted, the vertical positioning control can be set to properly center the picture in the mask opening.

9-37 Checking the Peaking Resistance. With receivers using magnetic deflection, another vertical scanning adjustment is usually necessary. In order to produce a sawtooth deflection current in the yoke, a voltage having the waveshape shown in Figure 52 must be generated. The output of the discharge tube is normally a sawtooth voltage. The waveform shown in Figure 52, required for linear deflection, is obtained by placing a peaking resistor in series with the charging capacitor. If, due to aging or changes in other components in the charging circuit, the peaking resistor is not of the correct value, the current in the yoke will no longer be a linear sawtooth, and the lines at the

Figure 53. Pattern produced in horizontal scanning amplitude test with 15,750-cps signal on grid.

top of the raster will begin to fold over into the picture. Since most receivers have a fixed resistor for "peaking", it must be replaced with a resistor of proper value. To do this, substitute a variable resistor to determine the correct value, after which a fixed resistor may be used in its place. This change will have to be made only if a resistor, capacitor, or other component in the charging circuit changes with age or becomes defective.

9-38 Adjusting Horizontal Sweep Circuits. A very similar procedure is followed for checking the performance of the horizontal sweep system. The external oscillator connections shown in Figure 50 are used. The oscillator should be set to 15,750 cps. The horizontal hold control should be adjusted until the sweep oscillator is synchronized with the applied 15,750 cps.

A pattern consisting of two vertical bars should appear on the screen, as shown in Figure 53. The positive half of the sine wave produces the bright bar, while the negative half produces the black bar.

With the horizontal oscillator synchronized at 15,750 cps, the scanning amplitude may be adjusted so that the pattern fills the mask aperture.

9-39 Effect of Line Voltage on Scanning Circuits. The vertical and horizontal sweep amplitudes are affected by changes in the power line voltages. When the a-c voltage falls, the receiver power supply voltage drops, and the picture is reduced in size. If the size controls have been set so that the picture just fills the mask aperture when the line voltage is at the nominal 117 volts, the picture will be smaller than the mask opening when the voltage drops below this value. Similarly, the picture will spread beyond the mask limits if the line voltage increases. Since the line voltage generally varies as much as plus or minus 10 per cent from the nominal 117 volts, a compromise must be made when setting the picture size. Usually the change in picture size will not be noticed if the picture always fills the mask opening or extends beyond its limits, whereas it becomes very obvious to the viewer when the picture does not fill the aperture. It is therefore best to set the picture size so that the mask opening is just filled when the line voltage is at its lowest (about 10% below 117 volts, or 105 volts). An excellent way to adjust the picture size is to connect the receiver to a variable transformer, such as a "Variac", and adjust the picture with the line voltage set at 105 volts.

9-40 Adjusting Horizontal Linearity. To check the linearity of the horizontal sweep, the oscillator frequency should be increased to a multiple of 15,750 cps in order to produce a sufficient number of vertical lines on the screen. To obtain a pattern of 40 vertical bars, such as shown in Figure 54, a frequency of 630,000 cps is necessary. The linearity controls should then be adjusted until the spacing between bars is uniform.

It is possible that no setting of the horizontal linearity controls will produce linear deflection. If such is the case, the damping tube may have failed. This condition is indicated by an overlapping of the vertical bars on the left side of the picture. Replacing the damping tube should cure the trouble. In receivers which use a resistor-capacitor combination for damping, instead of a tube, these components should be checked.

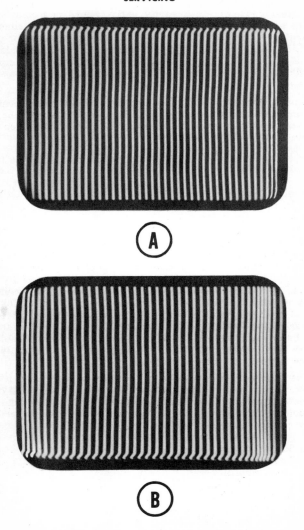

Figure 54. Linearity bars for checking horizontal scanning. A. Linear scanning, B. Non-linear scanning.

Another cause of non-linearity is the failure of a component in the horizontal deflection circuit, as for example a defective charging resistor or capacitor in the sawtooth generator circuit, or a faulty sweep-amplifier tube. Such faults should be isolated by signal tracing the entire sweep circuit and comparing the waveforms with those shown in the manufacturer's service manual.

This completes the adjustment of the circuits which control the motion of the electron beam across the face of the tube. It remains now to describe the methods for aligning the video and audio amplifier circuits.

ALIGNMENT

9-41 Since the band width and selectivity of a television receiver determine the quality of the picture and sound, it is important that the alignment of the tuned circuits be carried out with care in order to obtain the band width and selectivity for which the receiver was designed. Poor alignment will result in loss of picture detail, noise in the picture or distortion of the sound. Before beginning the alignment of a receiver, the technician should determine the intermediate frequencies, sensitivity, band width, and response characteristics of the receiver when it is properly aligned. This information can usually be found in the manufacturer's literature.

When complete alignment of a receiver is necessary, it can be performed most conveniently in the order given below (If only a section of the receiver must be aligned, as determined during troubleshooting, some of the alignment procedures described here can be bypassed):

1. Sound discriminator.
2. Sound limiter.
3. Sound i-f transformers.
4. Video amplifier.
5. Picture i-f transformers.
6. Picture i-f traps.
7. R-F tuner.
8. Overall band width check.
9. Sensitivity check.

Variations in this order may be necessary, depending upon the design of the receiver. As a rule, however, the order given will be the best one.

The various sections of a receiver and the order in which they are aligned are indicated in the block diagram of Figure 55.

It will be noted that the sound system is aligned first, working from the discriminator toward the i-f amplifier input. The sound system is aligned first because once it is properly tuned, it serves as a reference for the alignment of the video circuits.

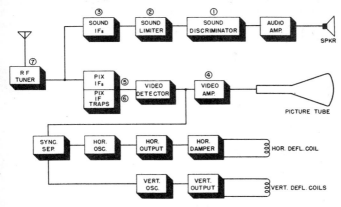

Figure 55. Order in which sound and video circuits are aligned.

It is common practice to tune a television receiver by adjusting for maximum sound and if the receiver is properly aligned, the best picture should be obtained simultaneously.

The video circuits should be aligned by working back from the grid of the picture tube to the video i-f circuits and finally to the r-f tuner. Using this procedure, the video amplifier is first aligned with an output-indicating instrument connected across its output (the output of the video amplifier is also the input to the picture tube). The indicator is left at this point, and each previous stage aligned in turn. Since the indicating instrument is at the last stage, it will show the overall band width of all of the preceding stages, as each is adjusted in turn.

Another technique is to move the output indicator to the output of each stage, as the alignment proceeds. The overall band width is then the sum of all the stages.

The quickest way to align tuned circuits is to use a sweep generator and cathode ray oscillograph. It is also possible to align

some circuits using a signal generator and vacuum tube voltmeter. Both methods are described here.

When making adjustments to i-f and r-f circuits a plastic
screwdriver several inches long should be used. If a metalic
screwdriver is used the circuit being adjusted will go out of
alignment each time the screwdriver is removed from its vicinity.

**9-42 Discriminator Alignment with Signal Generator and
VTVM.** The alignment of the discriminator using a VTVM and

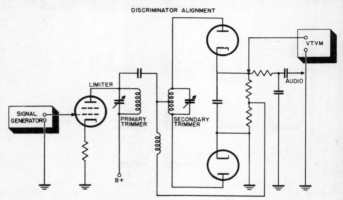

Figure 56. Connections used when aligning discriminator using
v.t.v.m.

signal generator may be accomplished using the following procedure:

1. Connect the VTVM between the cathode of the discriminator and ground as shown in Figure 56.
2. Connect the signal generator to the grid of the last limiter
stage.
3. Adjust the output of the signal generator to about 0.1 volts
and set its frequency to the sound i-f carrier frequency specified by the manufacturer (this will be about 21 Mc).
4. The polarity of the voltages indicated by the VTVM will
be plus or minus depending upon the setting of the secondary of
the discriminator coil.
5. Adjust the secondary of the discriminator coil to obtain a
zero reading on the voltmeter. The secondary trimmer capacitor can be located by checking the two capacitors in the dis-

criminator transformer with a voltmeter. The secondary trimmer will not have any voltage present on it while the primary trimmer has the plate voltage of the previous stage applied to it.

6. Move the VTVM probe to the junction of the two cathode resistors.

7. Adjust the primary of the discriminator coil to secure maximum output, as indicated by the VTVM.

8. Change the frequency of the signal generator to 50 kc above the i-f frequency and note the output voltage developed. Then change the signal generator frequency to 50 kc below the center frequency and note the output voltage. The voltages should be

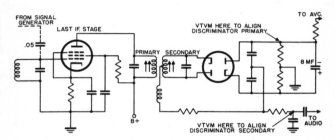

Figure 57. Connections used when aligning ratio detector using v.t.v.m.

equal at equal frequency intervals on either side of the center frequency. The primary should be adjusted until this condition exists.

If the receiver to be aligned uses a ratio detector, the alignment should be carried out in the following manner:

1. Connect the VTVM across the detector as shown in Figure 57.

2. Set the signal generator to the sound i-f frequency.

3. Tune the primary of the detector transformer to secure maximum reading on the VTVM.

4. Move the VTVM to the input of the first audio stage as shown in Figure 57.

5. Adjust the secondary of the detector transformer to secure zero output as indicated by the VTVM.

If the circuit in the receiver is similar to that shown in Figure 58, in which the center tap of the load resistor is not grounded, an effective center tap can be secured as shown. Connect two resistors in series across the load resistor. These resistors should each have a resistance equal to about five times the value

of the load resistor. The VTVM should be connected to the
junction of the resistors when adjusting the secondary of the
detector transformer for zero output at the i-f carrier frequency.

**9-43 Discriminator Alignment with Sweep Generator and Os-
cillograph.** A frequency modulated signal generator, marker
oscillator, and oscillograph can be used to accurately and quick-

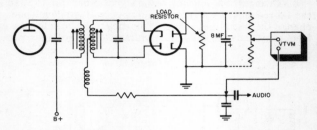

Figure 58. Use of series resistors to obtain midpoint when
aligning ratio detector.

ly align the discriminator stage. The procedure to align a discriminator using this equipment is as follows:

1. Connect the sweep generator between the grid of the last
limiter tube and ground as shown in Figure 59. If the sweep
generator has a built in synchronizing voltage for locking the
sweep signal of the oscillograph to the sweep frequency, this
sync voltage should be connected to the ''sync'' terminal of the
oscillograph. Some sweep generators supply a sweep voltage
which can be applied directly to the horizontal amplifier terminals of the oscillograph.

2. Set the center frequency of the signal generator to the i-f
frequency specified by the manufacturer. Adjust the frequency
deviation to approximately 200 kc.

3. Connect the oscillograph across the discriminator output.
The oscillator sweep circuit should be adjusted so that a single
pattern is obtained on the oscillograph screen. Either a double
pattern or a single pattern can be obtained, depending upon the
type of sweep signal furnished by the sweep generator. To provide a single pattern most sweep generators are equipped with
a phasing control.

4. Set the marker oscillator to the i-f frequency and connect
it across the output terminals of the sweep signal generator.
Another method of inserting the marker signal is to connect the
high side of the marker generator output to the point on the
chassis where the sweep signal generator is grounded. Connect

the ground side of the marker generator to another point on the chassis. While it appears that the output of the marker generator is shorted, this is not the case, since there is sufficient impedance between the two points on the chassis to serve as a load for the marker generator. This method of inserting the marker signal avoids loading the grid of the limiter during alignment.

5. Adjust the secondary trimmer of the discriminator transformer so that the marker signal occurs at the center of the

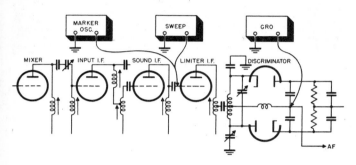

Figure 59. Connections used when aligning discriminator using oscillograph and sweep generator.

straight portion of the output curve. The curve will actually appear as shown in Figure 60A. The marker signal causes the breaks in the curve.

6. Readjust the marker generator frequency to the band width extremeties specified by the manufacturer. The marker signal, or "birdie", as it is called, should appear at one and then the other of the signal peaks as shown in Figure 60B.

7. Adjust the primary trimmer of the discriminator transformer so that the positive peak of the output curve is equal to the negative peak.

If a ratio detector is used, it may be aligned in much the same manner. The sweep generator should be connected to the grid of the last sound i-f stage and the oscillograph to the output of the detector.

9-44 Checking the Limiter. When the limiter in an f-m circuit is operating properly, it passes all signals up to a certain amplitude. Signals (such as noise riding on top of the sound signal) which exceed this amplitude, are greatly compressed. The

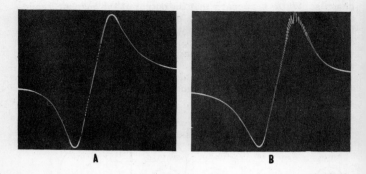

Figure 60. Signal on oscillograph produced by discriminator output. A. Marker signal at center frequency, B. Marker signal at signal peak.

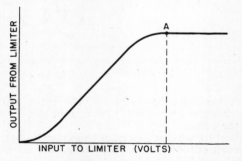

Figure 61. Limiter curve.

characteristic curve of the limiter is shown in Figure 61. This curve represents the output of the limiter for various input voltages. As the input voltage increases, the output voltage increases proportionately. When the input signal exceeds a certain level, a change in input will not produce a corresponding change in output. Above point A (which is referred to as the "knee" of the curve and is the voltage at which limiting action starts), the output voltage stays the same even though increasing signal voltages are fed to the input.

To check the action of the limiter, a signal generator and v.t.v.m. are connected as shown in Figure 62. The signal generator is coupled to the grid of the limiter and the v.t.v.m. to the junction of the resistors in the cathode circuit of the detector. Set the v.t.v.m. to read negative d-c volts.

The signal generator output voltage should be adjusted to give about 100 microvolts input to the grid of the limiter. The signal generator output should then be gradually increased while the reading on the v.t.v.m. is observed. The manufacturer's manual should be consulted for the voltage which corresponds to the knee of the limiter response curve. The d-c output, as

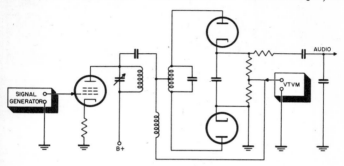

Figure 62. Connections used when checking limiter performance.

indicated by the v.t.v.m. snould increase up to this point, after which the voltage should remain constant. The limiter is operating correctly if the knee point corresponds to the specified value. If not, the voltages on the tube should be measured and compared with the manufacturer's specifications.

9-45 Aligning the Sound I-F Amplifiers. Several methods are available for aligning the sound i-f amplifier stages of the receiver. The quickest and most effective method requires a sweep generator, an oscillograph, and a marker oscillator. Using this equipment, the i-f amplifier stages may be aligned individually or all together. If a stage is aligned individually, the oscillograph should be connected to its output through a probe and the sweep generator and marker generator connected to its input. The probe required consists of a diode and other components necessary to detect the signal so that it may be observed on the oscillograph. The construction of such a probe is described in Section 10.

While stage-by-stage alignment is considered the best procedure to follow when working with wide band, overcoupled amplifiers, it consumes an excessive amount of time. Since overall alignment, if carefully done, will give generally satisfactory results, it is recommended, except in isolated instances. The following procedure for aligning the sound i-f amplifiers of a television receiver is described with reference to the circuit shown in Figure 63.

1. Connect the oscillograph through the probe detector across resistor R27 (point A), which is in the grid circuit of the first

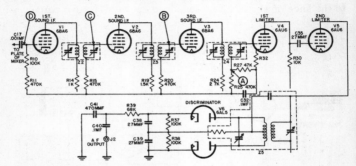

Figure 63. Simplified schematic of sound channel showing points used to connect instruments for alignment.

limiter tube V4. The oscillograph is left at this point during the alignment procedure.

2. Connect the sweep generator between the grid of V3 (point B), the last sound i-f amplifier, and ground.

3. Set the center frequency of the sweep generator to 21.9 Mc. Adjust the sweep frequency for approximately 200 kc.

4. Adjust the oscillograph to a sweep frequency of 60 cycles and synchronize the pattern which appears on the screen. Then, by increasing the horizontal gain control and adjusting the horizontal positioning control, obtain a single i-f curve on the screen, as shown in Figure 64A.

5. Frequency markers may be inserted externally (if the sweep generator does not have built-in markers) by connecting the marker generator in parallel with the sweep generator, point B.

6. Set the output of the marker oscillator to 21.9 Mc to produce a birdie as shown in Figure 64B. Do not feed too large a birdie signal to the amplifier, otherwise the pattern will be distorted as shown in Figure 64C.

7. Adjust the tuning capacitors in Z4, the i-f transformer between V3 and V4, to obtain a nearly flat response curve which is symmetrical on both sides of the center frequency, as in-

dicated by the birdie. An example of this response curve is shown in Figure 64D. In performing this alignment procedure, it is worth noting that the a.v.c. need not be disconnected, since the low impedance of the sweep generator, which is connected

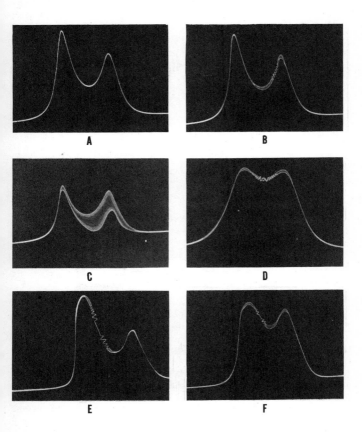

Figure 64. Response curves of sound i-f amplifiers.
A. Single i-f response curve, B. Response curve with birdie at 21.9 Mc, C. Effect of too much birdie, D. Response curve of properly aligned i-f amplifier, E. Effect produced by slight overload, F. Effect produced by excessive overload.

across the grid resistor, automatically shunts the a.v.c. and previous stages.

8. To align the sound i-f amplifier, leave the oscillograph at point A and move the sweep generator and marker oscillator to the grid of V2 (point C).

9. Adjust Z3, the i-f transformer between V2 and V3 to obtain a flat response curve, using the procedure just described.

10. The first i-f stage is adjusted in a similar manner. Move

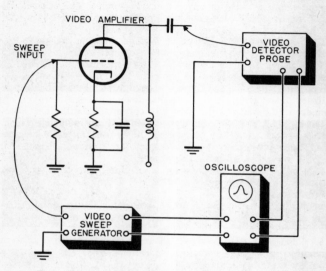

Figure 65. Connections used to adjust video amplifier using sweep generator and oscillograph.

the sweep generator and marker oscillator to the grid of V1 (point D).

11. Adjust Z2, to obtain a flat response curve. In making this adjustment, be sure that the output of the sweep generator is not so high that it overloads the second and third i-f stages. Figure 64E and 64F show conditions of overload when the sweep generator signal is set too high.

9-46 Adjusting the Video Amplifier. In order to secure the broad band response required of them, one or more peaking coils are used in the video amplifier circuits of the television receiver. As a rule, the impedance of the coils is variable, and they must be adjusted to secure the required band width characteristics.

Three methods are available for adjusting the peaking coils in the video amplifier: (1) Using a signal generator and v.t.v.m., (2) using an oscillograph and sweep generator, and (3) using a square wave generator and oscillograph. The first method mentioned is tedious and time consuming, since it requires that the output of the amplifier be measured at several different frequencies each time an adjustment is made. The second and third methods are both good ones and will be described here.

The following procedure is used when aligning the video amplifier with a sweep generator and oscillograph:

1. Connect the output of the sweep generator to the input of the amplifier to be tested, as shown in Figure 65. Set the sweep deviation to approximately six megacycles. Some video amplifiers are d-c coupled so that the sweep generator cannot be connected directly to the grid without upsetting the d-c level. If the sweep generator is not provided with an isolating capacitor, a series capacitor of approximately 0.01 mf must be used when the sweep generator is connected to a video amplifier in which d-c voltage is present at the grid.

2. Connect the probe detector (the same probe that was used for aligning the sound i-f amplifiers) from the output of the stage to ground.

3. Adjust the attenuator of the sweep generator until sufficient signal input is obtained to give a pattern on the oscillograph screen.

4. Connect the marker oscillator in parallel with the sweep generator.

5. By varying the marker frequency, the birdie can be moved to any position on the pattern and the band width measured.

6. If the correct response curve is not obtained, tune the adjustable peaking coils until the amplifier is properly aligned. If all the frequency compensating components in the video amplifier stage are fixed, but the response is poor, it is necessary to substitute a variable peaking coil which can be adjusted to provide the proper response.

9-47 Aligning the Video Amplifier with a Square Wave Generator and Oscillograph. A square wave generator offers a convenient method for checking the frequency response of a video amplifier. A square wave is formed by combining a sine wave with its odd harmonics as shown in Figure 66. Square waves contain harmonics as high as fifteen or twenty times the fundamental frequency. Thus, when a 200 kc square wave is applied

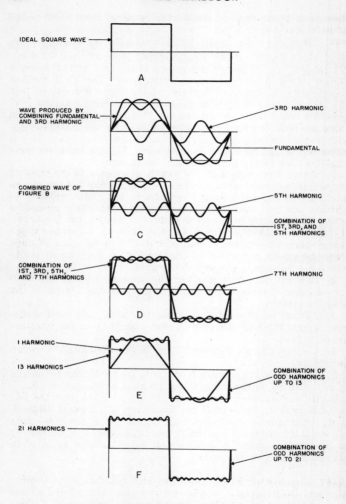

Figure 66. Creation of a square wave.

to an amplifier circuit, it tests the frequency response from 200 kc to 4 Mc (200 kc x 20). By noting the shape of the square wave output from the video amplifier on an oscillograph, one can check the high frequency response. Similarly, a low frequency square wave of about 30 cycles will indicate the video amplifier response between 30 cycles and 600 cycles. There is no need to check the response between 600 cycles and 200 kc, because most video amplifiers are substantially flat in this region.

One precaution should be taken when using the oscillograph with a square wave generator. So that the oscillograph does not introduce distortion to the square waves, it must have good fre-

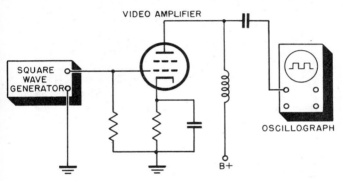

Figure 67. Connections used to adjust video amplifier using square wave generator and oscillograph.

quency response between 30 cycles and 4 megacycles. If the oscillograph amplifier does not have good response, the output signal from the video amplifier may be connected directly to the deflection plates of the oscillograph cathode-ray tube. Terminals for connecting the deflection plates are generally found on the front or rear of the oscillograph. To quickly check the response of the oscillograph amplifier, connect the square wave generator to the oscillograph amplifier terminals and set the square wave frequency to 30 cycles and then 200 kc. No perceptible distortion of the square waves should be noted if the amplifiers are flat from 30 cycles to 4 megacycles.

To check the high-frequency response, connect the square wave generator and oscillograph to the video amplifier as shown in Figure 67. Set the square wave frequency to 200 kc. With a little experience in interpreting the square wave patterns obtained on the oscillograph, the technician will be able to determine the approximate high-frequency response of the video amplifier. Typical patterns are shown in Figure 68. The rounded front edge of the square wave shown at A is typical of an amplifier without sufficient high-frequency compensation. The good square wave shown in B results from an amplifier that is correctly compensated to 4 Mc. The slight amount of overshoot on the leading edge of the square wave shown at C is typical of an amplifier which is overpeaked. The corresponding frequency

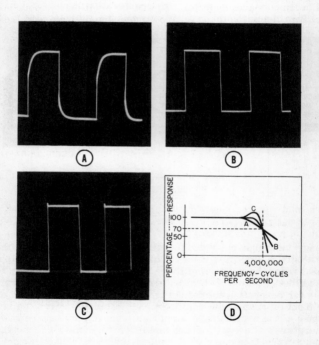

Figure 68. Patterns obtained on oscillograph when checking high frequency response of video amplifier.
A. Insufficient high-frequency compensation, B. Good square wave response, C. Overshoot caused by overpeaking.

response curves for each square wave are shown on the graph in D.

The low frequency response is checked in the same manner, only the square wave frequency is reduced to 30 cycles. The oscillograms shown in Figure 69 are examples of good and poor low-frequency response of a video amplifier. Poor low-frequency response is recognized by the sloping of the top and bottom portions of the square wave.

9-48 Checking the D-C Restorer. After the video amplifier has been properly adjusted, the d-c restoration should be checked. This check should be made only if some radical change has

Figure 69. Square wave patterns obtained when checking low-frequency response of video amplifier. A. Good low-frequency response. B. Poor low-frequency response.

been made in the video circuits. Otherwise, the d-c restorer should not require changes when an alignment of the amplifier is made. The following is the procedure used:

1. Measure the residual d-c voltage on the grid of the picture tube without any signal.

2. Measure the d-c voltage at the same point with a 15-kc sine wave fed to the video amplifier from the signal generator (this simulates the horizontal sweep frequency upon which the d-c restoration depends). Be careful not to overload the amplifier.

3. Measure the peak-to-peak amplitude of the sine wave at the grid of the picture tube, using an oscillograph and voltage calibrator.

4. If the d-c restorer is working properly, the change in d-c voltage from the residual value to that when the sine wave is fed to the video amplifier should be 85 percent of the peak-to peak sine voltage at the grid.

For example, if the d-c restoration is correct, a 15-kc, 2.5-volt peak-to-peak sine wave fed into the video amplifier, which would result in a 50-volt amplified signal at the grid of the picture tube, would cause a change in the d-c bias on the grid of about 42 volts.

A d-c voltage change as low as 65 percent is permissible, since this amount will maintain good d-c restoration and picture contrast. If the restorer is not working properly, the constants of the circuit must be changed.

9-49 Aligning Wide-Band Video I-F Amplifiers - Stage-by-Stage. A sweep generator, marker oscillator, and oscillograph are used to align over-coupled, wide-band, video i-f amplifiers. Either a stage-by-stage or overall alignment technique may be employed. The more complete stage-by-stage method is described first, with reference to the circuit shown in Figure 70.

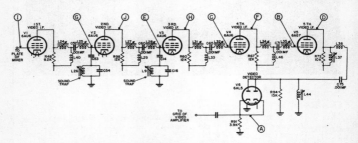

Figure 70. Simplified schematic of wide-band video i-f amplifier, showing points at which instruments are connected when alignment is performed.

This circuit should have a flat response from 22.4 to 25.65 megacycles. The 26.4-megacycle point on the response curve is down 6 db (50%); and the 22.4-Mc point is down 1 db, as shown in Figure 71.

Since the overall response calls for the 26.4-Mc point on the curve to be down 6 db, each individual i-f stage should be aligned so that this point is down about 1 db. This will result in an overall i-f response curve on which the 26.4-Mc point is down a total of 6 db. In order to maintain this overall response, it is necessary to align each i-f stage separately. To be sure that each stage is separately aligned without the influence of other sections of the circuit, it is recommended procedure to remove, from their sockets, the tubes preceding and following the stage being aligned.

The alignment procedure begins with the last video i-f stage and proceeds, stage-by-stage, toward the first i-f amplifier, as follows:

1. Connect the oscillograph between the cathode (point A in Figure 70) of V6 and ground. It is not necessary to use a probe detector at this point because the signal has already been detected by the video detector.

2. Connect the sweep generator between the grid of V5 (point B) and ground, in the 5th video i-f amplifier stage.

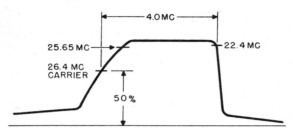

Figure 71. Ideal response curve for video i-f amplifier.

3. Set the sweep generator to furnish a sweep signal between 21 and 28 Mc.

4. Remove V4 from its socket.

5. The pattern obtained on the oscillograph should appear similar to that shown in Figure 72A. This pattern shows a dual response curve on the screen of the oscillograph.

6. Connect the high side of the marker oscillator to the point on the chassis where the sweep generator is grounded. Connect the ground side of the marker oscillator to another point on the chassis several inches from the point where the sweep generator is grounded.

7. Set the frequency of the marker oscillator to 26.4 Mc. This places a birdie on both the i-f curves, as shown in Figure 72B. Since these response curves are too narrow to permit accurate work, it is necessary to expand the horizontal sweep of the oscillograph. This gives the single response curve shown in Figure 72C.

8. Adjust variable inductors L37 and L34 to obtain a response curve similar to that shown in Figure 72D. The adjustment should be made so that the point indicated by the birdie is down about 1 db (10%) below the flat top of the response curve.

9. Figure 72E shows the position of the birdie when the marker generator is set to 22.4 Mc. It is not absolutely necessary to check this point now, because the 22.4-Mc point is determined in the overall response by the sound traps.

10. The output of the sweep generator should be set to about 0.1 volts when aligning each stage. Be certain that the output is not too high or the video amplifier may be overloaded.

11. Replace V4 and remove V3.

12. Connect the sweep generator between the grid (point C) of V4 and ground.

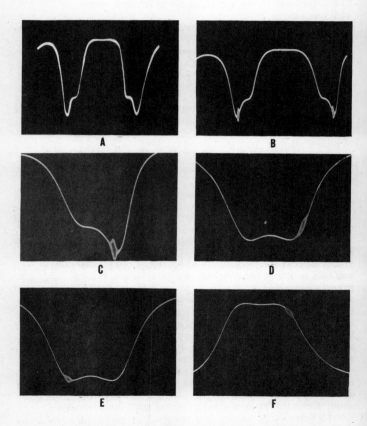

Figure 72. Response curves obtained when aligning video i-f amplifiers. A. Dual response curve. B. Birdie at 26.4 Mc. C. Single response curve. D. Birdie 1 db down from flat top. E. Birdie at 22.4 Mc. F. Birdie at 26.4 Mc.

13. Connect the oscillograph between the plate (point D) of V5 and ground, through the probe detector.

14. Set the marker generator to 26.4 Mc.

15. Tune inductors L34 and L35 to obtain the response curve shown in Figure 72F. Adjust this curve so that the 26.4 Mc point is 1 db down.

16. Replace V3 and remove V2 and V5 from their sockets.

17. Connect the sweep generator between the grid (point E) of V3 and ground.

18. Connect the probe detector between the plate (point F) of V4 and ground.

19. Repeat the alignment procedure, tuning this time inductances L31 and L32. The frequency response curve obtained by tuning these inductances is shown in Figure 73A. It will be noted that a slight nick in the response curve appears at its low-frequency end. This nick is at 21.9 Mc and is due to the sound trap in the grid circuit of V3. The sound trap should be adjusted at this time.

20. Change the setting of the marker oscillator to 21.9 Mc to check the tuning of the sound trap.

21. If the sound trap is not properly aligned, vary inductance L9, until the birdie appears at the bottom of the nick in the response curve.

22. Replace tubes V2 and V5, and remove V1 and V4 from their sockets.

23. Connect the sweep generator between the grid (point G) of V2 and ground.

24. Connect the probe detector between the plate of V3 (point H) and ground.

25. Repeat the alignment procedure tuning inductances L27 and L28 to obtain the response curve shown in Figure 73B. The presence of the two sound traps, one in the grid circuit of the second i-f stage, and the other in the grid circuit of the third i-f stage, are additive and produce a very pronounced dip in the response curve. Adjust sound trap L26 in the grid circuit of V2 until the dip in the curve occurs at 21.9 Mc. The birdie is barely visible in the region of 21.9 Mc, because of the severe attenuation of the signal by the sound trap.

26. Replace V1 and V4 and remove V3.

27. Connect the sweep generator between the grid (point I) of V1 and ground.

28. Connect the probe detector between the plate (point J) of V2 and ground.

29. Repeat the alignment procedure, tuning inductances L24 and L25 to obtain the response curve shown in Figure 73C.

30. Return V3 to its socket.

After aligning all the video i-f amplifier stages, an overall check of the response should be made. If the receiver chassis has a bottom plate, it should be in place when the response check is made. Otherwise, regeneration in the video i-f amplifier stages may distort the output signal, as shown in Figure 73D. This regeneration is not evident when a stage-by-stage examination is made, because the signal is isolated to the stage being adjusted.

31. Connect the sweep generator to the grid (point I) of V1.

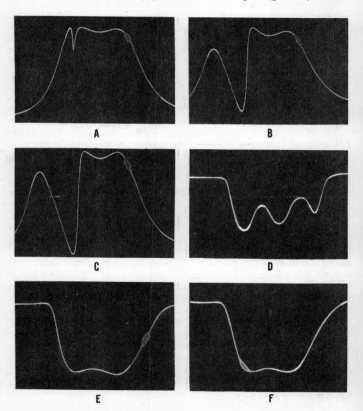

Figure 73. Response curves obtained when aligning video i-f amplifiers.

32. Connect the oscillograph directly to the grid of the picture tube. (It is assumed that the video amplifier stages have been previously aligned.)

33. Note the response curve as it appears on the screen of the oscillograph. Figure 73E shows a typical overall response curve. The 26.4 Mc point is indicated by the birdie and is 6 db down on the right edge of the curve. Figure 73F shows the same response curve with the birdie set at 22.4 Mc. These two response curves indicate that the overall alignment of the five stages is correct.

9-50 Overall Alignment of the Video I-F Amplifiers. Stage-by-stage alignment requires an oscillograph equipped with comparatively high gain deflection amplifiers. If such an instrument is not available, a low gain oscillograph may be used to align the video i-f amplifier stages by connecting it to the output of the video detector. The following procedure is used:

1. Connect the oscillograph to the output of the video detector, point A, in Figure 70. The probe detector is not necessary since the signal has already been detected at this point.

2. Connect the sweep generator and marker oscillator to the grid of the last video i-f stage (point B, Figure 70).

3. Following the procedure described in the paragraph on stage-by-stage alignment, adjust the last video coupling transformer.

4. Move the sweep generator and marker oscillator to the grid of the next video i-f stage and repeat the procedure, adjusting the coupling between the last and next to last i-f stages.

5. The sweep generator and marker oscillator should be moved to the grid of each i-f stage in turn, until all stages have been aligned.

9-51 Checking The Sound Trap Attenuation. The effect of the two sound traps, one in the grid circuit of the second i-f stage of V2, Figure 70, and the other in the grid circuit of the third video i-f stage, V3, is additive. The overall attenuation to the sound signal should be approximately 40 db. Therefore, each trap is responsible for 20 db attenuation. 40 db down corresponds to an attenuation of the sound signal 100 times more than the video signal; that is, for every volt of sound signal which is passed by the amplifier, there are 100 volts of video signal. 20 db attenuation means that for every volt of sound signal passed, there are 10 volts of video signal.

To measure the total attenuation of the sound traps, the following procedure should be followed:

1. Connect a marker oscillator between the grid of V1 and ground.

2. Set the frequency of the signal generator to the sound i-f frequency of 21.9 Mc.

3. Modulate the 21.9 Mc signal with a 400-cycle sine wave.

4. Connect the oscillograph between the grid of the picture tube and ground. With sufficient input signal and the gain control of the oscillograph set to a high level, a 400-cycle wave will appear on the screen of the oscillograph.

5. Set the amplitude of the 400-cycle wave to give a 2-inch deflection (20 scale divisions).

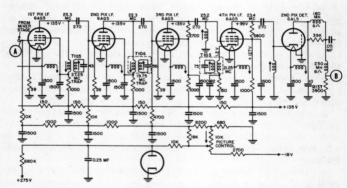

Figure 74. Schematic diagram of stagger-tuned video i-f amplifier.

6. Adjust the wave traps to give minimum deflection of this 400-cycle wave.

7. Again adjust the gain control of the oscillograph to secure a two-inch deflection on the screen.

8. Change the frequency setting on the signal generator so that it falls at some other point in the passband of the video i-f amplifier (for example, 25 Mc). The pattern appearing on the oscillograph will be greatly increased and much overloaded.

9. Utilizing the calibrated attenuator in the output circuit of the signal generator, step down the input signal until the amplitude of the 400-cycle wave is again 2 inches.

10. Note the change in gain setting of the calibrated attenuator of the signal generator. This is the attenuation introduced in the input signal by the sound traps in the video i-f channel.

If the total overall attenuation is less than 100:1, each trap must be checked in turn. If insufficient attenuation of the sound carrier exists, sound signals may enter the picture.

9-52 Aligning Stagger-Tuned Video I-F Amplifiers. Stagger-tuned i-f amplifiers are easier to align than over-coupled, wide-band amplifiers. A signal generator and v.t.v.m. are used to peak each of the stagger-tuned stages to a particular frequency. The v.t.v.m. is connected to the output of the second video detector and the signal generator to the grid of the first i-f stage.

The alignment of a typical stagger-tuned, video i-f amplifier is described with reference to the circuit shown in Figure 74.

1. Connect the signal generator to the grid (point A) of the first i-f amplifier.

2. Connect the v.t.v.m. across the video detector load resistor R137 (point B).

3. Set the signal generator to each of the following frequencies and peak the specified adjustment for maximum indication on the v.t.v.m.

21.25 Mc	-	T105
27.25 Mc	-	T103 (secondary)
19.75 Mc	-	T104 (secondary)

It may be desirable at times to observe the individual i-f stage response. This can be accomplished in the following way:

1. Connect a sweep generator to the grid of the first i-f amplifier.

2. Shunt all i-f transformers and coils with a 330-ohm carbon resistor, except the one whose response is to be observed.

3. Connect the oscillograph across the video detector load resistor and observe the response curve. The response obtained will be essentially that of the unshunted stage. The effects of the various traps on the response of the stage are also visible.

4. Figure 75 shows the response characteristics of each stage obtained in the above manner. Relative stage gain is not shown.

9-53 Aligning R-F Tuners. After the i-f system of the receiver has been adjusted for satisfactory bandwidth and selectivity, the r-f stages can be aligned. A sweep generator is of value here, but not as essential as in i-f amplifier alignment. The bandpass characteristics may be determined simply by applying three test frequencies (with 400-cycle modulation) to the antenna input, (1) at the picture carrier, (2) at the upper edge of the channel, and (3) at the lower edge of the channel. If substantially equal response is obtained on a v.t.v.m. or oscillograph connected across the second video detector, the amplifier is correctly aligned. It is not necessary to observe the shape of the r-f response curve, because the i-f response curve will provide sufficient selectivity if the three test frequencies show that the r-f amplifier is substantially flat.

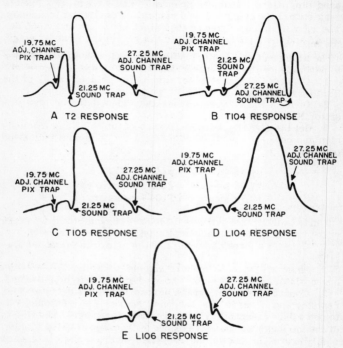

Figure 75. Response curves of stagger-tuned video i-f amplifiers.

If a sweep generator is used, it must have a frequency deviation sufficient to cover each r-f channel and one megacycle above and below it. Connections for r-f alignment with a sweep generator and oscillograph are shown in Figure 76. The procedure is the same as described for aligning a single overcoupled i-f amplifier stage. The only difference is that the center frequency of the sweep generator is now set at the r-f frequency corresponding to the midpoint of the channel under test. For example, if the r-f amplifier is tuned to Channel two

(54 to 60 Mc), the sweep generator center frequency is set at 57 Mc.

The type of r-f circuits used in receivers will vary, and the reader is referred to the manufacturer's service manual for information on the adjustable elements of these stages.

The continuous tuning "Inputuner" described in Section 7 calls for an entirely different approach to the alignment problem. The Inputuner must be first aligned by feeding a 71.25 Mc signal to it, setting the dial to channel 4 and adjusting the oscillator trimmer capacitor to obtain maximum output at the sound

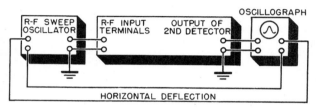

Figure 76. Connections used when aligning r-f section.

i-f frequency. A 215.75 Mc signal is then fed to the antenna input and the oscillator coil pulled or squeezed. After the tuner has been aligned a sweep generator and marker oscillator are used to adjust the bandwidth.

9-54 Final Sound Trap Adjustment. The tuning of a television receiver is determined by the exact setting of the discriminator. When the discriminator is aligned properly, a television channel may be best received by adjusting the tuner for maximum sound. The best picture will be obtained under these conditions.

To obtain a clear picture free from interference, it is also equally important that the sound channel fall precisely on a frequency to which the sound traps are adjusted. In order to assure that the sound traps and the discriminator transformers are in exact agreement, a final adjustment must be made after the rest of the receiver has been completely aligned.

1. Connect the signal generator to the antenna terminals of the receiver.

2. Connect the oscillograph between the grid of the picture tube and ground.

3. Adjust the receiver to a free channel (one on which no station is transmitting) in the lower television band.

4. Set the signal generator to the sound carrier frequency for the particular channel.

5. Adjust the tuner until a null is obtained on a v.t.v.m. connected across the discriminator output.

6. Reduce the contrast level until no overload is obtained in the video i-f when the signal generator is modulated 30% with 400 cycles.

7. Adjust the sound trap coils until a minimum of 400 cycle output is obtained on the oscillograph.

9-55 Sensitivity Check. A comparative sensitivity check can be made by operating the receiver on a weak signal from a television station and comparing the picture and sound obtained to that on other receivers of the same make under the same conditions. This weak signal can be simulated by connecting the shop antenna to the receiver through an attenuator pad of the type described in Section 8. A sufficient number of stages should be inserted in the pad so that somewhat less than normal picture contrast is obtained when the contrast control is set for maximum gain. Only carbon type resistors should be used to construct the attenuator pad.

To obtain an absolute measure of the receiver sensitivity, use the following procedure:

1. Connect the signal generator to the antenna terminals of the receiver.

2. Connect the oscillograph between the grid of the picture tube and ground.

3. Calibrate the oscillograph so as to be able to read 25 volts peak-to-peak (this value is used as an approximate standard and is about the average peak-to-peak voltage required in most receivers for normal contrast and brightness levels).

4. Tune the receiver to a free television channel in the lower television bands.

5. Adjust the calibrated signal generator to the center of the television channel.

6. Amplitude modulate the signal generator 30% with a 400 cycle sine wave signal.

7. Set the receiver contrast control to maximum and adjust the output of the signal generator until 25 volts peak-to-peak of the 400-cycle signal is obtained on the oscillograph.

The input signal (read on the signal generator output attenuator) required to obtain this level is the voltage sensitivity of the receiver.

9-56 Troubleshooting Charts. On the following pages the reader will find a series of charts which summarize common television receiver faults. These charts are useful when attempting to diagnose a defective receiver.

TELEVISION TEST EQUIPMENT

10-1 In the past, a signal generator, multimeter, and tube checker have been considered adequate test equipment for service shops. Such instruments as oscillographs and vacuum tube voltmeters, while extremely useful, were definitely not necessities.

With the advent of television, the three basic test instruments are no longer adequate. New test equipment, generally of a highly specialized nature, is required. In this section, the instruments required for the troubleshooting and adjustment of television receivers are described.

The instruments available for testing and adjusting television receivers can be divided into two groups: (1) those which are essential and (2) those which, although not essential, will simplify maintenance procedures and save time.

The following instruments are generally considered essential:
1. Cathode-Ray Oscillograph.
2. Sweep Frequency Signal Generator.
3. Audio Frequency Signal Generator.
4. R-F Frequency Signal Generator.
5. Vacuum Tube Voltmeter and Probe.
6. Multimeter.
7. Kilovoltmeter, or High-Voltage Probe.

In addition to the above instruments, the following are useful:

1. R.F. Probe for Oscillograph.
2. Square Wave Generator.
3. Oscillograph Voltage Calibrator.
4. Grid Dip Meter.
5. Q Meter.
6. R-C Bridge.
7. Crosshatch Generator.

Before a piece of test equipment is selected, its specifications should be examined carefully. The requirements for each type of instrument are outlined in this section. The unit chosen should meet, and if possible exceed, the specifications given. In addition, each new instrument selected should supplement the abilities of those instruments already in the possession of the purchaser. For example, a high voltage probe may be purchased instead of a kilovoltmeter if a suitable high resistance voltmeter is available. Other things which should be noted are the construction, accuracy, versatility, and freedom from obsolescence of the equipment under consideration.

CATHODE-RAY OSCILLOGRAPH

10-2 One of the most versatile and useful instruments for servicing all sections of the television receiver is the cathode-ray oscillograph or, as it is often called, the scope or CRO.

The oscillograph is used to examine voltage waveforms in the horizontal and vertical sweep circuits. It can be used to locate the causes of such video amplifier faults as clipping due to improper bias and loss of amplification due to faulty components. The causes of improper operation of synchronizing-pulse "clipper" stages can easily be located with the oscillograph, and excessive hum from power supplies is quickly identified, both as to amplitude and frequency.

One of the most important uses of the cathode-ray oscillograph is in the visual alignment of tuned circuits.

A block diagram of a typical oscillograph is shown in Figure 1. This oscillograph employs an electrostatically focused and deflected cathode-ray tube as do all oscillographs intended for television servicing. Shown in the block diagram are the horizontal (X) and vertical (Y) amplifiers and gain controls. In addition, the oscillograph is equipped with vertical and horizontal positioning controls and intensity and focus controls.

The vertical amplifier amplifies the signal which is to be observed. The output of the amplifier is fed to the vertical deflection plates of the cathode-ray tube. The gain control is provided in the vertical amplifier for adjusting the pattern to a convenient size. In some oscillographs, provision is also made to

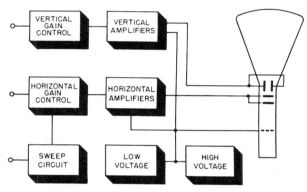

Figure 1. Block diagram of cathode-ray oscillograph.

permit connecting the vertical amplifier to a calibrating voltage source in order to measure the amplitude of the applied waveform.

The output voltage of the horizontal amplifier is used to deflect the electron beam from left to right, in accordance with the voltage applied to it. An attenuator of some type is provided, so that the pattern width may be adjusted to a convenient size. Normally a sawtooth voltage is fed to the horizontal amplifier from the built-in sweep circuit, so that the voltage applied to the vertical amplifier is plotted as a function of time. The sweep circuit is usually equipped with coarse and fine frequency controls for adjusting the sawtooth frequency to the desired value. In addition, a synchronizing control is provided for synchronizing the sawtooth frequency with the signal being examined, the 60-cycle power line, or an other external source. The oscillograph is also equipped with high and low voltage power supplies which provide operating potentials for the amplifiers, sweep circuits and the cathode-ray tube.

10-3 The Vertical and Horizontal Amplifiers. The vertical amplifiers of oscillographs suitable for television servicing usually consist of one or more single ended stages of amplification, working into a push-pull deflection amplifier.

Since an ordinary resistance-capacitance coupled amplifier stage does not provide sufficient bandwidth, some form of low and high frequency compensation must be used. High frequency compensation is secured by placing a suitable inductance in the plate circuit of an amplifier as shown in Figure 2. Its function

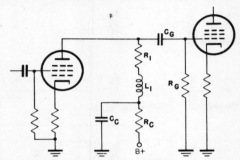

Figure 2. Oscillograph amplifier with high frequency compensation.

is identical to similar inductances utilized in the video amplifiers of television receivers.

Low frequency compensation takes the form of resistor Rc and Capacitor Cc. These components, and Cg and Rg, are chosen for optimum low frequency response.

To permit the study of signals of various amplitudes, some form of input attenuation must be used. Special circuits are necessary to obtain the required high impedance input and freedom from frequency discrimination. If the signal were coupled to the amplifier input through a high resistance potentiometer, a suitably high input impedance would be obtained, but frequency discrimination would result. If a low resistance potentiometer were used, the frequency discrimination would be avoided, but the input impedance would be too low. The problem is solved by the addition of a cathode follower input stage, as shown in Figure 3. A stepped frequency compensated input attenuator is used. Intermediate gain adjustments are made using a low resistance potentiometer located in the cathode follower output.

It is difficult to obtain sufficient voltage to deflect the cathode-ray tube if single-ended deflection is employed, and therefore most high-frequency oscillographs have push-pull output stages.

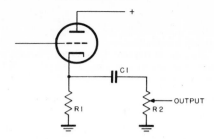

Figure 3. Cathode follower input stage.

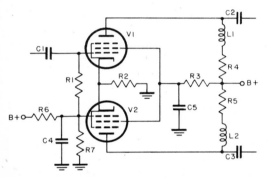

Figure 4. Cathode-coupled output stage.

Almost all oscillographs having push-pull output stages use the cathode-coupled, self-inverting output stage shown in Figure 4. In this circuit, the signal is applied to the grid of V1, causing an in-phase voltage to appear across the common cathode resistor R2. Since the grid of V2 is grounded by condenser C4, the grid-cathode voltage of V2 is equal to the signal voltage across R2. However, since a positive voltage on the cathode is equivalent to a negative voltage on the grid, the plate voltage of V2 is 180° out of phase with the plate voltage of V1. By using a large value of common cathode resistor, the amplitudes of the two outputs will approach each other within a few percent. Since such a large cathode resistor would result in entirely too large a negative bias on the tubes, a small amount of positive bias is placed on both grids through the network consisting of R6 and R7.

The design of the horizontal amplifier of a cathode-ray oscillograph is similar to that of its vertical amplifier, except that the gain of the horizontal amplifier is usually lower, and the frequency response not as great. The horizontal amplifier receives its signal from either an external sweep signal, such as that provided by most wobbulators, or from an internal sawtooth generator. To provide blanking of the return trace, an out-of-phase signal from the horizontal sweep amplifiers is often applied to the grid of the cathode-ray tube.

10-4 Sawtooth Generators. The simplest type of sawtooth generator utilizes a gas triode, as shown in Figure 5. In this type of circuit, when B voltage is applied, condenser C starts

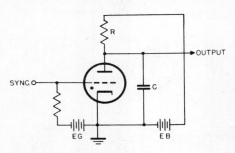

Figure 5. Gas triode sawtooth generator.

charging through series resistor R. When the voltage across the condenser reaches the ionization potential of the gas triode, the tube suddenly conducts and rapidly discharges the condenser. A sawtooth voltage is thus generated whose frequency is determined by the size of the resistor and condenser, the plate voltage, and the ionization potential of the tube. Since the ionization potential is controlled by the grid bias of the tube, the frequency of oscillation can be determined by a signal applied to the grid. For example, the sawtooth oscillator can be synchronized by the same voltage that is applied to the vertical amplifier by feeding this voltage to the grid of the gas triode.

A recurrent sawtooth, such as that produced by the circuit just described, is a suitable sweep voltage waveform if the signal to be examined is recurrent in nature. If it is irregular in occurrence, or if a small portion of it is to be spread out and examined in detail, a driven, or triggered-sweep sawtooth generator is required. Such a generator produces one sawtooth of voltage each time it is triggered. Hence, the start of the sawtooth sweep always occurs at the same time as the signal to be viewed. It is possible to convert the recurrent sawtooth generator into a triggered-sweep generator by modifying the circuit as shown in Figure 6.

In this circuit, the cathode potential of the diode is set to such a value that the diode will conduct at a slightly lower plate-to-ground potential than the triode. Thus, when the sweep condenser C charges to the potential of the diode cathode, the diode will conduct and prevent the condenser voltage from reaching the ignition potential of the gas triode. However, if a positive sync

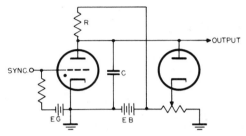

Figure 6. Gas triode circuit for generating driven or triggered sweep.

signal is momentarily impressed on the triode grid, it will lower the triode ignition potential below the voltage of the diode cathode, allowing the triode to conduct and discharge the condenser. The condenser will then charge, through the resistor, until it reaches the diode cathode potential again, where it will be "clamped" by the diode. During this time, the spot on the oscillograph screen has made a fast retrace from right to left, and then a single sweep from left to right, producing the required single sweep.

10-5 The Cathode-Ray Tube and High Voltage Supply. The cathode-ray tubes used in present day cathode-ray oscillographs are of the electrostatically-focused, electrostatically-deflected type. A P-1, green-fluorescent, medium persistence screen is employed instead of the P-4 screen employed in television picture tubes.

The power supplies used in oscillographs are somewhat similar to those used in television receivers. A typical supply for a high gain oscillograph is shown in Figure 8. It will be noted that the high voltage winding is an extension of the low voltage winding on the single power transformer used. Half-wave rectification and a two section filter consisting of C28, C29, C31, R49, and R55 is used.

The low voltage supply is regulated in order to minimize the effects which line voltage variations have upon the deflection amplifiers. The regulated supply also has very little ripple, a necessity in high gain instruments.

10-6 Oscillograph Requirements for Television Servicing. The many uses to which the oscillograph may be put in the maintenance of television receivers call for such wide versatility that few oscillographs meet all service requirements. For television servicing, an oscillograph should meet the following specifications:

1. High gain - The vertical amplifier should have a sensitivity of at least 25 millivolts RMS per inch in order to permit stage-by-stage alignment of i-f amplifiers in conjunction with a sweep frequency signal generator, or wobbulator. If an overall alignment procedure is used in which the oscillograph is connected to the output of the i-f amplifier system, a sensitivity of 0.1 volts RMS is adequate.

2. Good 60-cycle square wave response - Since most sweep frequency signal generators operate at 60 cps, the vertical amplifier should have good 60-cycle response to pass the wobbulated signal. Good low-frequency response is necessary, too, for observing the 60-cycle vertical sweep and sync signals in the receiver. If the instrument is to be used with a square wave generator to adjust video amplifier stages, it should have good square wave response down to 30 cycles.

3. Good high-frequency response - Vertical amplifier response extending to 100 kc is adequate for alignment work with a wobbulator. If the oscillograph is used for examining video and horizontal sweep signals, and for checking video amplifiers by means of a high-frequency square wave, the response should extend to at least 2 Mc, and preferably to 4 Mc.

4. Low input capacity to vertical amplifier - This is required when checking horizontal sweep circuits and video amplifiers. If the input capacity of the oscillograph is too high, the instrument will distort the response of the circuit it is being used to test. The input capacity should be less than 15 mmf.

5. Suitable tube size - For most television applications, 3-inch or 5-inch tubes are suitable.

10-7 The Du Mont Type 208B Cathode-Ray Oscillograph. The Du Mont Type 208B Cathode-Ray Oscillograph, shown in Figure 7, is a typical 5-inch instrument. It has a vertical sensitivity of .01 volts RMS/inch, and a frequency response uniform within

10% from 2 cps to 100 kc, at all positions of the gain control.

A schematic diagram of the 208B is shown in Figure 8. A capacity-compensated input attenuator feeds a cathode follower, V1, which has a low impedance gain control in its cathode circuit. This circuit eliminates frequency discrimination in the low-impedance gain control. Tubes V2 and V3 are high-frequency compensated amplifier stages, which have sufficiently

Figure 7. The Du Mont Type 208B Cathode-Ray Oscillograph.

large grid resistors and coupling capacitors to give the required low-frequency response. The signal is then fed to another cathode follower, V4, whose output is directly coupled to the two output tubes V5 and V6. V5 and V6 feed separate vertical plates of the cathode-ray tube V12, and provide balanced deflection. R16, which changes the d-c bias on V5 and V6, serves as a positioning control.

The horizontal amplifier employs two cathode followers, V8 and V9, which serve the same function as V1 and V4 in the vertical circuit. The horizontal amplifier output stage is identical to the vertical amplifier. A gas triode, V7, is employed in a standard sawtooth sweep circuit, with a range of 2 cps to 50 kc. The power supply of this instrument is necessarily more com-

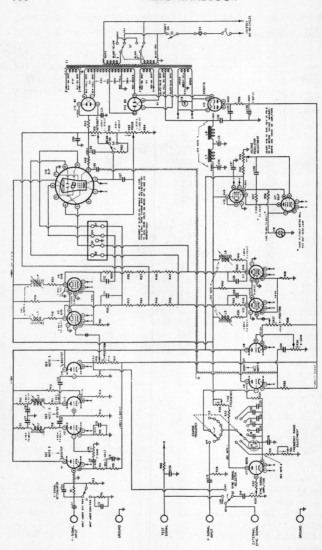

Figure 8. Schematic circuit of Du Mont Type 208B.

plex than those found in lower gain oscillographs. A full wave rectifier, V14, feeds a degenerative-type voltage regulator composed of V16, V17, and V18. The voltage regulator prevents line voltage variations from affecting the operation of the deflection amplifiers. A half-wave rectifier, V15, is used to supply a negative voltage for the cathode followers, so that a large cathode resistor may be used without having excessive bias. An additional half-wave rectifier, V13, is used to supply the accelerating voltage for the cathode-ray tube.

Because of its high gain, good low-frequency response, and extended high-frequency response, this instrument is excellent for most television work. The Type 208B may be used for visual alignment of individual i-f stages, and for troubleshooting the sync and sweep circuits. Its high frequency response is not adequate for checking the high frequency square wave response of video amplifiers.

SWEEP FREQUENCY GENERATOR

10-8 The sweep frequency generator, or wobbulator, is used to align the wide-band r-f and i-f stages of the television receiver. While it is possible to adjust the tuned circuits of a video i-f amplifier by using a signal generator and a voltmeter, and checking many points along the curve, the time and labor involved in this method is considerable.

There are two types of sweep frequency generators: (1) those in which the oscillator operates directly at the desired output frequency (or a subharmonic of it), and (2) those in which the output frequency is obtained by mixing the outputs of two separate oscillators together to obtain a beat frequency in the desired range. A block diagram of a fundamental type wobbulator is shown in Figure 9. In the fundamental frequency type wobbulator, an oscillator operating at the desired frequency has its frequency varied periodically, by one of several methods. A blanking circuit is often provided to disable the oscillator during the deviation cycle to produce a zero base line. A sweep voltage which is properly phased to move the cathode-ray oscillograph beam in synchronism with the frequency deviations of the oscillator is usually built into the wobbulator.

10-9 Generating the Sweep Frequency. In order to vary the

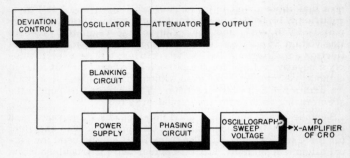

Figure 9. Block diagram of fundamental frequency wobbulator.

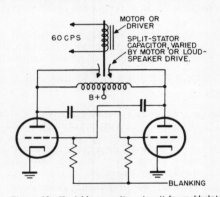

Figure 10. Variable capacitor circuit for wobbulator.

frequency of most oscillators, it is necessary to vary the reactance of some part of the tuned circuit. Commercial wobbulators employ one of four methods to generate sweep frequencies: (1) a rotating capacitor, (2) a vibrating capacitor, (3) a vibrating inductor, or (4) a reactance tube.

Rotating capacitor units utilize 1800 or 3600-rpm synchronous motors, driving small, ball hearing capacitors. Most test equipment manufacturers have discarded this method of frequency modulating an oscillator in favor of other, less expensive, and more flexible methods.

Vibrating capacitor units employ driver units, similar to PM loudspeaker drivers, to vary a split-stator concentric capacitor.

The capacitor is used in a push-pull oscillator circuit, as in Figure 10. The voice coil is normally driven with a 60-cycle voltage, so that one complete excursion of frequency, from the lower limit to the upper limit and back, takes place in one sixtieth of a second.

The vibrating inductor method employs a driver unit similar to the vibrating capacitor type. A disk of metal, instead of a capacitor, is mounted on the vibrator. The oscillator coil is wound in a spiral shape, and the metal disk is located close and parallel to the coil, so that it acts as a closely coupled shorted turn. As the metal disk is vibrated toward and away from the coil by the driver unit, the coupling varies and therefore the effective inductance of the coil varies, producing the required frequency modulation. The coil may be used in either a push-pull or single-ended oscillator circuit.

All of the above methods of frequency modulation utilize an electro-mechanical method of varying the oscillator frequency. It is possible, however, to produce the effect of a varying inductance or capacitance by electronic means, using a reactance tube. When a reactance tube is used in a wobbulator, a 60-cps sine wave is fed into its grid, causing the oscillator frequency to vary at a 60-cps rate.

All of the methods for generating sweep frequencies so far described have the shortcoming of not being able to produce a constant frequency deviation at different center frequencies. For example, if the sweep oscillator is designed for the alignment of the r-f channels in a television receiver, its center frequency must be varied from 54 to 216 Mc. To properly align each of the 12 channels in this range, the center frequency should deviate plus and minus 5 Mc. It is difficult to obtain this deviation over a wide range with the sweep generator methods just described. With the methods described, the deviation may be plus or minus 3 Mc at the lower center frequencies, and as much as 7 or 8 Mc at high center frequencies. The deviation problem is overcome in many instruments by using a beat method for obtaining the desired sweep frequency range. A block diagram of such an instrument is shown in Figure 11. With this method, the frequency modulated oscillator is operated at a fixed frequency, and an auxiliary oscillator is tuned to obtain the center frequency. The outputs of the two oscillators are mixed to produce a sweep frequency signal at the desired frequency. For example, if the center frequency of the frequency modulated oscillator is 114 Mc., and the variable oscillator can be tuned from 37 Mc to 112 Mc, output may be obtained from 114 + 37, or 151 Mc, to 114 + 112, or 226 Mc, with a deviation equal to that of the frequency modulated oscillator.

In order to produce the proper sweep voltage for the oscillo-graph, a 60-cycle sine wave or a 60-cycle triangular wave (if blanking of the oscillator is not provided) is required to super-impose the forward and return traces. If the oscillator is blanked, either of the above waveforms, or a 120-cycle sawtooth volt-age may be used. When sine wave sweep is used, it is usually

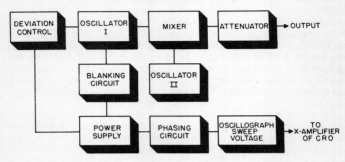

Figure 11. Block diagram of beat frequency wobbulator.

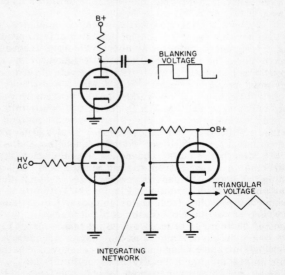

Figure 12. Circuit for generating triangular wave and blanking pulse.

fed through a phasing network to allow the sweep voltage to reach its maximum at the same time the wobbulator reaches its maximum output frequency. The same type of network is used to adjust the phase of the blanking voltage. A 60-cps triangular wave is usually produced by integrating a 60-cps square wave voltage formed by clipping a sine wave in a circuit similar to that shown in Figure 12. This circuit includes a tube used to provide blanking voltage for the sweep oscillator.

10-10 Sweep Generator Requirements. The sweep frequency generator must cover a wide range of frequencies if it is to be used for aligning all the amplifiers in a television receiver. The center frequencies and the deviations which the sweep generator must be capable of producing are listed below.

21.5	Mc	$\pm$ 500 kc	Sound i-f amplifiers
4.5	Mc	$\pm$ 500 kc	Intercarrier sound i-f amplifiers
24	Mc	$\pm$ 5 Mc	Video i-f amplifiers
57	Mc	$\pm$ 6 Mc	Channel 2 r-f amplifiers
63	Mc	$\pm$ 6 Mc	Channel 3 r-f amplifiers
69	Mc	$\pm$ 6 Mc	Channel 4 r-f amplifiers
79	Mc	$\pm$ 6 Mc	Channel 5 r-f amplifiers
85	Mc	$\pm$ 6 Mc	Channel 6 r-f amplifiers
177	Mc	$\pm$ 6 Mc	Channel 7 r-f amplifiers
183	Mc	$\pm$ 6 Mc	Channel 8 r-f amplifiers
189	Mc	$\pm$ 6 Mc	Channel 9 r-f amplifiers
195	Mc	$\pm$ 6 Mc	Channel 10 r-f amplifiers
201	Mc	$\pm$ 6 Mc	Channel 11 r-f amplifiers
207	Mc	$\pm$ 6 Mc	Channel 12 r-f amplifiers
213	Mc	$\pm$ 6 Mc	Channel 13 r-f amplifiers
8.5	Mc	$\pm$ 500 kc	Prewar sound i-f amplifiers
12.75	Mc	$\pm$ 5 Mc	Prewar video i-f amplifiers
5	Mc	$\pm$ 5 Mc	Video amplifiers

At the frequencies listed above, the only practical method of carrying the r-f voltage from the wobbulator to the receiver is by means of a coaxial cable, since a length of coaxial cable, terminated in its characteristic impedance, has a response which is flat over the frequencies listed. Approximately 500 millivolts of wobbulated r-f signal should be available at the end of the cable. For aligning i-f amplifiers, and r-f sections which are normally connected to the antenna by a coaxial line, the wobbulator should have single-ended output. For aligning r-f sections which are normally connected to the antenna with twinlead, the wobbulator should have a balanced-to-ground, push-pull output. An attenuator should be provided to permit varying the output of the wobbulator.

Since few oscillographs have a sweep voltage which can be adjusted to the proper phase, the wobbulator should supply its own sweep voltage. If varying the bandwidth varies the phasing, as it usually does in electro-mechanical wobbulators, a phasing control should be provided.

10-11 The RCA WR-59A Television Sweep Generator. This unit, shown in Figure 13 is an extremely versatile instrument which covers all the intermediate frequencies required for

Figure 13. RCA WR-59A Television Sweep Generator.

aligning modern television receivers. Frequency modulation is accomplished by means of a vibrating capacitor unit, and both direct and beat frequency outputs are used. For the r-f and sound i-f channels, where the percentage deviation is small, the oscillator operates directly at the desired output frequency. Three other ranges of 0 - 10 Mc, 5 - 15 Mc, and 20 - 30 Mc are provided for aligning video i-f and video amplifiers. In these ranges, the frequency modulated oscillator sweeps from 80 to 90 Mc, and an auxiliary oscillator, set at either 80, 75, or 60 Mc, beats with it to produce the desired output. For the 13 r-f channels, balanced output is provided, as required by the r-f sections used in most television receivers, while for i-f alignment single-ended output is provided.

When used with an external marker signal generator, this unit meets the requirements for television alignment. The switching arrangement for selecting frequency ranges makes it simple and convenient to operate.

10-12 The Kay Electric Mega-Sweep. The Kay Electric Mega-sweep (Figure 14) is a wide-band beat-frequency wobbulator

Figure 14. Kay Electric Mega-Sweep.

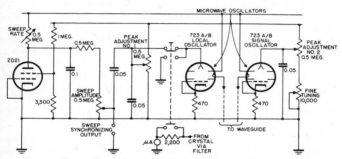

Figure 15. Basic schematic circuit of Mega-Sweep.

having a bandwidth adjustable up to 30 Mc with a center frequency adjustable from 50 kc to 500 Mc. An internal adjustment allows center frequencies up to 1000 Mc to be obtained. The output across a terminated 50-ohm coaxial cable is approximately .05 volts up to 500 Mc, and drops somewhat for higher frequencies.

The basic schematic of the instrument is given in Figure 15, showing the two 2K25/723 A-B reflex klystron oscillators and the 2D21 sawtooth voltage generator. The outputs of the two oscillators, which operate in the 10,000 Mc region, are injected into a special microwave waveguide, where they are mixed and detected by a crystal diode. By mechanically varying the dimensions of the internal cavity of the klystron, their frequency may be varied as much as 1000 Mc. By varying the repeller voltage, the klystron frequency may be swept as much as 30 Mc. This is accomplished by the sawtooth voltage generated by the 2D21 gas tetrode. Attenuation of the r-f output voltage is provided by a microwave attenuator which varies the output of the fixed frequency klystron.

The power supply for this unit is regulated to maintain the required voltage stability.

SIGNAL GENERATORS

10-13 The advent of television has imposed much broader and stricter requirements on signal generators, among them wider frequency ranges, increased accuracy, and special output systems adapted for the higher frequencies. The main uses of the signal generator in television are in setting the receiver local oscillator to the correct frequency for each channel, aligning stagger-tuned i-f's (which should be given a final touch-up with a sweep frequency signal generator), adjusting sound traps, making sensitivity and stage gain measurements, and providing "birdie" markers to indicate particular frequencies on the response curve obtained with a sweep frequency generator.

Signal generators are also useful for producing linearity bars, which are used to adjust the linearity of the vertical and horizontal sweep circuits.

For television service work, a signal generator must cover the range from the low audio frequencies up to at least 220 megacycles. Because of the nature of the circuits necessary two separate units are normally required, one for the audio frequencies and a second for the higher frequencies. The accuracy requirements are unusually strict, especially at the higher frequencies, where as little as a 1% error in frequency is equivalent to approximately 2 Mc. For precise alignment work, the signal generator must be either crystal-controlled or crystal-calibrated, for ordinary LC oscillators cannot maintain a precise calibration over a period of time.

In the audio and low radio frequency ranges (O-100 kc), two different types of circuits are in wide use, the beat frequency oscillator and the RC oscillator. In the remainder of the radio frequency range (100 kc - 230 Mc), self-excited Colpitts and Hartley oscillators are used. Crystal controlled oscillators are used in units designed specifically for generating marker signals.

The beat frequency type of signal generator employs two r-f oscillators, operating at slightly different frequencies. One oscillator generates a fixed frequency which is heterodyned with the voltage from another, variable, oscillator. The output signal has a frequency equal to the difference between the two oscillator frequencies.

In addition to the two oscillators, an amplifier is provided to bring the beat frequency up to the required voltage level. An a.v.c. circuit is usually employed to maintain the output voltage constant as the frequency is varied. This type of oscillator is used to cover the audio and low i-f frequencies.

The RC oscillator can be conveniently made to cover a frequency range of 1 cps to 100,000 cps.

Between 100 kc and about 400 Mc, ordinary Colpitts or Hartley oscillators are commonly used.

Crystal controlled oscillators are used in units designed to produce marker signals. Since above 12 Mc, fundamental frequency crystals are not available, overtone or harmonic mode crystals must be used. These crystals have dimensions that would normally permit them to oscillate between 5 and 15 Mc. They are cut in such a manner that in the proper circuit they will oscillate at their third, fifth, and seventh harmonics. The circuit used must be designed so that the feedback is provided only at the desired harmonic frequency, and not at the fundamental.

10-14 Signal Generator Requirements. To furnish markers for wobbulator alignment, the signal generator should have a frequency range from about 8 to 240 Mc. For aligning stagger-tuned i-f amplifiers, it is desirable to have a 400-cycle modulator in the generator. In checking overall and stage-by-stage gain, a calibrated attenuator, which controls the level of the signal output, is helpful. A terminated coaxial cable should be provided for the signal generator to couple the signal to the receiver under test. An r-f voltage of 500 millivolts should be available at the end of the cable.

Usually, two or more generators will be required for completely servicing the receiver. In addition to the r-f generator, a wide-range audio oscillator, of the RC or beat frequency type, is useful for checking audio amplifiers and for producing linearity bars. This unit should cover a range of from 20 cps to 200 kc, with less then five percent total distortion. An output of at least five volts should be available.

10-15 The Vacuum Tube Voltmeter. The vacuum tube voltmeter (v.t.v.m.) is used in all sections of the receiver. The extremely high input impedance of this instrument makes it possible to measure voltage at almost any point in a circuit without disturbing the circuit's operation. The v.t.v.m. should have an a-c voltage range of 0.5 volts to 250 volts. The instrument should have a constant input impedance of 10 megohms or more over its entire range.

The instrument should be equipped with a suitable probe to extend its range into the radio frequencies. The r-f voltage range should be from 0.5 to 250 volts. Response should be uniform from 10 kc to approximately 250 Mc. The input capacitance of the probe should not be more than four or five mmf.

10-16 The Multimeter. The multimeter is one of the most used servicing instruments. To provide maximum flexibility, it should have a wide variety of ranges. The following ranges are generally considered adequate.
1. D-C volts - 0.5 to 1000 volts.
2. A-C volts - 0.5 to 1000 volts.
3. Direct Current - 1 milliampere to 10 amperes.
4. Resistance - 2 ohms to 20 megohms.

The d-c sensitivity of the instrument should be at least 20,000 ohms per volt. Many v.t.v.m.'s include some or all of the ranges listed above. If such an instrument is available, a multimeter is not required.

10-17 The Square Wave Generator. A square wave generator and an oscillograph offer the most practical means of checking the frequency response of a video amplifier. Generally, it is sufficient to feed a 30-cycle and 200-kc square wave into a video amplifier to check its performance.

For checking the frequency response of video amplifiers, therefore, the square wave generator should have a frequency range extending from 30 cycles to 200 kc. The square wave generator can also be used to produce linearity bars and, if available, is preferable to a sine wave signal generator. For checking video amplifiers, an output of at least 2 volts peak-to-peak is required. To produce linearity bars, 10 volts peak-to-peak is necessary.

10-18 Detector Probe. In order to align individual i-f amplifier stages using an oscillograph and sweep generator, some form of detector probe is necessary. This probe is connected to the output of the stage being aligned. It detects the output signal before it is fed to the oscillograph.

Most of the probes designed for use with vacuum tube voltmeters are suitable for use with an oscillograph. Probes which use crystal rectifier units are preferred because they do not require provision for heater supply. The circuit of a suitable probe is shown in Figure 16. The components should be mounted in a shielded tube. A length of coaxial cable should be provided

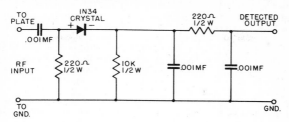

Figure 16. Probe detector.

for connecting the probe to the input terminals of the oscillograph.

10-19 The Voltage Calibrator. The voltage calibrator is a very useful accessory for use with the oscillograph. It enables the technician to determine the peak-to-peak voltage of any waveform appearing on the oscillograph screen. Since many television receiver manufacturers give this data for all the important points in the sweep and video circuits, measurement of the voltages at these key points in the receiver makes it possible to quickly locate faulty circuits and components. Commercial calibrators use either a sine or square wave voltage, of known adjustable magnitude, for measuring the amplitudes of unknown signals.

The voltage range that the calibrator should have is determined at the low end, by the maximum sensitivity of the oscillograph, as there is no need for calibrator voltages corresponding to less than a quarter-inch deflection on the screen. The maximum output voltage of the calibrator should be at least 100 volts. The instrument should be calibrated to an accuracy of at least five percent.

10-20 The Grid Dip Meter. The grid dip meter is a very useful instrument for troubleshooting high frequency circuits. It can be used as an indicating wavemeter to identify the frequency to which an oscillator is tuned, or it can be used to identify the frequency to which any circuit in a television receiver is tuned, even if the receiver is not operating. The grid dip meter is actually a wide range oscillator whose mechanical design is so arranged that it can be easily coupled to a circuit. When the circuit is tuned to the same frequency as the grid dipper, energy is absorbed from the dipper. The frequency to which the circuit is tuned is indicated by a dip in the reading of a meter, which is connected to the dipper, as it is tuned through the circuits resonant frequency.

For television work the frequency range of the grid dipper should extend from below 4 Mc to about 240 Mc. Usually, a switch is provided to disconnect the oscillator plate voltage, so that the tuned circuit and grid-cathode-meter circuit may be used as a calibrated wavemeter to check spurious responses of oscillators. The instrument can also be used to check resonant frequencies of antennas, or the capacities of unknown capacitors.

10-21 Q-Meters. In all tuned amplifiers, performance depends not only upon the inductances of the coils used, but also upon their Q, which is equal to Xl/R.

In high frequency circuits, the Q of the coil is very critical. If a coil must be replaced in an r-f, i-f, or video amplifier of a television receiver, it is often helpful to use a Q-meter to check the replacement coil, or to help wind one of equivalent value.

10-22 Resistance-Capacitance Bridges. The technician will often find it necessary to measure resistance or capacitance values more accurately than is possible with an ohmmeter or capacitance meter. In such cases, the required accuracy may be obtained by measuring the component on a resistance-capacitance bridge. This type of instrument is capable of measuring the values of capacitors, resistors, and the turns ratios of transformers. In addition, insulation resistance measurements can be made, and electrolytic condensers may be checked for excessive leakage current at rated working voltage with such an instrument. The following ranges are adequate: Capacitance from 5 mmf to 200 mf. Resistance from 5 ohms to 20 megohms.

10-23 Kilovoltmeter and High Voltage Probes. A high voltage voltmeter with a range to 30 kv is required to check and adjust the various types of power supplies which furnish the accelerating potential to the picture tube. Since most high voltage power supplies used in television receivers delivers only a few hundred microamperes, the high voltage meter should not draw more than 50 microamperes for full scale deflection.

Most vacuum tube voltmeter and volt ohm-milliammeters

have a maximum voltage range of 2 kv to 5 kv. It is possible to extend the range of these meters by using a high voltage probe. The probe contains a multiplying resistor which is inserted in series with the meter and increases its internal resistance, thereby raising the voltage range which the voltmeter can handle. A probe should be used only if the voltmeter available has a sensitivity of 20,000 ohms per volt or more.

10-24 Linearity Signal Generator. Several instruments are manufactured for the specific purpose of checking and adjusting the linearity or the vertical and horizontal sweep circuits. These instruments are known as bar generators, or crosshatch

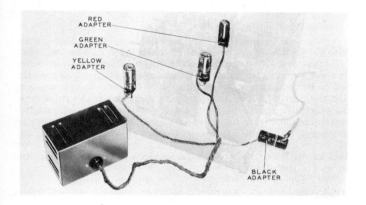

Figure 17. Philco Crosshatch Generator.

generators. They produce about 15 to 40 horizontal and vertical lines on the receiver screen or, in some cases, just dots representing the junctions of the bars. It is necessary only to adjust the receiver linearity controls until the bars are equally spaced on the screen to obtain linear sweep.

The Philco Model 5072 Crosshatch Generator, shown in Figure 17 is designed to receive its operating voltages and synchronizing signals from the receiver under test. A special harness, made for the particular receiver, plugs into the receiver and feeds synchronizing, plate, and filament voltages to the crosshatch generator. The circuit diagram of the unit is shown in Figure 18. V1 and V3 are the vertical and horizontal control tubes, while V2 and V4 serve as oscillators and shapers. Normally, the second half of each control tube is cut off by a

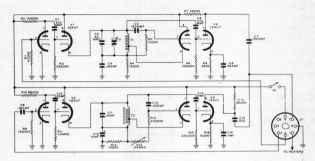

Figure 18. Schematic circuit of Crosshatch Generator

large cathode bias voltage, and hence does not affect the oscillators. Negative pulses, obtained from the receiver sync circuits, are amplified and fed to the control tubes as short positive pulses, causing them to conduct momentarily and load the oscillator down heavily enough to block them. This is done so that the oscillators will always have the same phase relative to the start of the horizontal and vertical sweeps. The bar signals which are generated by the oscillator will then be stationary on the screen. The oscillator voltages are shaped into narrow pulses, mixed, and fed to the video amplifier tube as narrow negative pulses, producing horizontal and vertical bars on the screen of the picture tube.

10-25 Other Instruments. At present, few instruments are available which meet all the requirements of television servicing. As an example, no one oscillograph has good low frequency, high gain, and 4-Mc bandwidth. The high frequency response of some high-gain, low-frequency oscillographs, such as the Du Mont Type 208-B, may be extended by using a Tel-Instrument video amplifier known as a Teledapter. Other accessory devices which increase the range of most television test equipment should be investigated as they appear on the market. Several new instruments, such as the portable Raytheon sync generator, have made their appearance; and undoubtedly, more useful aids for television servicing will become available in the future.

BUILDING A TELEVISION RECEIVER

No better way can be found to learn the inner workings of a television receiver than to build one. The result of such a project can be a receiver useful for pre-installation surveys, laboratory experiments, demonstrations, and for entertainment in the home.

Included in this section are the schematic circuit, parts list, and chassis layouts for a television receiver which can be operated with non-ion trap 10, 12, or 15 inch magnetic picture tubes. If the builder wishes to use an ion trap picture tube, permanent magnet ion traps are available.

The schematic circuit for all sections of the receiver, except the r-f tuner, is shown in Figure 1. The audio and video circuits use pre-aligned i-f transformers which are tuned for i-f carrier frequencies of 21.9 Mc. and 26.4 Mc., respectively.

It is difficult to construct and align an r-f tuner that will perform well at the high television frequencies without proper test equipment. Several pre-aligned r-f tuners can be purchased which are built up as complete assemblies. The tuner that is selected should provide a sound i-f frequency of 21.9 Mc. and

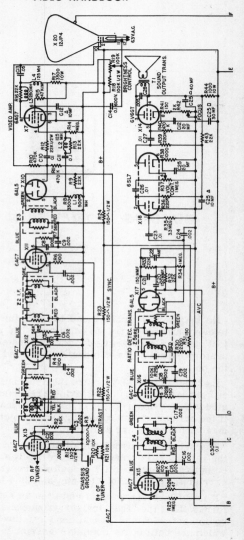

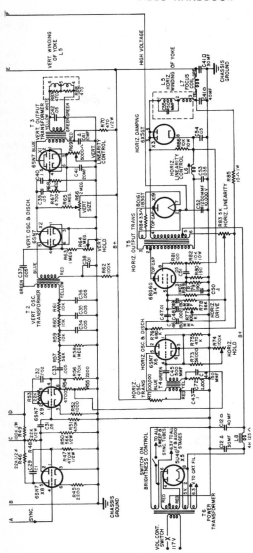

Figure 1.

a video i-f frequency of 26.4 mc. The circuit for coupling the
mixer stage in the r-f tuner to the first video i-f stage is shown
in Figure 2.

The main chassis contains all the parts shown in the schematic
diagram of Figure 1. Figure 3 shows the layout of parts on the
skirts of the chassis. A bottom view of the chassis is shown in
Figure 4. The r-f tuner assembly is mounted in the space indicated in the upper left hand corner. The location of terminal
strips for mounting the small parts is also shown. The socket
for the 8016 high voltage rectifier should not be mounted directly on the chassis, but should be supported on stand-off insulators.
It is suggested that a metal shield be built around the high voltage tube and transformer.

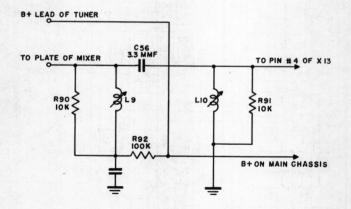

Figure 2.

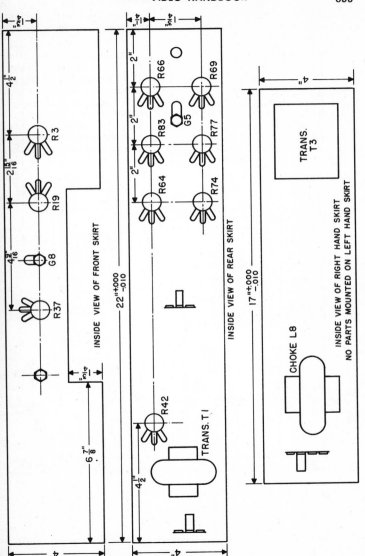

Figure 3.

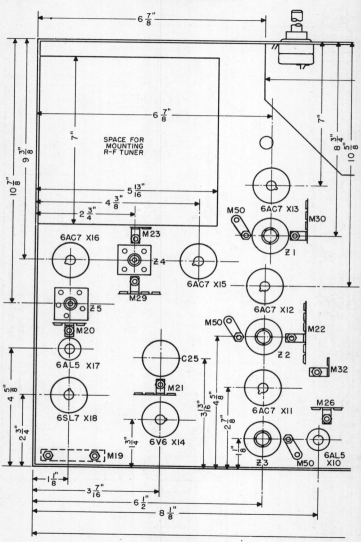

Figure 4

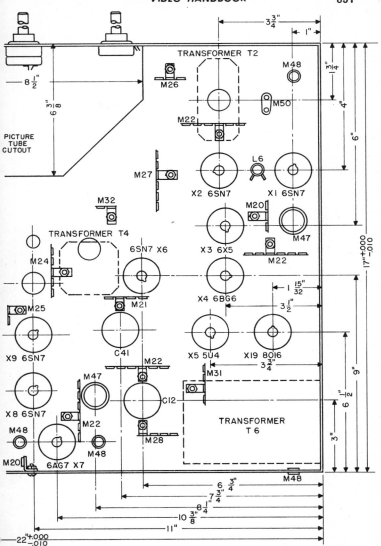

R1,R22,R23,R24,R28,R31,R41—150 ohms, ½ watt

R2,R5,R7,R50,R57,R73,R78—56,000 ohms, ½ watt

R3—Potentiometer, 10,000 ohms — c bias taper, 1-1/4" shaft (contrast control)

R4,R6,R81,R92—100 ohms, ½ watt

R8—3300 ohms, ½ watt

R9,R12,R13,R16,R32,R33,R43,R46,R48 R53,R72—22,000 ohms, ½ watt

R10,R11,R40,R47,R51,R56,R75—470,000 ohms, ½ watt

R14,R25,R34,R58,R63,R65,R68,R89—1.0 meg., ½ watt

R15,—47,000 ohms, 1 watt

R17—3,500 ohms, 10 watt

R18,R27,R29,R49,R62,R71—100,000 ohms, ½ watt

R19—Potentiometer, 100,000 ohms 1/2 watt — linear taper, with switch, 1-1/4" shaft (brightness control)

R20,R21,R59,R60,R61,R86,R90,R91—10,000 ohms, 1 watt

R26,—47 ohms, ½ watt

R30—2200 ohms, ½ watt

R35—3.3 meg., ½ watt

R36,R39—220,000 ohms, ½ watt

R37—Potentiometer, 1 meg., ½ watt—audio taper with switch, 1-1/4" shaft (volume control)

R38,R52—1000 ohms, ½ watt

R42—Potentiometer, 2,000 ohms—linear taper, screw driver slot (focus control)

R44—1000 ohms, 10 watt

R45,R55—2200 ohms, ½ watt

R54,R67—4700 ohms, ½ watt

R64—Potentiometer, 1 meg.—linear taper, screw driver slot (vertical hold control)

R66—Potentiometer, 2 meg.—linear taper, screw driver slot (vertical size control)

R69,R83—Potentiometer, 5,000 ohms—linear taper, screw driver slot (vertical linearity control, horizontal linearity control)

R70,R87,R88—470 ohms, ½ watt

R74,R77—Potentiometer, 100,000 ohms —linear taper, screw driver slot (horizontal hold control, horizontal drive control)

R76—680,000 ohms, ½ watt

R79,R80—190 ohms, 1 watt

R82—10,000 ohms, 10 watt

R84—3.3 ohms, ½ watt

R85—10 ohms, 1 watt

C1-C9,C15-C19,C24,C32,C48—.002 mfd., 600 volts, paper

C10,C11,C14,C30,C38,C40,C43,C50—0.1 mfd., 600 volts, paper

C12,C25,C41—40-30-10/450-10/25 electrolytic (can, negative)

C13,C31,C39,C42,C51,C54—.05 mfd., 600 volts, paper

C20,C21,C44,C46,C49—150 mmf., 500 volts, ceramic or mica

C22—4 mfd., 50 volts, electrolytic, pigtail leads

C23,C26,C27,C29,C47—.01 mfd., 600 volts, paper

C28—.005 mfd., 600 volts, paper

C33-C37—.005 mfd., 600 volts, paper

C45—500 mmf., 500 volts, mica

C52—.0012 mfd., 10,000 volts, ceramic

C53—.035 mfd., 600 volts, paper

C55—50 mmf., 500 volts, ceramic

C56—3.3 mmf., ceramic

L1—500 mh., pigtail leads—peaking coil—Transvision 0-319

L2,L4—125 mh., pigtail leads—peaking coil—Transvision 17

L3—250 mh., pigtail leads—peaking coil Transvision 16

L5—Deflection yoke—RCA 201D1

L6—Horizontal linearity control—RCA 201R3

L7—Focus coil—RCA 202D1 or Stancor FC10

L8—4h, 250 mil. filter choke

L9—Balancing coil—Transvision 0-365

L10—Balancing coil—Transvision 0-365

T1—Output transformer—6V6 to V.C.

T2—Vertical blocking oscillator transformer—RCA208T2

T3—Vertical output transformer—RCA 204T2

T4—Horizontal blocking oscillator transformer 0-307

T5—Horizontal output transformer—RCA 211T1

T6—Power transformer—400-0-400v-225ma., 5v-3a, 6.3v-10a, 6.3v-1.75a.

Z1—First video i-f transformer—Transvision 175

Z2—Second video i-f transformer—Transvision 174

Z3—Video detector i-f transformer—Transvision 176

Z4—First sound i-f transformer—Transvision 318

Z5—Ratio detector i-f transformer—Transvision 317

X1,X2,X6,X8,X9—6SN7

X3—6x5GT

X4—6BG6

X5—5U4G - 5V4G

X7—6AG7

X10,X17—6AL5

X11,X12,X13,X15,X16—6AC7

X14—6V6GT

DATA SECTION

Sample Installation and Service Agreement — The following is the wording of a typical agreement between a service organization and a set owner. It provides for the installation and servicing of the customers receiver for a period of one year.

DEFINITIONS, STIPULATIONS AND CONDITIONS

STANDARD INSTALLATION — The installation will be considered standard if:

1. The signal strength from desired television stations is sufficiently high and reflection and interference can be reduced to an acceptably low value by simple manipulation and orientation of a dipole type of antenna to obtain acceptable results.
2. Not more than approximately 100 feet of suitable transmission line is required.
3. A 60 cycle single phase 110 volt power outlet is available at the desired location of the receiver.
4. The installation can be satisfactorily completed by a two-man crew in time not to exceed four hours.
5. Not more than the standard 8 foot antenna mast is required.

NON-STANDARD INSTALLATION — If the installation falls in the category of "non-standard" where a special antenna or several antennae are required, unusual structural or technical difficulties are encountered in mounting the antenna or in running the transmission line, or where a 60 cycle single phase power outlet is not available at the location of the receiver, The Company will quote the Contract holder at the time of installation on the additional costs that may be involved over the standard installation and service rate quoted by the dealer. The amount of these extra charges will be determined on a basis of time over the standard four hour installation plus extra material and equipment used at prevailing prices. Extra charges for non-standard installations will be paid to THE SERVICE ORGANIZATION'S installer upon completion of the work. Final judgment as to the classification of the installation as standard or non-standard rests solely with THE SERVICE ORGANIZATION.

INSTRUCTION — THE SERVICE ORGANIZATION'S installer at the time of initial installation shall instruct the Purchaser or his agent, if the Purchaser is absent, in the proper operation of the television receiver.

APPOINTMENT AND ARRANGEMENTS FOR INSTALLATION — THE SERVICE ORGANIZATION shall make an appointment with the Purchaser specifying a definite time and place for the installation. It is the Purchaser's responsibility to obtain approval from the owner of the premises where the installation is to be made to permit such installation and access to the roof and other portions of the building and grounds by THE SERVICE ORGANIZATION'S installer. If THE SERVICE ORGANIZATION'S installer does not gain access of the appointed time for any reason resulting from (a) failure of Purchaser to arrange access or (b) Purchaser's absence or (c) Purchaser's refusing access or admittance of installer or service man, then, in such case, the Purchaser shall be liable to THE SERVICE ORGANIZATION for the time spent unnecessarily, bringing the total time above the maximum standard of four hours requiring a call back at a later appointed time. Such extra amounts shall be paid to THE SERVICE ORGANIZATION by the Purchaser in addition to other charges which might be due.

MOVE OF RECEIVER — The terms of this contract apply only to the initial installation of the specified receiver and antenna and do not cover subsequent installations resulting from structural alteration of the premises, redecorating, or movement of the receiver to a new location. If the receiver is moved from the point of original installation during the term of this contract, THE SERVICE ORGANIZATION shall be entitled to charge a regular fee for making an installation at the new address or location. It will be the duty of the owner to promptly notify THE SERVICE ORGANIZATION if the receiver is moved in order to arrange for the continuance of the protection provided by this contract.

SERVICE — THE SERVICE ORGANIZATION will furnish labor and material including replacement parts, components and all tubes except kinescope that may be required to maintain the television receiver covered by this contract in normal working order, and including up to six visits by the Company Service Man, without any charge other than the service fee paid, provided any failure requiring such service is the result of normal usage and, further, that no person other than an authorized representative of THE SERVICE ORGANIZATION has rendered service or installed material or components in the receiver or antenna and, further, that the receiver has not been removed from its originally installed location. The contract does not cover defects resulting from abuse, carelessness, Acts of God, tornado, wind storms, fire, flood, storms, nor does THE SERVICE ORGANIZATION agree to supply any material, components or labor to cover such defects. If the receiver or antenna has been subjected to misuse through negligence or otherwise, or if the receiver has had its serial number altered, its seal broken, effaced or removed, this contract shall be void.

This contract does not cover replacement or repair due to loss or damage incurred in transportation of the receiver, fire, lightning, theft, negligence or other causes beyond the control of THE SERVICE ORGANIZATION.

NEW TELEVISION STATIONS — In some cases it may be necessary to reorient, move, add to or replace any part of the antenna system as a result of new stations coming on the air, or changes in transmitting conditions. The company will then, at the request of the customer, perform any necessary work at its prevailing rates for materials and labor.

RECEIVING RANGE — In certain instances it may not be possible to obtain satisfactory reception from the television station or stations which are now in existence or which may hereafter come on the air, even though such stations may be considered, from a distance standpoint, to be within a normal service range. This is due to conditions beyond our control, and no responsibility is assumed for inability to receive such station or stations.

OPERATION FROM CENTRALIZED ANTENNA SYSTEM — In the event the television receiver to which this contract relates is operated from a centralized antenna system, the company shall not be held responsible under this contract for either the performance or maintenance of such system or its associated distribution elements.

AVAILABILITY OF SERVICE — The services provided by the company under this contract shall normally be available and rendered during the regular working hours of the customary work-week.

CHANGES MADE NECESSARY BY FEDERAL COMMUNICATIONS COMMISSION REGULATIONS — If circuit or component adjustments or alterations become necessary as a result of changes in transmission standards or changes in or additions to band assignments by the U. S. Government, such work, if technically feasible, will be performed by the company for the customer upon request, as promptly as possible at a reasonable charge for labor and materials.

TRANSFER OF CONTRACT — This contract is not transferable except with the written consent of THE SERVICE ORGANIZATION.

ELIMINATION OF INTERFERENCE — The television receiver specified herein and its antenna have been designed and will be installed to minimize the effects of external interference that may be created by passing automobiles, appliances, diathermy machines, aircraft, short wave and FM transmitters and other electrical equipment such as motors and converters. Liability on the part of THE SERVICE ORGANIZATION will, however, undertake to report such disturbances to the Federal Communications Commission and other controlling governmental or official agencies.

ACCESSORY EQUIPMENT — THE SERVICE ORGANIZATION assumes no liability with respect to the installation, service or maintenance of motor generators or other accessory devices that may be used under certain circumstances to supply power to the specified receiver, nor to the effect produced by such equipment on the performance of the receiver, unless furnished and installed by THE SERVICE ORGANIZATION.

LIMIT OF LIABILITY — THE SERVICE ORGANIZATION'S liability shall never exceed the amount of premium paid. THE SERVICE ORGANIZATION shall be credited in all cases with the amount of premium earned and in the event of default, breach or cancellation, the remission to the customer of the unearned premium shall constitute the limit of liability.

APPLICATION

We, the undersigned, hereby make application to The TELEVISION MAINTENANCE COMPANY OF NEW JERSEY, for a contract of Installation and Service on television set described on within form for one year; said Contract, if issued, to be on the within form, the terms, conditions, stipulations and definitions as agreed to by us. We herewith tender our check for $............to the order of the said Company as a deposite premium payment, and we agree to pay any additional costs which may become due as provided for in the conditions of this contract.

This application and said contract, if issued, shall, within the terms, conditions, stipulations and definitions herein, constitute the entire agreement between the undersigned and The TELEVISION MAINTENANCE COMPANY OF NEW JERSEY, any verbal or written statement, promise or agreement, by any Agent of the said Company, or notice to or knowledge of such Agent or any other person to the contrary notwithstanding. It is also agreed that this application, whether as respects anything contained therein or omitted therefrom, has been made, prepared and written by the applicant, or by his proper agent.

Dated at ....this ....day of ....19 ....

Signature of Applicant ....Address ....

TELEVISION CHANNEL ASSIGNMENTS

CITY	CHANNEL NOS.	TOTAL STATIONS
Akron	11	1
Albany		
Schenectady	2, 4, 7, 9, 11	5
Troy		
Altoona	9	1
Amarillo	2, 4, 5, 7	4
Asheville	5, 7, 12	3
Atlanta	2, 5, 8, 11	4
Augusta, Ga.	6, 12	2
Austin	8, 10, 12	3
Baltimore	2, 11, 13	3
Beaumont		
Port Arthur	3, 6, 8, 10	4
Binghamton	12	1
Birmingham	4, 9, 13	3
Boston	2, 4, 7, 9, 13	5
Buffalo		
Niagara	4, 7, 9, 13	4
Cedar Rapids	7, 11	2
Charleston, S.C.	7, 10, 13	3
Charleston, W. Va.	7, 11, 13	3
Charlotte	3, 9, 11	3
Chattanooga	3, 6, 10, 12	4
Chicago	2, 4, 5, 7, 9, 11, 13	7
Cincinnati	2, 4, 7, 11	4
Cleveland	2, 4, 5, 7, 9	5
Columbia	2, 4, 8	3
Columbus, Ga.	3, 12	2
Columbus, Ohio	3, 6, 8, 10	4
Corpus Christi	3, 6, 8, 10	4
Dallas	4, 8, 12	3
Davenport		
Rock Island	2, 4, 5, 9	4
Moline		

CITY	CHANNELS NOS.	TOTAL STATIONS
Dayton	5, 13	2
Decatur	2	1
Denver	2, 4, 5, 7, 9	5
Des Moines	2, 5, 9	4
Detroit	2, 4, 5, 7, 9	5
Duluth Superior	3, 6, 8, 10	4
Durham	4, 7	2
El Paso	2, 4, 5, 7	4
Erie	12	1
Evansville, Ind.	2, 11	2
Flint	11	1
Fort Wayne	2, 4, 7, 9	4
Fort Worth	2, 5, 10	3
Fresno	2, 4, 5, 7	4
Galveston	9, 11, 13	3
Grand Rapids	7, 9	2
Greensboro	2, 10	2
Hamilton Middletown	9	1
Harrisburg	8	1
Hartford New Britain	8, 10,	2
Houston	2, 4, 5, 7	4
Huntington, W. Va. Ashland, Ky.	5	1
Indianapolis	3, 6, 8, 10, 12	5
Jackson	2, 4, 5, 7	4
Jacksonville	2, 4, 6, 8	4
Johnstown, Pa.	13	1
Kalamazoo	3	1
Kansas City, Mo Kansas City, Kans.	2, 4, 5, 9	4
Knoxville	2, 4, 8, 11	4
Lansing	6	1
Lincoln	10, 12	2
Little Rock	3, 6, 8, 10	4
Los Angeles	2, 4, 5, 7, 9, 11, 13	7
Louisville	5, 9	2
Lowell Lawrence Haverhill	6	1
Macon	4, 7, 10	3
Madison	9	1
Memphis	2, 4, 5, 7, 9	5
Miami	2, 4, 5, 7	4
Milwaukee	3, 6, 8, 10	4
Minneapolis St. Paul	2, 4, 5, 7, 9	5
Mobile	3, 5, 9, 11	4
Montgomery	6, 10	2
Nashville	4, 5, 7, 9	4
New Orleans	2, 4, 6, 7, 10	5
New York Northeastern New Jersey	2, 4, 5, 7, 9, 11, 13	7
Norfolk Portsmouth Newport News	4, 7, 11, 13	4

CITY	CHANNELS NOS.	TOTAL STATIONS
Oklahoma City	2, 4, 5, 9	4
Omaha Council Bluffs	3, 6, 7	3
Peoria	3, 6, 12	3
Philadelphia	3, 6, 10, 12	4
Phoenix	2, 4, 5, 7	4
Pittsburgh	3, 6, 8, 10	4
Portland, Maine	3, 8	2
Portland, Oreg.	3, 6, 8, 10, 12	5
Providence, R. I.	11	1
Pueblo	3, 6, 8, 10	4
Richmond	3, 6, 8, 10	4
Roanoke	5, 9, 12	3
Rochester	2, 6, 11	3
Rockford	12	1
Sacramento	3, 6, 10	3
Saginaw Bay City	3, 8, 13	3
St. Joseph	13	1
St. Louis	4, 5, 7, 9, 13	5
Salt Lake City	2, 4, 5, 7, 9	5
San Antonio	2, 4, 5, 7, 9	5
San Diego	3, 6, 8, 10	4
San Francisco Oakland	2, 4, 5, 7, 9, 11	6
San Jose	13	1
Savannah	3, 5, 9, 11	4
Scranton Wilkes-Barre	11	1
Seattle	2, 5, 7, 11	4
Shreveport	2, 4, 6, 8	4
Sioux City	4, 9, 11, 13	4
Spokane	2, 4, 5, 7, 9	5
Springfield, Ill.	8, 10	2
Springfield, Mass. Holyoke	3	1
Springfield, Mo.	2, 4, 5, 9	4
Stockton	8	1
Syracuse	5, 8, 10	3
Tacoma	4, 9, 13	3
Tampa St. Petersburg	2, 4, 5, 7	4
Terre Haute	4	1
Toledo	13	1
Topeka	7, 11	2
Tulsa	3, 6, 8, 10	4
Utica Rome	3, 13	2
Waco	3, 6, 9, 11	4
Washington	4, 5, 7, 9	4
Waterbury	12	1
Waterloo	3, 6, 13	3
Wheeling	12	1
Wichita	2, 4, 5, 9	4
Winston-Salem	6, 8	2
Worcester	5	1
Youngstown	13	1

TELEVISION PICTURE TUBE CHART

Type	Dimensions Diam. in.	Dimensions Length in.	Raster Size in.	Base	Socket Conn.	Bulb Contact	Solid Defln. Angle	Type of Defln.	Type of Focus	Deflection Factor-Volts Hor.	Deflection Factor-Volts Ver.	Heater Volts	Heater Amp	Ion Trap	Grid Bias Cut-Off	Grid Drive Volts	Grid No.2 Volts	Anode No.1 Volts	Anode No.2 Volts
3KP4	3-1/16	11½	1-7/8 x 2½	Magnal 11 Pin	3KP4	None		E	E	76 to 104	100 to 136	6.3	0.6		-64		2,000	450	2,000
3NP4	2½	10	1.48x1.8	Special 5 Prong	Special 3NP4	Cup	42°	M	M			6.3	0.6	Metal Screen	-65				24,000
TP 400A	4	12-3/4	2-1/4 x 3	Octal	TP 400A	Cavity		M	M			6.3	0.6	Metl Screen	-70				20,000
5BP4	5-1/4	16-3/4	3 x 4	Magnal 11 Pin	11A	None		E	E	76	84	6.3	0.6		-40	35		450	2,000
5TP4	5	11-3/4	3 x 4	Duo-decal	12C	Cavity Cap	50o	M	E			6.3	0.6	Metal Screen	-70		200	4,900	27,000
7DP4	7-3/16	14-1/16	4 x 5½	Duo-decal	12C	Cavity	50°	M	E			6.3	0.6	Mag.	-45		250	1,430	6,000
7EP4	7	14-1/2	4 x 5½	Magnal 11 Pin	11D	None		E	E	95	110	6.3	0.6		-60	38		650	2,500
7GP4	7	14½	4 x 5½	Diheptal 12 Pin	14G	None		E	E	25 to	31 to 41	6.3	0.6		-60			1,000	3,000
7HP4	7-3/16	13	4 x 5½	Duo-decal	12D	Ball Cap		M	M			6.3	0.6		-55	30	250		6,000
7JP4	7	14½	4 x 5½	Diheptal 11 Pin	14G	None		E	E	150 204	186 246	6.3	0.6		-180 -120		1,620 2,400	1,620 2,400	4,000 6,000
9AP4	9	21	5-3/8x7-1/4	6 Prong	9-12AP4	Metal Cap		M	M			2.5	2.1		(i)	25	250	1,460	7,000
10BP4	10½	17-5/8	6 x 8	Duo-decal	12D	Cavity	50°	M	M			6.3	0.6	Mag.	-45	30	250		9,000
10CP4	10½	16-5/8	6 x 8	Duo-decal	12D	Small Ball Cap		M	M			6.3	0.6		-55	38	250		8,000 to 10,000

Type	Screen	Length	Screen Size	Base	Base No.	Cap	Angle					Heater V	Heater A	Focus	Grid				Anode V
10EP4	10½	17-5/8	6 x 8	Duo-decal	12D	Small Ball Cap	50°	M	M			6.3	0.6	Mag.	-45	38	250		8,000
10FP4	10½	17-5/8	6 x 8	Duo-decal	12D	Cavity		M				6.3	0.6	Metal Screen	-45	38	250		9,000
10HP4	10	19-1/4	6 x 8	Diheptal 12 Pin	14G	None	40°	E	E	80 100	104 130	6.3	0.6		-100			960 to 1,440 / 1,200 to 1,800	4,000 / 5,000
12AP4	12	25	7-3/8x9-3/4	6 Prong	9-12AP4	Metal Cap	50°	M	E			2.5	2.1		-45	38		1,460	7,000
12CP4	12½	18-3/4	7-3/4x10-1/4	Duo-decal	12D	Cavity Button	50°	M	M			6.3	0.6	Mag.	-45	38	250		9,000
12DP4	12	20-1/8	7-3/4x10-1/4	Octal	5AN	Metal Cap	50°	M	M			6.3	0.6		-45	38	250		7,000
12JP4	12	17½	7-3/4x10-1/4	Duo-decal	12D	Small Ball Cap	50°	M	M			6.3	0.6	Metal Screen	-45	30	250		10,000
12KP4	12-7/16	17-5/8	7½x10	Duo-decal	12D	Cavity	54°	M	M			6.3	0.6	Mag.	-45	30	250		9,000
12LP4	12-7/16	18-3/4	7-3/4x10-1/4	Duo-decal	12D	Small Ball Cap	54°	M	M			6.3	0.6	Mag.	-45	30	250		11,000
12QP4	12-7/16	17-1/2	7-3/4x10-1/4	Duo-decal	12D	Small Ball Cap	54°	M	M			6.3	0.6	Bent Gun	-45	30	250		10,000
K1003	12	23½	7-3/4x10-1/4	12 Contact	K1003	Metal Cap		E	E	103	159	2.5	2.1		-100	85		1,375	5,000 (n)
15AP4	15½	20½	9½x12-3/4	Duo-decal	12D	Small Ball Cap	52°	M	M			6.3	0.6		-45	38	250		12,000
15CP4	15½	21½	150 sq.in. Area	Duo-decal	12D	Cavity Button	50°	M	M			6.3	0.6	Mag.	-45	38	250 and up		9,000 to 15,000
16AP4	15-7/8	22-1/4	10x13-1/4	Duo-decal	12D	Metal Cone Rim	53°	M	M			6.3	0.6	Mag.	-60	38	300		12,000
20BP4	28-3/4	20	12-7/8x17-1/4	Duo-decal	12D	Metal Cap	50°	M	M			6.3	0.6		-45	38	250		15,000

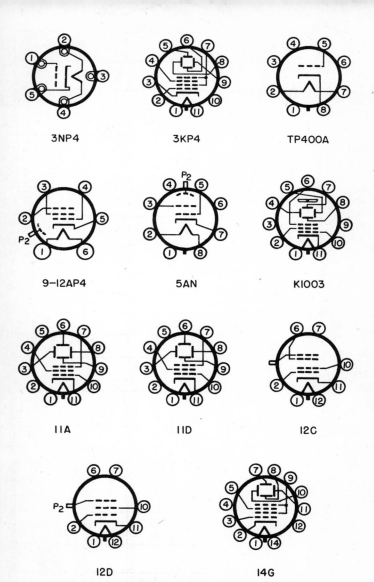

3NP4

3KP4

TP400A

9–12AP4

5AN

K1003

11A

11D

12C

12D

14G

BOTTOM VIEW OF SOCKET

TELEVISION TERMS

(A)

accelerating electrode. Otherwise known as the second anode of a cathode ray tube. This electrode serves to increase the velocity of the electron beam so that when it strikes the screen, light is emitted.

active lines. Those lines, of the 525 possible lines in a television image, which appear on the screen. The inactive lines are blanked out during the time that the beam is returning from the bottom of the picture to start of the next frame.

adjacent sound carrier frequency. The sound carrier in the television channel on the low frequency side of the channel.

align. To adjust two or more tuned circuits in radio so that they respond to the same frequency.

alternating current. (abbr: ac). An electric current which reverses its direction of flow at regular intervals.

amplitude modulation (am). A method of conveying information by changing the amplitude of a radio frequency carrier.

amplitude separation. The process of separating the synchronizing signal from the video information in the composite television signal utilizing the difference in their amplitude levels.

antenna. (Abbr: ant.). The portion, usually wires or rods, of a radio or television station or receiving set, for radiating waves into space or receiving them from space. Also called aerial.

antenna array. An arrangement of two or more antennas (or reflectors) coupled together so as to improve transmission or reception in a given direction.

aspect ratio. The ratio of picture width to picture height. 4 to 3 in the present television system.

associated sound carrier frequency. The sound carrier in the television channel under consideration.

astigmatism. A condition of focus of the electron beam wherein the spot is not perfectly round, resulting in different trace widths when the beam is deflected from the center of the screen.

audio. The Latin word for "hear". Used synonymously with the word sound.

audio carrier. The frequency modulated r-f signal which carries the sound information.

audio frequency (Abbr: af). A frequency corresponding to a normally audible sound wave — about 20 to 15,000 cycles a second.

automatic brightness control. A circuit which automatically controls the average brightness in the received image so that it corresponds with that being transmitted.

automatic frequency control (Abbr: afc). A circuit that keeps a radio receiver from "drifting" off the frequency to which it is tuned.

automatic volume control. A circuit which varies the amplification of a receiver so that its output remains constant despite changes in input signal strength.

average brightness. The average illumination in the television picture.

bandwidth. The number of continuous frequencies required to convey the information being transmitted, either visual or aural. The bandwidth of a television channel is 6 mc.

band-pass filter. A filter which passes a group of continuous frequencies and rejects all others.

beam. The stream of electrons which travels from the electron gun toward the screen in a cathode ray tube.

beat frequency. A frequency resulting from a combination of two frequencies.

black level. The amplitude level of the television signal which corresponds to black in the picture. At this level the beam in the cathode ray tube is biased to cutoff.

blacker-than-black level. The portion of the television signal devoted to the synchronizing pulses. These synchronizing signals are transmitted at higher amplitudes than those representing the blackest part of the picture.

blanking. The process of cutting off the picture tube beam during the time it is not forming the picture. This occurs when the spot returns from the far right to begin the next line and from the bottom to the top of the next picture.

blanking pulse. The pulse used to blank out the electron beam in both the camera and picture tubes during the blanking interval.

blocking oscillator. A type of oscillator used for triggering horizontal and vertical sweep generators.

blooming. The defocusing of the white regions of the television picture when an excess of electrons increases the spot size.

brightness control. A receiver control used to regulate the overall brightness of the picture.

camera. The unit housing the optical system and light sensitive pick-up tube which converts the visual image into electrical impulses.

camera tube. A cathode-ray tube used to transform an image into electrical impulses.

carrier frequency. The frequency of the unmodulated radio signal produced by the transmitter.

cathode-ray tube. An electron tube in which a stream of electrons from a cathode are formed into a narrow beam and deflected by means of electrostatic or magnetic fields over a target, usually a mosaic or fluorescent screen which glows wherever the beam strikes. The iconoscope, kinescope, picture tube, etc. fall into this category.

centering controls. The controls which are used to move the image in the vertical and horizontal directions to properly center it on the screen.

center frequency. As applied to frequency modulation, it is the frequency of the un-modulated carrier. With modulation, the instantaneous frequency swings above and below the center frequency.

channel. A band of frequencies assigned to a station for the transmission of the television and sound signals.

clipper. A vacuum tube circuit which removes a portion of a signal above or below a fixed amplitude level. In television, it refers to the stage which separates the video and sync signals.

clipping level. The amplitude level of a signal, above or below which a clipper removes part of the signal.

co-axial cable. A type of conductor which transmits a wide range of frequencies efficiently. Such a cable in its simplest form consists of a hollow metallic conductor with a single wire accurately centered along the axis of the hollow conductor, and held in position by a suitable insulating material.

composite television signal. The television signal composed of the video information and the synchronizing and blanking pulses.

composite sync signal. The portion of the television signal consisting of the horizontal, vertical, and equalizing pulses.

contrast. The difference in brightness between black and white portions of a picture. Pictures having high contrast have very deep blacks and brilliant whites, while a picture with low contrast has an overall gray appearance.

contrast control. The control which is used to vary the contrast of the picture by changing the gain of the video stages. It corresponds to the volume control in an aural receiver.

control electrode. The metal structure adjacent to the cathode in a cathode-ray tube to which a voltage is applied to regulate the electron flow. Sometimes called the grid, this electrode controls the light intensity of the image on the screen.

cross-over point. The point, between the grid and pre-accelerator, of a cathode-ray tube where the electrons emitted by the cathode converge.

damping tube. A vacuum tube used in horizontal sweep circuits to prevent transient oscillations.

d-c restorer. A circuit used to reinsert the d-c component of the video signal lost during amplification. The d-c component determines the average brightness of the received image.

d-c transmission. A system of transmission which retains the d-c component of the signal.

definition. The ability of a system to reproduce small details in an image.

deflection. The moving of the cathode ray beam by electrostatic or magnetic fields.

deflecting plates. Two pairs of metal plates used in an electrostatic cathode-ray tubes. Potentials applied to these plates cause the electron beam to move.

demodulation. The process of removing the modulating signal from a modulated radio frequency carrier.

diathermy interference. Interference which results from the signals generated by diathermy machines operated by doctors or hospitals in the vicinity of the television receiver.

differentiating circuit. A circuit used to separate the high frequency horizontal sync pulses from the low frequency vertical sync pulses.

dipole. A simple antenna whose total length is equal to one half the wavelength of the frequency for which it is tuned.

diplexer. A coupling unit which allows two transmitters to operate simultaneously or separately from the same antenna.

directional antenna. An antenna designed to receive radio signals better from some directions than from others.

director. A rod slightly shorter than a dipole, placed in front of it to provide greater directivity.

direct view receiver. A television receiver in which the image is viewed on the face

director. A rod slightly shorter than a dipole, placed in front of it to provide greater directivity.

direct view receiver. A television receiver in which the image is viewed on the face
of the picture tube.

discriminator. A circuit used in f-m receivers to convert the frequency modulated signal into an audio frequency signal.

dissector tube. A pick-up tube containing a continuous photosensitive cathode on which an electron image is formed.

dissolve. A camera technique whereby two images from different cameras are momentarily overlapped and then one is gradually faded out.

discharge tube. A tube used in sawtooth generating circuits to discharge a capacitor.

double-sideband transmission. A system of transmission wherein the sum and difference frequencies of the modulating and carrier signals are transmitted.

electromagnetic deflection coil. A current carrying coil placed over the neck of a cathode-ray tube. The resulting magnetic field deflects the electron beam. Two sets of coils, the vertical and horizontal, are combined into one case, called a yoke.

electron beam. The stream of electrons in a cathode-ray tube. The stream is focused to a sharp point on the tube's fluorescent screen.

electron emission. The releasing of electrons by the surface of an electrode, usually due to heat.

electron gun. That part of a cathode-ray tube in which the electrons are emitted and focused into a beam.

electron lens. The electromagnetic or electrostatic fields in a cathode-ray tube which cause the electrons to converge into a narrow beam.

electronic scanning. The deflection of an electron beam by means of electromagnetic or electrostatic fields.

electrostatic focusing. The process by which electrons are confined into a thin stream by an electrostatic field.

equalizing pulses. A series of six pulses occurring at twice the horizontal frequency. The equalizing pulses precede and follow the vertical sync pulse and are used to maintain proper interlace.

fidelity. The ability of a circuit to reproduce faithfully signals impressed upon it.

field. One half of a television image. With present standards, pictures are transmitted in two fields of $262\frac{1}{2}$ lines each, which are interlaced to form 30 complete frames or images per second.

field frequency. The repetition rate of the field which in present systems is 60 per second or twice the frame frequency.

field pick-up. The televising of remote events by mobile camera and transmitting equipment.

film pick-up. The televising of motion picture films.

flicker. Objectionable low frequency variation in intensity of illumination of a television picture.

fine tuning control. A control on the receiver which varies the frequency of the local oscillator over a small range so as to compensate for drift and permit fine adjustment to a station's carrier frequency.

fluorescent screen. The chemical coating on the inside face of a cathode-ray tube which emits light when struck by electrons.

flyback time. The period during which the electron beam is returning from the end of a scanning line to begin the next line.

flywheel synchronization. Another term for automatic frequency control of a scanning circuit. In such a system the sweep oscillator responds to the average timing of the sync pulses and not to each individual pulse.

focus. In a cathode-ray tube, this refers to the size the spot of light on the fluorescent screen. The tube is said to be focused when the spot is smallest. This term also refers to the optical focusing of camera lenses.

focusing control. The potentiometer control on the receiver which varies the first anode voltage of an electrostatic tube or the focus coil current of a magnetic tube and so focuses the electron beam.

focusing electrode. A metal cylinder in the electron gun, sometimes called the first anode. The electrostatic field produced by this electrode in combination with the control electrode and the accelerating electrode act to focus the electron beam to a small spot on the screen.

frame. One complete television image which consists of 525 lines or two interlaced fields.

frame frequency. The number of times per second the picture area is completely scanned. This frequency is 30 times per second in the present television system.

frequency modulation. A system for transmitting intelligence wherein the frequency of a radio signal is varied in proportion to the modulating signal.

ghost. A secondary picture formed on a television receiver by a signal from the transmitter which reaches the antenna by a longer path. Ghosts are usually caused by reflected signals.

halation. The ring of illumination which surrounds the point at which the electron beam strikes the fluorescent screen.

height. The vertical dimension of the television image.

height control. The control which varies the vertical size of the picture.

heterodyne frequency. A frequency which is produced by combining two other frequencies and which is their numerical sum or difference.

high voltage. The accelerating potential used to increase the velocity of the electrons in a cathode-ray tube beam.

hold control. A potentiometer in either a vertical or horizontal sweep oscillator circuit which varies the natural frequency of the oscillator and enables it to synchronize with applied sync pulses.

horizontal. This term refers to the direction of sweep of the electron beam from left to right.

horizontal blanking. The blanking pulse which occurs at the end of each horizontal line and cuts off the electron beam while it is returning to the left side of the screen.

horizontal centering-control. The potentiometer used to move the picture in the horizontal direction.

horizontal hold control. A control used to vary the natural frequency of the horizontal sweep oscillator so that it locks with the applied sync pulses.

horizontal resolution. The ability of a television system to reproduce small objects in the horizontal plane.

horizontal retrace. A line on the screen which is formed by the electron beam during the time the spot is returning from the right to the left side of the screen.

iconoscope. A camera tube in which a high velocity electron beam scans a photosensitive mosaic which stores an electrical image.

image dissector. A television camera tube in which the photoelectrons are moved past a pickup aperture by deflection circuits. (See Dissector)

image orthicon. A highly sensitive camera tube which combines the principles of the image dissector, orthicon, and image multiplier.

integrating circuit. A circuit which combines the vertical pulses into a single composite pulse.

intensifier electrode. Otherwise known as the third anode. It imparts additional kinetic energy to the electron beam after it has been deflected.

interference. Spurious signals which enter a receiver and mar the picture or sound.

interlaced scanning. A system of scanning whereby the odd and even numbered lines of a picture are transmitted consecutively as two separate fields which are superimposed to create one frame or complete picture at the receiver. The effect is to double the apparent number of pictures and so reduce the amount of flicker.

intermediate frequency (abbr: i.f.). The frequency resulting from the combination of two frequencies in one circuit.

ion. A particle carrying an electric charge. Ions may be positive or negative.

ion spot. A discoloration at the center of the screen of a picture tube due to bombardment of the fluorescent material by negative ions.

ion trap. An electron gun structure and magnetic field which permits electrons to flow toward the screen but diverts negative ions thereby avoiding the formation of an ion spot.

jitter. The tendency of either several lines or the entire picture to vibrate because of poor synchronization.

keystone effect. Distortion of a television image which results in a keystone shaped pattern.

kickback-supply. A high voltage power supply which derives its energy from the pulses occurring in the primary of the horizontal sweep output transformer when the magnetic field collapses during the retrace period.

lens turret. A part of a television camera on which several lenses are mounted for rapid selection.

limiter. The last i-f stage in the f-m audio circuits. This stage is so biased that it removes amplitude variations above a given level.

line. The path traced by the electron spot as it moves across the width of the screen. The intensity of the spot is changed as it moves to create varying shades in the picture. In present systems, 525 lines make up a complete picture.

linearity. The relative spacing of picture elements in the television image.

linearity control. A potentiometer in a vertical or horizontal sweep circuit which is used to adjust the spacing and distribution of the picture elements.

line scanning frequency. The number of lines scanned each second. In any system it is equal to the number of scanning lines per frame, multiplied by the frame frequency. Under present standards this is 525 lines x 30 frames per second or 15,750 lines per second.

local oscillator. The heterodyne oscillator in a superheterodyne receiver.

lock-in. A term describing the condition which exists when a sweep oscillator is in synchronism with the applied sync pulses.

magnetic focus. The focusing of the electron beam by means of a magnetic field set up by a coil placed over the neck of the cathode-ray tube.

microsecond. One millionth of a second.

megacycle. One million cycles.

mixing amplifier. An amplifier which combines several signals of different amplitudes and waveshapes into a composite signal. Such an amplifier is used to mix the blanking and sync pulses in the sync generator.

modulation. The variation of the amplitude, phase, or frequency of a radio carrier frequency by a lower frequency signal.

modulation grid. An electrode interposed between the cathode and focusing electrodes in a cathode-ray tube to control the amount of emission and thereby the brilliance of the spot. This controlling effect is produced by altering the voltage of the grid with respect to the cathode.

monitor. A cathode-ray tube and associated circuits, used in a television station to check the transmitted picture.

monoscope. A cathode-ray tube which produces a stationary pattern for the testing and adjusting of television equipment.

mosaic. The photosensitive plate in the iconoscope which emits electrons when struck by light.

multipath reception. The condition in which the radio signal from the transmitter travels by more than one route to a receiver antenna, usually because of reflections from obstacles, resulting in ghosts in the picture.

multivibrator. A type of oscillator, using R-C components, commonly used to generate the sawtooth voltages in television receiver circuits.

negative ghosts. Ghosts which appear on the screen with intensity variations opposite to those of the picture.

negative transmission. The modulation of the picture carrier by a picture signal whose polarity is such that the sync pulses occur in the blacker-than-black level.

noise. Spurious impulses which modulate the picture or sound signals.

non-linearity. The unequal distribution of picture elements in the vertical and/or horizontal direction.

odd-line interlace. A type of interlace system, such as is now used, in which there are an odd number of lines in each frame.

open-wire transmission line. A transmission line formed by two parallel spaced wires. The distance between the two wires and their diameters determine the surge impedance of the transmission line.

orthicon. A camera tube in which a low velocity electron beam scans a photosensitive mosaic.

oscillograph. An indicating instrument consisting of a cathode-ray tube and a sweep generator for plotting an alternating voltage against time.

over-coupled circuit. A tuned circuit in which the coupling is greater than critical coupling resulting in a broad-band response characteristic.

pairing. A condition of improper interlacing which exists when the lines in alternate fields are superimposed. The fields may "pair" intermittently or continuously.

panning. The movement of the camera head from right to left or up and down.

peaking resistor. A resistor placed in series with the charging capacitor of the vertical sawtooth generator in order to add a negative peaking pulse to the sawtooth voltage to create the waveform required to produce a linear sawtooth current in the yoke.

peaking coil. A small inductive coil placed in an amplifying circuit in order to increase its response at certain frequencies.

pedestal. The portion of the television video signal used to blank out the beam as it flies back from the right to the left side of the screen.

phosphor. A chemical compound which fluoresces when struck by electrons. The screen material of cathode-ray tubes.

photocell. A device containing a photosensitive cathode which emits electrons when exposed to light.

photoelectric emission. The discharge of electrons by a photosensitive material when exposed to light.

pick-up tube. A camera tube used to transform a light image into an equivalent electrical signal.

picture element. The smallest portion of an image that can be resolved by the electron beam.

picture tube. The receiving cathode-ray tube.

polarization. The direction of the electrostatic and electromagnetic fields surrounding an antenna.

pre-amplifier. An auxiliary amplifier, usually located near the camera in order to minimize effects of noise pickup.

pre-emphasis. The increasing of the relative amplitude of the higher audio frequencies in order to minimize the effects of noise during transmission.

projection receiver. A television receiver in which the image is optically enlarged and projected onto a screen.

projection television. A combination of lenses and mirrors which project an enlarged television picture onto a screen.

raster. The pattern obtained when the electron beam sweeps across the screen vertically and horizontally without being modulated.

R-C circuit. A circuit consisting of a combination of resistors and capacitors. The time constant of such a circuit is the product of the resistance and capacitance.

resolution. A measure of the ability of a system to reproduce small details.

resolution chart. A pattern of black and white lines used to determine the resolution capabilities of equipment.

return trace. Lines on the cathode-ray screen formed by the beam when it moves back to its starting position.

sawtooth. A voltage or current whose variation with time follows a sawtooth configuration.

sawtooth voltage. A voltage that varies between two values at regular intervals. Since the voltage drops faster than it rises it gives a waveform pattern resembling the teeth of a saw. Used in television to help form the scanning raster.

scanning. The process of breaking down a picture into elements by means of a moving electron beam.

scanning line. A horizontal line, whose width is equal to the diameter of the scanning electron beam, composed of elements varying in intensity.

scanning raster. See raster.

Schmidt system. An optical system adapted for television projection receivers in which the light from the image is collected by a concave mirror and directed through a correcting lens onto a scfeen.

second anode. The positively charged electrode in the electron gun which accelerates the beam.

serrated vertical pulse. A vertical pulse broken up into shorter duration pulses so that the horizontal oscillator does not fall out of synchronization during the vertical sync interval.

shading. The process of correcting for distorted light distribution in the image by injecting a voltage into the signal.

side bands. The radio frequencies on each side of the carrier produced by modulation.

signal. An electrical wave.

spot. The point of light produced by the electron beam as it strikes the fluorescent screen.

stagger tuning. The tuning of amplifier stages to slightly different frequencies in order to obtain broad-band response.

sweep. The uniform motion of the electron beam across the face of the cathode-ray tube.

synchronization. The process of maintaining the frequency of one signal in step with that of another.

synchronizing generator. An electronic generator which supplies synchronizing pulses to television studio and transmitter equipment.

sync pulses. Pulses transmitted as part of the video signal for the purpose of synchronizing the sweep circuits in the receiver with those in the transmitter.

station selector. The switch or tuning element in the receiver which is used to select the desired television signal.

tearing. An effect observed on the screen when the horizontal synchronization is unstable.

television channel. The group of frequencies allotted to a television station for the transmission of the sound and picture signals.

test pattern. A geometric pattern containing a group of lines and circles, used for testing the performance of a receiver or transmitter.

turnstile antenna. One or more layers of crossed horizontal half-wave antennas arranged vertically on a mast, resembling an old-fashioned turnstile. Used in television and other ultrahigh-frequency systems where a symmetrical radiation pattern is desired.

vertical blanking pulse. A pulse transmitted at the end of each field to cut off the cathode-ray beam while it is returning to the top of the picture for the start of the next field.

vertical centering control. The potentiometer in the vertical positioning circuit which raises or lowers the entire image on the screen.

vertical hold control. A potentiometer which varies the natural frequency of the vertical sweep oscillator to enable it to synchronize with the applied sync pulses.

vertical resolution. A measure of the ability of a system to reproduce fine horizontal lines.

vertical scanning. The motion of the electron beam in the vertical direction.

vestigial side-band transmission. A type of transmission in which one side band is suppressed to limit the bandwidth required.

video. Latin meaning "I see".

video amplifier. A wideband amplifier for the video frequencies. In a television receiver, this term generally refers to the amplifier located after the second detector and whose frequency response extends from approximately 30 cycles to about 4 megacycles.

video frequency. The frequency of the signal voltage containing the picture information which arises from the television scanning process. In the present television system, these frequencies are limited to 4 mc.

view finder. A term applied to an attachment to a television camera to enable the cameraman to observe the area covered by the camera.

viewing screen. The face of a cathode-ray tube on which the image is produced.

video transmitter. The radio transmitter used for transmitting the picture signal.

width control. The control in the horizontal sweep circuit which varies the size of the picture in the horizontal direction.

yoke. A set of coils placed over the neck of a cathode-ray tube which produce horizontal and vertical deflection of the electron beam when suitable currents are passed through them.

BIBLIOGRAPHY

Antenna Book
American Radio Relay League, Inc. West Hartford, Conn.

Cathode-Ray Tube in Television, I.G. Maloff and D.W. Epstein
McGraw-Hill Book Co., New York

Cathode-Ray Tube at Work, The
J.F. Rider, Publisher, New York

Electron Optics in Television, I.G. Maloff and D.W. Epstein
McGraw-Hill Book Co., New York

Electronics, Jacob Millman and Samuel Seeley
McGraw-Hill Book Co., New York, 1941

4000 Years of Television, Richard W. Hubbell
G.P. Putnam Sons, New York

F.M. Transmission and Reception, John F. Rider and
    Seymour D. Uslan
J.F. Rider, Publisher, 1948

Future Television, Orin E. Dunlap, Jr.
Harper Bros., New York

Here is Television, T.H. Hutchinson
Hastings House, New York

Photofact Television Course, Albert C.W. Saunders;
    B.V.K. French, Ed;
Howard W. Sams & Co., Indianapolis, Ind.

Practical Television
R.C.A. Service Division, Camden, N.J.

Practical Television Servicing, J.R. Johnson and J.H. Newitt
Murray Hill Books, New York

Principles of Television Engineering, Donald G. Fink
McGraw-Hill Book Co., New York

Radio at Ultra High Frequencies, Vol. II
R.C.A. Review, Princeton, New Jersey

Radio Data Book, W.F. Boyce and J.J. Roche
Boland & Boyce, New Jersey

Radio Engineers' Handbook, Frederick Emmons Terman, Sc.D.
McGraw-Hill Book Co., New York

Telecasting and Color, K.S. Tyler
Harcourt, Brace & Co., New York

Television, W.C. Eddy
Prentice-Hall, Inc., New York

Television, V.K. Zworkin and G.A. Morton
John Wiley and Sons, New York

Television, Vols. I, II, III, and IV.
R.C.A. Review, Radio Corporation of America, Princeton, N.J.

Television and F-M Receiver Servicing, Milton S. Kiver
D. Van Nostrand Co., Inc., New York

**Television Antennas - Design Construction, Installation and
    Troubleshooting,** Donald A. Nelson
Howard W. Sams and Co., Inc. Indianapolis, Ind.

Television Broadcasting: Production, Economics, Technique,
    Lenox R. Lohr
McGraw-Hill Book Co., New York

Television Encyclopedia, Stanley Kemper
Fairchild Publishing Co., New York

Television How It Works, John F. Rider
Publisher, Inc. New York

Television Primer on Production and Direction
    Louis A. Sposa
McGraw-Hill Book Co., New York

Television Production Problems, J.F. Royal
McGraw-Hill Book Co., New York

Television Programming, Richard Hubbell
Murray Hill Books, Inc., New York

Television Show Business, Judy Dupuy
General Electric Co., Schenectady, New York

Television Simplified, Milton S. Kiver
D. Van Nostrand Co., Inc. New York

Television Standards and Practice, Donald G. Fink
McGraw-Hill Book Co., New York

Television Techniques, Bettinger
Harper Bros., New York

Television - The Eyes of Tomorrow, Captain W.C. Eddy
Prentice-Hall, Inc., New York

Television Today and Tomorrow, Lee De Forest
Dial Press, Inc. New York

The Servicing of Television Receivers
Philco Service Div., Philco Corp., Philadelphia, Pa.

INDEX